Computer Organization

Principles, Analysis, and Design

Lan Jin

California State University, Fresno, CA

Bo Hatfield

Salem State University, Salem, MA

Andover • Melbourne • Mexico City • Stamford, CT • Toronto • Hong Kong • New Delhi • Seoul • Singapore • Tokyo

CENGAGE
Learning®

Computer Organization: Principles, Analysis, and Design

Lan Jin and Bo Hatfield

Publishing Director:
Roy Lee

Editorial Manager:
Han Lian Siew

Senior Development Editor (Media):
Tanmayee Bhatwadekar

Development Editor:
Joe Ng

Publishing Executive:
Deborah Yip

Senior Regional Director:
Janet Lim

Senior Product Manager:
Charles Ho

Regional Manager, Production and Rights:
Pauline Lim

Senior Production Executive:
Cindy Chai

Creative Manager:
Melvin Chong

Copy Editor/Proofreader:
Mahtab K. Dubash

Cover Designer:
Ong Lay Keng

Compositor:
diacriTech, Inc.

Cover Image:
istockphoto.com/Petrovich9

For product information and technology assistance, contact us at
Cengage Learning Asia Customer Support, 65-6410-1200

For permission to use material from this text or product,
submit all requests online at **www.cengageasia.com/permissions**
Further permissions questions can be emailed to
asia.permissionrequest@cengage.com

ISBN-13: 978-981-4392-51-8

ISBN-10: 981-4392-51-0

Cengage Learning Asia Pte Ltd
151 Lorong Chuan
#02-08 New Tech Park
Singapore 556741

Cengage Learning is a leading provider of customized learning solutions with office locations around the globe, including Andover, Melbourne, Mexico City, Stamford (CT), Toronto, Hong Kong, New Delhi, Seoul, Singapore, and Tokyo. Locate your local office at **www.cengageasia.com/global**

Cengage Learning products are represented in Canada by Nelson Education, Ltd.

For product information, visit **www.cengageasia.com**

Printed in Singapore
1 2 3 4 5 15 14 13

Contents

Preface

SCOPE AND COVERAGE

We wrote this book with the intention that it would be used in a first-level course on computer organization in computer science and computer engineering curricula. The book is self-contained, so that readers need only have a basic knowledge of computer programming in a high-level language. The breadth of material has been chosen to provide fundamental knowledge of computer information and basic digital logic. The depth of material has been chosen to provide students with a solid foundation for their future studies and a career as a computer professional.

One of the difficulties of writing a textbook on computer organization is the lack of universally accepted definitions for the terms "computer organization" and "computer architecture." Usually the two terms are distinguished conceptually in the research literature as follows: "Computer architecture" refers to those attributes of a system visible to an assembly-language programmer. "Computer organization" refers to the functional units and the interconnections that realize the architecture. We prefer this terminology and consider "computer organization" as a lower-level hardware-oriented course, and "computer architecture" as a higher-level system-oriented course. On the other hand, we understand that the disciplines of computer organization and computer architecture are so closely interrelated that it is difficult to clearly distinguish between them. We would rather treat the "hardware" in computer organization as a "logical" entity rather than a "physical" entity.

From the system point of view, a computer system can be conceived as an abstraction structured as a hierarchy of levels, and this conception has a major impact on the understanding of computer architecture and organization. Some textbooks on computer organization explicitly recognize the necessity of presenting the teaching material according to this hierarchy of levels, either top-down or bottom-up. This approach is especially suitable for teaching introductory courses to students with a basic computer science background, that is, students with no prior knowledge of such a concept. However, most computer organization textbooks present the material based on the major functional blocks of a computer (CPU, memory, I/O, control unit, and so on) while still keeping in mind the overall hierarchical structure of a computer system. This latter approach has the advantage of concentrating on the theory and design of separate functional blocks of a computer and avoids creating too broad a scope for the course. Our book follows the second approach and introduces the hierarchical structure of a computer system in Chapter 1. Thus, students will learn how to relate the contents of separate chapters to the overall structure of a computer.

We assume a hierarchical model of six levels as shown by the figure below:

Higher-Level Language
Operating System
Assembly Language
Conventional Machine (or Register Transfer)
Microprogramming
Digital Logic

If we attempt to differentiate between architecture and organization, then the higher-level language and operating system levels are most suitably addressed in "architecture," and the conventional machine, microprogramming, and digital logic levels are better addressed in "organization," while the assembly language level probably lies between the two.

Given this understanding, the book will elaborate on the following topics at the lower levels of the hierarchical model:

- Assembly language level (The lower end of this level deals with machine instructions and data as binary information and various operations on them):
  - Machine-level Representation of Data and Information (Chapter 2)
  - Complex Arithmetic Operations (Chapter 6)
  - Instruction Set Architecture (Chapter 7)
- Conventional machine or register-transfer level (assembly-level machine organization and functional organization, in which computer hardware is considered to be information storage and processing

units interconnected in a datapath for the transfer of data and control information):

- Arithmetic Logic Unit (Chapter 5)
- Central Processing Unit (Chapter 8)
- Control Unit (Chapter 9, part of hardwired control)
- Memory System Organization (Chapter 10, primary memory)
- Interfacing and Communication (Chapter 11, I/O)

■ Microprogramming Level (Chapter 9, part of microprogrammed control)

■ Digital Logic Level (digital logic and digital systems, in which the above-mentioned functional units are considered to be logic circuits and finite-state machines constructed from basic building blocks):

- Combinational Logic (Chapter 3)
- Sequential Logic (Chapter 4)

■ Advanced Computer Organization (Chapter 12, pipelining)

The *Summary* at the end of each chapter provides a recap of the topics covered in the respective chapter.

HOW TO USE THE BOOK?

This book has been designed to incorporate our experiences in teaching a Computer Science course entitled "Introduction to Computer Organization." Generally speaking, a computer science curriculum such as ours does not have a special course on digital logic, but it may have a course on "Computer Systems." Such a course could include some concepts of digital logic, but mostly teach assembly language programming or, at least, the basic concept of assembly languages as an important layer of a computer system. Therefore, this book does not advocate a specific assembly language for students to practice programming.

However, the book includes a chapter entitled "Instruction Set Architecture" that focuses on topics closely related to computer organization (such as instruction format, addressing modes, and instruction set design). Thus, we have de-emphasized assembly languages and emphasized digital logic in this book.

Furthermore, we treat the material on digital logic from the practical point of view, emphasizing its fundamental importance to the design of computer circuits and modules. Students must learn the analysis and design of these circuits and modules in the two introductory chapters on digital logic (Chapters 3 and 4). Resources and class schedule permitting, instructors can even implement and test these circuits and modules using simulation software. This hands-on experience would give students a sound basis for learning the material in later chapters related to the design of computers at the level of functional blocks.

This book's subtitle emphasizes analysis and design in computer organization. However, we do not attempt to teach students to design a practical computer as a commercial product. Our goal is to strengthen the students' understanding of computer organization by way of analysis and design according to the methods taught in this book. Therefore, this book does not emphasize case studies of commercially available processors because their complexity would prevent students from learning the basic-level design methods. Our intent is to teach students the concepts and techniques of designing modern computers. As an example, we use a simplified version of a practical processor on which we can show the design methods of its datapath and control unit from the upper level of the instruction set down to the basic level of logic circuits or microprogramming. In "learning by doing," students can not only design a simple processor, but also implement a "real" working model on a PC using appropriate simulation software. Our teaching experience has demonstrated the effectiveness of this teaching method for computer science students, who can learn the inner workings of a modern computer without attending additional hardware courses.

To use this book in the different curricula of different majors, we make the following recommendations for teaching a one-semester course on computer organization:

For Students Who Have Not Taken a Course on Digital Logic

Option A. All chapters except Chapter 12 can be covered, with the exclusion of these sections on special topics:

- the dynamic characteristics of logic circuits (Section 3.5),
- the design of the finite-state machine (Section 4.6),
- double-precision arithmetic (Sections 6.2 and 6.4),
- CPU bit-slice devices (Section 8.5),
- error detection and correction codes (Section 11.6.2), and
- bus standards except PCI (Sections 11.7.2 to 11.7.5).

Option B. To accommodate the basic contents of the book in a semester, each chapter can be taught with emphasis on selected basic topics such as the following:

- two's complement representation and operations (Sections 2.3.2 and 2.4.2),
- combinational circuit design and implementation on adders and MSIs (Sections 3.1 to 3.4 and 3.6),

- clocked sequential circuit design and implementation on counters and MSIs (Sections 4.2 to 4.5),

- ALU design and implementation (Sections 5.2, 5.3, 5.4.1, 5.4.2, and 5.5.2),

- floating-point operations (Section 6.5),

- instruction format and addressing modes (Sections 7.1 and 7.2),

- CPU based on accumulator and general-purpose registers (Sections 8.3.1 and 8.4),

- the design of the operation chart and the microprogram flowchart according to the basic instruction cycles (Sections 9.4.1 to 9.4.3 and 9.5.3 to 9.5.4),

- memory hierarchy and main memory (Sections 10.1 and 10.2), and

- I/O accessing and I/O interfaces (Sections 11.3 to 11.5).

For Students Who Have Taken a Course on Digital Logic

Option C. Students can be taught (or asked to read on their own) the design examples from Chapters 3 and 4 (Sections 3.3 to 3.5 and Sections 4.3 to 4.5) to review selected topics. This provides instructors an opportunity to teach the optional or advanced topics that are listed above in Option A, as well as pipelining in Chapter 12.

Option D. The teaching of the regular topics listed above in Option B can be taught with more emphasis on design and implementation down to the level of logic circuits. If possible, laboratory activities should be incorporated.

Acknowledgments

We wish to express our thanks to many people who have provided encouragement, support, and help during the writing of this book. We would especially like to thank Dr. Christopher W. Hatfield for editing the text of the entire manuscript and consistently enhancing the clarity of the presentation of the material. We gratefully acknowledge Tsinghua University Press, its chief editors, and acquisitions editor for their foresight and vision to initiate and guide the publishing of this book.

We wish to thank Dr. Henderson Yeung, Chair of the Department of Computer Science at California State University, Fresno, for his constant support during the writing of this book. We also thank our students who provided important proving and enhancing grounds for the material of this book during many years of class-testing of its earlier versions.

Since we have had to balance our regular teaching duties and the creation of this book, there will undoubtedly be room for further improvement. We would appreciate feedback and any comments that the readers may have regarding this book.

About the Authors

Dr. Lan Jin received his PhD in Electrical Engineering from Moscow Electrical Engineering Institute, and BS in Electrical Engineering from Tsinghua University, Beijing. From 1957 to 1983, he was Associate Professor and Professor at the Department of Computer Science and Technology at Tsinghua University, Beijing. During 1984 to 1988, he served in the faculty of Massachusetts Institute of Technology (MIT) and The Pennsylvania State University.

Since 1989, he is the Professor of Computer Science at California State University, Fresno. During his academic career, Dr. Jin taught computer science courses to undergraduate and graduate students. He has been engaged in teaching and research in advanced computer architecture and parallel processing since 1978 and has published two books: *Parallel Processing Computer Architecture* (Beijing: Tsinghua University Press, 1982) and *Computer Organization and Architecture* (Beijing: Tsinghua University Press, 1986). Both books have been used as course texts for undergraduates majoring in computer science and computer engineering in China. His current research interests are parallel and distributed computer systems.

Dr. Bo Hatfield received her MS and PhD in Computer Engineering from The Pennsylvania State University and BS in Computer Science from Southwest Jiaotong University, Chengdu, Sichuan Province, China. From 1993 to 1995, she served as Assistant Professor of Computer Science at the Christopher Newport University, Virginia, and was the faculty at Meredith College, North Carolina between 1995 and 1999. Thereafter, Dr. Hatfield joined Motorola as a senior design engineer for almost a year. She also worked as a senior software engineer for Multilink (now known as Spectel, Inc.).

Since 2001, Dr. Hatfield is the Professor of Computer Science at Salem State University, Massachusetts. She has taught many computer science and computer engineering courses. Her current research interests are data mining, artificial neural networks, and parallel and distributed computer systems.

List of Figures

List of Tables

1

Introduction

1.1 THE SCOPE OF COMPUTER ARCHITECTURE AND ORGANIZATION

A computer is a very complex system. A computer system is made up of application software, system software, major functional blocks, semiconductor chips, various types of peripheral devices, a communication subsystem, hardware assembly, and a power supply unit. A computer system may be viewed as a multilayered structure, as shown in Figure 1.1. Of the four layers, the highest layer is the application software. The computer system may be accessed through user interfaces, for example, graphical user interfaces (GUIs) or a client-server

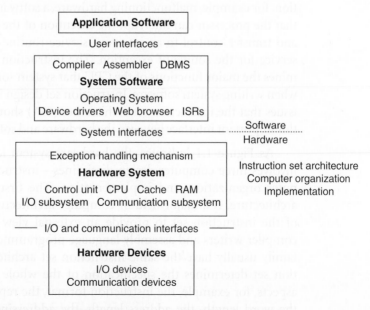

Figure 1.1 The multilayered structure of a computer system

communication interface. The second layer is the system software with an operating system at its center. The operating system provides both data abstraction and resource abstraction. For the former function, it services users through system libraries, such as an assembler, a compiler, and a database management system (DBMS). For the resource abstraction function, it supervises the processor, memory, input/output (I/O), and the communication subsystem through system calls. The system call interface serves as the boundary between the software and hardware of a computer system.

On the hardware side, there exist two layers. One is the hardware system layer consisting of the following five major functional blocks:

- central processing unit (CPU),
- primary memory (including cache),
- the control unit,
- the I/O subsystem (including secondary storage), and
- the communication subsystem.

The other layer is the hardware device layer, which includes I/O devices and communication devices. From the system point of view, the hardware system layer is crucial in determining the function and performance of the hardware system. Hardware provides two system interfaces. One interface is provided by the exception handling mechanism, and the other is represented by the instruction set of the processor. The exception handling mechanism responds to various exception requests from I/O devices, communication devices, and other sources of exception, for example, malfunctioning hardware, a software error, and a system call, so that the processor can interrupt the execution of the currently running program and transfer control to an interrupt service routine (ISR) that provides system service for the source of exception. The instruction set of the processor determines the major functions of the CPU that system software programmers rely on when writing system software. Instruction set design is one of the major technical issues that the instruction set architecture (ISA) should address for determining this important interface between the hardware and software of a computer system.

As Figure 1.1 indicates, the hardware system layer of a computer system involves three computer design disciplines—instruction set architecture, computer organization, and implementation. The first discipline, instruction set architecture, is a major field of computer architecture that involves the design of the instruction set to provide an external view of a computer system for compiler writers and assembly language programmers. Computers in the same family usually have the same instruction set architecture because the instruction set determines the specification of the whole computer family in many aspects, for example, the instruction format, the repertoire of CPU operations, the word length, the address length, the addressing modes, and the number of CPU registers. The second discipline—computer organization—designs the major functional blocks, their interconnections, that is, the datapath and the bus system, and the control unit for realizing the instruction set based on state-of-the-art technologies. Although all the members of a computer family usually share the same instruction set, each member may have a different organization depending on cost-performance requirements. The third discipline, implementation, uses concrete integrated circuit modules and other hardware components and devices (including the power unit) to implement the logic circuits and logic functions specified by the computer organization design.

1.2 MODELING COMPUTER ORGANIZATION

In this section, we discuss the layered structure of the computer design process, the register-transfer level (RTL) model of computer organization, and the performance model of a computer system.

1.2.1 The Layered Structure of the Computer Design Process

In the last section, we learnt that computer organization realizes the instruction set of a computer in the logical domain, and implementation realizes the instruction set in the physical domain. We combine these two closely related domains into a unified field called computer organization. In a broad sense, computer organization treats computer design as a multilayered structure, as shown in Figure 1.2. The basis of computer organization design process is the specification of an instruction set by the instruction set architecture that must be realized by the computer organization design. The computer organization design realizes the instruction set in two layers—system design and logic design. The system design includes two parallel parts—datapath design and control unit design. These two parts are closely related such that their design processes must be interleaved to produce an optimal design scheme.

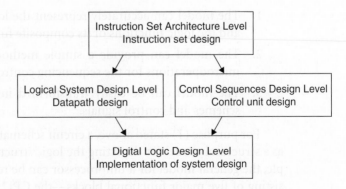

Figure 1.2 The multilayered structure of the computer design process

First, datapath design should choose between a nonpipelined organization and a pipelined organization, depending on the speed requirement. In a pipelined processor design, a superscalar organization could be chosen to determine how many pipelines should work in parallel to satisfy the required throughput, measured as the number of instructions executed per clock cycle. Based on these choices, the control unit design will further choose between hardwired control and microprogrammed control, with a compromise between speed (optimized with hardwired control) and flexibility (optimized with microprogrammed control). After both the datapath design and control unit design are completed, digital logic design is used to achieve an implementation at the logic level. This second stage is extensively technology-dependent. The highest level technology is the system-on-chip (SOC) implementation or the design of application-specific integrated circuit (ASIC) chips. If the design prefers less costly general purpose integrated circuit chips, then the choice can be made among regular programmable logic devices (PLDs) or complex programmable logic devices (CPLDs) and field-programmable gate arrays (FPGAs). This choice will depend on many factors, such as cost, volume of production, time-to-market requirements, and the availability of computer-aided design (CAD) tools for electronic design automation (EDA).

1.2.2 The Register-Transfer Level (RTL) Model of Computer Organization

Computer organization is a discipline of system design that involves the design of the logic organization of a computer. Since a computer system is very complex, we utilize modeling to describe it. In general, a model provides a means of abstraction that presents the major characteristics of a system and avoids irrelevant details. For computer organization, the major characteristics are contained in the logic structure of the hardware system, and the implementation details are hidden. Different models could be used depending on the purpose of the modeling. For the limited purpose of system design, the model should help describe the procedure of operation of the system and also the method of its design. Therefore, it should satisfy the following requirements:

1. The model can accurately represent the logic structure of the datapath and the logic functions of its composite functional blocks;

2. The model can provide a simple method of specifying sequences of microoperations for the sequencing control of the instruction set; and

3. The model can be easily transformed into hardware implementation schemes and control signals.

For purpose (1) stated above, a circuit schematic in graphical form can serve as a structural model for depicting the logic structure of a computer. For example, the general model for a uniprocessor can be represented as a structure consisting of five major functional blocks—the CPU, memory, control, input, and output—connected by a unified bus. This is called the processor-memory-switch (PMS) model. This model can best be used for multiprocessors because these are usually composed of multiple processors and multiple memory modules connected by an interconnection network. The PMS model can be used to compare different architectures of multiprocessors. Another model is the register-transfer level (RTL) model—a specific level of computer design. This model has both a graphical form and a textual form. The graphical form uses diagrams to describe the logic structures of the datapath, and the textual form uses a RTL language to describe the control process.

To describe the execution process of an instruction in the CPU at the register-transfer level, we need to understand how an instruction is executed in it. Almost all modern-day computers work as stored program computers, which are based on the von Neumann computer model. A program is a sequence of instructions, and each instruction performs a basic operation from the instruction set. Before execution, the program is stored in memory along with the data to be manipulated. When the program is executed, instructions are fetched from memory in a sequential fashion. The CPU decodes each instruction, fetches the data from its register or memory, performs the operation, and stores the result into a register or memory. Therefore, a von Neumann computer typically has the CPU organized as a datapath and a control section. At the register-transfer level, the datapath is abstracted as a set of data storage registers carrying information, and the information is processed by way of transfer between registers through information-transformation units. The control section controls the sequencing of microoperations performed in various datapath components.

An example of an RTL model for a simple datapath is shown in Figure 1.3 (Ashenden 2002). At the center of the datapath is an arithmetic-logic unit (ALU) that performs various arithmetic-logic operations on the data items fetched from registers. The results of these operations can be sent to any register(s) except the instruction register (IR). The registers are divided by functions into three groups:

1. *CPU group.* The general purpose register (GPR) set contains registers to be used as data registers or address registers. The size could be 32 registers of 32 bits each, as indicated in Figure 1.3. A temporary register (Temp) may be used as a working register to save temporary data. All registers can send data to the CPU.

2. *Control group.* The program counter (PC) stores the address of the next instruction to be fetched from memory. Every time a new instruction is fetched from memory, the content of the PC (the previous address) is immediately updated so that it always points to the next instruction. The new instruction is loaded into the IR and stays there for execution.

3. *Memory group.* The memory address register (MAR) may send addresses to the memory module through the memory bus, and receive addresses from the ALU. Memory will then perform a read/write operation according to the address in MAR and use the memory buffer register (MBR) to output/input data from/to memory.

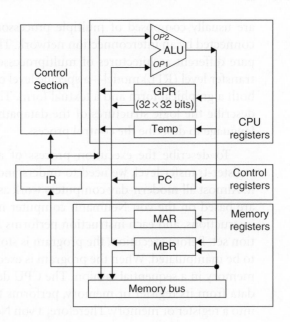

Figure 1.3 The RTL model of a CPU

The RTL model in Figure 1.3 describes the structure of the datapath that matches the general datapath of the CPU quite well. However, to describe the sequential operations in the control section of the CPU, we need to augment the RTL model by introducing a hardware description language (HDL) in textual form. Although there is a rigorous and standard HDL called VHDL,[1] we need a simpler informal language that serves to satisfy our limited purposes (2) and (3) stated at the beginning of this section.

We will use the RTL language to describe a short sequence of control statements and apply it to the control section in Figure 1.3. The control sequence describes only the first step of a basic instruction cycle—instruction fetch—consisting of the following microoperations:

1. Send the address of the instruction to be fetched from the PC to the MAR.

2. Assert a "read memory" command to the memory module and wait until the instruction is available in the MBR.

3. The content of the PC is incremented by "1" so that it will point to the address of the next instruction.

4. Load the new instruction from the MBR to the IR.

5. De-assert the "read memory" command.

---

[1] VHDL is the acronym for VHSIC hardware description language.

This short sequence of control statements, written in RTL language, is shown below:

MAR ← PC	through the ALU using its "*OP*1 forward" operation
memory_read ← 1	
PC ← PC + 1	using an "*OP*1+1" ALU operation
wait until ready = 1	
IR ← MBR	a dedicated path from MBR to IR is provided
memory_read ← 0	

In this book, the RTL language will be used in Chapter 9, when we will learn a design method for a control unit. We assume that the control cycles for an instruction fetch are synchronized with the central clock, so the wait command in the above sequence is omitted. Furthermore, for the purpose of clarity, we will make a distinction between a register number and the contents of a register. Therefore, the first command of the above sequence, MAR ← PC, for example, will be written as MAR ← (PC), using parentheses to specify the contents of a register. The above control sequence is written as follows:

MAR ← (PC)	
ReadM	implies ReadM ← 1
	effective only in one cycle, so ReadM ← 0 is unnecessary
PC ← (PC) + 1	
IR ← (MBR)	

1.2.3 The Performance Model of a Computer System

In Section 1.1, we described a computer system as a multilayered structure, with each layer implemented by some technical means. When the computer system is running a program, all the layers of software and hardware resources work in close cooperation and contribute in different ways to system performance. Therefore, the evaluation of the overall performance of the entire computer system is a complicated problem. Generally speaking, hardware characteristics and program behavior are the two fundamental factors that determine this overall performance. For a given computer system, most of the basic hardware parameters are fixed, and so the measurement of hardware performance is relatively easier. However, the programs running on a computer system are not fixed. To make a comparison of performance possible, the computing community has adopted the use of standardized benchmark programs to measure computer performance. We can use the averages of program execution time on different types of benchmark programs, as a performance measure. Because there still exist different categories of choosing benchmark programs and different algorithms of averaging their results, the method of measuring performance through benchmark programs is not easy to implement.

For the purpose of gaining a basic understanding of performance, we can examine two performance measures. One measure uses the number of *MIPS* (million instructions per second) or *Mflops* (million floating-point operations per second) to measure the hardware speed of a computer system. The other measure uses the CPU execution time (T) to quantify the effective speed of the combined hardware/software system. Both measures can be calculated using the assumption that we know the average number of cycles per instruction (CPI_{ave}) for the given computer. Once we have calculated CPI_{ave} from the statistical data generated by running a large number of benchmark or real programs, we can calculate the above performance measures using the following formulae:

$$MIPS = \frac{f(\text{MHz})}{CPI_{ave}}$$

$$T(\text{sec}) = \frac{IC \times CPI_{ave}}{f(\text{Hz})}$$

(1.1)

where f is the clock frequency and IC is the instruction count, that is, the total number of instructions in the running program.

Example 1.1 Calculation of the Original Performance of a Computer

Suppose a computer with a clock frequency of 100 MHz has four types of instructions, and the frequency of usage and the *CPI* for each of them are given in Table 1.1. Find the *MIPS* of the computer and the CPU time required to run a program of 107 instructions.

Table 1.1 The frequency of usage and *CPI* for four types of instructions

Instruction Operation	Frequency of Usage (%)	Cycles per Instruction
Arithmetic-logic	40	2
Load/Store	30	4
Compare	8	2.5
Branch	22	3

To obtain the solution, find the average *CPI* first, and then use the formulae in equation (1.1).

$$CPI_{ave} = 0.4 \times 2 + 0.3 \times 4 + 0.08 \times 2.5 + 0.22 \times 3$$
$$= 0.8 + 1.2 + 0.2 + 0.66 = 2.86$$
$$MIPS = 100/2.86 = 35$$
$$T = 10^7 \times 2.86/(100 \times 10^6) = 0.286 \text{ s}$$

∎

Example 1.2   Calculation of the Updated Performance of a Computer

There is a proposal to define a new type of instruction called Compare & Branch that combines compare and branch instructions so that compare instructions can be replaced and removed from the instruction set. Suppose that each compare instruction was originally used with one branch instruction, and now each branch instruction is changed to a Compare & Branch instruction. Also, suppose that the new proposal would decrease the clock frequency by 5% because the new Compare & Branch instruction needs more time to execute. Find the new CPI_{ave}, *MIPS*, and *T*.

The proposed method would remove all the compare instructions from the program, resulting in only three types of instructions. The new CPI_{ave} is smaller—it is equal to 2.66, if referred to the original base value of *IC*. However, since the new base value has been reduced to 92% of the original base, we need to refer all the percentages to the new base value by dividing them by 92%. This results in a new CPI_{ave} value equal to 2.9. This value, in turn, decreases *MIPS*, but reduces CPU time. The calculations are as follows:

$$\text{New } CPI_{ave} = \frac{0.4 \times 2 + 0.3 \times 4 + 0.22 \times 3}{0.92} = \frac{2.66}{0.92} = 2.9$$

$$\text{New } MIPS = \frac{100 \times (100\% - 5\%)}{2.9} = 32.76$$

$$\text{New } T = \frac{(0.92 \times 10^7) \times 2.9}{0.95 \times 100 \times 10^6} = 0.28 \text{ sec}$$

∎

Comparing the results of Examples 1.1 and 1.2, we see that the new proposal reduces the *MIPS* rate, but decreases the execution time of the program. This contradiction can be explained by saying that the new proposal is a software means that improves the software code, but worsens the hardware performance. Only the program execution time reflects the true performance of the computer.

The above performance model can be applied to superscalar and pipelined processors as well. Since these are parallel systems, we will use a measure called *speedup* to describe their performances. Speedup is defined as the ratio of the sequential execution time relative to the parallel execution time under the assumption that both the parallel system (e.g., multiprocessor) and the sequential system (e.g., the uniprocessor) are made of the unit processor of the same performance. The principle of operation of a pipeline is similar to an industrial production pipeline, for example, an automobile assembly line. If a *d*-stage instruction pipeline can work full speed without CPU stall, its maximum speed is equal to one instruction per clock cycle. If the instructions are executed sequentially in a nonpipelined machine, each instruction will take *d* clock cycles. So, the maximum speedup of the pipeline processor equals *d*, where the number of stages, *d*, is called the *depth* of the pipeline.

A *k*-issue superscalar processor consists of *k* instruction pipelines, each with depth *d*, working in parallel. If all the instruction pipelines can work at full speed without CPU stall, the maximum speed of a *k*-issue superscalar processor is equal to *k* instructions per clock cycle, with each pipeline outputting the result of one instruction per clock cycle. The same program of *IC* instructions would take $IC \times d$ cycles to execute on a sequential machine without pipelines. Therefore, the maximum speedup of a *k*-issue superscalar processor, S_k, will be equal to *kd*, as derived below:

$$S_k = \frac{T_{\text{unpipelined}}}{T_{\text{superscalar}}} = \frac{IC \times d}{\frac{IC}{k} \times 1} = kd \qquad (1.2)$$

1.3   A HISTORICAL SKETCH OF THE COMPUTER EVOLUTION

It is generally recognized that modern computer history began in 1946 with the development of the Electronic Numerical Integrator And Computer (ENIAC) in the United States. However, the first stored program computer based on the von Neumann model was the Electronic Delayed Storage Automatic Calculator (EDSAC) developed in 1949. The computers built during 1945–1955 used vacuum tubes as components for arithmetic-logic operations, and are classified as first-generation computers. They offered a hundred- to thousand-fold speed-up relative to the mechanical and electromechanical machines developed prior to 1945. The components used for memory were mercury or nickel delay lines and cathode-ray tubes, and hence, first-generation computers had a very small memory capacity of no more than 4,096 words. The devices used for I/O were punched cards, punched tapes, and typewriters.

Second-generation computers, built during 1955–1965, were characterized by the use of transistors. The vacuum tubes for arithmetic-logic operations were replaced by transistors. Tiny magnetic cores were used for random-access memory, and magnetic drums were used for memory storage. These components offered another hundred- to thousand-fold increase in the speed of computers. With respect to software, high-level languages such as FORTRAN and ALGOL were developed,[2] and this ended the history of handwriting the programs in machine code used in the case of first-generation computers.

The use of integrated circuit chips in computers signified the advent of third-generation computers; this era lasted for 15 years from 1965 to 1980. Semiconductor memory chips gradually replaced magnetic cores for main memory, and magnetic disks replaced magnetic drums for memory storage. This led to the mass production of commercialized computers, such as the IBM System/360 mainframes, which were introduced as the first computer family in 1964, and DEC (Digital Equipment Corporation) PDP-11 minicomputers in the 1970s. There were many innovative technical developments during this period. Microprogramming, pipelining, and parallelism were incorporated into processor design. Cache and virtual memory were introduced into memory systems. These technical achievements made it possible to develop supercomputers. The first scientific supercomputer was the CDC 6600 (introduced by Control Data Corporation in 1964) and the first vector supercomputer was the Cray-1 introduced in 1976.

The fourth-generation computers came about with the development of very-large-scale integration (VLSI) technology in 1978, when the Intel 8086 microprocessor with 29,000 transistors on a single chip became a technical reality. It was the first 16-bit microprocessor on a single chip. Its slower, but cheaper successor model, the 8088, was chosen by IBM as the CPU for the original IBM PC in 1981. The introduction of the IBM PC began the era of personal computers in the 1980s. Reduced instruction set computing (RISC) was proposed as a new design philosophy as opposed to complex instruction set computing (CISC). MIPS was the first RISC machine introduced in 1985.[3] The SPARC® (scalable processor architecture) was the first RISC workstation introduced in 1987.[4] The widespread use of microcomputers shifted the development of computer systems from centralized mainframes to distributed systems made up of a large number of microcomputer nodes connected by a network. Supercomputers also shifted from centralized multiprocessors to distributed clusters of workstations (COW). The Internet has been developed into the world's largest distributed computer system, bringing to reality the phrase "the network is a computer."

---

[2] The IBM Mathematical FORmula TRANslating (FORTRAN) System was developed by IBM on their San Jose, California, campus for scientific and engineering applications. ALGOL stands for ALGOrithmic Language, a family of programming languages. Both programming languages were developed in the 1950s.

[3] The original acronym of MIPS was Microprocessor without Interlocked Pipeline Stages. MIPS Computer Systems released their first design (R6000) of the MIPS architecture in 1985.

[4] This was developed and released by Sun Microsystems in mid-1987.

1.4 REPRESENTATIVE COMPUTER FAMILIES

In this section, we will present a brief introduction to a few important computer families to show the current technical level of computer development (Stallings 2003).

1.4.1 The Pentium® Family

The Pentium® family originated from low-end microprocessor chips produced by Intel Corporation starting in 1971. After 40 years of development, it has become the biggest microprocessor family in the personal computer market. The high-end microprocessors developed after the Intel 80486 were successively called Pentium®, Pentium® Pro, Pentium® II, III, and IV. These machines are high-performance models with high clock frequencies, quick instruction execution speeds, and rich system resources. A mapping of the Pentium® development process is shown in Figure 1.4.

From the map in Figure 1.4, it can be seen that two major improvements were made in the Pentium® architecture—the implementation of a superscalar pipelined architecture and the introduction of special instruction types facilitating the parallel processing of multimedia and vector operations. As a result, two types of special instructions are used in Pentium® machines: MMX (multimedia extension) and SSE [streaming "single instruction, multiple data" (SIMD) extension]. The former facilitates parallel processing of short numbers in multimedia operations on the pixels that describe graphical data, and the latter performs vector operations in the SIMD parallel processing mode. The inclusion of these two classes of instructions in the instruction repertoire reflects the change of function of next-generation personal computers in the modern era of information technology (IT).

1.4.2 The SPARC® Family

The SPARC® family originated from the development of high-performance workstations by Sun Microsystems Corporation starting in 1987. The workstations were specifically designed to be more powerful than ordinary personal computers. They were aimed at high-end applications and for use as part of a network. The early models of these workstations—SUN-1, SUN-2, and SUN-3—used a Motorola 68020 CPU. Starting in 1987, a new processor called the SPARC® was proposed for the SUN-4, which was a 32-bit, 36-MHz RISC machine. In 1995, Version 9 of the SPARC® architecture became the UltraSPARC I, which was a 64-bit machine with 23 new instructions called the VIS (Visual Instruction Set). Like the MMX and SSE instructions of the Pentium® family, VIS was aimed at providing general multimedia capability by facilitating parallel vector operations for graphics and signal processing. The V9 UltraSPARC Model II and Model III computers are the successors of the UltraSPARC I. The UltraSPARC can be a symmetrical multiprocessor with dozens (potentially hundreds)

Processor Model	Year Released	Specifications
4004	1971	4 bits, 0.108 MHz, 2,300 transistors on a chip, 640 bytes memory
8008	1972	8 bits, 0.108 MHz, 3,500 transistors, 16 KB memory
8080	1974	8 bits, 2 MHz, 6,000 transistors, 65 KB memory
8086	1978	16 bits, 5–10 MHz, 29,000 transistors, 1 MB memory
8088	1979	A slower and cheaper version of the 8086 with the same parameters.
80286	1982	16 bits, 8–12 MHz, 134,000 transistors, 16 MB memory
80386	1985	32 bits, 32-bit bus, 16–33 MHz, 275,000 transistors, 4 GB memory
80486	1989	32 bits, 25–100 MHz, 1.2 million transistors
Pentium®	1993	32-bit datapath, 64-bit bus, 60–233 MHz, 3.1M transistors, 2-issue superscalar of pipeline depth = 5
Pentium® Pro	1995	64-bit datapath, 64-bit bus, 150–200 MHz, 5.5M transistors, 3-issue superscalar of pipeline depth = 12
Pentium® II	1997	32 bits, 230–400 MHz, 7.5M transistors, Pentium® II plus MMX instructions
Pentium® III	1999	64-bit 1-Gbps system bus, 500–1000 MHz, 95M transistors, SSE instructions, superscalar processor with pipeline depth ≥ 20
Itanium®	2001	IA 64-bit architecture, 6-wide 10-stage deep pipeline

Figure 1.4 The developmental roadmap of the Pentium® family

of CPUs and physical memory of up to 2 TB (terabytes; 2^{40} or 10^{12} bytes). It can also work as a large Web server on the Internet.

The architecture of the UltraSPARC machines has the following characteristics:

- *UltraSPARC-I*: 0.5-micron (μm) CMOS technology and 167 MHz clock frequency.

- *UltraSPARC-II*: 0.25-micron technology and 250–480 MHz clock frequency; a pipeline of nine stages.
- *UltraSPARC-III*: 0.18-micron technology and 750–900 MHz clock frequency; 14-stage pipeline with four integer execution units and three floating-point units; offering superscalar performance.

1.4.3 The PowerPC family

The PowerPC family has been manufactured by IBM, Motorola, and Apple since the early 1990s. The POWER architecture was first used in the processors of the famous IBM RISC System RS/6000 line of computers.[5] The PowerPC architecture was a successor to the POWER architecture. Its first processor, the 601, was introduced in 1993, and represented a transition between the two architectures. Later, models utilizing only the PowerPC architecture were developed. The following list specifies the basic characteristics.

PowerPC 601 in 1993
32-bit processor, 50–100 MHz clock frequency, 2.8 million transistors on a chip, three independent execution units—integer, floating-point, and branch processing—for 3-issue superscalar operation with pipeline depths equal to 4 for integer instructions and 6 for floating-point instructions.

PowerPC 603 in 1994
32-bit processor, 100–300 MHz clock frequency, 1.6–2.6 million transistors on a chip, low-power design consuming about 3 watts, five execution units working in parallel.

PowerPC 604 in 1994
32-bit processor, 166–350 MHz clock frequency, 3.6–5.1 million transistors on a chip, six independent execution units—three integer units, a floating-point unit, a memory load/store unit, and a branch processing unit—for 4-issue superscalar operation.

PowerPC 620 in 1997
64-bit processor, superscalar architecture like the PowerPC 604, out-of-order execution of instructions and dynamic branch prediction, targeted for high-end systems.

MPC 740/750 (G3) in 1997
64-bit processor, 200–366 MHz clock frequency, 6.35 million transistors on a chip, integrating 2×32 KB level-1 cache and 256 KB to 1 MB level-2 cache in the main processor chip.

MPC 7450 (G4) in 1999
64-bit processor, 733 MHz clock frequency, 11 execution units—a load/store unit, a branch unit, four integer units, a floating-point unit, and four vectored operation units—for 4-issue superscalar operating with pipeline depth equal to 7.

---

[5] The original acronym of POWER was Performance Optimization With Enhanced RISC.

The G4 processor includes four special instructions for parallel operations on packed vector data operands, similar to the MMX and SSE instructions in Intel Pentium® processors. The special hardware consists of thirty-two 128-bit vector registers that provide vector data for these instructions. Each vector register can hold sixteen 8-bit integers, eight 16-bit integers, four 32-bit integers or four 32-bit floating-point numbers. The four vector instructions are *load*, *store*, *multiply-accumulate*, and *vector dot product*. The multiply-accumulate instruction multiplies the operands in the two vector registers and adds the product to a third vector register. This operation is common in digital signal processing.

1.5 PERSPECTIVES OF THE COMPUTER EVOLUTION

With the evolution of computing in the twenty-first century, besides overcoming the challenge of building a one-billion-transistor IC processor, researchers and companies will need to determine what the new role of the next-generation PC would be, and also how embedded systems will play an important role with the Internet and mobile devices becoming ubiquitous in everyday life.

1.5.1 The Challenges of a Billion-Transistor IC

The history of computer evolution indicates that the basic hardware elements used for computing have been the driving force for the development of each new generation of computer. The first three generations of computers survived about 10 to 15 years each; every generation was replaced by the next generation of computers that came with a thousand-fold greater processing speed. With each successive generation, the time scale of the clock period has been reduced by a factor of 1,000 from seconds, milliseconds, microseconds to nanoseconds. What will fifth-generation computers be like is anyone's guess. When will the fifth generation begin? What will be the driving force behind it? These questions have been of interest for quite some time. From the computer hardware point of view, an analysis of the development of the billion-transistor IC perhaps provides preliminary answers to these questions.

The evolution of semiconductor chip density versus time is shown in Figure 1.5 (Chiang 2001; Kavi *et al*. 1999). According to Moore's Law, computing power becomes half as expensive every 18–24 months. Single-chip transistor counts have doubled roughly every 18 months, increasing at a rate of 58% per year. Over the course of a decade, this reduces the cost by a factor of 30 to 100. This evolution rate is predicted to continue, at least, through the next decade. Figure 1.5 predicts that the billion-transistor IC chip will most likely appear beginning in 2006.[6] How to fully utilize the colossal computing power of one

---

[6] Intel released the duo-core Itanium-2 64-bit microprocessor in late 2005. "Intel enters billion-transistor processor era," *EE Times*, November 14, 2005. Available online: http://www.eetimes.com/electronics-products/processors/4079511/Intel-enters-billion-transistor-processor-era (last accessed 1 July 2013).

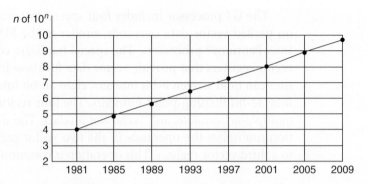

Figure 1.5   Evolution of semiconductor chip density in 10^n transistors/chip vs. time

billion transistors on one chip is a daunting challenge for computer architects. Researchers are using different approaches to seek solutions. One straightforward approach might be to integrate more functions, devices or systems on a single chip. For example, it is possible to integrate a symmetric multiprocessor (SMP) or a simultaneous multithreaded processor (SMT) on a single chip. Another approach is to extend and further improve the currently available architectures to yield even higher performance. For example, the number of parallel instruction pipelines could be increased. To explore instruction-level parallelism, more sophisticated branch prediction and speculation mechanisms could be used to overcome the obstacles caused by the branch instructions in the program. A third, more ambitious approach is to develop new architectural forms based on distributed processing, clustered architecture, a hardware-software codesign virtual machine, and so on.

Implementing a fully functional computer system on a billion-transistor chip is also a challenging task. This represents a new area of system-level integration (SLI), which represents the next level beyond VLSI with SOC capabilities. It is a significantly different computer architecture at both the system and processor levels. The system to be integrated on the chip may not be a pure digital system. It may have to integrate different functions such as logic, memory, mixed-signal blocks (analog, radio-frequency, CMOS image sensors, and high voltage), and megacells (digital signal processors, microcontrollers, microprocessors, and application-specific blocks) into a single chip. The IC design paradigm for the SOC is also different from the traditional design paradigm. It has changed from early transistor-component based designs to cell-based and RTL-based designs, and further to IP (intellectual property)-based designs. SOC technology caused the IC design to be vertically divided into two levels: one focused on IP core design, and another focused on system-level integration. This evolution in disintegration design facilitates the growth of SOC technology and enhances operational efficiency by shortening time-to-market and reducing chip cost.

1.5.2 The New Role of the Next-Generation PC

The rapid development of the Internet has significantly changed the role of computers. However, this is not the first time that computer roles have changed. Mainframes were replaced by distributed microcomputers connected by networks. Minicomputers eventually became obsolete. However, the current change in the role of computers is more fundamental than before. Today, computers perform many tasks other than computing. Many computers, especially personal computers, are used less frequently as number crunchers and more increasingly as communication devices, which create documents and send messages. People use PCs to access the Internet from wherever a telephone line is available. New computers are designed to be as mobile as cellular phones or wearable devices (such as eyeglasses or wristwatches). Therefore, a new spectrum of computers is currently being created, emphasizing reduction of size and increased mobility (Vajapeyam & Valero 2001). New areas of computing are appearing in the academic field, for example, the concepts of pervasive computing and mobile computing are being applied to mobile, wireless, and ubiquitous systems.

The role of large computing systems is also changing. The functions of mainframes have been taken over by distributed servers. More computing resources are shifted to the Internet, which realizes a new concept: The Internet is the computer. Client/server systems focused on a single enterprise will be phased out and replaced by computing systems that are Internet-based and fully distributed. This worldwide distributed system will be implemented as a large collection of server farms, including specialized computing servers to share the work of computing, and a large collection of disk farms to hold the data that feed the network.

The change in the role of computers has created new requirements for computer architecture and organization. Besides, general requirements such as intelligence, small size, low cost, and low power consumption are becoming the major requirements for new-generation PCs, because long battery life not only increases portability, but also tempers the availability of billions of transistors. A billion-transistor chip may consume hundreds of watts on a surface measuring 25 cm^2, requiring heat dissipation even higher than that of a domestic radiator. Therefore, designers of mobile computers pay special attention to cool-chip technology. The basic principle is to lower the transistor threshold voltage based on the following formula:

$$\text{Dynamic power} \propto \frac{\text{clock}}{\text{frequency}} \times \frac{\text{transistor}}{\text{switching}}{\text{activity}} \times \text{voltage}^2 \qquad (1.3)$$

The constant trend of lowering supply voltage to 1.5–1.8 volts can be observed for deep submicron feature-size ICs.

However, reducing the threshold voltage makes transistors increasingly leaky, which, in turn, makes the static power consumption increase. Therefore, practical low-power circuit technology involves a compromise between these two conflicting factors. Multithreshold voltages and speed-adaptive variable-threshold CMOS circuits are used that automatically adjust bias voltage based on the operation's speed and mode.

A special type of PC called a network processor has been proposed to serve as a special-purpose computer dedicated to Internet activities. It would be optimized to process data packets and dispatch them at a data rate of 10 GB/sec. It would also be programmable so that new features can be added and new Internet standards can be adopted. It would be versatile enough to address a wide range of networking applications. Several models have been designed since 2000.

1.5.3 Embedded Systems

In the last section, we looked at the changing roles of computers on account of new communication and Internet-oriented tasks. Another application area in which computers are changing roles is process control. This is an area where computers have traditionally played important roles in the manufacturing industry since the advent of third-generation computers. After 30 years of development, computers are now much more powerful, versatile, and reliable, and this application area has experienced significant changes. As a result, computers can do much more in this traditional application area than ever before. This expanding application domain covers all digital consumer products—vehicles, video, audio, cameras, washing machines, kitchen appliances, and so on. This domain is steadily increasing its share of the microcomputer market, forming a new application area under a new name—embedded systems (Rau & Schlansker 2001). This implies that the computer is embedded into an application system, either as a product or a process, and works as an intelligent component. Another implication is that the computer's hardware as well as software is embedded. This relationship between embedded hardware and embedded software is called a hardware-software partnership. Hardware refers primarily to parallel execution with higher speed, while software means primarily sequential execution at lower cost. Most embedded systems involve a combination of both hardware and software designs. If the speed requirement is not critical, we should use software means. For hard real-time functions, we should assign concurrent tasks to distinct processors. This hardware-software codesign should lead to the best quality of products in terms of cost, performance, size, power, and time-to-market goals.

Another special property of embedded systems is that it may require a novel architecture for traditional applications. For example, multimedia applications contain enormous parallelism and thus consume a vast number of transistors in relatively simple ways, for example, for video images, fixed small loop nests with fixed parameters are required. This demand for traditional techniques to solve current or even future problems is described as "back to the future."

One example is vector processing and SIMD processing that dates back three decades. New processors meet this "back to the future" demand by adding special packed-vector type instructions in the instruction set, such as MXX, SSE, VIS and other special instructions in the Pentium®, SPARC®, and PowerPC families of processors.

The third special property of embedded systems concerns its IC technology requirements. Besides the SOC technology discussed before, MEMS (microelectromechanical system) for highly-integrated communication ICs might be the new devices required for embedded systems. Electromechanical devices with tiny moving parts, built using IC-compatible materials, such as polysilicon, can be integrated on a silicon chip along with semiconductor circuits. They can result in RF devices that are smaller, faster, and cheaper. An example is experimental filters operating at hundreds of megahertz. An MEMS-based phased-array radar antenna might be able to reduce the cost of radar by over an order of magnitude.

From the viewpoint of system design, an embedded computing architecture has three general features:

1. *Specialization.* This refers to the design of datapaths of embedded systems. The datapaths are usually specialized depending on the application requirements of the target embedded system. They often minimize the logic complexity of the ASIC chips specially designed for the specialized application. The degree of specialization could be divided into three categories: general purpose systems, domain-specific systems, and application-specific systems. For example, the ARM is a general purpose microprocessor designed for low-power and low-cost embedded systems. Besides general purpose microcontrollers, some microcontroller chips are designed for domain-specific applications, such as video games.

2. *Customization.* This refers to the implementation techniques of embedded systems. There are two styles of implementation—off-the-shelf (OTS) or customization. The former implies the use of existing commercially available components, and the latter is a level of specialization used when no adequately specialized OTS products are available. CPLD and FPGA are examples of OTS products. Using different IP cores to design SOC chips is an example of customization. Customization incurs nonrecurring expenses in architectural design, in physical design, as well as in the creation of mask sets. Reusing IP blocks and electronic design automation are the means of reducing customized design costs.

3. *Automation.* This refers to the design techniques of embedded systems. As the chip density increases rapidly, electronic design automation is critical for the SOC design of embedded systems. It reduces the design cost incurred by customization and makes low-volume products viable.

SUMMARY

In Section 1.1, a computer system is described as a multilayered structure consisting of two software layers (application software and system software) and two hardware layers (hardware system and hardware devices). The hardware system layer, in turn, involves three computer design disciplines—instruction set architecture, computer organization, and implementation. In Section 1.2, the computer design is treated as a multilevel process, in which the RTL model is most suitable for describing the logical structure of the hardware system, especially the CPU and control. Also, the performance model of the computer is introduced. Only the program execution time on a computer can reflect the overall performance of a computer system with consideration of both hardware and software.

Section 1.3 briefly outlines the history of computer evolution; this is followed by modern representative computer families in Section 1.4 and perspectives of computer development in Section 1.5. The challenges of a billion-transistor IC and the new role of next-generation PCs and embedded systems are also emphasized.

2

The Representation of Information on a Computer

Generally speaking, a computer is a tool for processing information. Information can exist in a variety of forms—mathematical, logical, and physical (e.g., voltage, current, and temperature in process control). Modern IT systems store a wider range of data type comprising numbers, text, audio signals, videos, and so on. This type of data forms a new category of information called multimedia. Before the information can be processed in a *digital* computer, it should be *digitized*, that is, converted into a discrete form characterized by digital values. Owing to the limitations of the present-day physical devices, the most widely adopted form of information representation is the *binary* system. Digital values are represented in sequences of binary digits (bits), each of which has a value of either "1" or "0", corresponding to the logic values "TRUE" or "FALSE," respectively.

In this chapter, we will not delve into the representation of all types of information. Instead, this chapter presents a basic introduction to representing information in three different categories in a computer. This is the minimum background required for learning the logic design of computer hardware discussed in subsequent chapters. More advanced knowledge of the representation of specific number systems such as floating-point numbers will be presented in Chapter 6, when we will learn about complex arithmetic operations.

2.1 DATA TYPES REPRESENTING INFORMATION IN A COMPUTER

Binary variables and binary codes serve as the basis for representing information and thus, play crucial roles in a computer. However, in order to represent different types of information, we need to apply different methods and systems of representation utilizing binary digits. Thus, we distinguish three types of data:

- unsigned numbers,
- signed numbers, and
- bit strings.

Unsigned numbers are created directly as ordinary binary codes. No sign bit is defined on them. They are used simply as the magnitudes of numbers. When we attach a sign bit to a magnitude, we obtain the sign-magnitude representation of a signed number. In the instruction set of a computer, special operations are defined to handle unsigned integers. Unsigned numbers are widely used in the instruction format to specify operation codes in the Opcode field, register numbers in the address fields, and so on. They are all unsigned numbers. Memory addresses are also specified as unsigned integers. When we use counters to count events in control, the count should be unsigned. Similarly, time, clock frequency, and many other variables are also unsigned.

Signed numbers are widely used in the mathematical and physical world, where we use computers for numerical and engineering computations to process arithmetic and physical data as signed numbers. Most arithmetic operations in the instruction set handle signed integers or floating-point numbers as their operands.

The third category of data types in a computer has even wider application coverage than signed numbers. It is called a bit string, which means the binary code is not necessarily being given any numerical value. For example, logic operations in the instruction set are bitwise operations whose operands are simply bit strings without meaningful numerical values. More frequently, bit strings are used to denote symbols such as characters. They include all-text data, which is the main type of information on the Internet and in everyday life. Bit strings are also used in the control unit of a computer, for example, in status words, tagged data, and control codes.

2.2 REPRESENTATION OF FIXED-POINT UNSIGNED NUMBERS

In this section, we learn about the representation of fixed-point unsigned numbers. We will discuss the decimal, binary, octal, and hexadecimal number systems and the representation of fractional numbers. We will also learn how to convert an integer from the decimal to binary systems using both binary and decimal arithmetic. Lastly, the conversion of a fractional number from decimal to binary using decimal arithmetic is also introduced.

2.2.1 The General Positional Number System

Before learning the encoding of numerical data in a computer, let us examine the representation of numbers in our daily life. The basic problem is how to use a finite number of *symbols* to denote the digits and use these digits to encode any number, large or small, with sufficient precision. In general, the necessary factors for defining a number system are: (1) the notation of the digits and (2) the rule of evaluating the digits. The general number system that we use is the *positional number system*. Its principle is to represent any number in terms of a sequence of digits, each contributing a prespecified value according to its position to determine the value of the number by rules. Although the same notation of the digit has the same formal value, it evaluates to different effective values if it appears at different positions. For example, "**DLX**" is a number in Roman numerals, which evaluates to $500(\mathbf{D}) + 50(\mathbf{L}) + 10(\mathbf{X}) = 560$. However, "**DXL**" uses the same symbols to denote digits, but arranges them in different positions, so it evaluates to $500 + (50 - 10) = 540$. Such a rule of evaluating the digits is quite complex, but can be an interesting example for understanding the positional number system.

More specifically, we use the *weighted positional number system*. It is a special kind of positional number system with simple rules of evaluation. Using these rules, a number is represented by a number of digits, each of which evaluates to a prespecified value so that the sum of the values contributed by all the digits equals the value of the number. The prespecified value contributed by a unit digit (i.e., the digit value $= 1$) at a given position is called the *weight* of that digit position. Thus, the effective value of each digit equals the formal value of the digit multiplied by the weight associated with the position at which the digit appears. For example, we can interpret the decimal number 2356 (using only 10 symbols) in a weighted positional number system as composed of 4 digits that contribute the values 2000, 300, 50, and 6 such that $2000 + 300 + 50 + 6 = 2356$. There are four digit positions in this number, each having a weight contributed by the unit digit, from left to right, equal to 1000, 100, 10, and 1, respectively.

It should be noted that the number of digits is not part of the definition of a positional number system. It depends on the range of numbers that needs to be represented. In a computer, the number of digits is part of the physical characteristics of the hardware determined by the *word length* of the computer.

The common weighted positional number system used in a computer is the *radix-r number system* whose weights equal to r^i, where r is the radix and i is the position number ranging from 0 to $n-1$ for an n-digit number [$i = 0$ corresponds to the least significant digit (LSD), and $i = n-1$ corresponds to the most significant digit (MSD)]. The above example with the number 2356 is an example of the radix-10 number system with $r = 10$ and $n = 4$.

A radix-r number system has to define r different notations for its digits, whose formal values are:

$$0, 1, 2, ..., r - 1$$

Let the number, N, be represented as a sequence of digits whose values lie in the above range, then

$$(N)_r = d_{n-1}d_{n-2} \ldots d_1 d_0 \tag{2.1}$$

where $0 \le d_i \le r - 1$ for $0 \le i \le n - 1$. Considering the weight, r^i, associated with each digit position, i, we can evaluate the number as

$$(N)_{10} = d_{n-1}r^{n-1} + d_{n-2}r^{n-2} + \ldots + d_1 r^1 + d_0 r^0 \tag{2.2}$$

if all the values on the right-hand side of the expression are represented and calculated in decimal.

The following radix-r number systems are most frequently used in a computer:

1. The Decimal System

The radix-10 number system is the most frequently used system in ordinary arithmetic and daily life. However, it is usually not used as the internal representation of numbers in a computer, except being used as a natural number system for implementation of input/output and decimal arithmetic operations. When $r = 10$, we use 10 notations for the digits

$$0, 1, 2, 3, 4, 5, 6, 7, 8, 9$$

and Expressions (2.1) and (2.2) become

$$
\begin{aligned}
(N)_{10} &= (d_{n-1}d_{n-2} \ldots d_1 d_0)_{10} \\
&= d_{n-1}10^{n-1} + d_{n-2}10^{n-2} + \ldots + d_1 10^1 + d_0 10^0
\end{aligned}
\tag{2.3}
$$

where $0 \le d_i \le 9$ for $0 \le i \le n - 1$.

2. The Binary System

The radix-2 number system is the system we must deal with most frequently in computer design. Almost all computers use the binary system (or the binary coded system) as the internal representation of numbers because the two logic values, "0" and "1", can most conveniently be implemented by physical devices with two stable states (e.g., switch *off* and *on*, voltage *low* and *high*). When $r = 2$, we use only two notations for the binary digits or bits

$$0, 1$$

and Expressions (2.1) and (2.2) become

$$(N)_2 = (d_{n-1}d_{n-2} \ldots d_1 d_0)_2 \tag{2.4}$$

$$(N)_{10} = d_{n-1}2^{n-1} + d_{n-2}2^{n-2} + \ldots + d_1 2^1 + d_0 2^0 \qquad (2.5)$$

where $0 \le d_i \le 1$ for $0 \le i \le n-1$.

3. The Octal System

The radix-8 number system is an alternative form of binary number representation. If we divide the binary digits of a number into groups of three [starting from the least significant bit (LSB) for an integer, or from the most significant bit (MSB) for a fraction], then we can write the number in octal representation, in which we use eight notations for the octal digits

$$0, 1, 2, 3, 4, 5, 6, 7$$

and Expressions (2.1) and (2.2) become

$$(N)_8 = (d_{n-1}d_{n-2} \ldots d_1 d_0)_8 \qquad (2.6)$$

$$(N)_{10} = d_{n-1}8^{n-1} + d_{n-2}8^{n-2} + \ldots + d_1 8^1 + d_0 8^0 \qquad (2.7)$$

where $0 \le d_i \le 7$ for $0 \le i \le n-1$.

4. The Hexadecimal System

The radix-16 number system is yet another written form of binary number representation. Now we divide the binary digits of a number in groups of four (starting from the LSB for an integer, or from the MSB for a fraction) and write the number in hexadecimal representation, in which we use 16 notations for the hexadecimal digits

$$0, 1, 2, 3, 4, 5, 6, 7, 8, 9, A, B, C, D, E, F$$

where A, B, C, D, E, and F stand for 10, 11, 12, 13, 14, and 15 in decimal, respectively.

Expressions (2.1) and (2.2) then become

$$(N)_{16} = (d_{n-1}d_{n-2} \ldots d_1 d_0)_{16} \qquad (2.8)$$

$$(N)_{10} = d_{n-1}16^{n-1} + d_{n-2}16^{n-2} + \ldots + d_1 16^1 + d_0 16^0 \qquad (2.9)$$

where $0 \le d_i \le 15$ for $0 \le i \le n-1$.

In comparison, the above four radix-r number systems have the following properties:

1. *Ease of use.* The decimal system is the easiest system to understand and is used in devices such as calculators, keyboards, and cellular phones. It is also the external language used by human beings to interact with a computer.

2. *Implementation.* The binary system can be easily and quickly implemented within a computer. It is used widely as the internal representation of data for numerical computation. Because of the mismatch between binary and decimal systems, rounding/truncation algorithms must be carefully designed and implemented to eliminate the errors created in calculation.

3. *Effectiveness.* Both octal and hexadecimal representations are less cumbersome than the binary system. They have the same effectiveness as the decimal system in representing data in assembly language programs. Since the word length and instruction length in contemporary computers are in multiples of 8 bits (called bytes), hexadecimal representation is more useful than octal representation in writing data, instructions, and addresses.

2.2.2 The Representation of Fractional Numbers

Expressions (2.2) to (2.9) derived in the previous section relate to the simplest case of representation of integers. They can be generalized to fractions and mixed integer-fractional numbers. All these are fixed-point representations since the position of the radix point is fixed during arithmetic calculations. Within the computer, the radix point is implicit and needs no additional hardware, so the same code can be viewed as an integer or a fraction without any difference in

---

Example 2.1   Radix-r Number Systems

The integer number $(1000101110100111)_2$ can be represented in different ways:

$(1000101110100111)_2$ as an integer

$$= (2^{15} + 2^{11} + 2^9 + 2^8 + 2^7 + 2^5 + 2^2 + 2^1 + 2^0)_{10}$$
$$= (32{,}768 + 2{,}048 + 512 + 256 + 128 + 32 + 4 + 2 + 1)_{10}$$
$$= (35{,}751)_{10}$$
$$= (105{,}647)_8 \quad \text{// by grouping bits in 3-bit digits from the LSB of the binary code}$$
$$= (8BA7)_{16} \quad \text{// by grouping bits in 4-bit digits from the LSB of the binary code}$$

■

their representations of digits, but the effective values contributed by these digits are different because of different weights. For a fraction, N, Expressions (2.1) and (2.2) become

$$(N)_R = (d_{n-1}d_{n-2}\ldots d_1 d_0)_r$$
$$= d_{n-1}r^{-1} + d_{n-2}r^{-2} + \ldots + d_1 r^{-(n-1)} + d_0 r^{-n} \qquad (2.10)$$

with the radix point located before the most significant digit of the number.

It can be seen that converting an integer to a fraction is equivalent to shifting the radix point from the rightmost position to the leftmost position, which, in turn, is equivalent to dividing an n-bit number by r^n. Therefore, all the weights for integers are reduced by the same factor, r^n, in order to be applied to fractions. Similarly, by combining Expressions (2.2) and (2.10), we can derive the weights for any mixed integer-fractional numbers. The general rule is that when we shift the radix point one digit to the right, we increase the number by a factor of r, and when we shift the radix point one digit to the left, we decrease the number by a factor of r.

From the above discussion, we see the following advantages for the weighted positional number system:

- *Number of notations*. The system requires the definition of a minimum number of notations for the digits. For example, the binary system requires using only two notations: "0" and "1".
- *Number of digits*. The notation is independent of the number of digits, that is, the system allows logically unbounded (but physically bounded) range of numbers to be represented.
- *Position of radix point*. The notation is independent of the position of the radix point, so the system can represent integers, fractions, and mixed integer-fractional numbers equally well.

Example 2.2 **Fractional Number Representation**

The fractional number $(1000101110100111)_2$ is evaluated as:

$$
\begin{aligned}
(1000101110100111)_2 &= (2^{-1} + 2^{-5} + 2^{-7} + 2^{-8} + 2^{-9} + 2^{-11} + 2^{-14} + 2^{-15} + 2^{-16})_{10} \\
&= [(32{,}768 + 2{,}048 + 512 + 256 + 128 + 32 + 4 \\
&\quad + 2 + 1)/2^{16}]_{10} \\
&= (35{,}751/65{,}536)_{10} \\
&= (427{,}234)_8 \quad \text{// by grouping bits in 3-bit digits} \\
&\qquad\qquad\qquad \text{from the MSB of the binary code} \\
&= (8BA7)_{16} \quad \text{// by grouping bits in 4-bit digits} \\
&\qquad\qquad\qquad \text{from the MSB of the binary code}
\end{aligned}
$$

∎

2.2.3 Conversion between Numbers of Different Representations

Expression (2.2) provided the conversion formula from $r = 2, 8, 16$ to $r = 10$ if we substitute the corresponding value for r in decimal and perform decimal arithmetic for calculation of the result N. Conversion between $r = 2, 8$, and 16 is also straightforward, just by grouping the bits to digits or ungrouping digits to bits, as stated above. The only problem we need to discuss here is the conversion from decimal to binary. We distinguish between the two calculation formulae, one uses binary arithmetic by the computer, and the other uses decimal arithmetic by manual calculation.

1. Conversion of an Integer from Decimal to Binary Using Binary Arithmetic

The same Expression (2.2) can be used for the conversion if it is calculated in a computer using binary arithmetic. We need to convert all the coefficients to binary so that Expressions (2.1) and (2.2) become Expression (2.11), which consists of pure binary operations and thus, generates a binary number $(N)_2$ equivalent to the given decimal number $(d_{n-1}d_{n-2} \ldots d_1 d_0)_{10}$.

$$(N)_2 = (d_{n-1}d_{n-2} \ldots d_1 d_0)_{10}$$
$$= (d_{n-1})_2 \times [(1010)_2]^{n-1} + (d_{n-2})_2 \times [(1010)_2]^{n-2} + \ldots$$
$$+ (d_1)_2 \times [(1010)_2]^1 + (d_0)_2 \times [(1010)_2]^0 \qquad (2.11)$$

where $0 \leq d_i \leq 9$ for $0 \leq i \leq n-1$ are the decimal digits, and $(d_i)_2$ means the decimal digit d_i encoded in binary or in so-called *binary-coded decimal* (BCD) representation.

BCD code is an 8–4–2–1 code using the 4-bit binary codes 0000–1001 to denote decimal digits 0–9 and leaving 1010–1111 defined as invalid (see Section 2.5.2, Table 2.6).

2. Conversion of an Integer from Decimal to Binary Using Decimal Arithmetic

An algorithm for the manual conversion of an integer from decimal to binary based on repeated decimal division by 2 is given below.

Example 2.3   Conversion of Decimal Integer 105 to Binary Using Binary Arithmetic

$$(105)_{10} = (0001)(0001)_2 \times (1010)^2 + (0000)_2 \times (1010)^1 + (0101)_2 \times (1010)^0$$
$$= (0001 \times 1010 \times 1010)_2 + (0101 \times 0001)_2$$
$$= (1100100)_2 + (0101)_2 = (1101001)_2$$
$$= (64 + 32 + 8 + 1)_{10}$$

■

Assume a decimal unsigned integer number $(N)_{10} = (d_{m-1}d_{m-2} \ldots d_1 d_0)_{10}$ with m digits, where $0 \le d_i \le 9$ for $0 \le i \le m-1$. Convert it into a binary integer number $(b_{n-1}b_{n-2} \ldots b_1 b_0)_2$ with n bits, where $0 \le bj \le 9$ for $0 \le j \le n-1$ and $m = $ decimal word length $\le [\log_{10} 2]$.

```
Q = (N)₁₀;
i = 0;
while ((Q > 0) && (i < n)) {
      if (Q % 2 = 0)           /* check if Q is even or odd */
            bᵢ = 0;
      else bᵢ = 1;
      Q = Q/2;                 /* decimal integer divide */
      i = i + 1;

}
if (i >= n)
      signal overflow          /* if 10ᵐ > 2ⁿ, the conversion
                                  causes overflow */
else
      for (j = i; j<=n-1; j++)
            bⱼ = 0;            /* set unused higher-order
                                  bits = 0 */
```

It should be noted that a similar algorithm can be applied to binary-decimal conversion using binary arithmetic, provided that in the above algorithm, 2 is replaced by 10 and 10 is replaced by 2.

3. *Conversion of a Fractional Number from Decimal to Binary Using Decimal Arithmetic*

An algorithm for the manual conversion of a fractional number from decimal to binary based on repeated decimal multiplication by 2 is as follows.

Example 2.4 **Conversion of Decimal Integer 105 to 8-bit Binary Using Decimal Arithmetic**

$105/2 = 52$	remainder 1	$b_0 = 1$
$52/2 = 26$	remainder 0	$b_1 = 0$
$26/2 = 13$	remainder 0	$b_2 = 0$
$13/2 = 6$	remainder 1	$b_3 = 1$
$6/2 = 3$	remainder 0	$b_4 = 0$
$3/2 = 1$	remainder 1	$b_5 = 1$
$1/2 = 0$	remainder 1	$b_6 = 1$
$i \le 7, b_7 = 0$	result = 01101001	

■

Assume a decimal unsigned fractional number $(N)_{10} = (d_{m-1}d_{m-2} \dots d_1 d_0)_{10}$ with m digits, where $0 \le d_i \le 9$ for $0 \le i \le m-1$. Convert it into a binary fractional number $(b_{n-1}b_{n-2} \dots b_1 b_0)_2$ with n bits, where $0 \le b_j \le 1$ for $0 \le j \le n-1$, where n is limited by the word length of the computer.

```
Q = (N)10;
i = n-1;
while ((Q > 0) && (i > 0)) {
    if (Q * 2 >= 1)          /* check if Q is greater than or
                                equal to 0.5 */
            bi = 1;
    else  bi = 0;
    Q = Q*2 - bi;            /* decimal integer multiply and
                                subtract */
    i = i - 1;
}
for (j = i-1; j>=0; j--)
    bj = 0;                 /* set unused lower-order bits =
                                0 if any */
```

It should be noted that this algorithm for the conversion of a fraction may result in a non-terminating fraction. Rounding may be needed in the algorithm to increase the accuracy. Furthermore, an algorithm for the conversion of a fraction using binary arithmetic is not given because the binary equivalent of $(10)^{-i}$ for $n-1 \le i \le 1$ is not simple to calculate.

Example 2.5	Conversion of Decimal Fraction 0.703125 to 8-bit Binary Using Decimal Arithmetic	
$0.703125 \times 2 = 1.40625 > 1$	$b_7 = 1$	$1.40625 - 1 = 0.40625$
$0.40625 \times 2 = 0.8125 < 1$	$b_6 = 0$	
$0.8125 \times 2 = 1.625 > 1$	$b_5 = 1$	$1.625 - 1 = 0.625$
$0.625 \times 2 = 1.25 > 1$	$b_4 = 1$	$1.25 - 1 = 0.25$
$0.25 \times 2 = 0.5 < 1$	$b_3 = 0$	
$0.5 \times 2 = 1 = 1$	$b_2 = 1$	$1 - 1 = 0$
$i \ge 0, b_1 = 0, b_0 = 0,$	result = 10110100	

2.3 REPRESENTATION OF FIXED-POINT SIGNED NUMBERS

For implementation of arithmetic operations on signed numbers in a computer, we need the following additional rules to specify:

Rule 1. How to denote the sign of a number (; and)

Rule 2. How to represent the numerical part of a number.

For Rule 1, we need to introduce two distinctive notations to denote the positive sign and the negative sign. The conventional notations used for the sign are "0" for positive and "1" for negative. A separate sign bit is placed at the MSB position of the number so that it is not confused with the numerical part.

For Rule 2, there are three different methods of representing the numerical part of a signed number, thus resulting in three possible fixed-point binary signed number representations.

2.3.1 Sign-Magnitude Representation

As specified above, an n-bit number can be represented as a sign bit at the MSB, "0" for positive and "1" for negative, attached to the remaining $n-1$ bits, which simply accommodates the magnitude of the number in unsigned binary code as defined in the previous section. This notation is called sign-magnitude representation of signed numbers. Table 2.1 lists the n-bit numbers represented in sign-magnitude notation in descending order from the positive maximum, $00\ldots00$, to the negative minimum, $11\ldots11$. A total of only 2^n-1 distinct numbers can be represented with n bits in sign-magnitude notation because there are two different representations of zero: $000\ldots00$ for $+0$ and $100\ldots00$ for -0. This inconsistency of zero is one of the disadvantages of sign-magnitude representation. Another disadvantage is that the addition/subtraction algorithm requires comparing the sign bits of the two operands, treating their magnitudes

Table 2.1 Numbers represented in sign-magnitude notation in descending order

Binary Numbers	Decimal Value	Example with $n=8$
$011\ldots11$	$2^{n-1}-1$	$01111111=+127$
$011\ldots10$	$2^{n-1}-2$	$01111110=+126$
$\ldots\ldots$	$\ldots\ldots$	
$000\ldots01$	1	$00000001=+1$
$000\ldots00$	$+0$	$00000000=+0$
$100\ldots00$	-0	$10000000=-0$
$100\ldots01$	-1	$10000001=-1$
$\ldots\ldots$	$\ldots\ldots$	
$111\ldots10$	$-(2^{n-1}-2)$	$11111110=-126$
$111\ldots11$	$-(2^{n-1}-1)$	$11111111=-127$

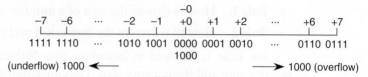

Figure 2.1 The range of representation for a 4-bit sign-magnitude number system

separately from the sign bits, and correcting the magnitude of the result if it is negative after subtraction. These steps make the algorithm quite complicated.

The range of representation for a sign-magnitude number system of 4 bits (including the sign bit) can be depicted on a coordinate axis as shown in Figure 2.1. When we increment the numbers in the increasing direction, positive number 0111 may incur overflow and become 1000. When we decrement the numbers in the decreasing direction, negative number 1111 may incur underflow and become 1000 too. The entire axis thus forms two separate cycles—one on the positive side and the other on the negative side. This explains the property of sign-magnitude representation that requires the magnitudes to be treated separately from the sign bits, leading to a complicated add/subtract algorithm.

2.3.2 Two's Complement Representation

First, we will present the rules of representation in the two's complement number system. It uses a different rule of representing the numerical part of negative numbers, while for the sign bit and positive numbers, the rule is the same as in the sign-magnitude representation. The rules are:

- For an n-bit positive number, the sign bit "0" at the MSB is attached to the magnitude in the remaining $n-1$ bits.

- For an n-bit negative number, the sign bit "1" at the MSB is attached to the two's complement of the magnitude in the remaining $n-1$ bits, where "two's complement" is derived from the magnitude by the following equation:

$$(n-1)\text{-bit two's complement} = 2^{n-1} - (n-1)\text{-bit magnitude} \qquad (2.12)$$

or alternatively,

$$(n-1)\text{-bit two's complement} + (n-1)\text{-bit magnitude} = 2^{n-1} \qquad (2.13)$$

For example, for $n = 4$, 011 and 101 are complement with each other since their sum equals $1000 = 2^3$. Therefore, in two's complement representation, we have

$$(+3)_{10} = (\underline{0}011)_2$$

$$(-3)_{10} = (\underline{1}101)_2$$

and

$$(+5)_{10} = (\underline{0}101)_2$$

$$(-5)_{10} = (\underline{0}101)_2$$

where the underlined bits denote the signs.

For simplicity, the rule for finding the two's complement from the magnitude of a negative number can be stated as follows:

> **1.** Invert all the bits of the magnitude to obtain its one's complement.
> **2.** Add "1" to the one's complement (at LSB) to obtain the two's complement of the magnitude.

It should be noted that the above rule applies only to the numerical part of a negative number without involving the sign bit. Conversely, if we want to evaluate a negative number in its two's complement notation, we can convert its complement (again the numerical part without the sign bit) back to its magnitude. In Expression (2.13), the magnitude and its two's complement for a negative number are related in a symmetrical manner. So, the conversion can occur in both directions, without the involvement of the sign bit.

Table 2.2 lists n-bit numbers represented in two's complement notation in descending order. All positive numbers are represented as in Table 2.1 for sign-magnitude notation; however, there is a considerable difference between the two

Table 2.2 Numbers represented in two's complement notation in descending order

Binary Numbers	Decimal Value	Example with $n = 8$
$011\dots11$	$2^{n-1} - 1$	$01111111 = +127$
$011\dots10$	$2^{n-1} - 2$	$01111110 = +126$
……	……	
$000\dots01$	1	$00000001 = +1$
$000\dots00$	0	$00000000 = 0$
$111\dots11$	-1	$11111111 = -1$
$111\dots10$	-2	$11111110 = -2$
……	……	
$100\dots01$	$-(2^{n-1} - 1)$	$10000001 = -127$
$100\dots00$	$-2^{n-1} - 1$	$10000000 = -128$

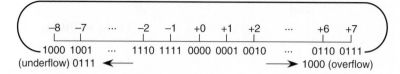

Figure 2.2   The range of representation for a 4-bit two's complement number system

systems for representation of negative numbers. A total of 2^n distinct numbers can be represented in n-bit two's complement number system since there is only one representation of zero, which is, $000\dots00$, while $100\dots00$ represents the most negative number of the value -2^{n-1}. The unique zero and wider range of representation of numbers are the two advantages enjoyed by the two's complement representation over the sign-magnitude one. A third and even more important advantage is that the two's complement addition/subtraction algorithm is much simpler than its sign-magnitude counterpart (described further in the next section).

The range of representation for a 4-bit two's complement number system (including the sign bit) can be depicted on a coordinate axis as shown in Figure 2.2. When we increment the numbers in the increasing direction, positive number 0111 may incur overflow and become 1000. When we decrement the numbers in the decreasing direction, negative number 1000 may incur underflow and become 0111. The entire axis thus forms only one cycle with all the positive and negative numbers involved. This explains the property of the two's complement representation, which allows the magnitudes to be treated together with the sign bits, leading to a very simple add/subtract algorithm.

From the definition of two's complement given above, we can derive the following unified expression for the evaluation of a signed number N in two's complement representation:

$$(N)_{\text{2's compl}} = (sd_{n-2}\dots d_1 d_0)_{\text{2's compl}}$$

$$= +\text{magnitude} = +(d_{n-2}\dots d_1 d_0) \qquad \text{with } s = 0 \text{ for a positive number}$$

$$\text{or} = -\text{magnitude} = (-2^{n-1} + 2^{n-1})$$

$$-\text{magnitude} \qquad \text{with } s = 1 \text{ for a negative number}$$

Example 2.6   Two's Complement Representation

$$(-52)_{10} = (\underline{1}\,0110100)_{\text{sign-mag}} = (\underline{1}\,(1001011 + 0000001))_{\text{2's compl}}$$

$$= (\underline{1}\,1001100)_{\text{2's compl}}$$

$$(\underline{1}\,1110101)_{\text{2's compl}} = (\underline{1}\,(0001010 + 0000001))_{\text{sign mag}}$$

$$= (\underline{1}\,0001011)_{\text{sign mag}} = (-11)_{10}$$

where the underlined bits denote the signs.   ∎

$$= -2^{n-1} + (2^{n-1} - \text{magnitude})$$
$$= -2^{n-1} + \text{two's complement of magnitude}$$
$$= -2^{n-1} + (d_{n-2} \ldots d_1 d_0)$$
$$= -2^{n-1} + d_{n-2} 2^{n-2} + \ldots + d_1 2^1 + d_0 2^0$$

Therefore,

$$(N)_{2's\,compl} = (sd_{n-2} \ldots d_1 d_0)_{2's\,compl} = -s2^{n-1} + d_{n-2} 2^{n-2} + \ldots + d_1 2^1 + d_0 2^0 \quad (2.14)$$

where $s = 0$ for a positive number and $s = 1$ for a negative number; $0 \le d_i \le 1$ for $0 \le i \le n-2$. This expression means that the sign bit for two's complement representation of an n-bit signed number has an effective weight equal to -2^{n-1}.

A very important rule called *sign-extension rule* for two's complement representation can be derived from the Expression (2.14). The rule is that if we extend the word length of a number in two's complement representation, we must repeat the sign bit as the extension of the numerical part, that is, extend "0"s for a positive number and extend "1"s for a negative number.

Example 2.7 Evaluation of Numbers in Two's Complement Representation

$$(\underline{1}\,1001100)_{2's\,compl} = -2^7 + 2^6 + 2^3 + 2^2 = -128 + 64 + 8 + 4 = -52$$

$$(\underline{0}\,1001100)_{2's\,compl} = -0 \times 2^7 + 2^6 + 2^3 + 2^2 = 64 + 8 + 4 = 76$$

∎

2.3.3 Motivation for the Two's Complement System

After we have learned the two's complement number system, we can now better understand the concept of complement using ordinary decimal arithmetic as an example.

In the decimal arithmetic implemented manually, the only method we use for representing signed numbers is the sign-magnitude representation. That is, the numerical part of a signed number is always represented as its magnitude, and the sign part of the number is attached to the magnitude without altering its notation. Therefore, in sign-magnitude representation, only the sign can distinguish a negative number from a positive number, while the magnitude of a negative number or a positive number has no knowledge of the sign. This representation is most familiar to us in ordinary algebra. Although it is useful for input/output, it is rarely used as an internal representation of signed numbers in a computer.

The difficulty of using sign-magnitude representation in a computer occurs in performing subtraction operations. Usually, when subtracting two numbers, we always subtract the smaller number from the larger number to keep the result positive, equal to its magnitude. However, this is not the case when a computer performs the subtract operation in sign-magnitude representation. There is no simple way of comparing two numbers, and the problem will occur if it subtracts a larger number from a smaller number. Look at an example in decimal. Suppose we want to perform the operation, 483 − 679. Typically, we will work it out as 679 − 483 = 196 and then attach a negative sign to produce the correct result equal to −196. However, the automated result would be 483 − 679 = 804 with a discarded borrow, no longer in sign-magnitude representation!

This simple example reveals, in general, the two major differences between computer arithmetic and manual arithmetic operations:

1. *Word Length.* The numbers represented in a computer always have a limited number of digits determined by the word length. So, it is always *modulo arithmetic* that is implemented in a computer. For example, two n-bit unsigned numbers, N_1 and N_2, can be added/subtracted only by the formula

$$N_1 \pm N_2 = (N_1 \pm N_2) \bmod 2^n \qquad (2.15)$$

   That means, only n bits of information can be retained by the computer hardware and the carry/borrow out of the MSB of the sum/difference is automatically discarded.

2. *Comparing Two Numbers.* There is no simple method of directly comparing two numbers in a computer. Before carrying out the subtraction of two numbers, it is difficult to predetermine which number is larger. Usually, we compare two numbers just by subtracting them. Therefore, a special result will be obtained after we subtract a larger number from a smaller one, and this result requires special treatment.

The special treatment inherent in the subtract operation of two arbitrary numbers, as described above, has motivated us to introduce a new concept of data representation called *complement*. In the above example of 483 − 679, we did not obtain the original result of −196, instead we obtained the result of 804 as the complement of 196, and the negative sign should be attached to it in order to indicate its complement nature. Even though the sign-magnitude representation attempts to keep the magnitude always positive, complement is an unavoidable result of computer arithmetic in some cases. A complement with a discarded borrow can be equivalent to a negative result. In the above example, considering the discarded borrow that lost a value 1 with the weight 103, we actually performed the following equivalent calculation:

$$483 - 679 = -10^3 (\text{lost}) + 804 = -196 \qquad (2.16)$$

Thus, we may consider 804 to be equivalent to -196 in computer arithmetic by calling 804 as the complement of 196. The relationship between 196 and 804 is that their sum equals 1000. In general, in any radix-r number system, two k-digit numbers are complement with each other if their sum equals r^k. The r's *complement* of a k-digit magnitude, $|N|$, can be defined as

$$|N|_{\text{r's compl}} = r^k - |N| \tag{2.17}$$

However, given a number 804, how can we determine whether it is positive 804 or negative 196? Therefore, we still need an additional sign digit to distinguish between them. For example, a positive sign followed by 804 is evaluated as $+804$, while a negative sign followed by 804 should be evaluated as -196. This concept created the method of complement representation we introduced in the previous section. The rule is defined as follows:

1. Use a positive sign and the original magnitude (same as unsigned number) to represent a positive number.
2. Use a negative sign and the complement of the magnitude to represent a negative number.

The concept of complement is useful not only for the representation of negative numbers, but also for performing subtraction itself. Take the example of $483 - 679$. We may replace it by adding -679 to 483, or adding 321 (using its 10's complement as the equivalent of -679) to 483. The sum will be 804, the same as before, that is, the equivalent of -196. Again, we need sign digits to be involved in the calculation. In general, subtraction in complement representation can be replaced by addition provided that we change the sign and complement the numerical part of the subtrahend. We will apply the concept of complement to the add/subtract operations of binary signed numbers in the next section.

2.3.4 One's Complement Representation

The third method of signed number representation is called one's complement representation. In principle, it is similar to two's complement representation, but uses one's complement to replace two's complement. Let the $(n-1)$-bit magnitude of a number be $|N|$, its one's complement is defined by the following expression:

$$1\text{'s compl of } |N| = (2^{n-1} - 1) - |N| \tag{2.18}$$

In other words, two $(n-1)$-bit unsigned numbers are one's complement to each other if their sum equals $2^{n-1} - 1$, that is,

$$|N| + \text{1's compl of } |N| = 2^{n-1} - 1 \qquad\qquad (2.19)$$

That means, the sum of a magnitude and its one's complement equals to 11 ... 11. In other words, if we invert every bit of a magnitude from "0" to "1" or "1" to "0", we can obtain its one's complement. The one's complement representation of signed numbers is defined by the following rules:

1. For an n-bit positive number, the sign bit "0" at the MSB is attached to the magnitude in the remaining $n-1$ bits.

2. For an n-bit negative number, the sign bit "1" at the MSB is attached to the one's complement of the magnitude in the remaining $n-1$ bits.

Table 2.3 lists the numbers represented in one's complement notation in a descending order. It can be seen that data in Tables 2.2 and 2.3 are quite similar. They have the same binary number sequence, but the negative numbers are evaluated differently: with the same binary representation, the value of the negative number represented in two's complement system is smaller by 1 than in one's complement system. This fact gives the simple rule of writing the numerical part of a negative number in one's complement system: just invert each bit of its magnitude (without the sign bit). Table 2.3 also shows that only 2^{n-1} distinct numbers can be represented in the n-bit one's complement system because there are two different representations of zero: +0 (000 ... 00) and −0 (111 ... 11). In addition to this disadvantage of one's complement representation, its addition/

Table 2.3 Numbers represented in one's complement notation in descending order

Binary Numbers	Decimal Value	Special Cases
011 ... 11	$2^{n-1} - 1$	$01111111 = +127$
011 ... 10	$2^{n-1} - 2$	$01111110 = +126$
......		......
000 ... 01	1	$00000001 = +1$
000 ... 00	+0	$00000000 = +0$
111 ... 11	−0	$11111111 = -0$
111 ... 10	−1	$11111110 = -1$
......		......
100 ... 01	$-(2^{n-1} - 2)$	$10000001 = -126$
100 ... 00	$-(2^{n-1} - 1)$	$10000000 = -127$

subtraction algorithm may need an extra cycle for special treatment of the result (see next section), which slows down the operation. The advantage of one's complement notation is the ease of conversion between positive and negative numbers.

The range of representation for a 4-bit one's complement number system (including the sign bit) can be depicted on a coordinate axis as shown in Figure 2.3. When we increment the numbers in the increasing direction, the positive number 0111 may incur overflow and become 1000. When we decrement the numbers in the decreasing direction, the negative number 1000 may incur underflow and become 0111. The entire axis forms almost a closed circle except only one number 1111 which equals −0.

From the definition of one's complement given above, we can derive the following expression for evaluation of a signed number N in one's complement representation:

$$(N)_{\text{1's compl}} = (sd_{n-2} \ldots d_1 d_0)_{\text{1's compl}}$$
$$= -s(2^{n-1} - 1) + d_{n-2} 2^{n-2} + \ldots + d_1 2^1 + d_0 2^0 \qquad (2.20)$$

where $s = 0$ for a positive number and $s = 1$ for a negative number; $0 \le d_i \le 1$ for $0 \le i \le n-2$. This expression indicates that the sign bit for the one's complement representation of an n-bit signed number has an effective weight equal to $-(2^{n-1} - 1)$.

The same sign-extension rule applies for one's complement representation, that is, if we extend the word length of a number in one's complement representation, we must repeat the sign bit as the extension of the numerical part by extending "0"s for a positive number and "1"s for a negative number.

In Example 2.8, we invert every bit of the magnitude 12 of the number to get its one's complement, and then add 1 to get the two's complement. All higher order "0" bits of the magnitude become "1" bits in two's and one's complement representations.

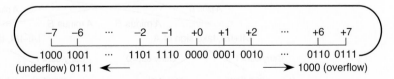

Figure 2.3   The range of representation for a 4-bit one's complement number system

Example 2.8   Three Representations of a Negative Number

Given a negative number -12, it can be represented with 8 bits as:

$$(-12)_{\text{sign-mag}} = 10001100$$

$$(-12)_{1's\,compl} = 11110011 = -(2^7 - 1) + 2^6 + 2^5 + 2^4 + 2^1 + 2^0 = -127 + 115$$

$$(-12)_{2's\,compl} = 11110100 = -2^7 + 2^6 + 2^5 + 2^4 + 2^2 = -128 + 116$$

■

2.4 BINARY ADDITION/SUBTRACTION

In this section, we will look at the algorithms of addition/subtraction for each of the binary signed number representations described in the previous section.

2.4.1 Sign-Magnitude Addition/Subtraction

The addition/subtraction algorithm for sign-magnitude representation is rather complicated. The sign bits must be treated separately from the magnitude parts. First, we compare the sign bits, s_a and s_b, of the two operands, A and B, and then test if we want to carry out A plus B or A minus B. The result of comparison and testing leads to two alternative decisions—addition or subtraction—as explained using the flowchart in Figure 2.4. We always choose one of the operations on the magnitudes $|A|$ and $|B|$, either $|A| + |B|$ or $|A| - |B|$, and take the sign of the first operand, A, as the sign of the result. After the operation, we may need to handle two exceptional cases. If the operation $|A| + |B|$ generates a carry-out, it means that the result of addition has exceeded the maximum range of representation, or we say the addition has caused an overflow. If the operation $|A| - |B|$ (executed

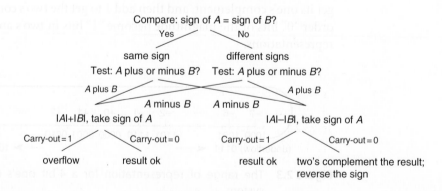

Figure 2.4   The flowchart of the algorithm for sign-magnitude addition/subtraction

Example 2.9 **Addition/Subtraction in Sign-Magnitude Representation**

0011	0101	0011	1011	1011	1011	1101
+ 0010	+ 0011	+ 1110	+ 0011	− 0101	+ 1101	+ 1110

$$\downarrow \qquad \downarrow \qquad \downarrow \qquad \downarrow \qquad \downarrow \qquad \downarrow \qquad \downarrow$$

011	101	011	011	011	011	101
+ 010	+ 011	− 110	− 011	+ 101	+ 101	+ 110
101	1000			1000	1000	1011

sign=0	sign=0	sign=0	sign=1	sign=1	sign=1	sign=1
carry=0	carry=1			carry=1	carry=1	carry=1
result=101 ok	overflow	↓	↓	overflow	overflow	overflow

$$
\begin{array}{cc}
 & \quad 011 \qquad\qquad 011 \\
 & + 010 \qquad\quad + 101 \\
 & \overline{\quad 101} \qquad\quad \overline{1000} \\[4pt]
 & \text{carry=0} \quad\ \text{carry=1} \\
 & \text{result=011} \ \ \text{result=000 ok} \\
 & \text{sign=1}
\end{array}
$$

∎

as $|A|$ plus one's complement of $|B|$ plus 1) does not generate a carry-out (which means a "borrow" is generated), we must take the two's complement of the result and reverse its sign. If the conditions for these two abnormal cases do not exist, both the result and the sign are correct.

2.4.2 Two's Complement Addition/Subtraction

Assume two signed numbers

$$(A)_{2\text{'s compl}} = (s_a a_{n-2} \ldots a_1 a_0)_{2\text{'s compl}}$$

$$(B)_{2\text{'s compl}} = (s_b b_{n-2} \ldots b_1 b_0)_{2\text{'s compl}}$$

Addition and subtraction can be performed directly on these two numbers with the sign bits treated together with the numerical parts. For addition, no conversion of codes is necessary and the result will be automatically corrected in two's complement representation. For subtraction, we may choose between two alternative rules. One is the subtract rule using borrow signals, same as that used in hand subtraction. The other is the difference rule by replacing subtraction with addition so that a unified rule of addition/subtraction can be derived. This is the rule normally followed by the computer, and we will examine it further.

Two's complement subtraction can be replaced by addition provided that we negate the subtrahend by inverting every bit (including the sign bit) of the subtrahend and adding "1" at the LSB position. This negation converts the subtrahend from positive to negative or vice versa. The expression is as follows:

$$(A)_{2\text{'s compl}} - (B)_{2\text{'s compl}} = (A)_{2\text{'s compl}} + [-(B)_{2\text{'s compl}}]$$
$$= (A)_{2\text{'s compl}} + [\text{inverted } s_b, b_{n-2}, \ldots b_1, b_0 + 00\ldots01] \quad \textbf{(2.21)}$$

It should be emphasized that the three terms, A, inverted B, and "1" at the LSB, in Expression (2.21) must be added together simultaneously. This guarantees that the overflow detection rule to be derived below in terms of carry signals can be applied correctly by the computer hardware (see Example 2.11).

Next, we will derive three algorithms of overflow detection. The first, most straightforward rule of detecting overflow is to compare the sign of the result $A \pm B$ with the signs of A and B. There are four cases that can cause errors of overflow: if two positive numbers add to generate a negative result, or two negative numbers add to generate a positive result, or a positive number minus a negative number to get a negative result, or a negative number minus a positive number to get a positive result, then overflow must occur. This condition contains too many parameters, so the implementation by hardware is not simple. However, this algorithm can help derive and verify the other two algorithms as we will see further.

Most frequently, we use the second, simplest algorithm. This algorithm is used to compare two carry signals created in the process of addition/subtraction. Suppose we have an n-bit addition/ subtraction performed in the computer. Let C_{n-2} denote the carry signal generated from the bit position $n-2$. It is the carry generated by the operation of the numerical parts of A and B, which provides a *carry into the sign bit* $= C_{n-2}$. Then, C_{n-2} is added to the sign bits of A and B, s_a and s_b, to generate a sign of the result, $s_{A \pm B}$. This operation, in turn, could generate a *carry out of the sign bit*, denoted as C_{n-1}. The second algorithm for detecting overflow is just to compare these two carry signals and can be written as: "overflow occurs whenever the carry into the sign bit, C_{n-2}, is different from the carry out of the sign bit, C_{n-1}."

This second algorithm can be proved by the first algorithm. Table 2.4 lists all possible cases of addition/subtraction of s_a, s_b, and C_{n-2} to produce $s_{A \pm B}$ and C_{n-1}. The eight cases for add operation are simple, but those for subtract operation need special consideration. According to the above-stated algorithm for subtraction, we replace subtraction with addition by inverting all the bits of B and plus 1 at the LSB, so s_b should be inverted. Furthermore, borrow signals in subtraction correspond to the inverted carry signals in addition. Therefore, in Table 2.4, we need to replace C_{n-2} and C_{n-1} for subtraction with their corresponding inverted signals for addition. Thus, we write two rows for each subtraction case: one for subtraction, and the other for the replacing operation.

Table 2.4 The cases of the sign and carry bits in two's complement addition/subtraction

Operation	s_a	s_b	C_{n-2}	s_{A+B}	C_{n-1}	Comments
Add	0	0	0	0	0	positive plus positive, result positive
Add	0	0	1	1	0	positive plus positive, overflow
Add	0	1	0	1	0	positive plus negative, result negative
Add	0	1	1	0	1	positive plus negative, result positive
Add	1	0	0	1	0	negative plus positive, result negative
Add	1	0	1	0	1	negative plus positive, result positive
Add	1	1	0	0	1	negative plus negative, underflow
Add	1	1	1	1	1	negative plus negative, result negative
(Subtract	0	0	0	0	0)	positive minus positive, result positive
Operation	0	1	1	0	1	
(Subtract	0	0	1	1	1)	positive minus positive, result negative
Operation	0	1	0	1	0	
(Subtract	0	1	0	1	1)	positive minus negative, overflow
Operation	0	0	1	1	0	
(Subtract	0	1	1	0	1)	positive minus negative, result positive
Operation	0	0	0	0	0	
(Subtract	1	0	0	1	0)	negative minus positive, result negative
Operation	1	1	1	1	1	
(Subtract	1	0	1	0	0)	negative minus positive, underflow
Operation	1	1	0	0	1	
(Subtract	1	1	0	0	0)	negative minus negative, result positive
Operation	1	0	1	0	1	
(Subtract	1	1	1	1	1)	negative minus negative, result negative
Operation	1	0	0	1	0	

The result of all 16 operations of addition and subtraction shows that only four overflow cases occur in the table. These cases are the only cases that have two unequal carry signals, C_{n-2} and C_{n-1}. This proves the second algorithm of detecting the overflow.

Example 2.10   Two's Complement Addition

0011	0101	0011	1101	1101	1011
+ 0010	+ 0011	+ 1010	+ 0011	+ 1011	+ 1010
0101	1000	1101	10000	11000	10101

$C_2 = 0$	$C_2 = 1$	$C_2 = 0$	$C_2 = 1$	$C_2 = 1$	$C_2 = 0$
$C_3 = 0$	$C_3 = 0$	$C_3 = 0$	$C_3 = 1$	$C_3 = 1$	$C_3 = 1$
result ok	overflow	result ok	result ok	result ok	overflow

∎

Example 2.11   Two's Complement Subtraction

0011	0101	0011	1101	1101	1011
− 0110	− 1000	− 1110	− 0011	− 0111	− 1010
↓	↓	↓	↓	↓	↓
0011	0101	0011	1101	1101	1011
1001	0111	0001	1100	1000	0101
+ 1	+ 1	+ 1	+ 1	+ 1	+ 1
1101	1101	0101	11010	10110	10001

$C_2 = 0$	$C_2 = 1$	$C_2 = 0$	$C_2 = 1$	$C_2 = 0$	$C_2 = 1$
$C_3 = 0$	$C_3 = 0$	$C_3 = 0$	$C_3 = 1$	$C_3 = 1$	$C_3 = 1$
result ok	overflow	result ok	result ok	overflow	result ok

∎

Although the second algorithm stated above is very simple, it requires two carry signals, C_{n-1} and C_{n-2}, to be used from the outside of the adder. However, if we use a commercial chip of the adder, the carry signal C_{n-2} may not be available for outside use. In this case, we need to derive a third algorithm from Table 2.4 for detecting overflow without using C_{n-2}. From the table, we can observe that the four overflow cases have a common feature not shown by the remaining cases. They have the values of s_a, s_b, $s_{A \pm B}$, and C_{n-1}, from top to bottom, equal to (0,0,1,0), (1,1,0,1), (0,0,1,0), and (1,1,0,1), respectively, all with an odd number of "1"s. That means, if an odd number of the parameters s_a, s_b, $s_{A \pm B}$, and C_{n-1} equal to 1, then an overflow must occur, otherwise, there is no overflow and the result is correct. The logic functions to implement the second and third algorithms are derived in Section 3.3.3 as Expression (3.21).

2.4.3 One's Complement Addition/Subtraction

Assume two signed numbers

$$(A)_{\text{1's compl}} = (s_a a_{n-2} \dots a_1 a_0)_{\text{1's compl}}$$

$$(B)_{\text{1's compl}} = (s_b b_{n-2} \dots b_1 b_0)_{\text{1's compl}}$$

The addition can be performed directly on these two numbers with the sign bits involved, and the sum will be automatically in one's complement. However, the result must be corrected if a carry-out of the sign bit, C_{n-1}, was generated during addition. This carry should be added back to the LSB of the sum and is thus called a *end-around carry*. In this case, an extra addition is needed which makes the one's complement representation less advantageous than the two's complement representation. The rule of overflow detection for two's complement addition/subtraction still holds if we consider each of C_{n-2} and C_{n-1} as the OR of the carry signals generated in two add operations.

One's complement subtraction is performed similarly as two's complement subtraction, that is, replaced with addition by just inverting every bit (including the sign bit) of the subtrahend. Different cases of one's complement addition/subtraction are shown in Example 2.12.

Example 2.12 One's Complement Addition and Subtraction

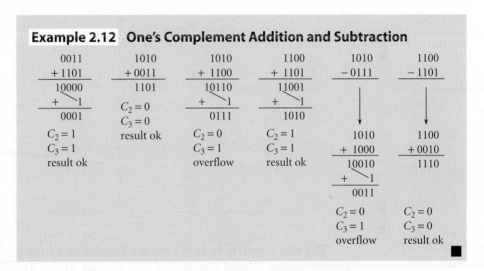

2.5 OTHER CODE SYSTEMS USING BIT STRINGS

In this section, we take a look at Gray codes, decimal codes, and character codes.

2.5.1 Gray Codes

The binary number system defined in Section 2.2.1 by Expression (2.4) is a weighted code system useful for counting numbers in a regular binary code sequence from $00\ldots00$ to $11\ldots11$. In general, any binary-coded system can be defined to code any number sequences with different counting orders. Table 2.5 defines a 4-bit Gray code sequence. It is an *unweighted* code system having the following valuable properties:

- Any two successive codes have only one bit changing.
- The code is *reflective*, as the code pattern of the bits $b_{i-1} - b_0$ lower than b_i is symmetrical with respect to the 2^i axes as indicated in the table.

Table 2.5 Gray codes

b_3	b_2	b_1	b_0	Comments
0	0	0	0	
0	0	0	1	____ 2^1 axis
0	0	1	1	
0	0	1	0	____ 2^2 axis
0	1	1	0	
0	1	1	1	____ 2^1 axis
0	1	0	1	
0	1	0	0	____ 2^3 axis
1	1	0	0	
1	1	0	1	____ 2^1 axis
1	1	1	1	
1	1	1	0	____ 2^2 axis
1	0	1	0	
1	0	1	1	____ 2^1 axis
1	0	0	1	
1	0	0	0	

The first property is useful for the generation of smoothly varying control signals, analog–digital conversion signals, and so on. The second property is useful for deriving any subset of the Gray codes by removing an equal number ($< 2^i$) of codes from each side of the 2^i axis. For example,

0000,   0001,   0011,   0010,   0110,   1110,   1010,   1011,   1001,   1000

can be obtained by removing six codes between 0110 and 1110.

0000,   0001,   0101,   0100,   1100,   1110,   1010,   1011,   1001,   1000

can be obtained by removing four codes between 0001 and 0101 and two codes between 1100 and 1110.

2.5.2 Decimal Codes

If the decimal number system defined in Section 2.2.1 by Expression (2.3) is implemented in a computer, each decimal digit should be, in turn, encoded in binary digits. Since a decimal digit may take one of 10 distinct values from 0 to 9, at least four binary digits are necessary to encode it. The enormous possibilities of selecting 10 codes from 4-bit, 5-bit, ..., or even 10-bit codes have created a large variety of decimal codes proposed in literature or realized in practice. Two of the most popular decimal codes are shown in Table 2.6. Except for the codes that could be chosen as the sign digit, all the other codes not used in the table are invalid.

BCD code is also called 8–4–2–1 code, indicating that it is a weighted code with the same weights assigned to its four bits as those assigned to binary numbers. Its advantage derives from its similarity to the binary number system. However, it does not have the convenience that the other decimal codes have for decimal arithmetic. The algorithm of one-digit BCD addition is as follows:

Add two BCD digits, $a_3a_2a_1a_0$ and $b_3b_2b_1b_0$, using binary arithmetic;

if the sum digit, $s_3s_2s_1s_0$, is greater than 1001 or it was created with a carry

> **then** add 0110 and save the carry generated during either one of the two addition times

> { correct the result between 10 and 15 if $s_3s_2s_1s_0 > 1001$ or

> correct the result between 16 and 19 if it was created with a carry }

> **else** no correction of the result is necessary;

Table 2.6 Decimal codes

Decimal Digit	Binary-Coded Decimal				Excess-3		
	b_3	b_2	b_1	b_0	b_3	b_2	b_1	b_0
0	0	0	0	0	0	0	1	1
1	0	0	0	1	0	1	0	0
2	0	0	1	0	0	1	0	1
3	0	0	1	1	0	1	1	0
4	0	1	0	0	0	1	1	1
5	0	1	0	1	1	0	0	0
6	0	1	0	0	1	0	0	1
7	0	1	1	1	1	0	1	0
8	1	0	0	0	1	0	1	1
9	1	0	0	1	1	1	0	0

The addition of two multi-digit BCD numbers is performed by successively applying this algorithm to all BCD digits, starting from the LSD position. The carry generated at each digit position is propagated and added to the next higher digit position.

Similar to signed binary numbers, signed decimal numbers can be represented in sign-magnitude, 10's complement, or nine's complement notation. The sign digit can be represented in various ways. One of the schemes involves selecting the notation of the sign from the remaining 4-bit codes not used by digits 0 to 9, for example, 1010, 1100, 1110 for positive, and 1011, 1101, 1111 for negative.

BCD subtraction can most conveniently be implemented in 10's complement representation. It can be replaced by BCD addition provided that the subtrahend is negated by changing the sign, converting each BCD digit to its nine's complement, and adding "1" to the LSD of the number. Special hardware is needed for transforming a BCD digit to its nine's complement according to Table 2.6.

Excess-3 code adds "3" (0011) to every 4-bit binary code used to denote decimal digits 0 to 9. For example, 0011 = 0000 + 0011 represents the decimal digit "0", 0100 = 0001 + 0011 represents the decimal digit "1", and so on (see Table 2.6). The following two properties make the excess-3 code more convenient for decimal arithmetic than the BCD code:

1. The nine's complement of an excess-3 digit is the same as its one's complement. For example, 0011 and 1100 for "0" and "9"; 0100 and 1011 for "1" and "8"; and so on. So, a simple inversion is sufficient for transforming an excess-3 digit to its nine's complement.

2. A carry in excess-3 addition (sum ≥ 10) corresponds to a carry in binary addition (sum ≥ 16) because the sum has an excess of "6". This simplifies the treatment of carry. However, excess-3 addition always requires correction of the sum digit according to the following algorithm:

Add two excess-3 digits, $a_3 a_2 a_1 a_0$ and $b_3 b_2 b_1 b_0$, using binary arithmetic;

if the sum digit, $s_3 s_2 s_1 s_0$, was created with a carry

    then add 0011 and save that carry { the sum 10 to 19 has lost 3 after generating a carry }

    else subtract 0011 and neglect the borrow;

        { the sum 0 to 9 has gained 3 from adding two excess-3 digits without carry }

2.5.3 Character Codes

Characters form a special data type important for computer processing of text information. There are two standard character codes in use: ASCII (American Standard Code for Information Interchange) and EBCDIC (Extended Binary Coded Decimal Interchange Code). The former uses 7 bits to encode a character set of 127 items, while the latter uses 8 bits. However, the ASCII code uses an extra bit for parity checking (see Section 3.3.3), so the standard length for a character code is 8 bits, which is called a *byte*. The ASCII code table is given in Table 2.7.

The ASCII character set consists of 32 control characters, 52 alphabetical characters, 10 numerals, and punctuation marks. The control characters are used internally by the computer, while the other characters are printable. Some properties of ASCII code are noteworthy:

- The four LSBs of the ASCII code of numerals and the BCD code of decimal digits are equivalent, which eases their mutual transformation.

- The transformation between lowercase letters and uppercase letters is also simple because they share the four common LSBs of ASCII code.

- The ASCII codes of lowercase letters, uppercase letters, and numerals form three sequences of characters with specific ordering. This property facilitates the sorting and searching of characters in text processing.

Table 2.7 ASCII code: $b_6 b_5 b_4 b_3 b_2 b_1 b_0$

$b_3 b_2 b_1 b_0$	$b_6 b_5 b_4$							
	000	001	010	011	100	101	110	111
0000	NULL	DLE	SP	0	@	P		p
0001	SOH	DC1	!	1	A	Q	a	q
0010	STX	DC2	"	2	B	R	b	r
0011	ETX	DC3	#	3	C	S	c	s
0100	EOT	DC4	$	4	D	T	d	t
0101	ENQ	NAK	%	5	E	U	e	u
0110	ACK	SYN	&	6	F	V	f	v
0111	BEL	ETB	'	7	G	W	g	w
1000	BS	CAN	(	8	H	X	h	x
1001	HT	EM	)	9	I	Y	i	y

(Continues)

Table 2.7   ASCII code: $b_6 b_5 b_4 b_3 b_2 b_1 b_0$ (continued)

$b_3 b_2 b_1 b_0$	$b_6 b_5 b_4$							
	000	001	010	011	100	101	110	111
1010	LF	SUB	*	:	J	Z	j	z
1011	VT	ESC	+	;	K	[	k	{
1100	FF	FS	,	<	L	\	l		
1101	CR	GS	–	=	M	]	m	}
1110	SO	RS	.	>	N	^	n	~
1111	SI	US	/	?	O	_	o	DEL

SUMMARY

Digitized information for processing in computers can be categorized into: unsigned numbers, signed numbers, and bit strings. Unsigned numbers are treated in Section 2.2 in binary, decimal, octal, and hexadecimal systems of representation. The algorithms of conversion among these systems and especially between the decimal system and other systems are derived.

In Section 2.3, signed numbers are treated in three different representations: sign-magnitude, two's complement, and one's complement. The algorithms of addition/subtraction for all three systems are derived in Section 2.4. The two's complement representation is most commonly used due to the simplicity of its addition/subtraction algorithms. Its other properties such as the overflow detection rule, the sign-extension rule, the ability of representing a unique most negative number (Table 2.2), and the evaluation of the sign bit with a negative weight by Expression (2.14) are also emphasized.

Three typical examples of bit strings are described in Section 2.5. They are Gray codes useful in control and analog–digital conversion (Section 2.5.1), decimal codes (Section 2.5.2), and character codes (Section 2.5.3).

EXERCISES

2.1 Convert the following unsigned numbers from the given radix to the other three radices as listed in Table 2.8.

Table 2.8 Table of answers to Problem 2.1

Decimal	Binary	Octal	Hexadecimal
369.3125	? ?	?	
?	10111101.101	?	?
?	?	326.5	?
?	? ?		F3C7.A

[Note: For the items whose solutions cannot be directly derived simply by observation, use the derivation processes.]

2.2 Convert the following signed numbers from the given number system to the other number systems as listed in Table 2.9. Indicate the unavailable answer, if any.

Table 2.9 Table of answers to Problem 2.2

Decimal	Sign-Magnitude	Two's Complement	One's Complement
715	?	?	?
−367	?	?	?
?	$(94AC)_{16}$	?	?
?	$(73CD)_{16}$	?	?
?	?	$(C5BF)_{16}$	?
?	?	$(8000)_{16}$	?
?	?	?	$(D680)_{16}$
?	?	?	$(5379)_{16}$

2.3 Given the 32-bit word length of integers, fill in the correct answers in Table 2.10.

2.4 Write the first 20 unsigned numbers in the radix-12 (or duodecimal) number system. Use "A" for decimal 10 and "B" for decimal 11.

2.5 Find the radix r for which the following equalities hold:

(a) $14_r + 52_r + 3_r = 113_r$

(b) $(23_r)^2 - 240_r = (14_r)^2 + 60_r$

(c) $35_r + 40_r + 26_r = 140_r - 15_r$

Table 2.10 Table of answers to Problem 2.3

	Sign-Magnitude	One's Complement	Two's Complement
Number of distinct numbers representable			
Range of nonzero numbers in hexadecimal			
Range of nonzero numbers in powers of 2			
Zero representation(s)			
The accuracy of representation			
Overflow and underflow boundaries			

2.6 Given a number in two's complement representation:

$$N = b_{n-1}b_{n-2} \ldots b_1 b_0,$$

where $b_i = 0$ or 1 for $0 < i < n-1$, and b_{n-1} is the sign bit.

(a) Write the expression which calculates the decimal equivalent of N.

(b) State the procedure to extend the n-bit number N into a $2n$-bit number N.

(c) Based on the expression in part (a), prove the correctness of the procedure in Part (b).

(d) Given the hexadecimal 16's complement numbers (having sign bit at the MSB position):

$$5BC0 \text{ and } D38A,$$

extend each of the numbers to eight hexadecimal digits. What general rule for this extension of hexadecimal numbers have you used?

2.7 Given the binary signed integers in two's complement representation below:

$$A = 10101001 \quad B = 11101010 \quad C = 10000000 \quad D = 010111001$$

(a) Find the decimal equivalent of A, B, C, and D.

(b) Convert A, B, C, and D into sign-magnitude and one's complement representations. Indicate the case in which the conversion will generate an illegal result.

(c) Show how the arithmetic operations $A + B$, $A - B$, $A - B$, and $A - D$ are performed in two's complement representation within a computer. Find the result for each operation. If any case will cause overflow, explain how the overflow can be detected.

(d) Repeat (c), but imitate the computer operations $A + B$, $A - B$, and $A - D$ in one's complement representation.

(e) Repeat (c), but imitate the computer operations $A + B$, $A - B$, and $A - D$ in sign-magnitude representation.

2.8 (a) Perform each of the following subtraction operations between the given two's complement numbers and check for overflow by the two algorithms by comparing carry signals given in Section 2.4.2.

$$01100101 - 10101000$$
$$10100111 - 00100110$$
$$01001010 - 10000000$$
$$10111010 - 10000000$$

(b) Using the above four examples, explain why it is incorrect to say that subtraction "A minus B" can be substituted by "A plus the two's complement of B." What should be the correct statement of this algorithm of subtraction in two's complement representation?

2.9 (a) Find directly the result of negation of the following signed hexadecimal numbers:

F0B3;   30D0.

(b) Perform the following operations directly on 16's complement hexadecimal numbers and indicate whether overflow occurs:

70C3 + A80D;   7FFF + FFFE.

2.10 Given the following integers of 32-bit word and 16-bit half-word, all in 16's complement representation with the sign bit at the MSB position:

$$N_1 = 987C4506; \quad N_2 = 78AE9000; \quad N_3 = 64FD; \quad N_4 = 8000.$$

(a) Perform the following operations in the same way as within a computer, but directly use the 16's complement representation to show the process for easy writing and calculation.

$$N_1 + N_2; \quad N_1 - N_2; \quad N_1 + N_3; \quad N_1 - N_3; \quad N_1 + N_4; \quad N_1 - N_4.$$

(b) If any case causes overflow, how can the overflow be detected by two different methods based on testing carry signals?

2.11 Given the following integers of 16-bit word, all in 16's complement representation with the sign bit at the MSB position:

$$N_1 = 978C; \quad N_2 = 78AE; \quad N_3 = 64FD; \quad N_4 = 8001.$$

(a)   Convert each number into sign-magnitude representation.

(b)   Perform the following operations directly in sign-magnitude representation according to the algorithm given in Section 2.4.1.

$$N_1 + N_2; \quad N_1 - N_2; \quad N_1 + N_3; \quad N_1 - N_3; \quad N_1 + N_4; \quad N_1 - N_4.$$

2.12 (a)   Suppose the sign is represented by "0" for positive and "1" for negative. Write the following given decimal integers in BCD representations using 10's complement signed number system:

$$A = +137 \quad B = -873 \quad C = -610 \quad D = +237$$

(b)   Show how the following arithmetic operations can be performed by the algorithm of decimal addition/subtraction using binary adders:

$$A + B \quad A - B \quad C + D \quad C - D$$

Show the process of digit-by-digit operation.

2.13 Repeat Problem 2.12, but use excess-3 representation.

2.14 Write the 8-bit ASCII code for the following characters using the MSB for odd-parity error detection:

(a)   D   d   7   6

(b)   E   e   8   0 (numerical zero)

[Note: Refer to Section 3.3.3.]

3

Logic Design of Combinational Circuits

In this chapter, we will discuss the following methods of specifying, analyzing, and designing combinational logic functions:

- Using a truth table to define a combinational logic function (Section 3.1.1).
- Using logic expressions to specify logic functions based on Boolean algebra (Sections 3.1.2–3.1.4).
- Using graphs to specify logic functions based on Karnaugh maps (Section 3.2).
- Using a logic circuit diagram to specify the implementation of a logic function (Sections 3.3 and 3.4).
- Using a waveform diagram to specify the dynamic behavior of a logic function (Section 3.5).

In addition, a method employing a program written in a hardware design language is used to specify a logic function and its circuit of implementation; however, we will not discuss this method here since it is beyond the scope of this book.

3.1   COMBINATIONAL LOGIC FUNCTIONS AND EXPRESSIONS

In this section, we will discuss the use of a truth table to define a combinational logic function and basic logic operations. We will also learn about Boolean algebra and logic expressions and the derivation of canonical sum-of-products and product-of-sums expressions.

3.1.1 Using a Truth Table to Define a Combinational Logic Function

The circuits that process discrete or logic signals are called *logic circuits*. Logic circuits deal with logic variables to implement logic functions. In a binary system,

Table 3.1   The truth tables of 16 two-variable (and one-variable) logic functions

A	B	F0	F1	F2	F3	F4	F5	F6	F7	F8	F9	F10	F11	F12	F13	F14	F15
0	0	0	0	0	0	0	0	0	0	1	1	1	1	1	1	0	1
0	1	0	0	0	0	1	1	1	1	0	0	0	0	1	1	1	1
1	0	0	0	1	1	0	0	1	1	0	0	1	1	0	0	1	1
1	1	0	1	0	1	0	1	0	1	0	1	0	1	0	1	0	1

a logic variable is also called a *binary variable*, which takes only two possible values: either "0" (FALSE) or "1" (TRUE). A *logic function* specifies the functional dependence between its dependent variable and independent variables. For each combination of values of the independent variables, we can assign a value to the dependent variable, so that the whole set of the output values corresponding to all the input combinations can define a unique logic function. As an example, all the 16 possible two-variable (including one-variable) combinational logic functions are specified in Table 3.1. The leftmost two columns list all the four combinations of two input variables in the order of $AB = 00, 01, 10$, and 11, and all the 16 different sets of the values of the dependent variable corresponding to these input combinations are specified in the remaining 16 columns, one in each column. This table is used for defining logic functions and is called a truth table.

There are two classes of logic functions: combinational and sequential. A *combinational logic function* is a logic function whose dependent variable is the function of merely its independent variables without the involvement of a time variable. A *sequential logic function*, on the other hand, must have an argument of time involved as an independent variable to reflect the function history. In a sequential logic circuit, memory is a necessary element that "memorizes" the history of the circuit. In a combinational logic circuit, there is no memory unit, so all the components, in principle, respond to the input signals instantaneously. The current output(s) of a combinational logic circuit is determined solely by the current inputs, with possible time delays caused by the physical components in the circuit. Most of the logic circuits in computer organization that merely process information can be constructed by combinational circuits.

It should be noted that using the truth table is an accurate and the simplest method of defining a logic function. A truth table can be created directly from the function specification and is unique to the function. If two functions have the same truth table, they must be identical. This is the simplest direct method of proving the equivalence of two or more logic functions.

3.1.2 Primitive Combinational Functions and Basic Logic Operations

To specify a combinational logic function using logic expressions requires the decomposition of a logic function in terms of predefined basic logic operations. The truth tables of all 16 primitive two-variable (and one-variable) logic functions and the frequently used basic logic operations defined by them are shown in Table 3.2.

Table 3.2 Truth tables for defining 16 primitive logic functions and basic logic operations

Input		Output Functions																
A	B	F0	F1	F2	F3	F4	F5	F6	F7	F8	F9	F10	F11	F12	F13	F14	F15
0	0	0	0	0	0	0	0	0	0	1	1	1	1	1	1	1	1
0	1	0	0	0	0	1	1	1	1	0	0	0	0	1	1	1	1
1	0	0	0	1	1	0	0	1	1	0	0	1	1	0	0	1	1
1	1	0	1	0	1	0	1	0	1	0	1	0	1	0	1	0	1
Expression		0	AB	$A\bar{B}$	A	$\bar{A}B$	B	$A \oplus B$	$A + B$	$\overline{A + B}$	$\overline{A \oplus B}$	$\bar{B}$	$\overline{\bar{A}B}$	$\bar{A}$	$\overline{A\bar{B}}$	$\overline{AB}$	1
Operation			AND					XOR	OR	NOR	XNOR	NOT		NOT		NAND	
Graphical symbols																	

If "1" is interpreted as TRUE and "0" is interpreted as FALSE, the basic logic operations defined and graphically represented in Table 3.2 have the following logic meanings:

A AND B written as $A \cdot B, A \wedge B$, or AB:
the function is true if and only if both A *and* B are true.
A OR B written as $A + B, A \vee B$, or A / B:
the function is true if and only if either A *or* B *or both* are true.
A XOR B written as $A \oplus B$:
the function is true if and only if either A *or* B but *not both* is true. So, the operation is called *Exclusive-OR*. Alternatively, the function is true if and only if A and B are *different*.
NOT A written as $\bar{A}$ or $\neg A$:
the function is true if and only if A is false. So, the operation is called *inversion*.
A XNOR B written as $\overline{A \oplus B}$ or $A \otimes B$ or $A = B$:
the function is *false* if and only if either A *or* B but *not both* is true. So, the operation is called *Exclusive-NOR*. Alternatively, the function is true if and only if A and B are the *same* or *equal*.
A NAND B written as $\overline{A \cdot B}$ or $\overline{AB}$:
the function is *false* if and only if both A *and* B are true.
A NOR B written as $\overline{A + B}$:
the function is *false* if and only if either A *or* B *or both* are true.

The above logic interpretation can be generalized to logic operations with more than two variables as follows:

- AND (or NAND) is true (or false) iff all its inputs are true.
- OR (or NOR) is true (or false) iff any nonzero number of inputs are true.
- Multistage XOR (or XNOR) is true iff any odd (or even) number of inputs are true, so it implements all odd (or even) functions (see Section 3.3.3).

3.1.3 Boolean Algebra and Logic Expression

A *logic expression* is an algebraic expression composed of literals of independent variables and logic operators acting on these literals. Here, a *literal* can be the identifier or inverted identifier of a logic variable, and the operator set is based on *Boolean algebra*, which is the algebra of binary variables and functions, named after the 19th-century mathematician George Boole. Therefore, a logic expression is also called a *Boolean expression*.

Boolean algebra is formulated on three basic logic operations: AND, OR, and NOT. All logic functions can be represented as the functional compositions of these three logic operations; hence, AND, OR, and NOT form a complete set which has the property of *logic completeness*. Boolean algebra provides a set of basic identities for the transformation of logic expressions. An identity is formed when both sides of it have the same truth table. Useful identities of Boolean algebra are listed below:

Identities		Properties
(a) $A \cdot B = B \cdot A$	$A + B = B + A$	Commutative
(b) $(A \cdot B) \cdot C = A \cdot (B \cdot C)$	$(A + B) + C = A + (B + C)$	Associative
(c) $A \cdot (B + C) = A \cdot B + A \cdot C$	$A + (B \cdot C) = (A + B) \cdot (A + C)$	Distributive
(d) $A \cdot 0 = 0$	$A + 1 = 1$	
(e) $A \cdot 1 = A$	$A + 0 = A$	
(f) $A \cdot \bar{A} = 0$	$A + \bar{A} = 1$	
(g) $A \cdot A = A$	$A + A = A$	
(h) $A \cdot (A + B) = A$	$A + A \cdot B = A$	Absorption
(i) $A \cdot (\bar{A} + B) = A \cdot B$	$A + \bar{A} \cdot B = A + B$	Absorption
(j) $\overline{A \cdot B} = \bar{A} + \bar{B}$	$\overline{A + B} = \bar{A} \cdot \bar{B}$	DeMorgan's Theorem
(k) $\bar{\bar{A}} = A$		

$$(3.1)$$

It is worthwhile to note the following properties of Boolean algebra:

1. All identities except (k) are arranged in two columns in order to show the *principle of duality*. The property of duality indicates that any identity remains an identity if all 0s are simultaneously changed to 1s, 1s to 0s, ANDs to ORs, and ORs to ANDs. If an identity is true, then its dual identity must be true. Therefore, in the above list, the identities in one column can be derived from their dual identities in the other column.

2. Shannon's Expansion Theorem is represented in two dual forms:

$$f(x_1, ..., x_n) = x_i f(x)\big|_{x_i=1} + \bar{x}_i f(x)\big|_{x_i=0} \qquad (3.2)$$

$$f(x_1, ..., x_n) = [x_i + f(x)\big|_{x_i=0}] \cdot [\bar{x}_i + f(x)\big|_{x_i=1}] \qquad (3.3)$$

3. DeMorgan's Theorem specifies the most important property of Boolean algebra. It can be expanded to more than two variables as follows:

$$\overline{A_1 \cdot A_2 \cdot ... \cdot A_n} = \overline{A_1} + \overline{A_2} + ... + \overline{A_n}$$

$$\overline{A_1 + A_2 + ... + A_n} = \overline{A_1} \cdot \overline{A_2} \cdot ... \cdot \overline{A_n} \qquad (3.4)$$

4. By repeatedly applying the above two forms of DeMorgan's Theorem, we have

$$\overline{A_1 B_1 + A_2 B_2 + ... + A_n B_n} = (\overline{A_1} + \overline{B_1}) \cdot (\overline{A_2} + \overline{B_2}) \cdot ... \cdot (\overline{A_n} + \overline{B_n})$$

$$\overline{(A_1 + B_1) \cdot (A_2 + B_2) \cdot ... \cdot (A_n + B_n)} = \overline{A_1} \cdot \overline{B_1} + \overline{A_2} \cdot \overline{B_2} + ... + \overline{A_n} \cdot \overline{B_n} \qquad (3.5)$$

3.1.4 Canonical Logic Expressions

The advantages of the algebraic method of description of a logic function are simplicity, flexibility, and convenience. However, it has a drawback compared with the tabular method of description. If the tabular representation of a logic function is unique, then the same function can be represented in many different Boolean expressions. To ensure the uniqueness of the algebraic representation of a logic function, *canonical expressions* are introduced and used in the design methodology of logic circuits. Given the truth table of a logic function, we can directly write its canonical logic expression in one of the following two formats:

1. Sum-of-Products (SOP) Form Written from the Output Values "1" of the Function

The *canonical sum-of-products (SOP) expression* is the sum (OR) of all product (AND) terms, each of which corresponds to an input combination causing an output value 1 of the function. The expression of each product term can be written as follows: if the input variable in this combination has a value 0, it enters an inverted variable identifier in the product; otherwise, if the input variable in this combination has a value 1, it enters an original variable identifier in the product. Thus, this product term contains the literals of all input variables, each of which is contained only once. It is called a *minterm*. To write the canonical SOP expression for a function from its truth table, we just pick up all the minterms corresponding to its values equal to "1" and OR them; thus, obtaining its canonical SOP expression.

2. Product-of-Sums (POS) Form Written from the Output Values "0" of the Function

The *canonical product-of-sums (POS) expression* is the product (AND) of all sum (OR) terms, each of which corresponds to an input combination causing an output value 0 of the function. The expression of each sum term can be written as follows: if the input variable in this combination has a value 1, it enters an inverted variable identifier in the sum; otherwise, if the input variable in this combination has a value 0, it enters an original variable identifier in the sum. Thus, this sum term contains the literals of all input variables; each of them is

Example 3.1   Exclusive-OR Function in a SOP Form

Derived below is the canonical SOP expression for the Exclusive-OR function:

Table 3.3   Deriving the canonical SOP expression for the Exclusive-OR function

A	B	$F = A \oplus B$	Product Term	Product Term That Outputs $F = 1$	Canonical SOP Expression
0	0	0	$\bar{A} \cdot \bar{B}$		
0	1	1	$\bar{A} \cdot B$	$\bar{A} \cdot B$	$\bar{A} \cdot B + A \cdot \bar{B}$
1	0	1	$A \cdot \bar{B}$	$A \cdot \bar{B}$	
1	1	0	$A \cdot B$		

∎

Example 3.2   Exclusive-OR Function in a POS Form

Derived below is the canonical POS expression for the Exclusive-OR function:

Table 3.4   Deriving the canonical POS expression for the Exclusive-OR function

A	B	$F = A \oplus B$	Sum Term	Sum Term That Outputs $F = 0$	Canonical POS Expression
0	0	0	$A + B$	$A + B$	
0	1	1	$A + \bar{B}$		$(A + B) \cdot (\bar{A} + \bar{B})$
1	0	1	$\bar{A} + B$		
1	1	0	$\bar{A} + \bar{B}$	$\bar{A} + \bar{B}$	

∎

contained only once. It is called a *maxterm*. To write the canonical POS expression for a function from its truth table, we just pick up all the maxterms corresponding to its values equal to "0" and AND them together, thus obtaining its canonical POS expression.

The following are some general conclusions drawn from the above examples:

1. The sum of a complete set of minterms equals to "1", for example,

$$\bar{A} \cdot \bar{B} + \bar{A} \cdot B + A \cdot \bar{B} + A \cdot B = 1 \tag{3.6}$$

$$\bar{A} \cdot \bar{B} \cdot \bar{C} + \bar{A} \cdot \bar{B} \cdot C + \bar{A} \cdot B \cdot \bar{C} + \bar{A} \cdot B \cdot C + A \cdot \bar{B} \cdot \bar{C}$$
$$+ A \cdot \bar{B} \cdot C + A \cdot B \cdot \bar{C} + A \cdot B \cdot C = 1 \tag{3.7}$$

2. If we take the sum of any part of a complete set of minterms, it is equal to the inversion of the remaining part, for example, from Expressions (3.6) and (3.7), we can derive

$$\overline{\overline{A} \cdot B + A \cdot \overline{B}} = \overline{A} \cdot \overline{B} + A \cdot B$$

$$\overline{\overline{A} \cdot B + A \cdot \overline{B} + A \cdot B} = \overline{A} \cdot \overline{B}, \text{ and so on.} \tag{3.8}$$

$$\overline{\overline{A} \cdot \overline{B} \cdot \overline{C} + \overline{A} \cdot B \cdot C + A \cdot \overline{B} \cdot \overline{C} + A \cdot B \cdot \overline{C} + A \cdot B \cdot C}$$
$$= \overline{A} \cdot \overline{B} \cdot C + \overline{A} \cdot B \cdot \overline{C} + A \cdot \overline{B} \cdot C, \text{ and so on.} \tag{3.9}$$

3. The product of a complete set of maxterms equals to "0", for example,

$$(A + B) \cdot (A + \overline{B}) \cdot (\overline{A} + B) \cdot (\overline{A} + \overline{B}) = 0 \tag{3.10}$$

$$(A + B + C)(A + B + \overline{C})(A + \overline{B} + C)(A + \overline{B} + \overline{C}) \cdot$$
$$\cdot (\overline{A} + B + C)(\overline{A} + B + \overline{C})(\overline{A} + \overline{B} + C)(\overline{A} + \overline{B} + \overline{C}) = 0 \tag{3.11}$$

4. If we take the product of any part of a complete set of maxterms, it is equal to the inversion of the remaining part, for example, from Expressions (3.10) and (3.11), we can derive

$$\overline{(A + \overline{B}) \cdot (\overline{A} + B)} = (A + B) \cdot (\overline{A} + \overline{B})$$

$$\overline{(A + \overline{B}) \cdot (\overline{A} + B) \cdot (\overline{A} + \overline{B})} = (A + B), \text{ and so on.} \tag{3.12}$$

$$\overline{(A + B + C)(\overline{A} + B + \overline{C})(\overline{A} + \overline{B} + C)(A + \overline{B} + \overline{C})}$$
$$= (A + B + \overline{C})(A + \overline{B} + C)(\overline{A} + B + C)(\overline{A} + \overline{B} + \overline{C}), \text{ and so on.} \tag{3.13}$$

We may use the binary number sequence of the input combinations to number the minterms and maxterms for writing the canonical expressions. Thus, for the four variables A, B, C, and D, the minterms $\overline{A} \cdot \overline{B} \cdot \overline{C} \cdot \overline{D}$ to $A \cdot B \cdot C \cdot D$ can be denoted by m_0 to m_{15}, while the maxterms $A + B + C + D$ to $\overline{A} + \overline{B} + \overline{C} + \overline{D}$ can be denoted by M_0 to M_{15}. The general canonical expression of a function $F(x_1, \ldots x_n)$ will then be written as:

$$F = \sum_{i=0}^{2^n - 1} f_i m_i \tag{3.14}$$

or

$$F = \prod_{i=0}^{2^n - 1} (f_i + M_i) \tag{3.15}$$

where $\sum$ denotes the cumulative OR operation,
$\prod$ denotes the cumulative AND operation,
f_i denotes the value of function F for the input combination i.

3.2 KARNAUGH MAPS FOR SIMPLIFICATION OF LOGIC FUNCTIONS

Canonical logic expressions are useful not only for the uniqueness of representation of logic functions, but also for the systematic approach to simplification of logic expressions. The most popular systematic approach is the use of a chart called a *Karnaugh map*, which is the graphical representation of a logic function in the form of a rectangular array with the following properties:

3.2.1 Correspondence with the Truth Table or the Canonical SOP Expression

An n-variable Karnaugh map has 2^n cells, each of which corresponds to one of 2^n combinations of input variables (or a minterm). To represent a logic function, we simply write its output values in the corresponding cells. Therefore, a Karnaugh map can be easily generated from the canonical SOP expression of a function or directly from its truth table.

3.2.2 Labeling Rule

A Karnaugh map should be labeled in such a way that any pair of adjacent cells has only one input variable changing. Here, adjacency refers to the relationship between a cell and its four neighbors—east, west, north, and south. For the neighborhood of a boundary cell, the map should be wrapped around so that the topmost row is adjacent to the bottommost row, and the leftmost column is adjacent to the rightmost column. The result is that the four corner cells of the map are all neighbors. To satisfy this requirement, the Karnaugh map applies Gray code to label its cells in both dimensions (horizontal and vertical) of the map. The resulting correspondence between the cells and the minterms with $n = 4$ is shown in Figure 3.1.

CD \ AB	00	01	11	10
00	$m_0 =$ $\overline{A}\overline{B}\overline{C}\overline{D}$	$m_4 =$ $\overline{A}B\overline{C}\overline{D}$	$m_{12} =$ $AB\overline{C}\overline{D}$	$m_8 =$ $A\overline{B}\overline{C}\overline{D}$
01	$m_1 =$ $\overline{A}\overline{B}\overline{C}D$	$m_5 =$ $\overline{A}B\overline{C}D$	$m_{13} =$ $AB\overline{C}D$	$m_9 =$ $A\overline{B}\overline{C}D$
11	$m_3 =$ $\overline{A}\overline{B}CD$	$m_7 =$ $\overline{A}BCD$	$m_{15} =$ $ABCD$	$m_{11} =$ $A\overline{B}CD$
10	$m_2 =$ $\overline{A}\overline{B}C\overline{D}$	$m_6 =$ $\overline{A}BC\overline{D}$	$m_{14} =$ $ABC\overline{D}$	$m_{10} =$ $A\overline{B}C\overline{D}$

Figure 3.1 Skeleton of a Karnaugh map for $F(A, B, C, D)$

3.2.3 Simplification Rule

Any pair of adjacent cells of a Karnaugh map containing output values of 1s can be combined to yield a product term with one input variable missing. The explanation is that by the above labeling rule, these two adjacent cells must correspond to two minterms that differ in exactly one input variable, so this input variable will be canceled when the two minterms are ORed together. This rule can be generalized as follows: any rectangle of a Karnaugh map with $2^k (k \le n)$ neighboring cells containing output values of 1s corresponds to a product term of the function with k input variables missing.

3.2.4 Writing the Maximally Simplified Expression

To use the above simplification rule, we must choose the rectangles of maximal area containing 2^k neighboring 1-cells in the Karnaugh map. The simplest product term thus obtained by combining these cells is called a *prime implicant*. Some cell(s) of the Karnaugh map containing the function value of "1" may be covered by more than one prime implicant. To write the final simplest expression of the function, we need to choose only a minimum, but necessary, number of prime implicants. We distinguish between two kinds of prime implicants. If a prime implicant contains at least one cell not covered by any other prime implicant, it is called an *essential prime implicant*, otherwise it is unessential. An unessential prime implicant has all its cells covered by other prime implicants. The final expression of the function must include all essential prime implicants plus a minimum number of unessential prime implicants selected in such a way that all the cells of the Karnaugh map containing function values of 1s are covered.

Example 3.3   Simplification of a Function by a Karnaugh Map

A Karnaugh map is shown in Figure 3.2. All the rectangles of maximal area containing 2^k 1-cells are enclosed by dashed lines, with the corresponding simplified expression attached. They are all essential prime implicants. So, we must consider all of them in order to cover all the function values of 1s. The final maximally simplified expression of the function is:

$$F = \overline{B}\overline{D} + ABD + B\overline{C}D \tag{3.16}$$

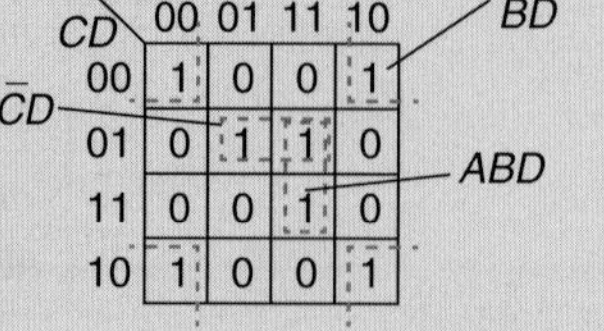

Figure 3.2   The Karnaugh map for Example 3.3

Example 3.4   Multiple Solutions for Simplification of a Function by a Karnaugh Map

A Karnaugh map is shown in Figure 3.3. There are five prime implicants: $\bar{B}\bar{D}$, $\bar{B}C$, and $B\bar{C}D$ are essential, while ABD and ACD are unessential. We must include the first three, but choose any one of the final two of these terms in the simplified expression of the function, thus generating two alternative solutions of the problem as follows:

$$F = \bar{B} \cdot \bar{D} + \bar{B}C + B\bar{C}D + ABD \qquad (3.17)$$

or

$$F = \bar{B} \cdot \bar{D} + \bar{B}C + B\bar{C}D + ACD \qquad (3.18)$$

A third expression may be obtained by using the seven cells containing 0s to write the simplified expression for the inverse function, $\bar{F}$, as follows:

$$F = \overline{B\bar{D} + \bar{B} \cdot \bar{C}D + \bar{A}BC} \qquad (3.19)$$

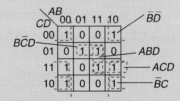

Figure 3.3   The Karnaugh map for Example 3.4

3.2.5 Don't Care Conditions

When some combinations of input variables either do not appear or are invalid, they constitute as *don't care conditions*. The output values of the function corresponding to don't care conditions are undefined and written as "x". Each "x" value in the Karnaugh map can be taken as either "0" or "1" depending on which value will make the final expression maximally simplified. The rule is to consider an "x" as "1" when identifying the largest rectangles as prime implicants or as "0" when writing the final expression to cover all function values of 1s.

3.3 IMPLEMENTATION OF COMBINATIONAL LOGIC FUNCTIONS

This section will study the implementation of logic functions with simple logic gates. The gates introduced in Table 3.2 for the functions of two logic variables are the basic logic gates that are usually implemented in small-scale integration (SSI) modules.

3.3.1 AND, OR, and NOT Gates

AND, OR, and NOT gates are the simplest gates directly implementing the logic operations defined by Boolean algebra. As an electronic circuit, a logic gate is

Example 3.5   A Karnaugh Map with Don't Care Conditions

The Karnaugh map given in Figure 3.4 contains six cells with don't care conditions. They may represent the case of BCD code whose input combinations from 1010 to 1111 are not used. During simplification, the "x" values inside the dotted-line rectangles are taken as "1", while those outside the dotted-line rectangles are taken as "0". The final expression is as follows:

$$F = \bar{B}C + B\bar{D} \tag{3.20}$$

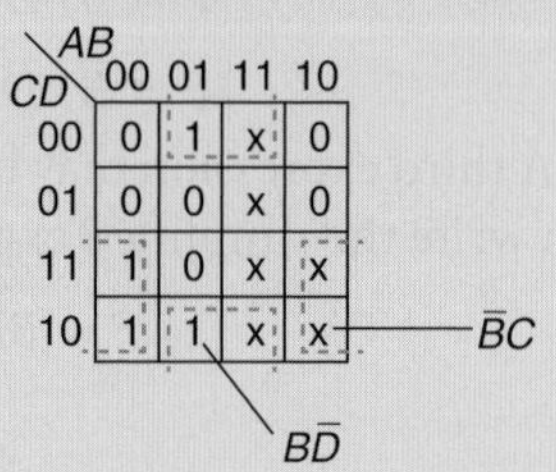

Figure 3.4   The Karnaugh map for Example 3.5

defined in the electric domain, where it uses electrical voltage levels H (high) and L (low) to represent logic values and provides the circuit behavior to represent the logic function. There are two possible ways of mapping the electric domain of the circuit to the logic domain of the function. *Positive logic* maps H to 1 and L to 0, while *negative logic* maps H to 0 and L to 1. Thus, using the same logic circuit, but different interpretations of the circuit behavior, will result in different logic functions. Example 3.6 shows how a circuit can be used as either an AND gate or an OR gate depending on the different logic used for mapping.

3.3.2 NAND and NOR Gates

NAND and NOR gates introduce inverters as the active elements in the pure AND and OR circuits, and thus, help to maintain valid voltage levels at the gate output. So, the number of permissible inputs (called *fan-in*) and permissible output loads (called *fan-out*) of NAND and NOR gates is greater than the number of gates with only passive elements in the circuit. Furthermore, NAND (or NOR) operation alone has the property of logic completeness. That means all other logic operations can be realized using only NAND (or NOR) operation. The circuit consisting of only NAND gates is called an *all-NAND circuit*, while that consisting of only NOR gates is called an *all-NOR circuit*.

Example 3.6 Creating AND and OR Functions from the Same Circuit

The same table in the electric domain can be mapped to two different truth tables in the logic domain as shown in Tables 3.5 and 3.6.

Table 3.5 Mapping a physical table to a logic table using positive logic

Inputs		Output		Inputs		Output
A	*B*	*F*		*A*	*B*	*F*
L	L	L	positive logic	0	0	0
L	H	L		0	1	0
H	L	L	$\longrightarrow$	1	0	0
H	H	H		1	1	1

We have a truth table of the AND operation, so we can use the circuit as an AND gate.

Table 3.6 Mapping a physical table to a logic table using negative logic

Inputs		Output		Inputs		Output
A	*B*	*F*		*A*	*B*	*F*
L	L	L	negative logic	1	1	1
L	H	L		1	0	1
H	L	L	$\longrightarrow$	0	1	1
H	H	H		0	0	0

We have a truth table of the OR operation, so we can use the circuit as an OR gate. ■

To help analyze and construct all-NAND and all-NOR circuits, we introduce the concept of equivalent gates as demonstrated in Figure 3.5. A NAND gate performs the same function as an OR gate with inverse inputs, and a NOR gate performs the same function as an AND gate with inverse inputs. This equivalence relation is a direct consequence of DeMorgan's Theorem. In fact, the graphical

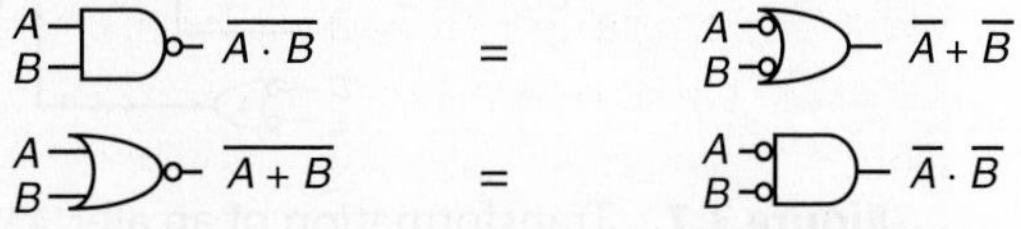

Figure 3.5 Derivation of equivalent gates by DeMorgan's Theorem

Example 3.7   **Show that the Two-Level NAND-NAND Is Equivalent to AND-OR, and that the Two-Level NOR-NOR Is Equivalent to OR-AND**

Figure 3.6 shows the graphical method of transformation by replacing the gate in the second stage with its equivalent gate and then canceling the two "inversion" symbols on the same line.

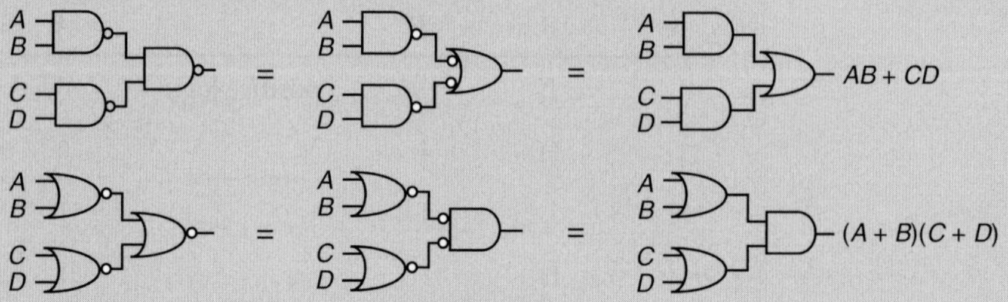

Figure 3.6   Equivalence between NAND-NAND (NOR-NOR) and AND-OR (OR-AND)

Example 3.8   **Analysis of an All-NAND Circuit**

Using the same method as illustrated in Figure 3.6, an all-NAND circuit can be transformed into its equivalent AND-OR-NOT circuit. In Figure 3.7, two solutions are derived: one replaces gates 1 and 3 with their equivalent gates, while the other replaces gates 2 and 4 with their equivalent gates. In the last step, if there is only one "inversion" symbol on a line, it can be replaced by an inverter. For an input line, the "inversion" symbol can be transferred to the input variable if the inputs of both polarities are available. Otherwise we need to insert an inverter in the input line.

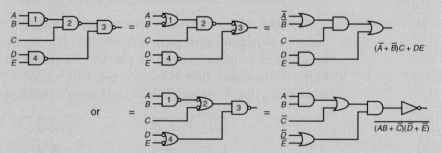

Figure 3.7   Transformation of an all-NAND circuit to an AND-OR-NOT circuit

symbols of two equivalent gates can be used interchangeably in drawing logic circuit diagrams. Using the concept of equivalent gates, it is easy to transform NAND and NOR circuits into equivalent AND, OR, NOT circuits, and vice versa.

The process of transforming an AND-OR-NOT circuit into an equivalent all-NAND or all-NOR circuit is the reverse of the process shown in Figure 3.7. It involves adding "inversion" symbols on the properly selected lines, two at a time on the same line, and then replacing the OR and AND gates carrying inverted inputs by their equivalent NAND and NOR gates respectively. For example, the reverse process of transforming AND-OR (or OR-AND) into NAND-NAND (or NOR-NOR) in Example 3.7 is as follows: add two inverse symbols on each of the lines between the two stages and then replace the second stage with its equivalent gate.

3.3.3 XOR **and** XNOR **Gates**

The XOR gate implements a half adder with the simple rule of 1-bit addition without considering the carry: $0 + 0 = 0$, $0 + 1 = 1$, $1 + 0 = 1$, and $1 + 1 = 0$. Both the XOR and XNOR gates are useful in the simplification of logic functions, reducing the number of gates and the number of inverted input variables. The following properties of XOR and XNOR gates are noteworthy:

- An XOR gate with one input variable inverted is equivalent to an XNOR gate with the inversion bar removed from the corresponding input variable.

- An XOR gate with both input variables inverted is equivalent to an XOR gate with both inversion bars removed from those input variables.

- An XOR gate with one input variable equal to "1" is equivalent to an inverter for inverting the other input variable.

- Based on the above property, we can use one input variable, B, of the XOR gate, $A \oplus B$, to control the inversion of another input variable, A, so that if $B = 0$, the gate outputs A; if $B = 1$, the gate outputs $\overline{A}$.

XOR and XNOR gates are useful for the generation of odd and even functions. An *odd function* equals the value 1 iff an odd number of its input variables takes the value 1 and the rest of the input variables take the value 0. An *even function* is the inverse of the odd function, that is, it equals to value 1 iff an even (including zero) number of its input variables take value 1 and the rest of the input variables take the value 0. In general, an odd function of n variables can be implemented with $n - 1$ XOR gates connected in a tree. The number of levels of the tree is equal to $\lceil \log_2 n \rceil$. The circuits implementing odd functions for $n = 3$, 4, 5, and 8 are shown in Figure 3.8. You will find in Figure 3.11 that the circuit of the full adder used for the generation of the sum is just an odd circuit with $n = 3$ in Figure 3.8. The derivation of the expression for its output can be seen from

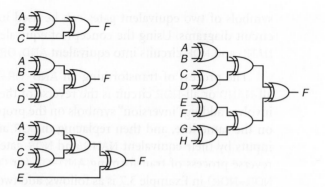

Figure 3.8 Tree-structured circuits using XOR gates for the implementation of odd functions

Expression (3.23). Furthermore, if the circuits in Figure 3.8 change their output stages to XNOR gates, they will implement even functions.

The XOR and XNOR gates find many applications in a computer. The simplest example is the generation of the overflow status, V, for the add/subtract operation. Among the three algorithms of detecting overflow derived in Section 2.4.2, two can directly use the XOR gates to implement the odd functions as shown below:

$$V = C_{n-1} \oplus C_{n-2} \quad \text{if both } C_{n-1} \text{ and } C_{n-2} \text{ are available}$$

$$V = s_a \oplus s_b \oplus s_{A\pm B} \oplus C_{n-1} \quad \text{if } C_{n-2} \text{ is not available} \qquad \textbf{(3.21)}$$

Odd/even functions are also useful in *parity checking*, which uses an extra bit called a *parity bit* attached to the binary code for the detection of single-bit errors in data transmission. The *odd parity bit* is created before transmitting a binary code such that the total number of 1s in the resultant code (including the parity bit itself) is always odd, while the *even parity bit* does the opposite, that is, makes the total number of 1s in the resultant code always even. After transmission of this code, the number of 1s will be checked by the parity-checking circuit to detect the occurrence of any possible single-bit error. If the number of 1s in the transmitted code changed to even (or odd) for odd (or even) parity, the circuit will output an error message of value 1.

3.4   DESIGN OF COMBINATIONAL LOGIC CIRCUITS

The design of a combinational logic circuit may follow the steps listed below:

1. Given the specification of a problem, the first step is to analyze it in order to obtain a truth table to specify the functional dependencies of its output variables on the input variables.

2. Based on the truth table, we may write the canonical SOP expressions for the logic functions of output variables. If Karnaugh maps are to be used

for simplification, the values of the minterms from the truth table can be transferred to the Karnaugh maps.

3. Now, we can simplify the logic expressions by Boolean algebra or Karnaugh maps. Because the simplification depends on the logic devices to be used for implementation, this step may have to be performed in parallel (i.e., overlapped) with Step 4.

4. Implementation is the most flexible step of design. Besides the SSI modules (basic gates) described above, we may use medium-scale integration (MSI) or large-scale integration (LSI) modules for implementation.

3.4.1 Design of a Full Adder

The parallel adder for the addition of two n-bit numbers can be constructed with n full adders connected in cascade, as shown in Figure 3.9. Each full adder at bit $i(i=0$ to $n-1)$ receives two 1-bit operands, A_i and B_i, from outside and 1-bit input carry, C_{i-1}, from the full adder at bit $i-1$ (or from outside as C_{-1} for $i=0$). It performs an *add* operation on these three components, and produces a 1-bit sum, S_i, and a 1-bit output carry, C_i, which is then propagated to the full adder at the next higher-order bit $i+1$ (or output to the outside as C_{n-1} for $i=n-1$). Since carry signals propagate through the chain of full adders in the process of addition, such an adder is called a *ripple-carry adder*. The carry propagation path causes a large delay whose maximum value is proportional to the number of bits, n, of the adder.

Thus, a single full adder, FA_i, has a truth table (see Table 3.7), and the canonical SOP expressions are derived as follows:

$$S_i = \overline{A_i}\,\overline{B_i}C_{i-1} + \overline{A_i}B_i\overline{C_{i-1}} + A_i\overline{B_i}\,\overline{C_{i-1}} + A_iB_iC_{i-1}$$
$$C_i = \overline{A_i}B_iC_{i-1} + A_i\overline{B_i}C_{i-1} + A_iB_i\overline{C_{i-1}} + A_iB_iC_{i-1} \tag{3.22}$$

The Karnaugh maps generated from the truth table are shown in Figure 3.10. The map for S_i has a chessboard pattern of 1s (which is characteristic for odd functions) and can only be simplified algebraically. The map for C_i allows simplification. The expressions obtained from the Karnaugh maps are as follows:

$$S_i = (\overline{A_i \cdot B_i} + A_iB_i)C_{i-1} + (\overline{A_i}B_i + A_i\overline{B_i})\overline{C_{i-1}}$$
$$= \overline{A_i \oplus B_i}C_{i-1} + (A_i \oplus B_i)\overline{C_{i-1}} = A_i \oplus B_i \oplus C_{i-1}$$
$$C_i = A_iB_i + A_iC_{i-1} + B_iC_{i-1} \tag{3.23}$$

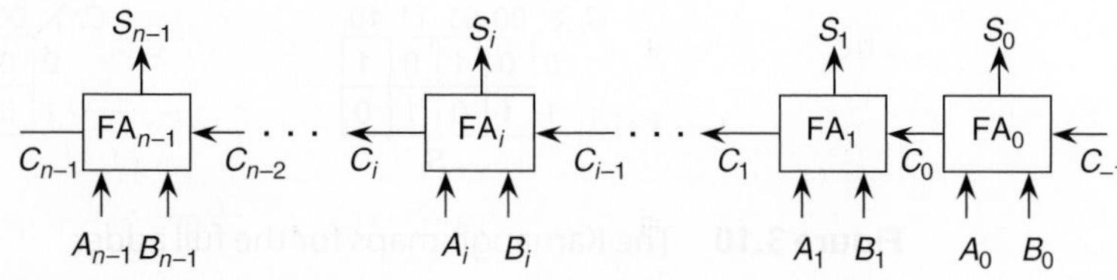

Figure 3.9   Block diagram of an n-bit ripple-carry adder

Table 3.7   Truth table of a full adder

Inputs			Outputs	
A_i	B_i	C_{i-1}	S_i	C_i
0	0	0	0	0
0	0	1	1	0
0	1	0	1	0
0	1	1	0	1
1	0	0	1	0
1	0	1	0	1
1	1	0	0	1
1	1	1	1	1

The rule of simplification of multiple functions of the same set of input variables requires that we make the best use of their common terms. The simplification of each function individually may not yield the best result. Four implementations are given in Figure 3.11, in which C_i is implemented based on different expressions using as few extra gates as possible.

The derivation of the expressions for the circuits in Figure 3.11 is as follows:

For (a) and (c):

$$F_i = A_i \oplus B_i \oplus C_{i-1} \tag{3.24}$$
$$C_i = (A_i \oplus B_i)C_{i-1} + A_i B_i$$

For (c):

$$A_i \oplus B_i = A_i \overline{B_i} + \overline{A_i} B_i = A_i \cdot \overline{A_i B_i} + B_i \cdot \overline{A_i B_i} = \overline{(A_i \cdot \overline{A_i B_i})} \cdot \overline{(B_i \cdot \overline{A_i B_i})} \tag{3.25}$$

which is the simplest implementation of $A_i \oplus B_i$ by a block of four NAND gates without using inverted input variables.

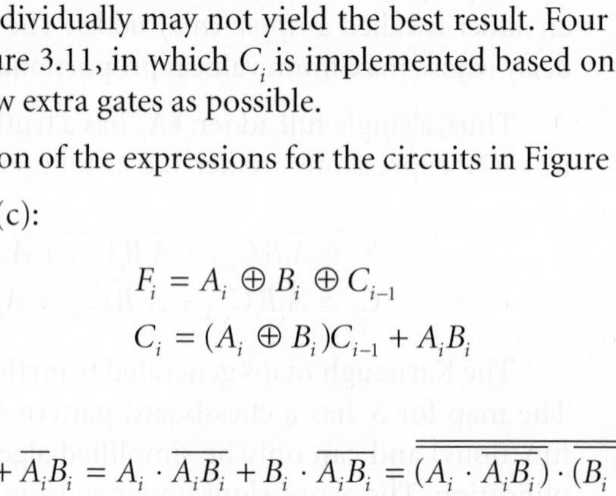

Figure 3.10   The Karnaugh maps for the full adder

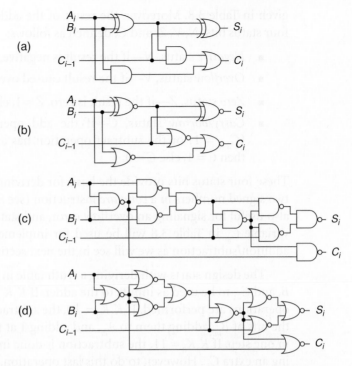

Figure 3.11 Four implementations of a full adder: (a) XOR-based circuit, (b) XNOR-based circuit, (c) all-NAND circuit, and (d) all-NOR circuit

For (b) and (d):

$$F_i = \overline{\overline{A_i \oplus B_i} \oplus C_{i-1}} = A_i \oplus B_i \oplus C_{i-1}$$

$$C_i = (\overline{A_i \oplus B_i} + C_{i-1})(A_i + B_i) = (A_i + B_i)C_{i-1} + A_iB_i \tag{3.26}$$

For (d):

$$\overline{A_i \oplus B_i} = (A_i + \overline{B_i})(\overline{A_i} + B_i) = (A_i + \overline{A_i + B_i})(B_i + \overline{A_i + B_i})$$

$$= \overline{\overline{A_i + \overline{A_i + B_i}} + \overline{B_i + \overline{A_i + B_i}}} \tag{3.27}$$

which is the simplest implementation of $\overline{A_i \oplus B_i}$ by a block of four NOR gates without using inverted input variables.

3.4.2 Ripple-Carry Adder/Subtractor with External Logic for Subtraction

In this section, we will design a ripple-carry adder/subtractor with the subtract and compare operations included in its functionality. The function table for controlling add/subtract operations using two function select signals, K_1 and K_0, is given in Table 3.8. Moreover, the result of the adder/subtractor should include four status bits, N, V, Z, and C, defined as follows:

- *Negative* status, N—if the result is negative, $N = 1$, else $N = 0$;
- *Overflow* status, V—if the result caused overflow, $V = 1$, else $V = 0$;
- *Zero* status, Z—if the result is zero, $Z = 1$, else $Z = 0$;
- *Carry/borrow* status, C—if the add operation has an output carry ($C_{n-1} = 1$) or the subtract operation has an output borrow ($C_{n-1} = 0$), then $C = 1$, else $C = 0$.

These four status bits provide the basis for deriving the result of comparison of two signed numbers in a *compare* instruction (see Section 9.4.3). The status V is also useful for signaling an overflow error, and status C together with the input variable C_{in} in Table 3.8 will be used for implementation of double-precision addition/subtraction as we will see in the next section.

The design starts with deriving a truth table in Table 3.9 for the variables A, B, and C_{-1} to be used as inputs to the adder. If $K_1 K_0 = 00$, ordinary add/subtract operations are performed. If $K_1 K_0 = 10$, the subtraction is done by inverting all the bits of B_{in}, adding them to A_{in}, and adding 1 at the LSB, all being performed in one step. If $K_1 K_0 = 11$, the subtraction is done in the same way, but subtracting an extra C_{in}. However, to do this last operation, we must add 1 and subtract C_{in} at the same time because there is only one input C_{-1} of the adder. So, we should transform $(1 - C_{in})$ to a single input value $\overline{C_{in}}$ for C_{-1} as indicated in Table 3.9.

Next, we derive the simplest expressions for the input variables of the adder as follows:

$$A = A_{in}$$

$$B = \overline{K_1} B_{in} + K_1 \overline{B_{in}} = K_1 \oplus B_{in} \tag{3.28}$$

Table 3.8 Function table of a parallel adder/subtractor

Function Select		Function	Comments
K_1	K_0		
0	0	$A_{in} + B_{in}$	A_{in} plus B_{in} in two's complement representation
0	1	$A_{in} + B_{in} + C_{in}$	same as above, plus an extra input carry C_{in}
1	0	$A_{in} - B_{in}$	A_{in} minus B_{in} in two's complement representation
1	1	$A_{in} - B_{in} - C_{in}$	same as above, but minus an extra input borrow C_{in}

Table 3.9 Truth table of a parallel adder

Function Select		Inputs of the Adder			Comments
K_1	K_0	A	B	C_{-1}	
0	0	$A_{in} + B_{in}A_{in}$	B_{in}	0	independent of C_{in}
0	1	A_{in}	B_{in}	C_{in}	supply C_{in} to the carry input C_{-1} of the adder
1	0	A_{in}	$\overline{B_{in}}$	1	independent of C_{in}
1	1	A_{in}	$\overline{B_{in}}$	$1 - C_{in} = \overline{C_{in}}$	supply 1 and minus $C_{in} \Rightarrow$ supply $\overline{C_{in}}$

$$C_{-1} = K_1\overline{K_0} + \overline{K_1}K_0C_{in} + K_1K_0\overline{C_{in}} = K_1\overline{K_0} + K_0(K_1 \oplus C_{in}) \qquad (3.29)$$

or alternatively,

$$C_{-1} = K_1\overline{C_{in}} + (K_1 \oplus K_0)C_{in} \qquad (3.30)$$

There are two alternative expressions for C_{-1}. They have the same complexity of implementation with four gates and the same three-gate delays with respect to the input carry, C_{in}. We have used Expression (3.30) for the implementation of C_{-1} in Figure 3.12.

The expressions for the status bits are derived in terms of the resultant sum/difference, S, and the resultant carry signals, C_{n-1} and C_{n-2}, as follows:

$$N = S_{n-1}$$
$$V = C_{n-1} \oplus C_{n-2}$$
$$Z = \overline{S_{n-1} \cdot \overline{S_{n-2}} \cdot ... \cdot \overline{S_0}} = S_{n-1} + S_{n-2} + ... + S_0$$
$$C = \overline{K_1}C_{n-1} + K_1\overline{C_{n-1}} = K_1 \oplus C_{n-1} \qquad (3.31)$$

Finally, the block diagram of the adder is shown in Figure 3.12. The NOR gate for Z is only conceptual. Practical NOR gates have limited fan-in and n may be too large.

3.4.3 Double-Precision Addition/Subtraction

In many scientific and engineering applications of computers, we often require high precision computation for handling 64-bit numerical data on 32-bit computers. Therefore, we need to derive algorithms for double-precision arithmetic on single-precision hardware. In this section, we will consider the

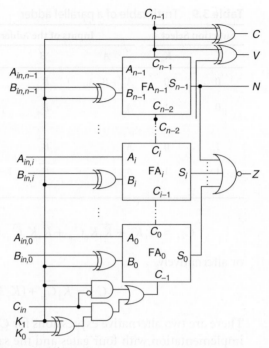

Figure 3.12 Block diagram of a ripple-carry adder with subtract operation

algorithms for double-precision fixed-point addition/subtraction. Algorithms for double-precision multiplication, division, and floating-point operations will be addressed in Chapter 6.

Suppose two double-precision words, A and B, are given as composed of least significant words, A_L and B_L, and most significant words, A_H and B_H, respectively, and the double-word result denoted by S is composed of the least-significant word, S_L, and the most significant word, S_H. The sign bit of each double-precision word is in the most significant word. All the double-precision words are represented in two's complement representation. The algorithm for a double-precision add/subtract, $A + B/A - B$, on a single-precision adder/subtractor, such as the adder/subtractor designed in Section 3.4.2, can be formulated as follows:

Suppose $A = 2^n A_H + A_L$ and $B = 2^n B_H + B_L$, where n is the single-word length.

3.4.4 Ripple-Carry adder for Sign-Magnitude Representation

In this section, we will examine the problem of how to design a ripple-carry adder for sign-magnitude representation based on the algorithm obtained in Section 2.4.1.

Step 1.	Perform the add/subtract operation on the least significant words, A_L and B_L, to obtain $S_L = A_L \pm B_L$, using the adder/subtractor designed in Section 3.4.2 by setting $K_1 K_0 = 00/10$, without considering C_{in}.
Step 2.	Generate the carry/borrow status, C, from the above operation. Also, record the Z status generated by the lower-order operation as Z_L for later use in Step 5.
Step 3.	Perform the add/subtract operation on the most significant words, A_H and B_H, together with the status, C, obtained in Step 2 to obtain $S_H = A_H \pm B_H \pm C$ by connecting C to C_{in} and setting $K_1 K_0 = 01/11$. Record the Z status resulting from the operation as Z_H.
Step 4.	S_H concatenated with S_L will be the double-precision result, $S = 2^n S_H + S_L$.
Step 5.	The status bits, N, V, and C, for the final result are determined solely from Step 3, according to the same algorithm as for a single-precision operation, while the overall status, Z, is determined from both Steps 1 and 3 as $Z = Z_H \text{ AND } Z_L$.

Example 3.9   Numerical Examples of Double-Precision Addition/Subtraction

Three sets of test data are provided, and their calculation processes along with the results obtained based on the above algorithm are shown in Figure 3.13. In these examples, when $A_L - B_L$ does not create an output carry, the C status equals 1. Then, we need to perform the subtraction $A_H - B_H - C$ in the next step. On the other hand, if $A_L - B_L$ produces an output carry, the status is $C = 0$, then we need to perform $A_H - B_H$ without involving C.

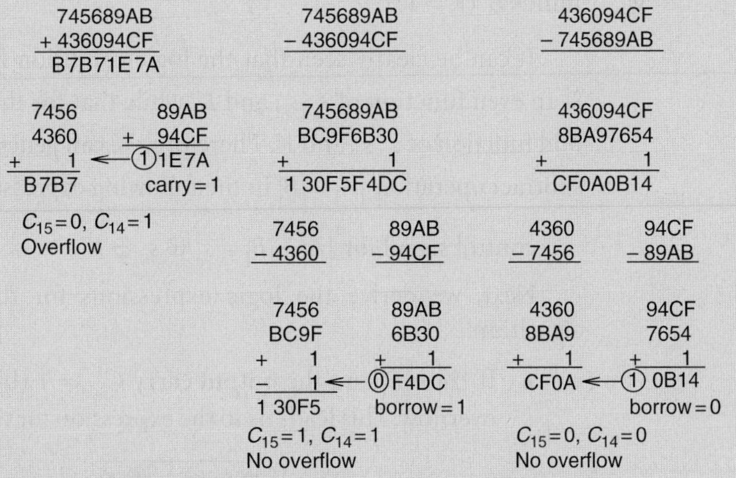

Figure 3.13   Double-precision add/subtract for Example 3.9

Table 3.10   Determining the operation on the magnitudes of A and B

Given Parameters			Operation for the Adder	Comments
s_a	s_b	K	$|A| + |B|$ or $|A| - |B|$	
0	0	0	$|A| + |B|$	same sign, A plus B
0	0	1	$|A| - |B|$	same sign, A minus B
0	1	0	$|A| + |B|$	different signs, A plus B
0	1	1	$|A| - |B|$	different signs, A minus B
1	0	0	$|A| + |B|$	different signs, A plus B
1	0	1	$|A| - |B|$	different signs, A minus B
1	1	0	$|A| + |B|$	same sign, A plus B
1	1	1	$|A| - |B|$	same sign, A minus B

First, we need to elaborate the algorithm so that its various conditions can be expressed in terms of logic operations. For example, the first step of the algorithm requires a comparing and checking procedure that generates a logic condition for controlling the adder to choose between the operations of $|A| + |B|$ and $|A| - |B|$. The truth table for deriving this logic condition is obtained in Table 3.10, where the parameter K distinguishes between "A plus B" ($K = 0$) and "A minus B"($K = 1$).

It can be clearly seen that the logic condition for the operation of $|A| + |B|$ is an even function of s_a, s_b, and K, while that for the operation of $|A| - |B|$ is an odd function of s_a, s_b, and K. Therefore, we can generate the control signal for the subtract operation $|A| - |B|$ in the following expression:

$$\text{control signal for } |A| - |B| = s_a \oplus s_b \oplus K \tag{3.32}$$

Next, we derive the logic expressions for the other conditions in the algorithm:

- If $|A| + |B|$ and the output carry $C_{n-2} = 1$ (bit $n - 1$ is the sign bit), then overflow. This leads us to the expression for the overflow signal as follows:

$$V = \overline{s_a \oplus s_b \oplus K} \cdot C_{n-2} \tag{3.33}$$

- If $|A| - |B|$ and $C_{n-2} = 0$, then recover the magnitude of the difference $|A| - |B|$ from its intermediate two's complement result and, at the same time, invert the sign of A. The control signal for these two operations is as follows:

$$U = (s_a \oplus s_b \oplus K)\overline{C}_{n-2} \tag{3.34}$$

The recovery operation uses the second adder by setting its first operand to 0 and performing the operation controlled by U.

- The carry/borrow status C equals the carry if $|A| + |B|$ or the borrow if $|A| - |B|$:

$$C = V + U \tag{3.35}$$

These expressions give rise to the block diagram of the sign-magnitude adder in Figure 3.14.

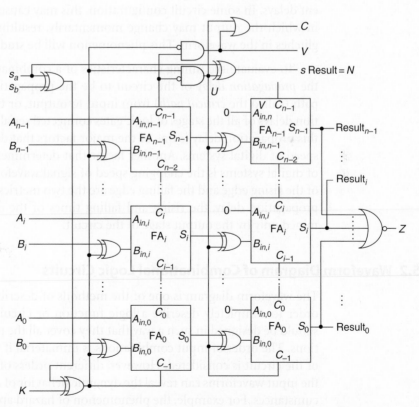

Figure 3.14   Block diagram of an adder in sign-magnitude representation

3.5   DYNAMIC CHARACTERISTICS OF COMBINATIONAL LOGIC CIRCUITS

Next, we learn about the dynamic characteristics of combinational logic circuits, such as propagation delay, waveform diagrams, and hazards.

3.5.1 Propagation Delay of Combinational Logic Circuits

In deriving the logic equivalence of two logic circuits in the previous sections, we neglected the fact that the physical circuits of logic gates have delay. Two combinational circuits are statically equivalent if they implement the same truth table or have identical logic expressions. However, it does not mean that they must have identical *dynamic behavior* because two circuits with the same truth table might be implemented with different circuit configurations, and even the same logic gates may have different physical parameters when manufactured. When two equivalent circuits receive the same input signals with the same waveforms, their output waveforms might be quite different. Different signals may pass through different paths to arrive at the same destination, incurring different delays. In some circuit configuration, this may cause an effect called *hazard*, in which the output may change momentarily, resulting in the appearance of glitches in the waveform. This phenomenon will be studied in Section 3.5.3.

To evaluate the timing characteristics of a combinational circuit, we define the *propagation delay* of the circuit to be the propagation delay of the longest path (called the *critical path*) from input to output, or the sum of the propagation delays of all the stages of logic gates connected serially. Later, we will see that this propagation delay is one of the major factors that determines the hardware speed of digital systems. Another factor that determines the dynamic behavior of digital systems is the changing speed of signal waveforms. The time duration of the rising edge and the falling edge are the two metrics in this category. Unlike propagation delay, the rising and falling times of the output signal are determined only by the output stage of the circuit.

3.5.2 Waveform Diagram of Combinational Logic Circuits

The waveform diagram is one of the methods of describing a logic function. In order to completely describe a logic function or circuit, the input waveforms should be designed in such a way that they cover all the possible input combinations. The order of input combinations is immaterial if only the static behavior of the circuit is considered. However, different orders of input combinations in the input waveforms can reveal the dynamic behavior of a circuit in different circumstances. For example, the phenomenon of hazard appears only at some specific transitions of input combinations. Since the Gray-code sequence of input waveforms changes only one input signal at a time, it usually produces smoother output waveforms than those produced by a binary code sequence.

Example 3.10 The Dynamic Behavior of an XOR-based Full Adder Circuit

To analyze the XOR-based full adder circuit for its output responses to given input transitions, two cases are indicated in the circuit diagram in Figure 3.15. The case of $A_iB_iC_{i-1} = 010 \to 011$ produces smooth changes of outputs S_i and C_i from $1 \to 0$ and $0 \to 1$, respectively, but the case $A_iB_iC_{i-1} = 001 \to 010$ produces a hazard $1 \to 0 \to 1$ in the waveform of S_i while both S_i and C_i should have no change. The calculation of time delays is based on the assumption that all the gates in the circuit have one unit delay. This is usually the default value in some simulating software. The results of the analyses of all the eight input transitions following a binary sequence are listed in Table 3.11. The waveform diagram with two cases of hazards in the output waveform of S_i is shown in Figure 3.16.

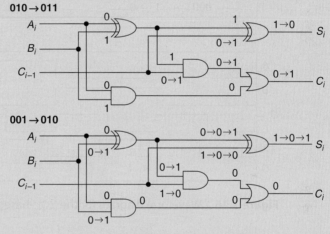

Figure 3.15 Analysis of the XOR-based full adder circuit

The method of calculation of the time delays in a combinational logic circuit is shown in Figure 3.15. Trace the circuit from the inputs to the outputs, gate by gate, through every gate. Look at the case of $A_iB_iC_{i-1} = 001 \to 010$. To indicate the effect of delay introduced by the first XOR gate, we repeat its original output value, that is, $0 \to 0 \to 1$. To indicate the value of the C_{i-1} that changes instantly but waits for another signal after change, we repeat its changed value, that is, $1 \to 0 \to 0$. When these two signals meet at the inputs of the second XOR gate, they cause a hazard $1 \to 0 \to 1$. To calculate the delay of the entire circuit, we count the total number of gates that change values from the input to the output along the longest path. Thus, the path that has the longest time delay for the worst case of the changing input combination is called the *critical path*. It is the critical path that determines the propagation delay of a combinational circuit.

Table 3.11   Output changes and delays for the input transitions in a binary sequence

$A_iB_iC_{i-1}$		S_i		C_i		Comments
From	To	Change	Delay	Change	Delay	
000	001	$0 \to 1$	1	none	–	
001	010	$1 \to 0 \to 1^*$	2	none	–	*Hazard
010	011	$1 \to 0$	1	$0 \to 1$	2	
011	100	$0 \to 1$	1	$1 \to 0$	2	
100	101	$1 \to 0$	1	$0 \to 1$	2	
101	110	$0 \to 1 \to 0^*$	2	none	–	*Hazard
110	111	$0 \to 1$	1	none	–	
111	000	$1 \to 0$	1	$1 \to 0$	2	

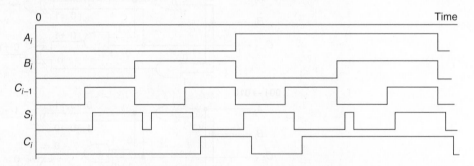

Figure 3.16   Waveform diagram for the XOR-based full adder circuit in Figure 3.15

3.5.3 Hazards in Combinational Logic Circuits

In general, the hazard in a combinational logic circuit occurs in the form of glitches in the output waveforms. The glitches can be positive if the signal change is $0 \to 1 \to 0$ or negative if the signal change is $1 \to 0 \to 1$. These are cases of *static hazards*, in which the signal should normally remain unchanged, but momentarily changes its value in a short period of time. Hazards can also be *dynamic*, in which the change can be $0 \to 1 \to 0 \to 1$ or $1 \to 0 \to 1 \to 0$, that is, the output function should normally change value from 0 to 1 or 1 to 0, but momentarily produces an oscillation. Hazards usually cause no harm to the normal function of a pure combinational logic circuit. However, when combinational logic circuits are used in connection with sequential circuits, the short-duration pulses (glitches) caused by the hazards may affect the normal operation of the sequential circuits, if the overall system works asynchronously.

Example 3.11 A Simple Circuit to Explain the Cause of Hazard and a Method of Avoiding it

A simple circuit of three variables and two disjoint prime implicants is shown in Figure 3.17. Its expression $F = A\overline{C} + BC$ and a Karnaugh map can be used to explain the cause of hazards. Any input transition between the two prime implicants of value 1, $A\overline{C}$ and BC, may cause a hazard $1 \rightarrow 0 \rightarrow 1$. Two classes of these input transitions are:

- Two variables changing at the same time: $ABC = 100 \leftrightarrow 111$ or $110 \leftrightarrow 011$.
- One variable changing: $ABC = 111 \leftrightarrow 110$.

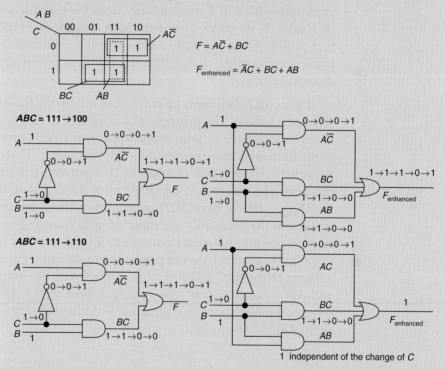

Figure 3.17 A simple example of analysis of hazards using a Karnaugh map

In the general case where the circuit has a complicated structure and its components have variable delays, hazards are not easy to detect and avoid. For the purpose of simplicity of analysis, we assume fixed and uniform gate delays in the circuit, so that the structure of the circuit becomes the major factor that we can use to predict and avoid hazards. We will look at a simple example, and then come back to the more complicated case of the full adder circuit. With respect to dynamic hazards, since they occur only in multilevel circuits in which there are at least three paths along which a change from a primary input can propagate with different delays, they will not be studied in this introductory section.

For the input transitions between two 0-valued minterms, for example, $ABC = 000 \leftrightarrow 101$ or $010 \leftrightarrow 101$, we can predict other possible hazards with positive glitches. Since C is the primary input that must change values across the two prime implicants and has two parallel paths with propagation having different delays in the circuit, the set of changing input variables must contain C. Two cases are checked in the figure, namely $111 \leftrightarrow 100$ and $111 \leftrightarrow 110$. Both cause real hazards. This is because during the transition, the prime implicant $A\overline{C}$ changes to "1" later than the prime implicant BC changes to "0", and F momentarily loses both prime implicants to support its 1 value. If we check these two input transitions in the opposite direction, that is, $100 \leftrightarrow 111$ and $110 \leftrightarrow 111$, we will see different pictures in which the prime implicant $A\overline{C}$ is "0" after the prime implicant BC is "1", so a hazard cannot occur.

Figure 3.17 also shows an example of modifying the structure of the circuit to avoid a hazard. The principle of hazard-free design is to add more product terms to bridge the disjoint prime implicants so that every pair of adjacent 1s in the Karnaugh map is covered by a product term. Therefore, the input transition between each pair of adjacent "1" minterms will not cause a hazard. By this principle, we can add a product term AB to F in order to make the function $F_{enhanced}$ free of hazards. However, this method can only be used for input transitions that have only one input variable changing because it is impossible to cover two non-adjacent minterms by a single product term. This conclusion is verified in Figure 3.16. The product term AB can remove the hazard between adjacent terms ABC and $AB\overline{C}$, but not between the non-adjacent terms ABC and $A\overline{B}\overline{C}$. For the latter case, adding a term $ABC + A\overline{B}\overline{C} = A \cdot \overline{B \oplus C}$ may solve the problem because it remains "1" during the entire period of input transition $ABC = 111 \leftrightarrow 100$.

Example 3.12   Hazard Detection and Avoidance in the XOR-based Full Adder Circuit

Now we can look at a more complicated example. We draw in Figure 3.18 the Karnaugh maps for the sum, S_i, and carry, C_i, of the full adder. We combine the minterms of value 1 in a way different from Figure 3.10 in order to fit the specific configuration of the XOR-based full adder circuit. The combined terms of value 1 thus obtained for S_i are $(A_i \oplus B_i)\overline{C_{i-1}}$ and

$\overline{A_i \oplus B_i} \cdot C_{i-1}$, and those obtained for C_i are $(A_i \oplus B_i)C_{i-1}$ and A_iB_i. Then, from the Karnaugh maps, we can detect a potential hazard $1 \to 0 \to 1$ whenever we have an input transition from a combined term of value 1 to another combined term of value 1. Similarly, we can detect a potential hazard $0 \to 1 \to 0$ whenever we have an input transition from a minterm of value 0 to another minterm of value 0. Therefore, the potential hazards for the XOR-based full adder circuit are as follows:

For S_i: $1 \to 0 \to 1$ hazards occur at input transitions $A_iB_iC_{i-1} = 001 \leftrightarrow 010$,

$$001 \leftrightarrow 100, 111 \leftrightarrow 010, 111 \leftrightarrow 100.$$

$0 \to 1 \to 0$ hazards occur at input transitions $A_iB_iC_{i-1}$

$$= 110 \leftrightarrow 101, 110 \leftrightarrow 011, 000 \leftrightarrow 101, 000 \leftrightarrow 011.$$

For C_i: $1 \to 0 \to 1$ hazards occur at input transitions $A_iB_iC_{i-1} = 110 \leftrightarrow 011$,

$$110 \leftrightarrow 101, 111 \leftrightarrow 011, 111 \leftrightarrow 101.$$

$0 \to 1 \to 0$ hazards occur at input transitions $A_iB_iC_{i-1} = 010 \leftrightarrow 100.$

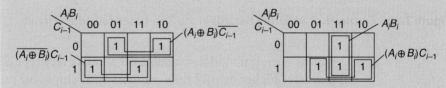

Figure 3.18 Karnaugh maps for the analysis of hazards in the XOR-based full adder circuit ∎

Some cases in the above example have been verified in Figure 3.19. The result shows that all the hazards for S_i in the above example are real hazards, but those for C_i are not, depending on whether one of the terms $(A_i \oplus B_i)C_{i-1}$ and A_iB_i changes to value 1 no later than the other changes to value 0. If the condition in this "whether"-clause is true, there will be no hazards, otherwise a hazard will occur. For example, in Figure 3.19, C_i has a hazard at transition $110 \to 011$ because $(A_i \oplus B_i)C_{i-1}$ gets a value 1 later than A_iB_i gets a value 0. On the contrary, $011 \to 110$ is not a real hazard for C_i because $(A_i \oplus B_i)C_{i-1}$ does not get a value 0 before A_iB_i gets a value 1.

3.6 COMBINATIONAL MSI MODULES

SSI modules are usually built with fewer than 10 gates on a chip. MSI modules contain 10 to 100 gates on a chip. Multiplexers, decoders (demultiplexers), encoders, comparators, and programmable logic devices (PLDs) are typical combinational MSI modules. Programmable logic devices are widely

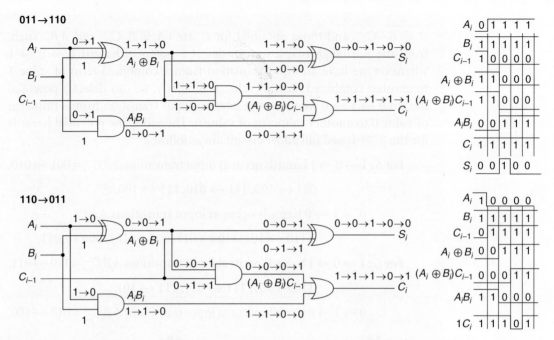

Figure 3.19 Examples of analyzing hazards in the XOR-based full-adder circuit

used as universal modules suitable for almost every type of logic circuit. A PLD may have higher density than ordinary MSI chips and can be classified as LSI chips, which contain 100 to 10,000 gates on a single chip. High-performance microprocessors are classified as very large-scale integration (VLSI) chips that accommodate millions of gates on a single chip. Combinational MSI modules have wide application in CPUs, control units, memory systems, and I/O. In this section, we will study only three types of MSI modules—the multiplexer, the decoder, and the encoder.

3.6.1 Multiplexer

A $2^n \times 1$ multiplexer has 2^n data inputs and n control inputs. It has either one output or two outputs (if an extra *complement* output is included). The multiplexer selects a value from one of the *data* inputs and directs it to the output. The selection is controlled by *data select* control inputs in such a manner that each combination of the control input variables corresponds to a data input line. The entire chip is enabled by an active-low *enable* input. The symbol and logic circuit of an 8×1 multiplexer, such as a 74151 chip, are shown in Figure 3.20. The truth table is shown in Table 3.12.

It can be seen from the truth table that when the chip is not enabled, y always outputs 0. When the chip is enabled, y outputs the value at the selected data input line di, $0 \leq i \leq 7$, determined by the value i of the control input combination $s2s1s0$.

Table 3.12 Truth table of an 8 × 1 multiplexer

enable	Inputs			Outputs	
	s2	s1	s0	y	$\bar{y}$
1	x	x	x	0	1
0	0	0	0	d0	$\overline{d0}$
0	0	0	1	d1	$\overline{d1}$
0	0	1	0	d2	$\overline{d2}$
0	0	1	1	d3	$\overline{d3}$
0	1	0	0	d4	$\overline{d4}$
0	1	0	1	d5	$\overline{d5}$
0	1	1	0	d6	$\overline{d6}$
0	1	1	1	d7	$\overline{d7}$

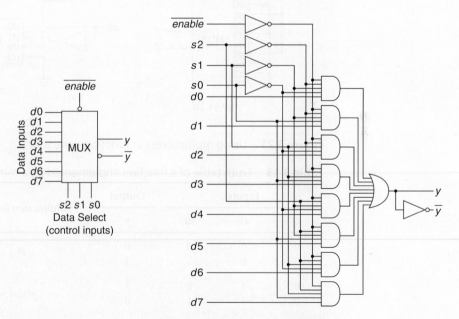

Figure 3.20 Symbol and logic circuit of an 8 × 1 multiplexer

Therefore, each data input line *di* will represent a value of the minterm m_i of the function $y(s2, s1, s0)$. The use of the multiplexer as a function generator is based on this principle.

Example 3.13 Multiplexer as a Function Generator

Implement by multiplexer the function

$$y(s2, s1, s0) = \sum m(1, 2, 4, 5) \qquad (3.36)$$

Solution 1—Using an 8 × 1 Multiplexer

Just connect "1" to the data input lines $d1$, $d2$, $d4$, and $d5$, and "0" to the rest, then y will output "1" for the minterms m_1, m_2, m_4, and m_5. The circuit is shown in Figure 3.21(a).

Solution 2—Using a 4 × 1 Multiplexer

Divide the truth table of $y(s2, s1, s0)$ into four independent tables corresponding to $s2s1 = 11, 01, 10,$ and 11, as shown in Table 3.13. Then, each subtable has only one input variable—$s0$. Obtain the function of $s0$ for the signal to be connected to each data input line of the multiplexer (see each subtable in Table 3.13). The circuit is shown in Figure 3.21 (b).

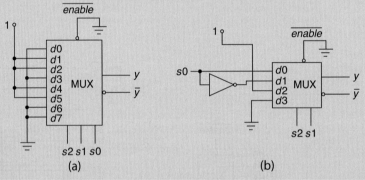

(a) (b)

Figure 3.21 Using multiplexers as function generators

Table 3.13 Truth table of a function implemented by a multiplexer

Inputs			Output	Subfunction from the Subtable
$s2$	$s1$	$s0$	y	
0	0	0	0	$y(s2s1 = 00) = s0$
0	0	1	1	
0	1	0	1	$y(s2s1 = 01) = \overline{s0}$
0	1	1	0	
1	0	0	1	$y(s2s1 = 10) = 1$
1	0	1	1	
1	1	0	0	$y(s2s1 = 11) = 0$
1	1	1	0	

The same result as that shown in Solution 2 of Example 3.13 can be obtained by an analytical method using Shannon's Expansion Theorem (see Expressions 3.2 and 3.3) as follows:

$$
\begin{aligned}
y(s2, s1, s0) &= \sum m(1, 2, 4, 5) = \overline{s2} \cdot \overline{s1} \cdot s0 + \overline{s2} \cdot s1 \cdot \overline{s0} + s2 \cdot \overline{s1} \cdot \overline{s0} + s2 \cdot \overline{s1} \cdot s0 \\
&= s2(y_{s2=1}) + \overline{s2}(y_{s2=0}) \\
&= s2(\overline{s1} \cdot s0 + \overline{s1} \cdot s0) + \overline{s2}(\overline{s1} \cdot s0 + s1 \cdot \overline{s0}) \\
&= s2[s1(\overline{s1} \cdot \overline{s0} + \overline{s1} \cdot s0)_{s1=1} + \overline{s1}(\overline{s1} \cdot \overline{s0} + \overline{s1} \cdot s0)_{s1=0}] \\
&\quad + \overline{s2}[s1(\overline{s1} \cdot s0 + s1 \cdot \overline{s0})_{s1=1} + \overline{s1}(\overline{s1} \cdot s0 + s1 \cdot \overline{s0})_{s1=0}] \\
&= s2[\overline{s1}(\overline{s0} + s0)] + \overline{s2}[s1(s1 \cdot \overline{s0}) + \overline{s1}(s0)] \\
&= \overline{s2} \cdot \overline{s1} \cdot s0 + \overline{s2} \cdot s1 \cdot \overline{s0} + s2 \cdot \overline{s1} \cdot 1 \tag{3.37}
\end{aligned}
$$

Two identical $2^n \times 1$ multiplexers can be combined into a double-sized $2^{n+1} \times 1$ multiplexer by the circuit connection shown in Figure 3.22 for $n = 4$. Then, the input *enable* becomes a control input. When $s2 = 0$, it enables the upper multiplexer to select among $d0$–$d3$, while $s2 = 1$, it enables the lower multiplexer to select among $d4$–$d7$.

This result can also be verified using Shannon's Expansion Theorem as follows:

$$
\begin{aligned}
f(s2, s1, s0) &= s2 \cdot f(s2, s1, s0)\big|_{s2=1} + \overline{s2} \cdot f(s2, s1, s0)\big|_{s2=0} \\
&= \text{MUX}_{\text{enabled by } s2} + \text{MUX}_{\text{enabled by } \overline{s2}} \tag{3.38}
\end{aligned}
$$

Another method of constructing a large-sized multiplexer from small-sized ones is to connect the small-sized multiplexers into a multistage structure so that the outputs of the lower-level small-sized multiplexers become the inputs of the

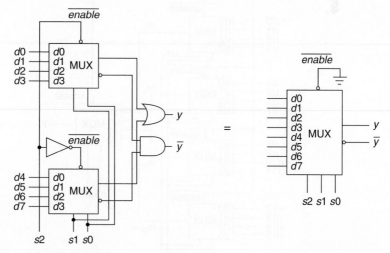

Figure 3.22 Combining two 4×1 multiplexers into one 8×1 multiplexer

higher-level large-sized multiplexer. This structure does not use $\overline{enable}$ inputs for interconnection, but effectively utilizes the control inputs of all small-sized multiplexers to extend the range of control. An example of combining five 4×1 multiplexers into one 16×1 multiplexer is given in Figure 3.23.

Besides the implementation of canonical SOP expressions of logic functions, multiplexers are very useful for constructing the datapath of the CPU, the memory, and the I/O controller of a computer. These applications include:

- A multiple source single-destination connection.
- A parallel-serial conversion.
- A combinational shifter.

3.6.2 Decoder/Demultiplexer

An $n \times 2^n$ decoder has n binary coded inputs and 2^n outputs (active high or active low, depending on the implementation). The decoder selects one of the mutually exclusive outputs corresponding to the value of combination of the n input variables (an n-bit binary code). The entire chip is enabled by one or two active-low $\overline{enable}$ inputs. The symbol and logic circuit of a 3×8 decoder are shown in Figure 3.24. The truth table is shown in Table 3.14.

It can be seen from the truth table that when any one or both of the $\overline{enable}$ inputs are "1", the chip is not enabled and all output lines have the value 0. When both $\overline{enable}$ inputs are "0", the chip is enabled and the output line m_i, $0 \leq i \leq 7$, that corresponds to the value i of the combination ABC, will take the value 1

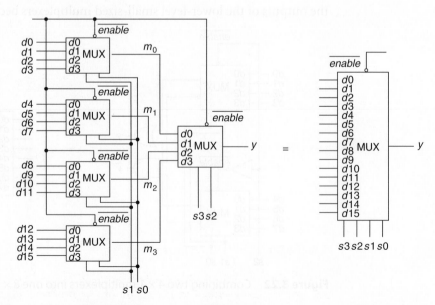

Figure 3.23   Combining five 4×1 multiplexers into one 16×1 multiplexer

Table 3.14 Truth table of a 3 × 8 decoder

$\overline{enable1}$	$\overline{enable2}$	Inputs			Outputs							
		$c2$	$c1$	$c0$	m_0	m_1	m_2	m_3	m_4	m_5	m_6	m_7
0	1	x	x	x	0	0	0	0	0	0	0	0
1	0	x	x	x	0	0	0	0	0	0	0	0
1	1	x	x	x	0	0	0	0	0	0	0	0
0	0	0	0	0	1	0	0	0	0	0	0	0
0	0	0	0	1	0	1	0	0	0	0	0	0
0	0	0	1	0	0	0	1	0	0	0	0	0
0	0	0	1	1	0	0	0	1	0	0	0	0
0	0	1	0	0	0	0	0	0	1	0	0	0
0	0	1	0	1	0	0	0	0	0	1	0	0
0	0	1	1	0	0	0	0	0	0	0	1	0
0	0	1	1	1	0	0	0	0	0	0	0	1

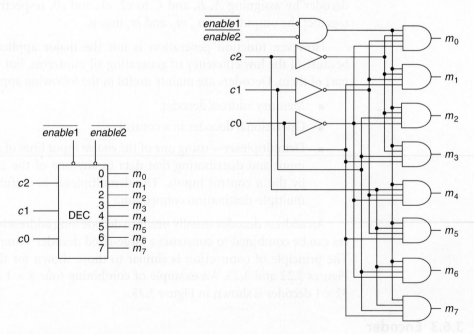

Figure 3.24 Symbol and logic circuit of a 3 × 8 decoder

and all the remaining output lines will take the value 0. Therefore, each output line m_i represents a minterm m_i of the function $F(c2, c1, c0)$. If we select the minterms required by the function $F(c2, c1, c0)$ and OR them together,

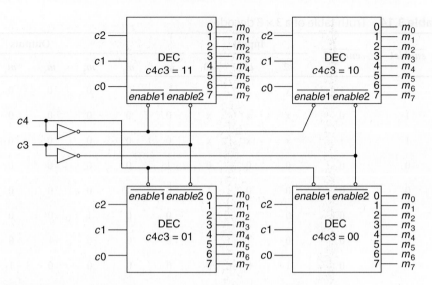

Figure 3.25   Combining four 3×8 decoders into a 5×32 decoder

we can use the decoder as a function generator. For example, the function $y(A, B, C) = \sum m(1, 2, 4, 5)$ in Example 3.14 can be generated from a 3×8 decoder by assigning A, B, and C to $c2$, $c1$, and $c0$, respectively, and then OR together the outputs m_1, m_2, m_4, and m_5 into y.

However, function generation is not the major application of decoders because of the low efficiency of generating all minterms, but using only a small part of them. Decoders are mainly useful in the following applications:

- Memory address decoder.
- Operational decoder in a control.
- Demultiplexer—using one of the $\overline{enable}$ input lines of a decoder as a data input and distributing that data to any one of the 2^n outputs selected by the n control inputs. The demultiplexer is useful for single-source multiple-destination connection.

An address decoder usually needs to decode long address bits. Several decoders can be combined to construct a large-sized decoder using the $\overline{enable}$ inputs. The principle of connection is similar to those shown for the multiplexers in Figures 3.22 and 3.23. An example of combining four 8×1 decoders into one 32×1 decoder is shown in Figure 3.25.

3.6.3 Encoder

A $2^n \times n$ encoder has 2^n inputs and n binary coded outputs. The encoder receives one of the mutually exclusive inputs, I_i (for $0 \le i \le 2^n - 1$), and generates its corresponding binary code i on the output lines. The symbol and logic circuit of an

8×3 encoder are shown in Figure 3.26. The truth table is shown in Table 3.15, where $y2$, $y1$, and $y0$ are binary coded outputs, and v is called the *presence bit* that validates the outputs when a value 1 is present on any one of the input lines.

The expressions for the output variables for the case of mutually exclusive inputs are

$$y2 = I_4 + I_5 + I_6 + I_7$$
$$y1 = I_2 + I_3 + I_6 + I_7$$
$$y0 = I_1 + I_3 + I_5 + I_7$$
$$v = I_0 + I_1 + I_2 + I_3 + I_4 + I_5 + I_6 + I_7 \tag{3.39}$$

Table 3.15   Truth table of an 8×3 encoder

Inputs								Outputs			
I_0	I_1	I_2	I_3	I_4	I_5	I_6	I_7	$y2$	$y1$	$y0$	v
0	0	0	0	0	0	0	0	0	0	0	0
1	0	0	0	0	0	0	0	0	0	0	1
0	1	0	0	0	0	0	0	0	0	1	1
0	0	1	0	0	0	0	0	0	1	0	1
0	0	0	1	0	0	0	0	0	1	1	1
0	0	0	0	1	0	0	0	1	0	0	1
0	0	0	0	0	1	0	0	1	0	1	1
0	0	0	0	0	0	1	0	1	1	0	1
0	0	0	0	0	0	0	1	1	1	1	1

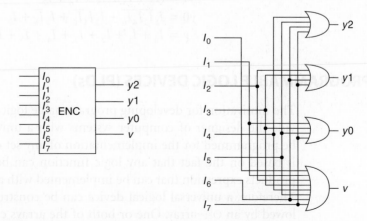

Figure 3.26   Symbol and logic circuit of an 8×3 encoder

Table 3.16   Truth table of an 8×3 priority encoder

Inputs								Outputs			
I_0	I_1	I_2	I_3	I_4	I_5	I_6	I_7	$y2$	$y1$	$y0$	v
0	0	0	0	0	0	0	0	0	0	0	0
1	0	0	0	0	0	0	0	0	0	0	1
x	1	0	0	0	0	0	0	0	0	1	1
x	x	1	0	0	0	0	0	0	1	0	1
x	x	x	1	0	0	0	0	0	1	1	1
x	x	x	x	1	0	0	0	1	0	0	1
x	x	x	x	x	1	0	0	1	0	1	1
x	x	x	x	x	x	1	0	1	1	0	1
x	x	x	x	x	x	x	1	1	1	1	1

The encoder is mainly used to encode the exception signal lines activated by various exception sources, such as I/O devices. Because the exception requests on these lines are issued randomly, they must be made mutually exclusive by using a priority encoder. Assume that the input line Ii has a higher priority than I_j, if $i > j$. Then, the truth table in Table 3.15 should be modified to that in Table 3.16.

The expressions for the output variables for the case of not mutually exclusive inputs are

$$
\begin{aligned}
y2 &= I_4 + I_5 + I_6 + I_7 \\
y1 &= (I_2 + I_3)\overline{I_2 I_5} + I_6 + I_7 \\
y0 &= I_1 \overline{I_2 I_4 I_6} + I_3 \overline{I_4 I_6} + I_5 \overline{I_6} + I_7 \\
v &= I_0 + I_1 + I_2 + I_3 + I_4 + I_5 + I_6 + I_7
\end{aligned}
\tag{3.40}
$$

3.7   PROGRAMMABLE LOGIC DEVICES (PLDs)

The motivation for developing programmable logical devices (PLDs) is to provide the designer of computer systems with a universal logic device that can be programmed for the implementation of any set of logic functions. The idea is based on the fact that any logic function can be represented in a sum-of-products expression that can be implemented with a two-level AND–OR circuit. Therefore, a universal logical device can be constructed as an AND–array followed by an OR–array. One or both of the arrays can be made programmable in order to generate various custom-designed logic functions. According to the programmability of the AND-arrays and/or OR-arrays, there are three types of programmable logical devices, namely:

- the programmable logic array (PLA),
- the read-only memory (ROM), and
- the programmable array logic (PAL).

3.7.1 Programmable Logic Array (PLA)

A programmable logical array (PLA) consists of a programmable AND-array and a programmable OR-array. We use three parameters to characterize its capacity: (1) the number of inputs, (2) the number of product terms, and (3) the number of outputs. The logic circuit diagram of a $3 \times 8 \times 4$ PLA is shown in Figure 3.27. If the AND-array and the OR-array are programmed by the manufacturer according to the program table provided by the customer, the PLA is called a *mask-programmable PLA*. If the AND-array and the OR-array can be programmed by the user by blowing fusible links or leaving them intact, the PLA is called a *field-programmable PLA* (FPLA). To achieve efficient utilization of the product terms of a PLA, it is important to optimize the logic design so that the multiple output functions of the same set of input variables can make use of as many common product terms as possible.

3.7.2 Read-Only Memory (ROM)

Although read-only memory (ROM) is used mainly as a memory chip, it is actually a combinational circuit. It is similar to a PLA, with the only difference that its AND-array is fixed, providing all 2^n product terms for n input variables. Therefore, the AND-array of a $2^n \times m$ ROM is an $n \times 2^n$ decoder, and the OR-array is programmable, generating m output functions by ORing selected product terms

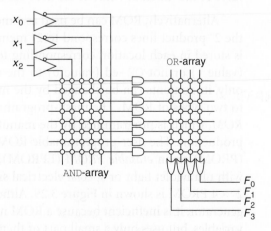

Figure 3.27 Logic circuit diagram of a $3 \times 8 \times 4$ PLA

Example 3.14   A Full Adder Implemented on a PLA

A full adder needs 3 inputs, 2 outputs, and 7 product terms of a PLA if we use Expression (3.22) with 7 distinct minterms. In order to maximize the number of common product terms sharable by S_i and C_i, we take advantage of the complemented outputs provided by the PLA. We can use the expression for the inverse carry-out signal and thus, reduce the total number of product terms to 5. A circuit implementing the full adder with a minimum size of PLA of $3 \times 5 \times 2$ is shown in Figure 3.28.

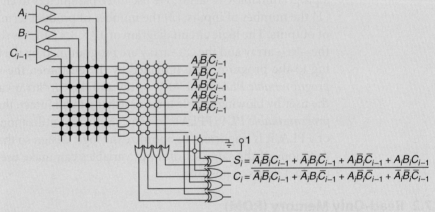

$$S_i = \bar{A}_i \bar{B}_i C_{i-1} + \bar{A}_i B_i \bar{C}_{i-1} + A_i \bar{B}_i \bar{C}_{i-1} + \overline{A_i B_i C_{i-1}}$$

$$C_i = \overline{\bar{A}_i \bar{B}_i C_{i-1} + \bar{A}_i B_i \bar{C}_{i-1} + A_i \bar{B}_i \bar{C}_{i-1} + \bar{A}_i \bar{B}_i \bar{C}_{i-1}}$$

Figure 3.28   Implementation of a full adder optimized to a minimum of $3 \times 5 \times 2$ PLA ∎

from the decoder. Therefore, the ROM is a direct implementation of the truth table of the function without the need for simplification.

Alternatively, ROM can be used as a memory device. For a $2^n \times m$-bit ROM, the 2^n product lines correspond to 2^n memory locations, and an m-bit number is stored in each location corresponding to whether the product line is OR-ed (value 1) or not OR-ed (value 0) to the output. Although the ROM is read-only, its contents can be changed by the manufacturer or the user, which leads to two types of ROM. The mask-programmable ROM is known as an *ordinary ROM*, which is programmed by the manufacturer through a mask during chip production. The user-programmable ROM is known as a *programmable ROM* (PROM) or an *erasable PROM* (EPROM), in which stored data can be erased with ultraviolet light or special electrical signals. The logic circuit diagram of a $2^3 \times 4$ PROM is shown in Figure 3.29. Although ROM can be used as a function generator, it is inefficient because a ROM must generate all minterms of n input variables, but uses only a small part of them.

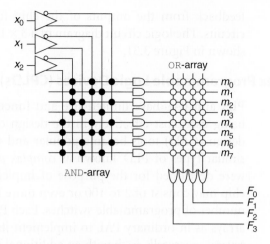

Figure 3.29 Logic circuit diagram of a $2^3 \times 4$ PROM

Example 3.15 A Full Adder Implemented on a ROM

A full adder implemented on a $2^3 \times 2$-bit ROM is shown in Figure 3.30.

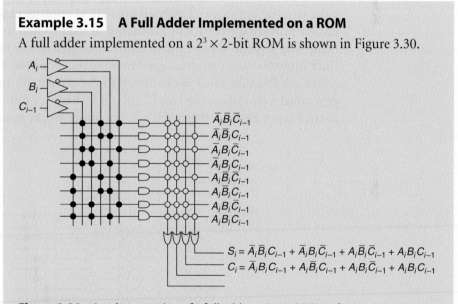

Figure 3.30 Implementation of a full adder using a PROM of minimum capacity of $2^3 \times 2$ bits ∎

3.7.3 Programmable Array Logic (PAL)

The programmable array logic (PAL) was developed from PLAs by making the OR-array fixed. The product terms generated by the AND-array are distributed properly among a number of outputs. The fan-in values of the output OR-gates are thus fixed. To overcome this limitation, the AND-array of the PAL allows feedback from the outputs of the chip for constructing multilevel AND–OR circuits. The logic circuit diagram of a $3 \times 12 \times 4$ PAL with two feedback paths is shown in Figure 3.31.

3.7.4 Complex Programmable Logic Devices (CPLDs)

PLA and PAL have limited size and functionality, which prevents them from being used cost-effectively in the design of large systems. As computer-aided design (CAD) tools became popular and widely used, special large devices of similar types of PLD, known as *complex programmable logic devices* (CPLDs), were developed for the purpose of implementing complex systems. A CPLD chip may consist of 2 to 100 or even more PAL-like blocks connected by a large number of programmable switches. Each PAL-like block has the same AND–OR arrays as in ordinary PAL to implement its basic logic functions, but contains several *macrocells*, each with an additional output circuit for enhancing its output capability. The block diagram of such an output circuit of the macrocell is shown in Figure 3.33. It contains a D-type flip-flop (see Chapter 4) that provides selective outputs and makes it possible to implement sequential circuits on PAL by providing feedback of the output of the flip-flop to the AND–array. The D flip-flop has two inputs: a data input coming from the PAL's OR–array and a clock input to store that data signal into the flip-flop. The output of the macrocell of the PAL-like block is connected to the outside through a special type of gate called a *tri-state device* (see Chapter 8), which is a buffer with an additional control input $K0$ such that if $K0 = 1$, the buffer works as usual with no change

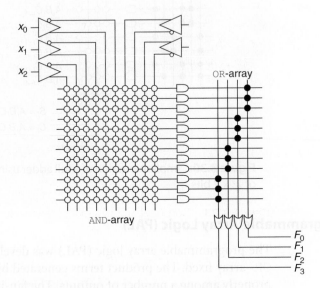

Figure 3.31   Logical circuit diagram of a $3 \times 12 \times 4$ PAL

Example 3.16 A Full Adder Implemented on a PAL without Inverted Output

A full adder can be implemented on a $3 \times 12 \times 4$ PAL, as shown in Figure 3.32. Compared with Figure 3.28, it can be seen that a PAL uses more product lines than a PLA to implement the full adder. Due to the lack of complemented outputs, the PAL must generate 7 minterms for the sum and carry-out functions of the full adder. Due to the fixed OR-array, the PAL must use 4 extra product lines for feedback and fitting the configuration of the OR-array (i.e., a product line cannot be shared among two or more OR-gates).

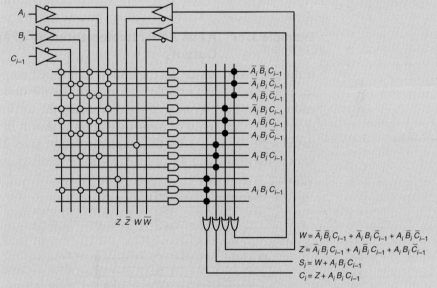

Figure 3.32 Implementation of a full adder using a $3 \times 12 \times 4$ PAL ∎

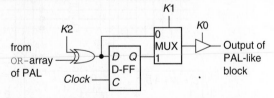

Figure 3.33 Output circuit of a macrocell of a PAL-like block

of input signal; if $K0 = 0$, the buffer is open-circuited, presenting a high impedance to the outside of the circuit. This *high impedance state* allows many tri-state devices to be directly connected together without mutual interference if only one of the tri-state devices is enabled at a time. Thus, the control signals $K2$–$K0$ of the macrocell perform their control functions according to Table 3.17.

Table 3.17   Function table of the macrocell in Figure 3.33

K2	K1	K0	Output of the PAL Device
0	0	1	Original output of the PAL OR-array
0	1	1	Original output of the PAL OR-array output through the D flip-flop
1	0	1	Inverted output of the PAL OR-array
1	1	1	Inverted output of the PAL OR-array output through the D flip-flop
x	x	0	Output is blocked and presents a high impedance to the outside

Example 3.17   A Full Adder Implemented on a PAL with Inverted Outputs

If the given PAL device has the option of inverted outputs, we can use the same method from Example 3.14 to optimize the design by generating S_i and $\overline{C}_i$ from the OR-array, thus minimizing the total number of product terms to 5. The circuit of implementation is shown in Figure 3.34. Compared with Example 3.16, this implementation saves 25% of the product lines of the device by fully utilizing the same feedback path for both output signals.

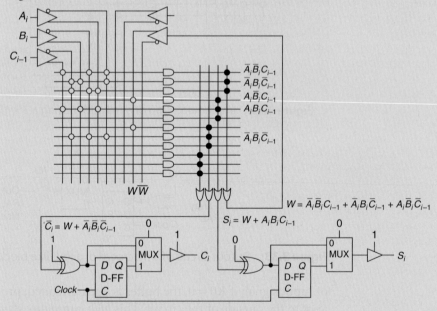

Figure 3.34   Implementation of a full adder using a $3 \times 12 \times 4$ PAL with macrocells

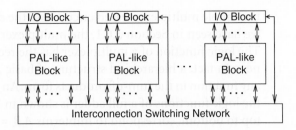

Figure 3.35 Block diagram of a CPLD based on PAL-like blocks

The block diagram of a CPLD is shown in Figure 3.35. It has a number of PAL-like blocks with a large number of input/output pins. Unlike ordinary PLAs and PALs, these I/O pins can be programmed for the required logic functions. The interconnection switching network can be configured for connections between the PAL-like blocks through a large number of horizontal and vertical wires, using switches for connections by programming. Although it is impractical to provide full connectivity between every pair of horizontal and vertical wires, an adequate connectivity should be achieved to satisfy the requirements of most application systems.

3.7.5 Field-Programmable Gate Arrays (FPGAs)

The development of CPLDs has been an important step toward the goal of computer design automation. However, their size and functionality are still somewhat limited because any function must be implemented as a sum-of-products form and uses one output pin. To overcome this limitation, another class of programmable devices known as *field-programmable gate arrays* (FPGAs) has been developed. The structures of these devices are based on two important concepts. One concept is the "gate array" implied in the name of the device. The array contains some types of universal functional units as the basic logic blocks. The other concept comes from the parallel architecture of "array processor," which interconnects hundreds or thousands of processing elements in a two-dimensional or multidimensional topology so that each processing element can be connected with its four or eight nearest neighbors. These two concepts led to the creation of a conceptual structure of FPGA as shown in Figure 3.36. A large array of basic logic blocks denoted by "LB" are interconnected through a large number of switching elements denoted by "S" according to a two-dimensional mesh topology. As the figure shows, each basic logic block is connected to its eight nearest neighbors through eight surrounding switching elements. All the boundary switching elements are connected to the I/O pins in corresponding I/O blocks.

Various functional units of highly modular and flexible structure can be used as the basic logic block of the FPGA. Two popular circuits are noteworthy: one is the simple multiplexer-based circuit, and the other is the simple lookup table. As we have seen in Section 3.6.1, the multiplexer is a good universal logic element. The logic function of a multiplexer has the required property of logic completeness. In fact, a hierarchical structure of basic 2×1 multiplexers can implement any function in the sum-of-products form. An example of the implementation of the logic functions of a full adder is shown in Figure 3.37. The four inputs, from top to bottom, correspond to minterms $A_i B_i = 00, 10, 01,$ and 11, respectively.

Another possible implementation of the basic logic block for the FPGA is the look-up table (LUT). It simply implements a truth table for completely defining and storing a logic function. For example, a four-input LUT can be stored in a 16-bit memory circuit that can be programmed to implement any function of

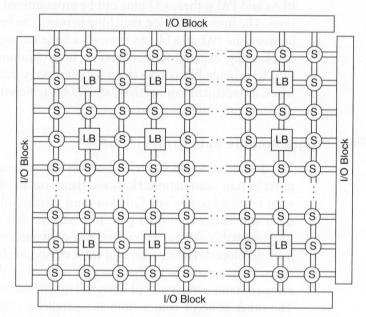

Figure 3.36 Conceptual structure of an FPGA

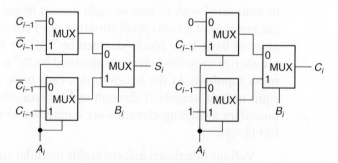

Figure 3.37 Implementation of the full-adder function in a simple multiplexer-based circuit

four variables. The basic logic block may also contain flip-flops for implementation of the sequential logic functions. Therefore, the FPGA chips actually need to include a substantial amount of memory not only for the LUTs, but also for many other purposes such as RAM, ROM, stacks, queues, and so on.

Compared to a CPLD, the FPGA chips have much larger size and greater functionality for the implementation of large application systems. Hence, an FPGA allows an application designer to design, implement, and test a prototype of the application system in a relatively short period of time rather than going a long way to design and fabricate a customized VLSI chip with a much higher cost. However, the major problem which FPGA chips may face is the slower speed than the less powerful but flexible CPLD chips.

SUMMARY

Combinational logic circuits are the most important basic circuits that are most widely used in performing all the basic arithmetic-logic operations involved in the instruction set of a computer. For example, operations such as add/subtract, AND/OR/NOT/XOR, shift, compare, memory address generation, branch address (next PC or target address) calculation all use combinational circuits. Sequential circuits (to be studied in the next chapter) also use combinational circuits as a basis. The combinational circuits can be represented, analyzed, and designed in many different ways, including the use of a truth table (Section 3.1.1), Boolean algebra (Section 3.1.2–3.1.4), a Karnaugh map (Section 3.2), a logic circuit diagram (Section 3.3–3.4), and a waveform diagram (Section 3.5). The design of combinational circuits is closely related to their hardware implementations. The simple implementation is to use basic logic gates, especially NAND, NOR, XOR, and XNOR gates, whose properties are described in Section 3.3. The design of parallel adders/subtractors, including double-precision and sign-magnitude add/subtract circuits, are given in Section 3.4. The implementations using MSI and PLD modules are studied in Sections 3.6 and 3.7, respectively.

EXERCISES

3.1 Using the algebraic method, simplify each of the following Boolean expressions for minimum implementation using a minimum number of basic gates selected from AND, OR, NOT, NAND, NOR, XOR, and XNOR. Those gates with inverted input(s) are not included. Assume that only the original input variables, not the inverted variables, are given.

(a) $AB + A\overline{B} + \overline{A}C + \overline{A} \cdot \overline{C}$

(b) $A \cdot \overline{B} \cdot \overline{C} \cdot \overline{D} + A \cdot \overline{B} \cdot C + A \cdot B \cdot D + \overline{A} \cdot C \cdot \overline{D}$

(c) $C(AB + \overline{ABC}) + AB\overline{C}$

(d) $\overline{CD} + A + A + CD + AB$

(e) $\overline{A + B} + (A \oplus B) + ABC$

(f) $(AB + \overline{A}C + BC)(A + B + \overline{C})$

(g) $(\overline{A} + C)(\overline{A} + \overline{C})(A + B + \overline{C}D)$

(h) $(AB + C + D)(\overline{C} + D)(\overline{C} + D + E)$

3.2 Prove the identity of each of the following Boolean equations, using algebraic manipulation:

(a) $\overline{A} + A \cdot B + A \cdot \overline{C} + A \cdot \overline{B} \cdot \overline{C} = \overline{A} + B + \overline{C}$

(b) $A \cdot \overline{B} + \overline{A} \cdot \overline{C} \cdot \overline{D} + \overline{A} \cdot \overline{B} \cdot D + \overline{A} \cdot \overline{B} \cdot C \cdot \overline{D} = \overline{B} + \overline{A} \cdot \overline{C} \cdot \overline{D}$

(c) $A \oplus B + B \oplus C + C \oplus A = A \oplus B + B \oplus C$

(d) $(X \oplus Y) + (Y \oplus Z) + (Z \oplus X) = \overline{X}Y + \overline{Y}Z + \overline{Z}X = X\overline{Y} + Y\overline{Z} + Z\overline{X}.$

3.3 Directly derive the complement (i.e., the inversion) of each of the following expressions using DeMorgan's Theorem, and then simplify algebraically the obtained expression to a minimum number of literals. Don't simplify the given expression before applying DeMorgan's Theorem.

(a) $AB(\overline{C}D + \overline{B}C)$

(b) $A(B + C)(\overline{C} + \overline{D})$

(c) $(A + C + \overline{D})(AB + \overline{A}C)$

(d) $\overline{\overline{C} + D(\overline{AD} + AB)}$

(e) $\overline{A \cdot B \cdot \overline{A} + \overline{AC} \cdot (\overline{A} + B + C)}$

(f) $(AB + C + D)(\overline{C} + D)(\overline{C} + D + E)$

3.4 Convert the following expressions to canonical SOP form using three methods:

(i) Use the basic formulae of Boolean algebra to expand each product to a sum of minterms.

(ii) Repeatedly use Shannon's Expansion Theorem on the original given expression.

(iii) Use the Karnaugh map in the reverse direction.

(a) $F(A, B, C, D) = \overline{ABC} + AC + BD$

(b) $F(A, B, C, D) = (\overline{B} + \overline{C} + \overline{D})(\overline{A} + \overline{D})(B + \overline{D})$

(c) $F(A, B, C) = (\overline{A} + C)(AB + \overline{A} \cdot \overline{B} + AC)$

(d) $F(A, B, C) = (\overline{A} + BC)(\overline{A} + \overline{B} + \overline{C})(AC + \overline{B})$

3.5 Convert the following expression to canonical POS form by the algebraic method:

(a) $F(A, B, C, D) = (\overline{C} + \overline{D})(\overline{A} + \overline{D})(\overline{B} + \overline{D})$

(b) $F(A, B, C, D) = AC + BD + \overline{A} \cdot \overline{B} \cdot \overline{C}$

(c) $F(A, B, C) = BC + \overline{A} \cdot \overline{B} + C$

(d) $F(A, B, C) = (A + \overline{B} + C)(AB + \overline{A}C)$

3.6 For each of the following expressions, use the Karnaugh map to find (1) all the essential prime implicants, (2) all the unessential prime implicants, and (3) all the possible simplest SOP expressions.

(a) $F_1(A, B, C, D) = \Sigma(m_3, m_4, m_5, m_7, m_{10}, m_{11}, m_{12}, m_{14}, m_{15})$

(b) $F_2(A, B, C, D) = \Sigma(m_0, m_2, m_4, m_5, m_7, m_{10}, m_{11}, m_{13}, m_{14}, m_{15})$

3.7 Use the Karnaugh map to simplify each of the following Boolean functions F together with the don't care sets d:

(a) $F(A, B, C, D) = \Sigma(m_0, m_5, m_{10}, m_{14})$ with $d(A, B, C, D) = \{m_1, m_6, m_7, m_{15}\}$

(b) $F(A, B, C, D) = \Sigma(m_0, m_6, m_8, m_{13}, m_{14})$ with $d(A, B, C, D) = \{m_2, m_4, m_{10}\}$

(c) $F(A, B, C, D) = \Sigma(m_3, m_5, m_7)$ with $d(A, B, C, D) = \{m_2, m_{11}, m_{13}, m_{15}\}$

3.8 (a) Prove that NAND is a universal operation, that is, it has the property of logical completeness.

(b) Prove that NOR is a universal operation, that is, it has the property of logical completeness.

(c) Prove that XOR gate can be universal when it is used in combination with OR.

(d) Prove that XOR gate can be universal when it is used in combination with AND.

3.9 Given a combinational circuit as shown in Figure 3.38.

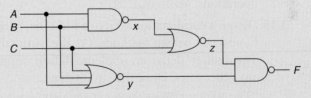

Figure 3.38 Circuit diagram for Problem 3.9

(a) Based on the circuit, directly write the expression for F and simplify it algebraically to the simplest form.

(b) Assume that each gate introduces a unit gate delay. Analyze the circuit to show that F has a hazard during the transition $ABC = 111 \rightarrow 000$.

(c) Based on the result of analysis in Part (b), draw a complete waveform diagram for all the variables, $A, B, C, x, y, z,$ and F. Find the delay of F in the number of unit gate delays.

3.10 Given the four circuits of a full adder as shown in Figure 3.11, analyze each of them for the state transition $A_i B_i C_{i-1} = 110 \rightarrow 101$ to find the state transitions (including hazards, if any) and the delays in the number of unit gate delays for the outputs S_i and C_i.

3.11 (a) Write a truth table for the comparison of two 3-bit binary unsigned numbers. The input variables are the numbers $A = A_2 A_1 A_0$ and $B = B_2 B_1 B_0$, and the output variables are $R = R_1 R_0$ such that if $A > B$, then $R = 10$, if $A < B$, then $R = 01$, and if $A = B$, then $R = 00$.

(b) Design the circuit.

(c) Redo the problem for a comparison of two 4-bit unsigned numbers, $A = A_3 A_2 A_1 A_0$ and $B = B_3 B_2 B_1 B_0$. The output is a single logic variable, R, which equals 1 if $A > B$, else R equals 0.

3.12 (a) Design a combinational circuit that converts a BCD digit, $a_3 a_2 a_1 a_0$, into an excess-3 digit, $b_3 b_2 b_1 b_0$, not using an adder. Your circuit must be constructed by no more than six basic gates selected from two-input AND, OR, NAND, NOR, XOR, and XNOR. Assume that the inverted input variables are not available. The logic for detection of invalid digits is not required.

(b) Repeat Part (a) for converting an excess-3 digit to a BCD digit with the same condition.

3.13 Design the logic circuit of a 4-bit Gray-to-binary code converter that converts a 4-bit Gray code, $x_3 x_2 x_1 x_0$, to a 4-bit binary code, $f_3 f_2 f_1 f_0$. Use a minimum number of XOR gates only.

3.14 Prove that a single 2×1 multiplexer is logically complete. That means, how you can use only a *single* 2×1 multiplexer to implement each of three basic logic operations, AND, OR, NOT.

3.15 Design a combinational circuit for a majority function of four variables, A, B, C, and D. Use two methods, (1) the truth table and (2) Shannon's Expansion Theorem, to derive an implementation using only 2×1 multiplexers without any other gates. Draw the circuit diagram.

[Note: Majority function equals 1 iff a majority of its input variables take value 1 and the rest take value 0. Constructing a 16×1 multiplexer and then mapping the function on it is not a required solution.]

3.16 Figure 3.39 is a combinational logic circuit with a multiplexer and some gates.

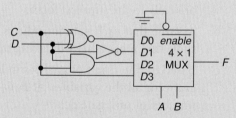

Figure 3.39   Circuit diagram for Problem 3.16

(a)   Using the basic functional expression of a multiplexer, write the logic expression for the output function F directly from the circuit.

(b)   Using the method of Karnaugh map, find three different simplest SOP expressions equivalent to the above-obtained expression.

3.17 Given three 4-input logic functions:

$$F_1(A, B, C, D) = \Sigma m(0, 3, 5, 6, 8, 9, 14, 15)$$
$$F_2(A, B, C, D) = \Sigma m(2, 3, 5, 6, 8, 11, 13, 15)$$
$$F_3(A, B, C, D) = \Sigma m(0, 3, 4, 7, 9, 10, 12, 14)$$

(a)   Implement each of them using a 8×1 multiplexer plus an inverter.

(b)   Implement each of them using a 4×1 multiplexer plus no more than three basic gates.

(c)   Try a third implementation using five 4×1 multiplexers without using external gates.

3.18 (a)   Construct a 5×32 decoder using four 3×8 decoders and one 2×4 decoder, each with one enable input.

(b)   If each 3×8 decoder has two enable inputs, can you use two 3×8 decoders to connect sixty-four 3×8 decoders into a 9×512 decoder? How would you implement this?

3.19 Given a single 8×3 binary encoder and three 2-input OR gates, construct a 10×4 BCD decimal encoder which encodes mutually exclusive input signals of decimal digits, $D0, D1, \ldots, D9$ (corresponding to $0, 1, \ldots, 9$, respectively) into an output BCD code, $y_3 y_2 y_1 y_0$.

3.20 (a)   Design a full subtractor that performs *direct* binary subtraction of $A_i - B_i - C_{i-1}$, where A_i is a 1-bit minuend, B_i is a 1-bit subtrahend, and C_{i-1} is the input borrow. Use similar circuits as those shown in Figure 3.11 to implement your design for generating the difference, S_i, and the output borrow, C_i.

(b)   Based on the same principle, design a full adder/subtractor with a control input K such that if $K = 0$, it performs addition, if $K = 1$, it performs subtraction in the same way as in Part (a).

3.21 (a)   Design a one-digit BCD adder that performs the addition $A + B + C_{in}$ to produce sum S and carry out C_{out}, where $A = A_3 A_2 A_1 A_0$, $B = B_3 B_2 B_1 B_0$, and $S = S_3 S_2 S_1 S_0$, all in BCD representation. Your design can use two standard 4-bit binary adders incorporated with a correction circuit for realization of the algorithm provided in Section 2.5.2.

(b)   Repeat Part (a) for a one-digit excess-3 adder.

3.22 (a)   Using the PLA given in Figure 3.27, form an implementation of the following functions:

$$F_1 = \overline{AB} + \overline{AC} + ABC$$

$$F_2 = A\overline{B} + AC + \overline{A}B\overline{C}$$
$$F_3 = \overline{A}B + B\overline{C}$$

Be sure to take advantage of the complemented outputs of the PLA to achieve an optimal design using a minimum number of product terms.

(b) Repeat the design in Part (a) using a PAL given in Figure 3.31.

3.23 Given below are three logic functions of four variables A, B, C, and D:

$$F_1(A, B, C, D) = \Sigma m(1, 3, 5, 7, 8, 10, 11, 14),$$
$$F_2(A, B, C, D) = \Sigma m(0, 1, 2, 4, 6, 8, 9, 12),$$
$$F_3(A, B, C, D) = \Sigma m(5, 7, 9, 11, 13, 15).$$

(a) Give an implementation of the functions on a PLA with a minimum number of product terms. The PLA has outputs with both original and inverted polarities.

(b) If the above functions are implemented with a ROM, what should be its minimum size?

3.24 Given three functions

$$F_1(A, B, C, D) = \Sigma m(0, 3, 4, 7, 9, 10, 12, 14),$$
$$F_2(A, B, C, D) = \Sigma m(0, 3, 4, 7, 9), \text{ and}$$
$$F_3(A, B, C, D) = \Sigma m(1, 2, 3, 5, 6, 7, 8, 10, 11).$$

(a) Implement them on a PLA with a minimum number of product terms. The PLA has outputs with both original and inverted polarities.

(b) Implement them using a PAL with the OR–array of the following configuration: two 4-input NOR–gates and two 2-input NOR gates.

3.25 Using a PLA of capacity $3 \times 4 \times 3$, form a design to generate the following three functions:

$$X = \overline{A} \cdot \overline{C} + A\overline{B}C,$$
$$Y = \overline{A} \cdot \overline{B} + B\overline{C},$$
$$Z = \overline{B \oplus C} + AB.$$

Derive the expressions for X, Y, and Z with the total number of product terms being minimum in order to fit the capacity $3 \times 4 \times 3$ of the given PLA, and then draw the internal connection diagram of the PLA.

4

Logic Design of Sequential Circuits

4.1   GENERAL MODEL OF SEQUENTIAL CIRCUITS

A sequential logic circuit implements a sequential logic function whose value is a function of not only its current input variables, but also its past history stored in *state variables*. The state variables, in fact, reflect the influence of the previous inputs on the current output of the circuit. Therefore, a sequential logic circuit must contain an internal *memory* element that stores the state variables and, through the state variables, introduces the parameter of time into the function of the circuit. Based on this principle, the operation of a sequential logic circuit can be illustrated by a general model as shown in Figure 4.1. It is composed of two parts—a combinational circuit and memory. The combinational circuit realizes the functional behavior of the circuit as specified by Expression (4.1).

$$\text{outputs} = f(\text{inputs, current states}) \tag{4.1}$$

The combinational circuit also generates necessary information for the *next state* variables according to Expression (4.2).

$$\text{next states} = g(\text{inputs, current states}) \tag{4.2}$$

The next state variables will be stored by the memory module of the sequential circuit in order to be used as *current state* variables in the subsequent time instant.

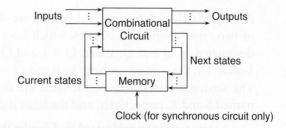

Figure 4.1   General model of a sequential circuit

Depending on how the memory elements are used to introduce the time parameter and generate the current state variables, we can distinguish between two types of sequential circuits, namely, *synchronous* and *asynchronous* sequential logic circuits. If the current state variables can change values only at discrete fixed-time instants (usually in fixed time periods determined by a central clock acting on the memory element), the sequential circuit is called synchronous. If the state variables change values in accordance with the change of input variables in a random fashion, not in synchronism with a clock signal, the sequential circuit is called asynchronous. Most of the sequential circuits encountered in computer organization are synchronous circuits.

Another distinction made among models of sequential circuits concerns the generation of the outputs. In Expression (4.1), if the outputs are functions of the current state variables only, the sequential circuit model is called a *Moore machine*; however, if the outputs reflect the current inputs as well as current state variables, it is called a *Mealy machine*. The behavior of a sequential circuit can be described using either model. In a Moore machine model, the outputs are associated with the states. In a Mealy machine model, the outputs are associated with the state transitions in terms of the functions of both the inputs and the state variables.

4.2   FLIP-FLOPS

The memory elements used in sequential logic circuits are of two types—*flip-flops* and *delay lines*. The *delay line* is a dynamic memory device, acting as a cyclic shift register, but it is rarely used today. A *flip-flop* is a static memory device storing one bit of information. A clocked flip-flop changes state during each clock pulse in keeping with the excitation signals, hence, it is most frequently used in synchronous sequential circuits. An unclocked flip-flop (also called a latch) acts only upon change of the input, so it is used in asynchronous sequential circuits. We will, at first, look at a simple latch constructed with two NOR gates, and then describe the four basic types of clocked flip-flops as the building blocks of many useful sequential circuits.

4.2.1   Analysis of a Simple SR Latch

A simple latch and its graphical symbol are shown in Figure 4.2. It is composed of two cross-coupled NOR gates, which have mutually complemented outputs, designated as Q and $\overline{Q}$. When $Q = 1$ and $\overline{Q} = 0$, the latch is said to be in the 1-state. On the contrary, when $Q = 0$ and $\overline{Q} = 1$, we say the latch is in the 0-state. The setting and resetting of the latch are controlled by two excitation signals named S and R, respectively, and the latch is called an *unclocked SR flip-flop*.

A *state transition table* used to describe the function of an SR latch is shown in Table 4.1. The main difference between a state transition table and a truth

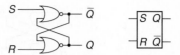

Figure 4.2 Logic circuit and the graphic symbol of an SR latch

table is that the current state variable, $Q(t)$, plays the role of an independent variable in determining the next state, $Q(t+1)$.

In deriving the state transition table in Table 4.1, we can use the same method of analyzing the combinational circuits we learned in Section 3.5. Four cases are shown in Figure 4.3.

Cases (a) and (b): When $S=0$, $R=0$, the SR latch can randomly stay in one of the two stable states, "0" or "1", depending on the physical condition of asymmetry of the two NOR gates.

Case (c): When R changes from 0 to 1, Case (a) will invoke Case (c), which makes a state transition from "1" to "0" with two gate delays, or Case (b) remains unchanged.

Case (d): When S changes from 0 to 1, Case (b) will invoke Case (d), which makes a state transition from "0" to "1" with two gate delays, or Case (a) remains unchanged.

If we consider the state transitions as the outcome of the table, then Table 4.1 can be simplified as Table 4.2, which is called a *reduced state transition table*. It can be seen that $S=1$ and $R=0$ always set Q to 1; $R=1$ and $S=0$ always reset Q to 0; if $S=0$ and $R=0$, Q does not change state; $S=1$ and $R=1$ is not allowed.

Table 4.1 State transition table of an SR latch

Excitations		Current State	Next State
S	R	$Q(t)$	$Q(t+1)$
0	0	0	0
0	0	1	1
0	1	0	0
0	1	1	0
1	0	0	1
1	0	1	1
1	1	0	not defined
1	1	1	not defined

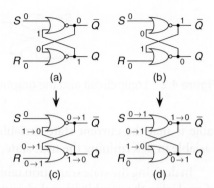

Figure 4.3 Analysis of the circuit in Figure 4.2 to derive its state transition table

Table 4.2 Reduced state transition table of an SR latch

Excitations		State Transitions
S	R	
0	0	$Q(t+1) = Q(t)$
0	1	$Q(t+1) = 0$
1	0	$Q(t+1) = 1$
1	1	not defined

The reason for the undefined state of an SR latch at $S = 1$ and $R = 1$ is that this combination of excitation signals will cause both gates of the latch to output "0" at the same time, thus totally violating the bi-state working condition of the latch with two stable states. Under this condition, if both S and R drop to 0 at exactly the same time, which gate turns to "1" is indeterminate, depending on the different delays of these two NOR gates.

With the SR latch mentioned above as an asynchronous circuit, we can extend it to form a synchronous circuit by simply adding a control input from a clock to turn the latch into a clocked flip-flop. There are four types of clocked flip-flops in use, namely, the SR flip-flop, the JK flip-flop, the T flip-flop, and the D flip-flop, as described in the following sections.

4.2.2 SR Flip-Flop

A clocked SR flip-flop can be conceptually constructed as shown in Figure 4.4. It consists of a flip-flop made of two cross-coupled NAND gates plus two input gates controlled by the clock. The circuit is conceptual because it is controlled by the clock level instead of the clock edge. Either S or R can pass the input gate only when the clock level is high or "1". Since the clock does not carry information

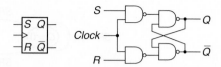

Figure 4.4   Conceptual logic circuit of a clocked SR flip-flop

other than this timing control action, the functional characteristics of the SR latch statically represented in Tables 4.1 and 4.2 (when *clock* = 1) can be applied to the clocked SR flip-flop without change.

Again, for the derivation of the same state transition table for the clocked SR flip-flop, we apply the same method of analysis to the circuit in Figure 4.5. Cases (a) to (d) are similar to those in Figure 4.3, but require *clock* = 1. Additional cases (e) and (f) show that the flip-flop will maintain its state unchanged when the *clock* returns to 0 after the change made during *clock* = 1.

The dependence of state transitions on excitation signals illustrated in Table 4.2 can be depicted by a *state transition diagram* as shown in Figure 4.6, where the states are denoted by circles with the state names, and the transitions are denoted by directed arcs labeled with the excitation conditions. A state transition takes place iff the corresponding excitation condition is true. Alternatively, this relationship can be represented by an *excitation table* as shown in Table 4.3, where x denotes a "don't care" condition.

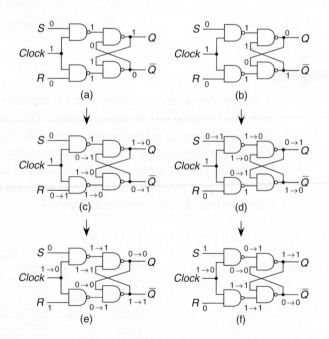

Figure 4.5   Analysis of the circuit in Figure 4.4 for derivation of the state transition table

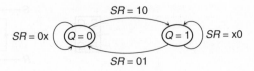

Figure 4.6 State transition diagram of an SR flip-flop

Table 4.3 Excitation table of an SR flip-flop

State Transitions		Excitations	
$Q(t)$	$Q(t+1)$	S	R
0	0	0	x
0	1	1	0
1	0	0	1
1	1	x	0

Moreover, the operation of a SR flip-flop can be represented by the Boolean expressions derived from Table 4.1. They are called the *characteristic equations* of the SR flip-flop.

$$Q(t+1) = S + \overline{R} \cdot Q(t)$$

$$SR = 0 \text{ (restriction)} \tag{4.3}$$

4.2.3 JK Flip-Flop

A JK flip-flop is an extension of a SR flip-flop that allows excitation signals J and K to be equal to 1 at the same time. This combination of excitation signals, $JK = 1$, corresponds to toggling the state of the flip-flop from 0 to 1 or from 1 to 0. The JK flip-flop can be constructed conceptually by feeding outputs $\overline{Q}$ and Q back to the J and K input gates, respectively, so that only one of the input signals, J or K, can pass through the input gate to act on the output gates of the flip-flop. The resultant circuit is shown in Figure 4.7.

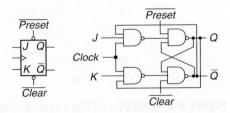

Figure 4.7 Conceptual logic circuit of a clocked JK flip-flop

____For completeness, the circuit in Figure 4.7 has two extra active-low inputs, *Clear* and *Preset*, which can be used to initialize the state of the flip-flop to 0 or 1. Only one of these two initializing signals can be "0" at any time, and both of them must be placed to "1" during the normal operation of the flip-flop. The full and reduced state transition tables and the excitation table of a JK flip-flop are shown in Tables 4.4, 4.5, and 4.6, respectively. The state transition diagram of a JK flip-flop is given in Figure 4.8.

Table 4.4   State transition table of a JK flip-flop

Excitations		Current State	Next State
J	K	$Q(t)$	$Q(t+1)$
0	0	0	0
0	0	1	1
0	1	0	0
0	1	1	0
1	0	0	1
1	0	1	1
1	1	0	1
1	1	1	0

Table 4.5   Reduced state transition table of a JK flip-flop

Excitations		State Transitions
J	K	
0	0	$Q(t+1) := Q(t)$
0	1	$Q(t+1) := 0$
1	0	$Q(t+1) := 1$
1	1	$Q(t+1) := \overline{Q(t)}$

Table 4.6   Excitation table of a JK flip-flop

State Transitions		Excitations	
$Q(t)$	$Q(t+1)$	J	K
0	0	0	x
0	1	1	x
1	0	x	1
1	1	x	0

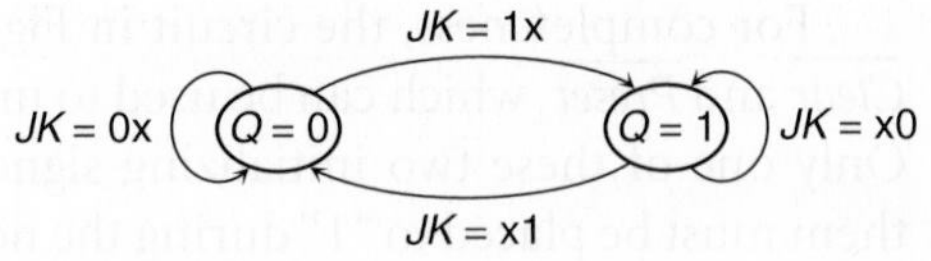

$$JK = 1x$$

$$JK = 0x \quad \big(Q = 0 \big) \qquad \big(Q = 1 \big) \quad JK = x0$$

$$JK = x1$$

Figure 4.8   State transition diagram of a JK flip-flop

Moreover, the characteristic equation for the JK flip-flop can be derived from Table 4.4 as follows:

$$Q(t+1) = J \cdot \overline{Q(t)} + \overline{K} \cdot Q(t) \tag{4.4}$$

4.2.4 T Flip-Flop

The T flip-flop is a special case of a JK flip-flop in which the excitation inputs J and K are connected together into a single input T, as shown in Figure 4.9. The excitation $T = 1$ corresponds to toggling the state of the flip-flop from 0 to 1 or 1 to 0. Thus, the symbol T is interpreted as *toggle*. The full and reduced state transition tables and the excitation table of the T flip-flop are shown in Tables 4.7, 4.8, and 4.9, respectively. The state transition diagram of the T flip-flop is given in Figure 4.10.

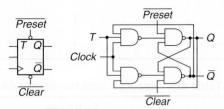

Figure 4.9   Conceptual logic circuit of a T flip-flop

Table 4.7   State transition table of a T flip-flop

Excitation	Current State	Next State
T	$Q(t)$	$Q(t+1)$
0	0	0
0	1	1
1	0	1
1	1	0

Table 4.8   Reduced state transition table of a T flip-flop

Excitation T	State Transitions
0	$Q(t+1) = Q(t)$
1	$Q(t+1) = \overline{Q(t)}$

Table 4.9   Excitation table of a T flip-flop

State Transitions		Excitation
$Q(t)$	$Q(t+1)$	T
0	0	0
0	1	1
1	0	1
1	1	0

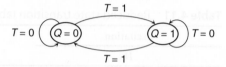

Figure 4.10   State transition diagram of a T flip-flop

Moreover, the characteristic equation for the T flip-flop can be derived from Table 4.7 as follows:

$$Q(t+1) = \overline{T} \cdot Q(t) + T \cdot \overline{Q(t)} \qquad (4.5)$$

4.2.5 D Flip-Flop

The D flip-flop is another special case of the JK flip-flop in which the excitation inputs, J and $\overline{K}$, are connected together into a single input D, as shown in Figure 4.11. The excitation $D = 0$ always changes the state of the flip-flop to 0, while $D = 1$ always changes it to 1. The effect is to make the output Q of the flip-flop always follow the input D, but with a delay of one clock period. Thus, the name D is interpreted as *delay*. The full and reduced state transition tables and the excitation table of a D flip-flop are shown in Tables 4.10, 4.11, and 4.12, respectively. The state transition diagram of a D flip-flop is given in Figure 4.12.

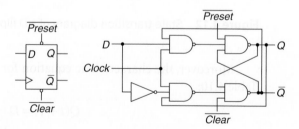

Figure 4.11   Conceptual logic circuit of a D flip-flop

Table 4.10 State transition table of a D flip-flop

Excitation	Current State	Next State
D	$Q(t)$	$Q(t+1)$
0	0	0
0	1	0
1	0	1
1	1	1

Table 4.11 Reduced state transition table of a D flip-flop

Excitation	State Transitions
D	
0	$Q(t+1) := 0$
1	$Q(t+1) := 1$

Table 4.12 Excitation table of a D flip-flop

State Transitions		Excitation
$Q(t)$	$Q(t+1)$	D
0	0	0
0	1	1
1	0	0
1	1	1

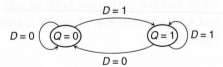

Figure 4.12 State transition diagram of a D flip-flop

Moreover, the characteristic equation for a D flip-flop can be derived from Table 4.10:

$$Q(t+1) = D \qquad\qquad (4.6)$$

4.2.6 Practical Flip-Flop Circuits

The logic circuit shown in Figure 4.7 for the level-triggered JK flip-flop is only a conceptual circuit. It cannot work correctly for the following reason. Suppose $J = 1$ and $K = 1$. As long as the clock level remains high to allow the flip-flop to toggle, the two input gates repeatedly change conditions, which ensure toggling, resulting in an undesired phenomenon of multiple triggering during the active clock level (see Figure 4.13). To eliminate this error, the practical circuit of a clocked flip-flop must be designed to trigger only in response to the transition edge of the clock rather than to its level. Such a circuit is called an *edge-triggered flip-flop*. If it responds to the rising edge of the clock, the flip-flop is called *positive edge-triggered*, otherwise, it is a *negative edge-triggered* flip-flop responding to the falling edge of the clock. For a level-triggered flip-flop, the output can change in the entire clock duration, while for an edge-triggered flip-flop, the output can change only once at the active edge of the clock pulse. The output of the flip-flop is determined only by the value of the excitation signals just prior to the active edge of the clock, and not by any change of the excitation signals thereafter. The waveform diagram for the edge-triggered JK flip-flop compared with its level-triggered counterpart is shown in Figure 4.13.

Two implementations of the edge-triggered flip-flop are possible: one uses a special circuit design to realize the edge-triggering property, and the other uses two conceptual flip-flops connected in cascade to form a *master-slave flip-flop*.

A practical circuit for a JK-type positive edge-triggered flip-flop can be constructed with six NAND gates connected as shown in Figure 4.14.

The circuit in Figure 4.14 is a 2-gate SR flip-flop supplemented by a 4-gate input circuit. The principle of operation of the circuit can be analyzed by tracing through the gates and drawing the corresponding waveform diagram as shown in Figure 4.15. We analyze a typical case in which the JK flip-flop works correctly

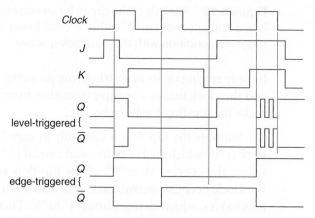

Figure 4.13 Timing diagrams of level-triggered and edge-triggered JK flip-flops

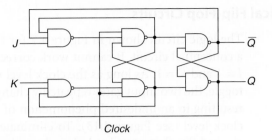

Figure 4.14 Logic circuit of an edge-triggered JK flip-flop

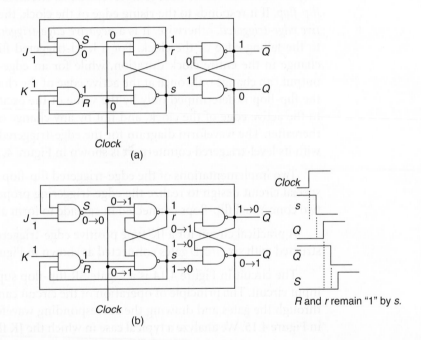

Figure 4.15 Analysis of the circuit for an edge-triggered JK flip-flop. (a) The flip-flop is in a stable condition "0" with the clock being idle. (b) The flip-flop is in an edge-triggered condition with the clock being active.

by only relying on its edge-triggering property, when both J and K inputs are "1" and the clock makes a positive transition from "0" to "1". This condition should make the flip-flop toggle only once.

Suppose the flip-flop is currently in state "0" with $J = 1$ and $K = 1$, and the *clock* is "0" which makes both r and s equal to "1". The values of $S = 0$ and $R = 1$ reflect the current state "0" of the flip-flop as shown in Figure 4.15(a). Now the clock becomes active, making a transition from "0" to "1". The first signal affected is s, which changes from "1" to "0". Then, s acts like a "set" signal to cause the transition of the flip-flop from "0" to "1". Following this transition, the signal S becomes 1. This state will not change as long as the *clock* stays at level "1". No changes of J and K signals will affect it. No multiple triggering is possible.

After the clock returns from "1" to "0", the flip-flop will be in a stable state "1" in which both r and s equal to "1", similar to the state as shown in Figure 4.15(a), but with $R = 0$ and $S = 1$.

It can be seen that in the above edge-triggered circuit, the feedback connections from r and s to the input gates play important roles to maintain the signal level of R or S, masking any changes of J and K. (The role of the r-connection should be shown in the analysis of another case when $J = 1$, $K = 1$ and the flip-flop is originally in state "1".) Also, the cross connections between the signals r and s play a positive role to block the changes of r and s at the same time. These four connections are added to the conceptual circuit to make its edge-triggered property possible.

The above analysis of the edge-triggered circuit of a flip-flop was based on the assumptions that all the gates have a unit delay and some stable conditions exist in the circuit before and after the clock makes an active transition. These assumptions lead to the timing diagram of a positive edge-triggered JK flip-flop as shown in Figure 4.16.

The output response of the flip-flop shown in Figure 4.16 is determined by three parameters related to gate delays:

- *Setup time*—the time during which the excitation signals must be maintained at a constant value prior to the active edge of the clock pulse.
- *Hold time*—the time during which the excitation signals must not change after the application of the active edge of the clock pulse.
- *Propagation delay time*—the time interval between the triggering edge of the clock pulse and the instant when the output of the flip-flop becomes stabilized.

The values of these and other parameters of a flip-flop can be found in the manufacturer's data book.

The logic circuit of a master-slave JK flip-flop is shown in Figure 4.17. It consists of two basic SR flip-flops, each with a simple circuit as shown in Figure 4.4.

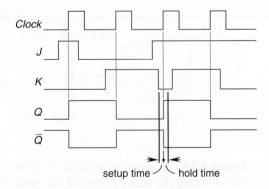

Figure 4.16   Timing diagram of a positive edge-triggered JK flip-flop

The feedback connections between the two flip-flops are similar to a JK flip-flop. The input stage serves as the master and receives the excitation signals J and K. It is triggered by the clock pulse CP. The output stage serves as the slave. It is driven by the master and triggered by the inverted clock pulse, $\overline{CP}$. As long as CP remains high, the slave is disabled. So, its output Q cannot be affected by any change of the external J or K signal. When CP returns to a low level, the master is disabled and isolated from the J and K inputs. The active high-level clock $\overline{CP}$ transfers the state P to the slave output Q.

A detailed analysis of the master-slave JK flip-flop circuit is shown in Figure 4.18. It explains how the circuit of the master-slave flip-flop, as shown in Figure 4.17, can work exactly as a negative edge-triggered flip-flop relative to the clock CP. From the analysis in Figure 4.18, we can see that the delay of the outputs of the master-slave JK flip-flop equals three gate delays relative to the falling edge of the clock.

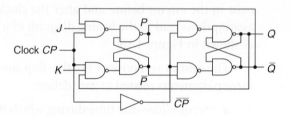

Figure 4.17 Logic circuit of a master-slave JK flip-flop

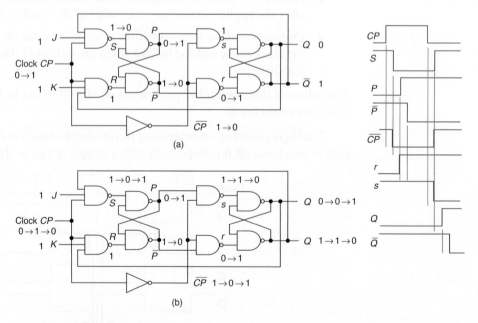

Figure 4.18 Analysis of the logic circuit of a master-slave JK flip-flop. (a) The master works during the active period of the clock CP. (b) The slave works during the active period of the inverted clock $\overline{CP}$.

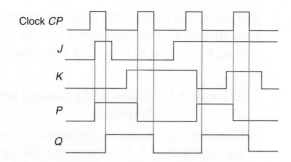

Figure 4.19 Timing diagram of a master-slave JK flip-flop

The timing diagram of the JK master-slave flip-flop is shown in Figure 4.19.

4.3 ANALYSIS OF SEQUENTIAL LOGIC CIRCUITS

In this section, we analyze sequential logic circuits using the state transition table and state transition diagram, and also learn how to transform the counter into a finite-state machine.

4.3.1 From Circuit to State Transition Diagram

The goal of analyzing a sequential circuit is to obtain its state transition table and state transition diagram. The process of analysis consists of the following steps:

Step 1: Write logic expressions for the excitation signals of all the flip-flops as well as the output variables. These expressions are written in terms of the input and current state variables.

Step 2: Derive the state transition table and the output table. The leftmost several columns of the table should contain all of the possible combinations of the input and current state variables. Corresponding to each combination, we find the excitation signals using the equations obtained in Step 1, and then find the values of the next state and output variables using the state transition table or characteristic equations of the corresponding type of flip-flop.

Step 3: Based on the state transition table, we can draw the state transition diagram. In the state transition diagram, states are represented as circles, and state transitions are represented by directed arcs between states. In a Mealy machine model, the number of states is determined by the number of flip-flops, and each state transition is specified as a corresponding pair of input and output, that is, the input that causes the transition and the output caused by that transition.

If the states involved in the closed cycle of a useful counting sequence are viewed as valid states, then the other out-of-cycle states are invalid. In Example 4.1, states 00, 01, and 10 are valid for $x = 0$, and 01 and 10 are valid for $x = 1$. If the counter happens to be in an invalid state with no initialization, it should be able to make transitions to finally reach a valid state. This is called the *self-correcting property* of the counter. For Example 4.1, when $x = 0$ or 1, $A_1 A_0 = 11$ goes to a valid state $A_1' A_0' = 00$, but when $x = 1$, the invalid state $A_1 A_0 = 00$ goes to itself, causing the counter to be not self-correcting as long as x is maintained at value 1.

Example 4.1   Analysis of a Counter with an Arbitrary Counting Sequence

Given the logic circuit of a counter as shown in Figure 4.20, find the counting sequences of $A_1 A_0$ and output F for input values $x = 0$ and $x = 1$.

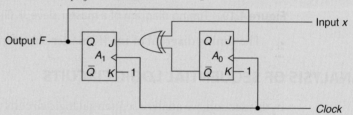

Figure 4.20   Logic circuit of a counter for Example 4.1

Step 1: Write the excitation equations and the output equation.

For flip-flop A_1:   For flip-flop A_0:

$$J_1 = x \oplus \overline{A_0} \qquad\qquad J_0 = A_1$$

$$K_1 = 1 \qquad\qquad\qquad K_0 = 1 \qquad\qquad\qquad (4.7)$$

For the output: $F = A_1$ (4.8)

Step 2: Determine the next states corresponding to each entry of the state transition table.

For example, for table entry $x = 0$ and $A_1 A_0 = 00$, we have $J_1 = 1$, $K_1 = 1$, $J_0 = 0$, $K_0 = 1$, and therefore $A_1' A_0' = 10$ and $F = 0$, where A_1' and A_0' denote the next states of A_1 and A_0, respectively. Do the same for the remaining seven table entries. Finally, we obtain the state transition table as shown in Table 4.13.

Table 4.13   State transition table for Example 4.1

Input	Current States		Next States		Output
x	A_1	A_0	A_1'	A_0'	F
0	0	0	1	0	0
0	0	1	0	0	0
0	1	0	0	1	1
0	1	1	0	0	1
1	0	0	0	0	0
1	0	1	1	0	0

Input	Current States		Next States		Output
x	A_1	A_0	A_1'	A_0'	F
1	1	0	0	1	1
1	1	1	0	0	1

Step 3: Obtain the state transition diagram as shown in Figure 4.21.

From the state transition diagram, it can be seen that when $x = 0$, the counter has a cyclic counting sequence $00 \rightarrow 10 \rightarrow 01 \rightarrow 00 \rightarrow \ldots$ and when $x = 1$, it has a cyclic counting sequence $01 \rightarrow 10 \rightarrow 01 \rightarrow \ldots$

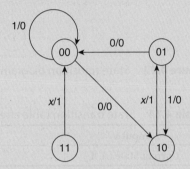

Figure 4.21   State transition diagram for Example 4.1

4.3.2 From State Transition Diagram to Finite-State Machine

With respect to Example 4.1, it is possible to transform the counter into a finite-state machine consistent with the general model of a sequential circuit, which we introduced in Figure 4.1.

Usually, the design of a finite-state machine begins with the derivation of a state transition diagram from the formal specification of a problem. For the problem in Example 4.1, this diagram is already available, so this discussion will start from Figure 4.21 by assuming that, before state assignment, the original state transition diagram should name the states as A, B, C, and D instead of 00, 01, 10 and 11, respectively. Thus, we have the state transition diagram as shown in Figure 4.22.

The state transition table can be derived by state assignment as shown in Table 4.14.

The functions for the next state variables, A_1' and A_0', and the output, F, can be derived from the state transition table as follows:

$$A_1' = \overline{A_1} \cdot \overline{A_0} \cdot \overline{x} + \overline{A_1} \cdot A_0 \cdot x$$

$$A_0' = A_1 \cdot \overline{A_0}$$

$$F = A_1$$

These expressions can be implemented as the combinational part of the general model of the sequential circuit, while the memory part of it can be implemented by the two flip-flops of the 2-bit counter. The resulting circuit of the finite-state machine is shown in Figure 4.23.

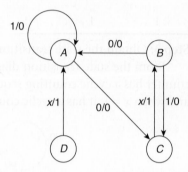

Figure 4.22 State transition diagram before state assignment

Table 4.14 State transition table after state assignment

Input x	0	1
Current State $(A_1 A_0)$	Next State $(A_1' A_0')$/ Output	
$A(00)$	$C(10)/0$	$A(00)/0$
$B(01)$	$A(00)/0$	$C(10)/0$
$C(10)$	$B(01)/1$	$B(01)/1$
$D(11)$	$A(00)/1$	$A(00)/1$

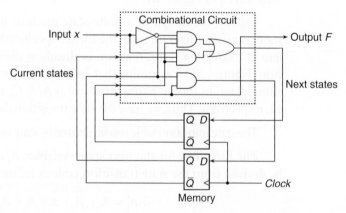

Figure 4.23 Model of a finite-state machine for the counter in Example 4.1

4.4 SYNTHESIS OF SEQUENTIAL LOGIC CIRCUITS

In Section 4.3.2, we studied two methods of analyzing sequential circuits. One is a method for considering a sequential circuit as a counter with any arbitrary counting sequence. The other is a general method of designing a finite-state machine. Both methods require the construction of state transition tables, but the former is simpler and the latter is more general. The former can determine the states directly from the given counting sequence, while the latter can handle the general case, in which the number of states of the finite-state machine may be unknown and must be determined in the process of design and optimization. This general procedure for designing a finite-state machine will be addressed here. In this section, we will introduce a simple method of designing a counter with a given counting sequence.

In a broad sense, any sequential circuit that generates a sequence of states, each being assigned a distinct binary code, can be viewed as a counter. The sequence of the binary codes resulting from the state assignment forms the counting sequence of the counter. Usually the counter simply generates the counting sequence for counting events without specifying the details of these events and how they are actually controlled. Therefore, a counter can be designed as a simple sequential circuit with n flip-flops that can count up to 2^n events in a given counting sequence. The steps of design are as follows:

Step 1: From the given problem specification, the state transition table can be written in a straightforward manner. Besides the outputs of all the flip-flops, if applicable, we can include output function(s) in the table. If only some of the 2^n states of the n flip-flops are involved in the given counting sequence, the table entries corresponding to the missing states should be filled in as "don't cares."

Step 2: Choose the type of flip-flops to be used in the counter, and then use the excitation table for the selected type of flip-flop to derive the excitation table for the counter corresponding to the state transitions in the table obtained in Step 1.

Step 3: From the excitation table obtained in Step 2, derive the simplest logic expressions for the excitation signals. Also, derive the expression for the output function(s) if needed.

Step 4: Check if the designed counter satisfies the requirement of the self-correcting property (see Section 4.3.1). If yes, go to Step 5, otherwise, go to Step 3 for necessary modification of the expressions for the excitation signals.

Step 5: Implement the expressions obtained in Step 3.

Example 4.2 **Design of a Gray Code Counter in Two Options Using JK and D Flip-Flops**

Given the counting sequence of the counter

$$000 \rightarrow 001 \rightarrow 011 \rightarrow 010 \rightarrow 110 \rightarrow 100 \rightarrow 000 \rightarrow \dots$$

Step 1: We can write the state transition table as shown in Table 4.15. Assume that the counter counts on every clock signal, so it does not need a control input. Since the given counting sequence is only a subset of a complete Gray code sequence, the next states for the invalid states should be "don't care."

Table 4.15 State transition table of Example 4.2

Current State	Next State
$y_2 y_1 y_0$	$y_2' y_1' y_0'$
0 0 0	0 0 1
0 0 1	0 1 1
0 1 0	1 1 0
0 1 1	0 1 0
1 0 0	0 0 0
1 0 1	x x x
1 1 0	1 0 0
1 1 1	x x x

Step 2: We choose JK and D flip-flops. Referring to their excitation tables, we can find the corresponding excitation tables of the counter as shown in Table 4.16. The excitation signals for D flip-flops simply duplicate the next state variables in Table 4.15.

Table 4.16 Excitation table of Example 4.2

Current State	D Flip-Flops			JK Flip-Flops					
$y_2 y_1 y_0$	D_2	D_1	D_0	J_2	K_2	J_1	K_1	J_0	K_0
0 0 0	0	0	1	0	x	0	x	1	x
0 0 1	0	1	1	0	x	1	x	x	0
0 1 0	1	1	0	1	x	x	0	0	x
0 1 1	0	1	0	0	x	x	0	x	1

Current State	D Flip-Flops			JK Flip-Flops					
$y_2 y_1 y_0$	D_2	D_1	D_0	J_2	K_2	J_1	K_1	J_0	K_0
1 0 0	0	0	0	x	1	0	x	0	x
1 0 1	x	x	x	x	x	x	x	x	x
1 1 0	1	0	0	x	0	x	1	0	x
1 1 1	x	x	x	x	x	x	x	x	x

Step 3: Using the Karnaugh maps shown in Figure 4.24 for JK flip-flops and Figure 4.25 for D flip-flops, we can derive the Boolean Expressions (4.9) and (4.10) for the corresponding excitation variables.

$$J_2 = y_1 \overline{y_0}$$
$$K_2 = \overline{y_1}$$
$$J_1 = y_0$$
$$K_1 = y_2$$
$$J_0 = \overline{y_2} \cdot \overline{y_1}$$
$$K_0 = y_1 \tag{4.9}$$

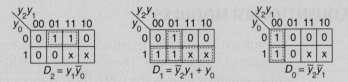

Figure 4.24 Karnaugh maps of the excitation signals of JK flip-flops for Example 4.2

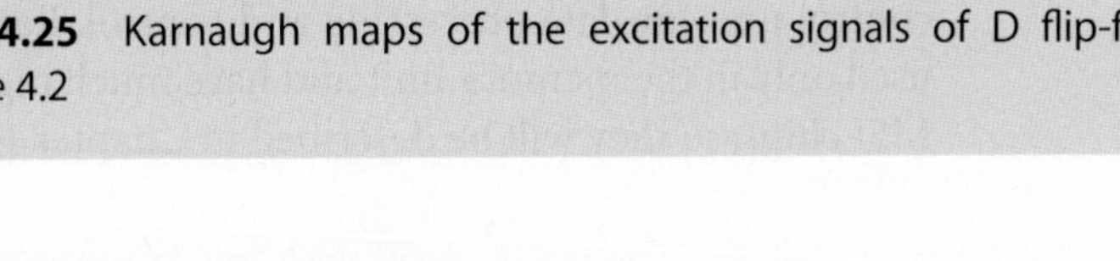

Figure 4.25 Karnaugh maps of the excitation signals of D flip-flops for Example 4.2

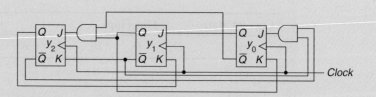

Figure 4.26 Logic circuit of the counter in Example 4.2 using JK flip-flops

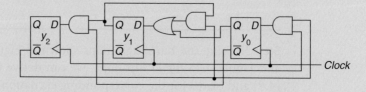

Figure 4.27 Logic circuit of the counter in Example 4.2 using D flip-flops

$$D_2 = y_1 \overline{y_0}$$
$$D_1 = \overline{y_2} y_1 + y_0$$
$$D_0 = \overline{y_2} \cdot \overline{y_1}$$

(4.10)

Step 4: We check the self-correcting property of the counter as follows:

When $y_2 y_1 y_0 = 101$, $D_2, D_1, D_0 = 0, 1, 0$, leading to the next state 010;

When $y_2 y_1 y_0 = 111$, $D_2, D_1, D_0 = 0, 1, 0$, leading to the next state 010;

When $y_2 y_1 y_0 = 101$, $J_2, K_2 = 0, 1$, $J_1, K_1 = 1, 1$, $J_0, K_0 = 0, 0$, leading to the next state 011;

When $y_2 y_1 y_0 = 111$, $J_2, K_2 = 0, 0$, $J_1, K_1 = 1, 1$, $J_0, K_0 = 0, 1$, leading to the next state 100;

010, 011, and 100 are all valid states.

Finally, we implement the logic circuit diagrams of the counter with JK and D flip-flops as shown in Figures 4.26 and 4.27, respectively. ∎

4.5 SEQUENTIAL MSI MODULES

In this section, we will describe registers, shift registers, and counters as typical sequential MSI modules. These modules are widely used in all functional units of a computer, such as the CPU, the memory unit, the I/O subsystem, and the control unit for data processing and control. Random access memory chips are used only in the memory unit and have much higher density of integration than MSI chips, so they will be described in Chapter 10.

4.5.1 Register

A register can be constructed using any of the flip-flop types mentioned in Section 4.2. Two circuits with JK and D flip-flops are shown in Figure 4.28. JK flip-flops are easier to control than D flip-flops when they are used in the register, because they have different mechanisms to maintain the register contents unchanged during the action of the clock. For JK flip-flops, when the control signal *Load* is 0, both *J* and *K* signals equal 0, so the flip-flops can maintain the stored contents and are not affected by the clock. However, this is not the case for D flip-flops. Even if the control signal *Load* is 0, which makes all the *D* signals equal to 0, it cannot maintain the contents of the register, but instead clears all the flip-flops during the clock transition. This problem can be resolved in two ways: (1) feedback the output *Q* of the flip-flop to its *D* input or (2) inhibit the clock from acting on the flip-flop. The circuit in Figure 4.28 uses the second method. It uses an OR gate to block the clock by keeping the control signal *Maintain* at the value 1, while the register is not being loaded (*Load* = 0). This method is used in a practical circuit of the shift register shown in Figure 4.30.

4.5.2 Shift Register

A shift register is used to store data that can be shifted left or right, usually one bit at a time by each clock transition. A shift register is typically used for bit manipulation or code transformation. For example, for parallel to serial conversion, the parallel binary code in the shift register is shifted out in sequential order, while for serial to parallel conversion, the serial binary code is shifted into the shift register. For logical shift, the value shifted into the register can be 0, while for arithmetic shift, it can be the sign bit of a number if that number is shifted right with sign extension. The logic circuits of left shift registers and right shift registers

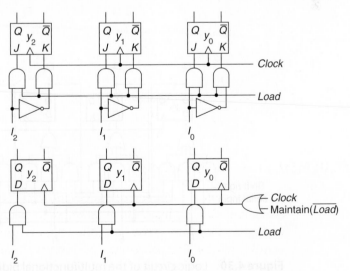

Figure 4.28 Logic circuits of registers with JK and D flip-flops

with JK and D flip-flops are shown in Figure 4.29, while that of a multifunctional bidirectional shift register on D flip-flops is shown in Figure 4.30. The circuit in Figure 4.30 connects three sets of input gates ORed together to the D inputs of the flip-flops: the left gates for right shift operation controlled by $\bar{s}_1$, the right gates for left shift operation controlled by $\bar{s}_0$, and the middle gates for parallel load operation controlled by $s_1 s_0$. It is possible to use only one-bit signal, $\bar{s}_1$ or $\bar{s}_0$, to control the shift operations because $\bar{s}_1 \cdot \bar{s}_0 = 1$ does block the clock signal from exerting any interference with them.

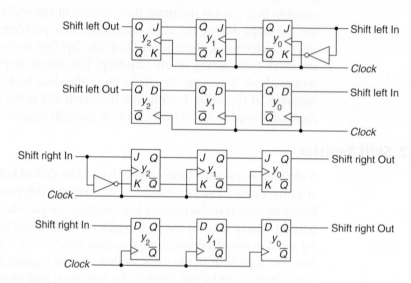

Figure 4.29   Logic circuits of shift registers with JK and D flip-flops

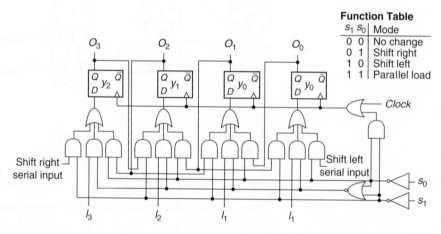

Figure 4.30   Logic circuit of the multifunctional bidirectional shift register

4.5.3 Counter

In this section, we describe ordinary binary counters with regular counting sequences. The state transition tables for the ordinary up-counter and down-counter are shown in Table 4.17. We will design these counters by inspecting the state transition table rather than going through the systematic procedure of using excitation tables. The logic relationships between the successive stages of the counter can be seen in the table and generalized as follows:

For counting up and down: y_0 triggers at every clock pulse;

For counting up: y_i triggers whenever $y_{i-1}y_{i-2} \dots y_0 = 1$

for $i = 1, 2, \dots n - 1$;

For counting down: y_i triggers whenever $\overline{y_{i-1}} \cdot \overline{y_{i-2}} \dots \overline{y_0} = 1$

for $i = 1, 2, \dots n - 1$; **(4.11)**

Logic circuits of up-counters with JK and D flip-flops are shown in Figure 4.31. Each JK flip-flop works as a T flip-flop by connecting together J and K inputs. A chain of AND gates is used for generating and propagating carry signals in a serial fashion. The counter implemented in this way is called a *ripple-carry counter*. If we replace each JK flip-flop with a D flip-flop and add an XOR gate to the D input, then the D flip-flop acts as a T flip-flop.

Ripple-carry counters work slowly because the carry propagation time is proportional to the number of stages. To improve the performance, we can construct parallel counters by directly generating all the products in Expression (4.11) at once, as shown in Figure 4.32. However, if the fan-in of the AND gates is

Table 4.17 State transition tables of the up-counter and the down-counter

Current States			Next States					
			Counting Up			Counting Down		
y_2	y_1	y_0	y_2'	y_1'	y_0'	y_2'	y_1'	y_0'
0	0	0	0	0	1	1	1	1
0	0	1	0	1	0	0	0	0
0	1	0	0	1	1	0	0	1
0	1	1	1	0	0	0	1	0
1	0	0	1	0	1	0	1	1
1	0	1	1	1	0	1	0	0
1	1	0	1	1	1	1	0	1
1	1	1	0	0	0	1	1	0

limited to five, the number of stages of the counter cannot exceed four. To construct a larger parallel counter, we need to use the carry-out signals to connect several 4-bit parallel counters together in the same way as we do within a 4-bit counter.

The down-counter can be constructed in a similar way, except that the $\overline{Q}$ outputs replace the Q outputs of the flip-flops. According to this principle, we can construct an up-down counter by connecting an XOR gate to the output of every flip-flop, as shown in Figure 4.33. The XOR gates are controlled by the signal *Countup / Countdown*, which should be "0" for counting up and "1" for counting down.

The circuit of a multifunctional up-down counter not using the built-in $\overline{Clear}$ inputs of the flip-flops is shown in Figure 4.34. This circuit inserts an

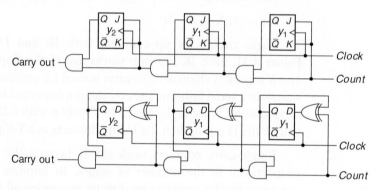

Figure 4.31 Logic circuits of ripple-carry up-counters with JK and D flip-flops

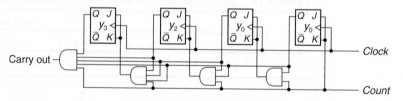

Figure 4.32 Logic circuit of a parallel up-counter on JK flip-flops

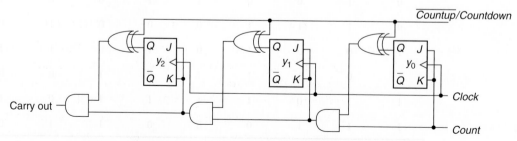

Figure 4.33 Logic circuit of an up-down counter with JK flip-flops

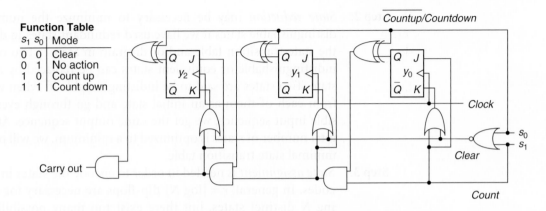

Figure 4.34   Logic circuit of an up-down counter with a clear function

OR gate into the J-K loop of each flip-flop in order to make $K = 1$ by the signal $clear = \overline{s_1} \cdot \overline{s_0}$ generated by a NOR gate. Since the function table assigns $s_1 = 1$ to both the functions of *Countup* and *Countdown*, we can use s_1 as the control signal *Count* and use s_0 as the signal $\overline{Countup} \,/\, Countdown$. All these considerations allow for a very simple implementation.

4.6   DESIGN OF A FINITE-STATE MACHINE

Registers and counters are not the only applications of sequential circuits in a computer. Generally speaking, any sequencing control of operations and events in a computer is based on the principle of sequential logic. In fact, sequential logic can be described as a finite-state machine that uses states to reflect information and the transitions of states to reflect the sequencing of events for processing the information. A *finite-state machine* is defined as a finite set of states being acted on by a finite number of inputs and generating a finite number of outputs according to a set of state-transition rules and output rules. This definition corresponds to the general model of a sequential circuit given in Figure 4.1. In this section, we will describe the major steps involved in designing a finite-state machine and present a simple example.

The major steps required for designing a finite-state machine are as follows:

Step 1:   Given the specification of the problem, the first step is to analyze the sequencing of events with associated input conditions in order to represent the state transition rule and output rule in a tabular or diagrammatic form. The result of this step will be the state transition table or state transition diagram that allows the functional dependence of the output and next state variables on the input and current state variables to be derived in the succeeding steps.

Step 2: *State reduction* may be necessary to minimize the number of distinguishable states if we have used redundant states in deriving the state transition table and/or diagram in Step 1. Two or more indistinguishable or equivalent states can be replaced by a single state. Two states are said to be indistinguishable iff when we start from each of them as an initial state and go through every possible input sequence, we get the same output sequence. After the total number of states is optimized to a minimum, we will obtain a minimal state transition table.

Step 3: *State assignment* is needed in order to encode the states in binary codes. In general, $r = \lceil \log N \rceil$ flip-flops are necessary for encoding N distinct states, but there exist too many possibilities to assign $N \leq 2^r$ values of the combinations of r state variables to N distinct states. *Race* is a potential problem (not discussed here) that may have to be solved in this step. A good state assignment must be not only be race-free, but also realize the state transition table with minimal combinational hardware. Substituting binary codes for the state names in the minimal state transition table provides the final binary-coded state transition table. For the simple finite-state machines such as binary counters and shift registers, whose number and encoding of states are fixed and already known, the previous step of state reduction and the current step of state assignment can be skipped.

Step 4: The binary-coded state transition table is implemented by choosing the proper type of flip-flops and deriving the corresponding excitation table.

Step 5: We can now derive logic expressions for the output function and the excitation inputs of the flip-flops and draw the circuit diagram, using the same simplification and implementation methods mentioned in Chapter 3 for implementing a finite-state machine.

Example 4.3   Synthesis of a Finite-State Machine with an Unknown Number of States

A finite-state machine has two inputs and one output. If the total number of 1s received is greater than or equal to four and at least three pairs of inputs have occurred, then the output should be 1, coincident with the reset of the machine. Design the machine using D flip-flops.

An example input set and the corresponding output follows:

Input sequence:

$$0 \quad 0 \quad 0 \quad 1 \quad 1 \quad 1 \quad 0 \quad 0 \quad 0 \quad 1 \quad 1 \quad 1 \quad 0 \quad 0 \quad 1 \quad 1 \quad 1 \quad 0 \quad 1$$
$$0 \quad 1 \quad 1 \quad 1 \quad 1 \quad 1 \quad 0 \quad 0 \quad 0 \quad 0 \quad 0 \quad 0 \quad 1 \quad 0 \quad 1 \quad 1 \quad 1 \quad 0 \quad 1$$

Output sequence (reset after every 1 of output):

$$0 \quad 0 \quad 0 \quad 1 \quad 0 \quad 0 \quad 1 \quad 0 \quad 0 \quad 0 \quad 0 \quad 0 \quad 1 \quad 0 \quad 0 \quad 1 \quad 0 \quad 0 \quad 1$$

Step 1: State Transition Table

The state transition table as shown in Table 4.18 can be derived by analyzing the sequencing of events under the actions of different input sequences of X_1 and X_2. For example, first we specify the reset state as S_0. The definition of the state is indicated in the first two columns of the table. When no value-1 input occurs in X_1 and X_2, the state changes to S_1. When a 1-input occurs in either X_1 or X_2, the state changes to S_2. When two 1s occur in X_1 and X_2, the state changes to S_3. The sequencing continues without output until the circuit reaches S_6, which means two 1s have occurred in at least two pairs of X_1 and X_2. When at this time two 1s occur in X_1 and X_2, the state S_6 will output a 1 and reset to state S_0.

Table 4.18 State transition table of Example 4.3

No. of Pairs	No. of 1s in X_1, X_2	Current State	Next State When $X_1 X_2 =$			
			00	01	10	11
0	0	S_0	S_1	S_2	S_2	S_3
1	0	S_1	S_4	S_5	S_5	S_6
1	1	S_2	S_5	S_6	S_6	S_7
1	2	S_3	S_6	S_7	S_7	S_8
≥ 2	0	S_4	S_4	S_5	S_5	S_6
≥ 2	1	S_5	S_5	S_6	S_6	S_7
≥ 2	2	S_6	S_6	S_7	S_7	$S_0, 1$
≥ 2	3	S_7	S_7	$S_0, 1$	$S_0, 1$	$S_0, 1$
2	4	S_8	$S_0, 1$	$S_0, 1$	$S_0, 1$	$S_0, 1$

Notes: S_0 is the reset state. $S_0, 1$ means reset to S_0 and output 1. All the other items output 0.

Step 2: State Reduction

Without delving into the problem of state reduction, we can see in Table 4.18 that the rows of S_1 and S_4 are identical, and the rows of S_2 and S_5 are also identical. Changing every S_4 to S_1 and S_5 to S_2, omitting the duplicated rows, and renumbering the other states S_6, S_7, and S_8 as S_4, S_5, and S_6, respectively, we get the minimal state transition table as shown in Table 4.19.

The state transition diagram is shown in Figure 4.35, where the values of the input and output variables are indicated as X_1X_2/F on each directed arc.

Table 4.19 Minimal state transition table of Example 4.3

Current State	Next State When $X_1X_2 =$			
	00	**01**	**10**	**11**
$S_0 S_0$	S_1	S_2	S_2	S_3
S_1	S_1	S_2	S_2	S_4
S_2	S_2	S_4	S_4	S_5
S_3	S_4	S_5	S_5	S_6
S_4	S_4	S_5	S_5	$S_0, 1$
S_5	S_5	$S_0, 1$	$S_0, 1$	$S_0, 1$
S_6	$S_0, 1$	$S_0, 1$	$S_0, 1$	$S_0, 1$

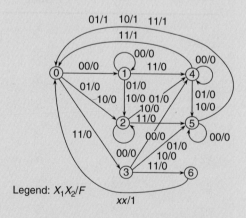

Figure 4.35 State transition diagram for Example 4.3

Step 3: State Assignment

Without discussing the problem of state assignment in detail, we simply assign a 3-bit binary sequence 000–110 to states S_0 to S_6 successively.

The binary-coded minimal state transition table is shown in Table 4.20. Each item of this table represents the next states of flip-flops y_2, y_1, and y_0, as well as the output of the machine corresponding to each combination of input variables X_1, X_2, and current states.

Table 4.20 Binary-coded minimal state transition table of Example 4.3

State	$y_2 y_1 y_0$	$y_2' y_1' y_0'$ when $X_1 X_2 =$			
		00	01	10	11
S_0	000	001	010	010	011
S_1	001	001	010	010	100
S_2	010	010	100	100	101
S_3	011	100	101	101	110
S_4	100	100	101	101	000, 1
S_5	101	101	000, 1	000, 1	000, 1
S_6	110	000, 1	000, 1	000, 1	000, 1

Step 4: Excitation Table and Output Table
Because the D flip-flop that we choose for implementation of this design has the excitation variable equal to the next state variable, Table 4.20 can be used as the excitation table and output table without change. Each item of the table represents the values of excitation variables $D_2 D_1 D_0$ and output function F.

Step 5: Boolean Expressions and Their Implementation in a Logic Circuit
Using any appropriate method mentioned in Chapter 3, including the Karnaugh map method, we obtain the following expressions:

$$D_2 = \overline{X_1} \cdot \overline{X_2} \cdot y_2 \overline{y_1} + \overline{X_1 X_2} \cdot y_2 \overline{y_1} \cdot \overline{y_0} + \overline{y_2} y_1 y_0 + \overline{\overline{X_1} \cdot \overline{X_2}} \cdot \overline{y_2} y_1$$
$$+ X_1 X_2 \overline{y_2} y_0$$

$$D_1 = \overline{\overline{X_1} \cdot \overline{X_2}} \cdot \overline{y_2} \cdot \overline{y_1} \cdot \overline{y_0} + (X_1 \oplus X_2) \cdot \overline{y_2} \cdot \overline{y_1} + \overline{X_1} \cdot \overline{X_2} \cdot \overline{y_2} y_1 \cdot \overline{y_0}$$
$$+ X_1 X_2 \overline{y_2} y_1 y_0$$

$$D_0 = \overline{X_1 \oplus X_2} \cdot \overline{y_2} \cdot \overline{y_1} \cdot \overline{y_0} + \overline{X_1} \cdot \overline{X_2} \cdot \overline{y_2} \cdot \overline{y_1} + X_1 X_2 \overline{y_2} \cdot \overline{y_0}$$
$$+ (X_1 \oplus X_2) \cdot \left(\overline{y_2} y_1 y_0 + y_2 \overline{y_1} \cdot \overline{y_0} \right) + \overline{X_1} \cdot \overline{X_2} \cdot y_2 \overline{y_1} y_0$$

$$F = X_1 X_2 y_2 + \overline{X_1} \cdot \overline{X_2} \cdot y_2 \overline{y_1} y_0 + y_2 y_1 \cdot \overline{y_0} \qquad (4.12)$$ ∎

The logic circuit for the designed finite-state machine is not discussed in this chapter.

SUMMARY

Sequential logic circuits are widely used in computers for performing many important functions related to time as an independent parameter. All the instructions in a computer are executed as various timing sequences of activities. The control units controlling the execution of instructions and I/O operations perform sequencing control using sequential circuits. The memory unit is itself a sequential circuit not only to implement large arrays of memory cells, but also to serve as the basic element for building sequential circuits in combination with their combinational parts. This latter use of a memory element forms the general model of a sequential circuit as stated in Section 4.1. The four types of flip-flops—SR, JK, T, and D—serving the basic memory element in this model are analyzed in Section 4.2. The state transition table and state transition diagram as well as the excitation table are used for the analysis and synthesis of sequential logic circuits as illustrated in Sections 4.2 to 4.4 through different examples. Even the sequential MSI modules such as registers, shift registers, and counters are analyzed and designed in Section 4.5 using the same method. Finally, the general method of designing a finite-state machine is illustrated in Section 4.6 using an example.

EXERCISES

4.1 Show that the four types of flip-flops—SR, JK, T, and D—are interchangeable, that means you can transform a flip-flop of any type (e.g., D or T) into a flip-flop of any other type (e.g., JK).

[Hint: For example, to transform a D flip-flop into a JK flip-flop, just derive the expressions for D in terms of J and K so that you can construct an input circuit to the given D flip-flop.]

4.2 Given the conceptual circuit of the NAND-based level-controlled clocked JK flip-flop as shown in Figure 4.7, derive its state transition table in the same way as for the SR flip-flop. That is, you should analyze the circuit, gate by gate, for different cases of J, K, and *clock* signals.

4.3 The circuit diagram of an *edge*-triggered D flip-flop is given in Figure 4.36. Following the sample of Figure 4.15, analyze the given circuit for different cases of D and *clock* signals, and draw the waveforms at all the named points in the circuit. Use the result of the analysis to explain the principle of edge-triggering operation of the flip-flop.

You need to analyze the given circuit of edge-triggered D flip-flop for, at least, two cases:

(1) When $D = 1$, $Q = 0$, and $Clock = 0$, show that the flip-flop can be in a stable state.

When $Clock$ turns to "1", how does the circuit work and change its state?

When $Clock$ keeps to "1" and D changes to "0", how does the circuit respond?

(2) Repeat Case 1 for the initial state when $D = 0$, $Q = 1$, and $Clock = 0$.

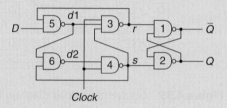

Figure 4.36 Logic circuit of an edge-triggered D flip-flop for Problem 4.3

4.4 As in Example 4.1, analyze the sequential circuit given in Figure 4.37 and find its (1) state transition table and output table, (2) state transition diagram, (3) counting sequences for $x = 0$ and $x = 1$, and (4) self-correcting property.

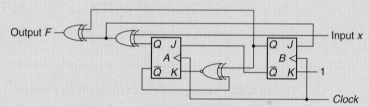

Figure 4.37 Sequential circuit for analysis in Problem 4.4

4.5 Repeat Problem 4.4 for the sequential circuit given in Figure 4.38. If the circuit is not self-correcting relative to the major counting sequence, make a minor modification of the circuit in order to correct the design without changing the original major counting sequence.

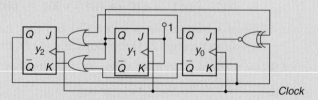

Figure 4.38 A counter circuit for Problem 4.5

4.6 Repeat Problem 4.4 for the sequential circuit given in Figure 4.39. If the circuit is used as a modulo-N counter, what are the values of N for $x = 0$ and $x = 1$? What is the meaning of the function of the input variable x and the output function F?

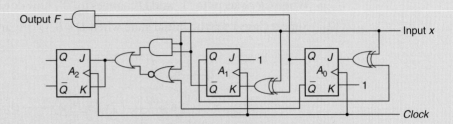

Figure 4.39 Sequential circuit diagram for Problem 4.6

4.7 It is known that the circuit given in Figure 4.40 is not self-correcting relative to the counting sequence. Verify it and make the necessary minor modification of the circuit in order to correct the design without changing the original counting sequence.

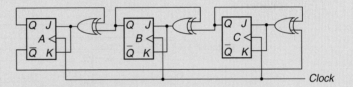

Figure 4.40 Sequential circuit diagram for Problem 4.7

4.8 Design a modulo-5 bidirectional counter under the control of an input signal x as follows:

if $x = 0$, the counter counts as

$000 \rightarrow 001 \rightarrow 100 \rightarrow 110 \rightarrow 011 \rightarrow 000 \rightarrow \ldots$, and

if $x = 1$, the counter counts as

$000 \rightarrow 011 \rightarrow 110 \rightarrow 100 \rightarrow 001 \rightarrow 000 \rightarrow \ldots$

Out-of-sequence states are invalid, but they must be self-corrected. Implement the counter using (1) D flip-flops and (2) JK flip-flops.

4.9 (a)   Design a counter using JK flip-flops with the following "add 3 mod 8" counting sequence:

$000 \rightarrow 011 \rightarrow 110 \rightarrow 001 \rightarrow 100 \rightarrow 111 \rightarrow 010 \rightarrow 101 \rightarrow 000 \rightarrow$ (repeat)

Give the detailed design process for deriving the simplest expressions for the excitation signals.

(b) Add two control signals s_1, s_0 to the circuit with the function table given in Table 4.21.

Table 4.21   Function table for Problem 4.9

Function Select		Functions	Explanation
s_1	s_0		
0	0	Maintain	No change
0	1	Clear to 000	
1	0	"add 1 mod 8" counting	Ordinary 3-bit binary up-counting
1	1	"add 3 mod 8" counting	Counting in the above sequence

4.10 Design a 3-bit multifunctional parallel counter, $y_2 y_1 y_0$, using JK flip-flops for the simplest implementation of the function table given in Table 4.22.

Table 4.22   Function table for Problem 4.10

Function Select Code		Count Mode
s_1	s_0	
0	0	add 1 mod 8
0	1	add 3 mod 8
1	0	add 5 mod 8
1	1	add 7 mod 8

4.11 Design a 3-bit bidirectional Gray code counter, which counts by the following Gray code sequences:

If $x = 0$,

$ABC = 000 \rightarrow 001 \rightarrow 011 \rightarrow 010 \rightarrow 110 \rightarrow 111 \rightarrow 101 \rightarrow 100 \rightarrow 000$

If $x = 1$,

$ABC = 000 \rightarrow 100 \rightarrow 101 \rightarrow 111 \rightarrow 110 \rightarrow 111 \rightarrow 010 \rightarrow 011 \rightarrow 000$

using (a) SR flip-flops;

(b) JK flip-flops;

(c) T flip-flops;

4.12 Design a multifunctional counter satisfying the following conditions:

- The counting sequence contains six states defined by a 3-bit Gray code starting from 000, with two of the eight states removed from both sides of the 2^2 axis.

- The counter is multifunctional and bidirectional under the control of two input variables s_1 and s_0 according to the function table given in Table 4.23.

Table 4.23 Function table for Problem 4.12

s_1	s_0	Function	Remarks
0	0	Clear	Clear to 000
0	1	Parallel load	From an external 3-bit input
1	0	Count in straight sequence	$000 \rightarrow 001 \rightarrow \ldots$
1	1	Count in reverse sequence	Reverse the above sequence

4.13 (a) Design the circuit of a 4-bit binary counter using four JK flip-flops—A_3, A_2, A_1, and A_0—and a minimum number of basic gates. The counter has two control inputs, *Count* and *Mode*, which operate as follows:

If *Count* = 0, *Mode* = 0,	the counter clears to zero.
If *Count* = 0, *Mode* = 1,	the counter maintains its current state.
If *Count* = 1, *Mode* = 0,	the counter counts the clock pulses in a mod16 sequence 0000, 0001, ..., 1111, 0000(repeat).
If *Count* = 1, *Mode* = 1,	the counter counts the clock pulses in a mod10 sequence 0000, 0001, ..., 1001, 0000(repeat).

[Note: The given JK flip-flops do not have *Clear* and *Preset* inputs.]

4.14 Design a 6-bit multifunctional binary up-counter whose function table is given in Table 4.24, based on the general formulae for the standard circuit of a binary up-counter.

Table 4.24 Function table for Problem 4.14

s_1	s_0	Operation	Counting Sequence
0	0	Clear	000000 (using *Preset/Clear* input of the flip-flop)
0	1	Count by 1	$000000 \rightarrow 000001 \rightarrow 000010 \rightarrow \ldots \rightarrow 111111 \rightarrow 000000$
1	0	Count by 2	$000000 \rightarrow 000010 \rightarrow 000100 \rightarrow \ldots \rightarrow 111110 \rightarrow 000000$
1	1	Count by 4	$000000 \rightarrow 000100 \rightarrow 001000 \rightarrow \ldots \rightarrow 111100 \rightarrow 000000$

The "Function Code" header spans the s_1 and s_0 columns.

4.15 Design a multifunctional counter, using JK flip-flops, A, B, and C, according to the function table given in Table 4.25, which combines the shift and count operations into a single sequential circuit. The count operation operates in the following counting sequence:

$$ABC = 000 \rightarrow 100 \rightarrow 110 \rightarrow 111 \rightarrow 011 \rightarrow 001 \rightarrow 010 \rightarrow 000 \rightarrow \text{(repeat)}$$

Table 4.25   Function table for Problem 4.15

s_1	s_0	Function	Remarks
0	0	Clear	Not using *Preset*/*Clear* input of the flip-flop
0	1	Count	Count in the above-given sequence
1	0	Left rotate	Rotate left the code *ABC* in the counter
1	1	Right rotate	Rotate right the code *ABC* in the counter

4.16 Change the circuit of the bidirectional shift register in Figure 4.30 into a similar circuit with the same function table, but using JK flip-flops instead of D flip-flops. Provide your design procedure and draw the circuit diagram. Besides flip-flops, you should use a minimum number of only NAND gates in your design.

4.17 (a)   Draw the schematic diagram of a 3-bit left-shift register using D flip-flops.

(b)   If the serial output signal is required to be a repeated binary sequence 0011010 0011010 0011010 …, what should be the initial content of the register? What should be the serial input sequence?

4.18 Design a binary sequence detector that recognizes four consecutive 1s, using D flip-flops. Give the detailed steps of your design. Display the state diagram, state table, excitation table, and final circuit. For example,

Input sequence x: 0011111011001110001111101 …

Output sequence F: 0000011000000000000011100 …

5

The Arithmetic Logic Unit

5.1 THE VON NEUMANN COMPUTER MODEL

The vast majority of computer systems used today are based on the *von Neumann computer model*, which was proposed by John von Neumann in 1946. Although computer science and technology have changed tremendously both in hardware and software, the basic model for computers has remained essentially the same.

A computer based on the von Neumann model is viewed as a *stored program computer*. Although problems to be solved on a computer can be described in any form most suitable for the target applications, these forms will ultimately be translated into programs that are understandable by the computer. A program is a sequence of instructions, each of which performs a basic operation. Before execution, the program is stored in memory along with data to be manipulated. When the program is executed, the instructions in it are retrieved from memory, sequentially, and brought into the processing unit. The processing unit decodes each instruction, retrieves the data from its register or from memory, performs the operation, and stores the result in the register or memory. Therefore, a computer based on the von Neumann model typically consists of three functional blocks, namely, main memory, a CPU, and an I/O subsystem, as shown in Figure 5.1. From the viewpoint of computer organization, main memory can be abstracted as a one-dimensional series of locations each bearing a unique address for storing and accessing information (instructions and data). The CPU is organized as a finite-state machine whose state changes as a result of the execution of instructions. From Chapter 4, we know that a finite-state machine such as the CPU should consist of a memory part in the form of registers, and a combinational part in the form of the arithmetic logic unit and the control unit, which realize the control sequences of instructions. The I/O subsystem serves as the interface between the computer and the outside world. The

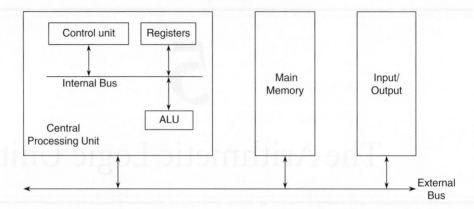

Figure 5.1   Basic organization of a stored program computer

external bus allows these functional blocks to be connected and communicate with each other.

5.2   PARALLEL FAST ADDERS

An arithmetic logic unit (ALU) is the heart of the CPU that works as a basic processing unit for all of the arithmetic logic operations (except for complex operations) defined in the instruction set. Even for instructions that do not directly perform arithmetic logic operations, the ALU may serve as a central datapath shared by all instructions for transmitting information. Therefore, we will study the ALU before we study the CPU. Furthermore, the ALU usually has a binary adder that lies in its central position and takes responsibility for processing and transmitting information. Thus, the performance of the ALU is mainly determined by its adder. As a result, we need to design a fast adder to eliminate the excessive carry-propagation time of the ripple-carry adder.

5.2.1   The Nature of Carry Propagation

In Chapter 3, we used a ripple-carry adder as a typical example for the design of a combinational logic circuit. In this section, we will study how the carry signals are generated and propagated along the carry propagation chain of the adder. Then, in a later section, we will see how to design a parallel fast adder by avoiding this carry propagation. First, the schematic diagram of an n-bit parallel adder is redrawn with n 1-bit full adders, as shown in Figure 5.2. Then, we will consider its implementation with emphasis on its carry propagation circuit. We start from the basic logic expressions of a full adder, which were derived in Chapter 3 as follows:

$$S_i = \overline{A}_i \overline{B}_i C_{i-1} + \overline{A}_i B_i \overline{C}_{i-1} + A_i \overline{B}_i \overline{C}_{i-1} + A_i B_i C_{i-1} = (A_i \oplus B_i) \oplus C_{i-1}$$
$$C_i = \overline{A}_i B_i C_{i-1} + A_i \overline{B}_i C_{i-1} + A_i B_i \overline{C}_{i-1} + A_i B_i C_{i-1} = (A_i + B_i)C_{i-1} + A_i B_i$$

(5.1)

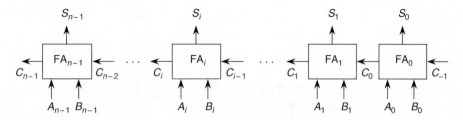

Figure 5.2 Block diagram of an n-bit ripple-carry adder

It can be seen from Expression (5.1) that the carry of the full adder of the current bit i, C_i, depends on the carry of the lower-order bit $i - 1$, C_{i-1}. Although n full adders work in parallel, the carry signals are, in fact, generated and propagated in sequence. The worst case of carry propagation occurs when a carry signal propagates from C_{-1} to C_{n-1} all the way along the carry propagation circuit. The time for this propagation is, therefore, directly proportional to the number of bits of the adder. It is the purpose of the following study to explain logically the nature of carry propagation and how to reduce its delay as much as possible.

There are two cases in which a carry is created, corresponding to the two terms $(A_i + B_i)C_{i-1}$ and A_iB_i in Expression (5.1b). The logic of the first term is that if either A_i or B_i is equal to "1" and there is a carry, $C_{i-1} = 1$, propagated from the lower-order bit, the current bit must create a carry. So, $(A_i + B_i)$ as a condition to continue or, more accurately, to relay the carry propagation, is called the *carry propagate*. The logic of the second term is that if both A_i and B_i equal to 1, the current bit must create a carry, independent of whether there exists a carry C_{i-1} equal to 1. So, A_iB_i is a condition to initiate a carry propagation and is called the *carry generate*. Distinguishing between the two components of a carry will help understand the concept of *carry look-ahead* to be described later.

5.2.2 The Ripple-Carry Parallel Adder (Revisited)

The logic circuit of a 4-bit ripple-carry parallel adder is shown in Figure 5.3. It is divided into three circuits: an input circuit, a carry propagation circuit, and an output circuit. For the input circuit, we introduce two variables, X_i and Y_i, for $0 \le i \le n-1$, related to carry propagate and carry generate, respectively, as determined by the following expressions:

$$X_i = A_i + B_i$$
$$Y_i = A_iB_i$$

(5.2)

These variables are independent of the carry signals, and thus, are available for all the bits simultaneously before the add operation begins. The input circuit is just designed to produce $\overline{X}_i$ and $\overline{Y}_i$, $0 \le i \le 3$, from the given inputs A_i and B_i by inverting the formula in Expression (5.2).

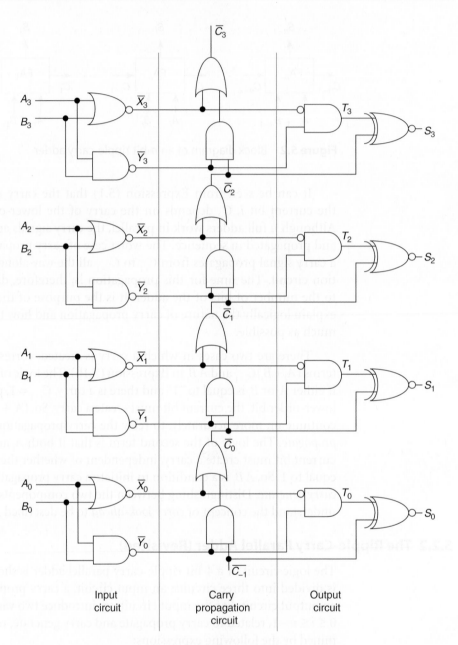

Figure 5.3   Logic circuit of a 4-bit ripple-carry adder

The carry propagation circuit may be designed in two different ways. One way is to keep the original carry signals on, and the other is to keep the inverted carry signals on. However, they are not mixed up. Since the input circuit in Figure 5.3 was designed on inverted signals, we will design the carry propagation circuit to propagate inverted carry signals too. Thus, we use the $\overline{X}_i$ and $\overline{Y}_i$ variables and the relation.

$$\overline{Y}_i \cdot \overline{X}_i = \overline{A_i \cdot B_i} \cdot \overline{A_i + B_i} = (\overline{A}_i + \overline{B}_i) \cdot \overline{A_i \cdot B_i} = \overline{A_i \cdot B_i} = \overline{A_i + B_i} = \overline{X}_i$$

to derive the carry signals $\overline{C}_i$ as follows:

$$\overline{C}_i = \overline{(A_i + B_i)C_{i-1} + A_iB_i} = \overline{X_iC_{i-1} + Y_i} = \overline{(X_i + C_{i-1})Y_i}$$

$$= \overline{Y_i \cdot C_{i-1}} + \overline{Y_i \cdot X_i} = \overline{Y}_i \cdot \overline{C}_{i-1} + \overline{X}_i \tag{5.3}$$

It can be seen from Figure 5.3 that the carry propagation circuit takes two gate delays for each bit i to propagate a carry signal.

Finally, the output circuit in Figure 5.3 receives variables $\overline{X}_i$ and $\overline{Y}_i$ from the input circuit and the carry signals $\overline{C}_{i-1}$ from the carry propagation circuit, and then generates the sum by the following expression:

$$S_i = (\overline{A}_iB_i + A_i\overline{B}_i) \oplus C_{i-1} = [(A_i + B_i)(\overline{A}_i + \overline{B}_i)] \oplus C_{i-1} = [(A_i + B_i)(\overline{A_iB_i})] \oplus C_{i-1}$$

$$= (X_i\overline{Y}_i) \oplus C_{i-1} = \overline{(X_i\overline{Y}_i)} \oplus \overline{C_{i-1}} = \overline{T}_i \oplus \overline{C}_{i-1} \tag{5.4}$$

where $T_i = X_i\overline{Y}_i$ \hfill (5.5)

5.2.3 The 4-Bit Carry Look-Ahead Adder

The carry look-ahead adder differs from a ripple-carry adder only in its carry look-ahead circuit. It reduces significantly the carry creation time by generating the carry signals for all the bits at once directly from the input carry C_{-1}. This is the basic idea of *carry look-ahead* that we can use to build a 4-bit parallel fast adder based on the same input and output circuits as we have built in Figure 5.3 for the ripple-carry adder. Since this input circuit generates the inverted variables, $\overline{X}_i$ and $\overline{Y}_i$, we should derive the expressions for all the inverted carry signals, $\overline{C}_i$, $3 \le i \le 0$, in terms of $\overline{C}_{-1}$ by iteratively applying Expression (5.3) in the following way:

$$\overline{C}_0 = \overline{Y}_0 \cdot \overline{C}_{-1} + \overline{X}_0$$

$$\overline{C}_1 = \overline{Y}_1 \cdot \overline{C}_0 + \overline{X}_1 = \overline{Y}_1 \cdot \overline{Y}_0 \cdot \overline{C}_{-1} + \overline{Y}_1 \cdot \overline{X}_0 + \overline{X}_1$$

$$\overline{C}_2 = \overline{Y}_2 \cdot \overline{C}_1 + \overline{X}_2 = \overline{Y}_2 \cdot \overline{Y}_1 \cdot \overline{Y}_0 \cdot \overline{C}_{-1} + \overline{Y}_2 \cdot \overline{Y}_1 \cdot \overline{X}_0 + \overline{Y}_2 \cdot \overline{X}_1 + \overline{X}_2 \tag{5.6}$$

$$\overline{C}_3 = \overline{Y}_3 \cdot \overline{C}_2 + \overline{X}_3 = \overline{Y}_3 \cdot \overline{Y}_2 \cdot \overline{Y}_1 \cdot \overline{Y}_0 \cdot \overline{C}_{-1} + \overline{Y}_3 \cdot \overline{Y}_2 \cdot \overline{Y}_1 \cdot \overline{X}_0$$

$$+ \overline{Y}_3 \cdot \overline{Y}_2 \cdot \overline{X}_1 \cdot \overline{Y}_3 \cdot \overline{X}_2 + \overline{X}_3$$

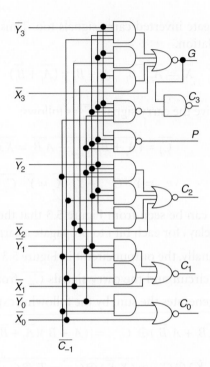

Figure 5.4   Logic diagram of a 4-bit carry look-ahead circuit

The circuit of a 4-bit carry look-ahead adder is shown in Figure 5.4.

Theoretically speaking, Expression (5.6) can be expanded to higher order bits up to $n - 1$ for $n > 4$. However, as the bit number increases, the number of product terms (i.e., the number of inputs of an OR gate) and the maximum number of literals in a product term (i.e., the number of inputs of an AND gate) in the expression would increase proportionally. If we limit the fan-in of an AND gate or an OR gate to 5, then the maximal allowable size of a single-stage carry look-ahead circuit is 4 bits, as we have implemented in Figure 5.4 according to Expression (5.6). If we replace the carry propagation circuit in Figure 5.3 with the carry look-ahead circuit of Figure 5.4, then we obtain a complete 4-bit carry look-ahead adder. Such a 4-bit carry look-ahead adder embedded in the ALU circuit will be seen in Figure 5.8.

5.2.4 The Block Carry Look-Ahead Circuit

As we have seen in the last section, the single-stage carry look-ahead adder cannot be implemented by simply generalizing Expression (5.6) to more than 4, if the fan-in of the basic logic gates is limited to 5. To eliminate this problem, we will introduce a solution that uses block carry signals to construct a multi-stage carry look-ahead adder of a larger size with a logic gate fan-in not exceeding 5.

We start from two extra signals, P and G, generated in Figure 5.4 according to the following expressions:

$$\overline{P} = \overline{Y_3} \cdot \overline{Y_2} \cdot \overline{Y_1} \cdot \overline{Y_0}$$
$$\overline{G} = \overline{Y_3} \cdot \overline{Y_2} \cdot \overline{Y_1} \cdot \overline{X_0} + \overline{Y_3} \cdot \overline{Y_2} \cdot \overline{X_1} + \overline{Y_3} \cdot \overline{X_2} + \overline{X_3} \tag{5.7}$$

Thus, we consider bits 3 to 0 as a 4-bit block and obtain the basic formula expressing the highest-bit carry, $\overline{C_3}$ in Expression (5.6) in terms of $\overline{C_{-1}}$:

$$\overline{C_3} = \overline{P} \cdot \overline{C_{-1}} + \overline{G} \tag{5.8}$$

This formula can be generalized to all the bit groups (3..0), (7..4), (11..8), (15..12), …, and thus, the general expression for the carry C_i of each 4-bit block i can be written as

$$\overline{C_i} = \overline{P_i} \cdot \overline{C_{i-4}} + \overline{G_i} \tag{5.9}$$

where $i = 3, 7, 11, 15, \ldots$

Comparing Expression (5.9) and the first Expression of (5.6), we can see the correspondence of P_i, G_i, and C_{i-4} with Y_0, X_0, and C_{-1}, respectively. Therefore, P is called a *block carry propagate*, and G is called a *block carry generate*, both being applied to a block of 4 bits. These P and G signals are useful for expanding the carry look-ahead adder in blocks of 4 bits. Applying Expression (5.9) to all bit groups (3..0), (7..4), (11..8), and (15..12), we obtain the following expressions:

$$\overline{C_3} = \overline{P_3} \cdot \overline{C_{-1}} + \overline{G_3}$$
$$\overline{C_7} = \overline{P_7} \cdot \overline{C_3} + \overline{G_7} = \overline{P_7} \cdot \overline{P_3} \cdot \overline{C_{-1}} + \overline{P_7} \cdot \overline{G_3} + \overline{G_7}$$
$$\overline{C_{11}} = \overline{P_{11}} \cdot \overline{C_7} + \overline{G_{11}} = \overline{P_{11}} \cdot \overline{P_7} \cdot \overline{P_3} \cdot \overline{C_{-1}} + \overline{P_{11}} \cdot \overline{P_7} \cdot \overline{G_3} + \overline{P_{11}} \cdot \overline{G_7} + \overline{G_{11}} \tag{5.10}$$
$$\overline{C_{15}} = \overline{P_{15}} \cdot \overline{C_{11}} + \overline{G_{15}} = \overline{P_{15}} \cdot \overline{P_{11}} \cdot \overline{P_7} \cdot \overline{P_3} \cdot \overline{C_{-1}} + \overline{P_{15}} \cdot \overline{P_{11}} \cdot \overline{P_7} \cdot \overline{G_3}$$
$$+ \overline{P_{15}} \cdot \overline{P_{11}} \cdot \overline{G_7} + \overline{P_{15}} \cdot \overline{G_{11}} + \overline{G_{15}}$$

The circuit of a 16-bit carry look-ahead adder based on Expression (5.10) is shown in Figure 5.5.

It should be noted that the block carry look-ahead circuit in Figure 5.5 is the practical circuit of an SN74182 look-ahead carry generator chip that implements

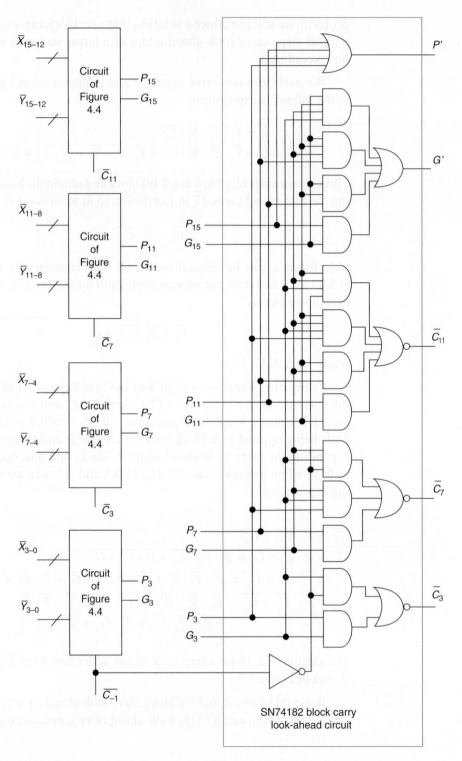

Figure 5.5 Logic diagram of a block carry look-ahead circuit and the configuration of a 16-bit two-stage carry look-ahead circuit

the product-of-sums (POS) Expression (5.11) instead of the sum-of-products (SOP) Expression (5.10) according to the following transformation:

$$\overline{C_3} = (G_3 + \overline{C_{-1}})(G_3 + \overline{P_3}) = \overline{G_3 C_{-1} + G_3 P_3}$$

$$\overline{C_7} = (G_7 + G_3 + \overline{C_{-1}})(G_7 + G_3 + \overline{P_3})(G_7 + \overline{P_7}) = \overline{G_7 G_3 C_{-1} + G_7 G_3 P_3 + G_7 P_7} \quad \textbf{(5.11)}$$

$$\overline{C_{11}} = (G_{11} + G_7 + G_3 + \overline{C_{-1}})(G_{11} + G_7 + G_3 + \overline{P_3})(G_{11} + G_7 + \overline{P_7})(G_{11} + \overline{P_{11}})$$

$$= \overline{G_{11} G_7 G_3 C_{-1} + G_{11} G_7 G_3 P_3 + G_{11} G_7 P_7 + G_{11} P_{11}}$$

Like the circuit in Figure 5.4, the block carry look-ahead circuit in Figure 5.5 generates two extra signals, P' and G':

$$\overline{P'} = \overline{P_{15} \cdot P_{11} \cdot P_7 \cdot P_3} = \overline{P_{15} + P_{11} + P_7 + P_3}$$

$$\overline{G'} = \overline{P_{15} \cdot P_{11} \cdot P_7 \cdot G_3} + \overline{P_{15} \cdot P_{11} \cdot G_7} + \overline{P_{15} \cdot G_{11}} + \overline{G_{15}} \quad \textbf{(5.12)}$$

$$= (G_{15} + G_{11} + G_7 + G_3)(G_{15} + G_{11} + G_7 + \overline{P_7})(G_{15} + G_{11} + \overline{P_{11}})(G_{15} + \overline{P_{15}})$$

$$= \overline{G_{15} G_{11} G_7 G_3 + G_{15} G_{11} G_7 P_7 + G_{15} G_{11} P_{11} + G_{15} P_{15}}$$

such that in Expression (5.10),

$$\overline{C_{15}} = \overline{P' C_{-1} + G'} \quad \textbf{(5.13)}$$

P' and G' signals produced by Expression (5.12) are the block carry propagate and block carry generate signals for a 16-bit group. They are useful for further expanding a carry look-ahead adder to an even larger size.

The configuration of a 16-bit two-stage carry look-ahead circuit is also shown in Figure 5.5. We use four basic 4-bit carry look-ahead circuits shown in Figure 5.4 as the building blocks and connect them to an SN74182 block carry look-ahead circuit to construct a 16-bit two-stage carry look-ahead circuit. All the P and G signals from the circuits in Figure 5.4 are connected to the corresponding P and G inputs of the SN74182. The output carry signals of the SN74182 are connected to the corresponding carry inputs of the circuits in Figure 5.4. The carry input to the LSB of the adder, $\overline{C_{-1}}$, should be connected to the carry input of the SN74182. The delays from this carry input to different carry outputs of the adder can be measured along different paths of the circuit. None of these delays totals more than five gate delays. If we don't have an SN74182 and sequentially connect the four circuits of Figure 5.4 in a cascade to form a blocked ripple-carry adder in a serial-parallel configuration, the maximum delay will be eight gate delays.

Since Expressions (5.9) and (5.13) have similar forms, we can use the same principle to build a 64-bit tree-structured carry look-ahead circuit using 16 of the circuits shown in Figure 5.4 and five SN74182 block carry look-ahead circuits.

5.3 ANALYSIS OF THE DESIGN OF A COMMERCIAL ALU CHIP

The ALU can have a large variety of designs depending on the functional requirement of a computer. The simplest ALU can implement basic arithmetic operations such as add and subtract, and logic operations such as AND, OR, and XOR. Complex operations, such as multiply, divide, and floating-point operations, can be performed either by software (at the assembly-language level), a microprogram, or a coprocessor. A more sophisticated ALU may have some complex operations included in its basic set of arithmetic logic operations and directly implement them via hardware. For example, multiplication can be performed either by a combinational fast multiplier or by a system of sequential circuits using special registers and timing control. To emphasize the basic principles, we will first consider the design of a standard ALU chip in this section and then give more examples of the design of customized ALU circuits in subsequent sections.

5.3.1 Organization of an ALU Based on an Adder

As we have studied above, the ALU can be built upon a parallel adder for performing basic arithmetic operations, and then special circuits can be designed to incorporate additional operations, especially logic operations, in the ALU. The general idea is to decompose an adder circuit into three parts—an input circuit, a carry creation circuit, and an output circuit—as we did in Figure 5.3. Thus, we can incorporate additional operations by changing the input circuit and the output circuit of the adder. Being controlled by the function select code of the ALU, the input circuit can feed various input operands to the adder for executing different operations. The output circuit can be modified to distinguish between arithmetic and logic operations by enabling/disabling the carry signals for different output logic structures of the adder. This scheme of changing the input and output circuits is shown in Figure 5.6 for a 4-bit ALU. The input circuit still outputs the same variable names, $\overline{X}_i$ and $\overline{Y}_i$ for $0 \leq i \leq 3$ as in Figure 5.3, but its logic functions may be changed to feed different input operands to the adder. The carry-creation circuit could be either the circuit in Figure 5.3 or the one in Figure 5.4. The output circuit is modified by introducing a control input M for enabling/disabling the carry signals. When $M = 0$, all C_i's for $-1 \leq i \leq 2$ are enabled so that the ALU can perform arithmetic operations on an ordinary adder:

$$F_i = T_i \oplus C_{i-1} = (X_i \overline{Y}_i) \oplus C_{i-1} \quad \text{General expression}$$
$$\text{with } X_i \text{ and } Y_i \text{ determined by the input circuit for } 0 \leq i \leq 3$$

$$F_i = [(A_i + B_i)\overline{A_i B_i}] \oplus C_{i-1} = A_i \oplus B_i \oplus C_{i-1} \tag{5.14}$$
$$\text{if } X_i = A_i + B_i \text{ and } Y_i = A_i B_i \text{ as in Figure 5.3}$$

When $M = 1$, all C_i's for $-1 \leq i \leq 2$ are disabled so that the ALU can perform bitwise logic operations according to the following expression

$$F_i = \overline{T_i} = \overline{X_i} + Y_i \qquad \text{for} \quad 0 \leq i \leq 3 \tag{5.15}$$

5.3.2 Design of the Input Circuit for Logic Operations

Now we will use the block diagram of the ALU in Figure 5.6 to analyze the design process of the commercial 4-bit ALU chip SN74181. Once we have a general block diagram, the problem of designing the ALU is simplified down to the design of the input circuit for implementing a given truth table of logic operations. The truth table of logic operations $F_i(A_i B_i)$ for the SN74181 ALU chip is given in Table 5.1, which contains the same set of 16 two-variable basic logic functions as we have defined in Table 3.2. Here, we need a 4-bit function code, $s_3 s_2 s_1 s_0$, for selecting one of the 16 logic operations. Because the input circuit works together with the output circuit to implement logic operations

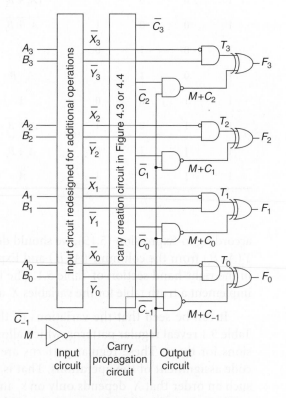

Figure 5.6   Block diagram of an ALU based on a parallel adder

Table 5.1 Truth table for the logic operations performed by an SN74181 ALU when $M = 1$

Function Code				Logic Operations	Intermediate Functions	
s_3	s_2	s_1	s_0	$F_i(A_i, B_i) = \overline{X_i} + Y_i$	$X_i(A_i, B_i)$	$Y_i(A_i, B_i)$
0	0	0	0	$\overline{A_i}$	A_i	0
0	0	0	1	$\overline{A_i} \cdot \overline{B_i}$	$A_i + B_i$	0
0	0	1	0	$\overline{A_i} \cdot B_i$	$A_i + \overline{B_i}$	0
0	0	1	1	0	1	0
0	1	0	0	$\overline{A_i} + \overline{B_i}$	A_i	$A_i \cdot \overline{B_i}$
0	1	0	1	$\overline{B_i}$	$A_i + B_i$	$A_i \cdot \overline{B_i}$
0	1	1	0	$A_i \oplus B_i$	$A_i + \overline{B_i}$	$A_i \cdot \overline{B_i}$
0	1	1	1	$A_i \cdot \overline{B_i}$	1	$A_i \cdot \overline{B_i}$
1	0	0	0	$\overline{A_i} + B_i$	A_i	$A_i \cdot B_i$
1	0	0	1	$\overline{A_i \oplus B_i}$	$A_i + B_i$	$A_i \cdot B_i$
1	0	1	0	B_i	$A_i + \overline{B_i}$	$A_i \cdot B_i$
1	0	1	1	$A_i \cdot B_i$	1	$A_i \cdot B_i$
1	1	0	0	1	A_i	A_i
1	1	0	1	$A_i + \overline{B_i}$	$A_i + B_i$	A_i
1	1	1	0	$A_i + B_i$	$A_i + \overline{B_i}$	A_i
1	1	1	1	A_i	1	A_i

according to Expression (5.15), we should derive a truth table for $X_i(A_i, B_i)$ and $Y_i(A_i, B_i)$ from the column $F_i(A_i, B_i)$ and Expression (5.15). The result is shown in the right-hand section of Table 5.1. The input circuit should be designed to implement a truth table for the variables X_i and Y_i.

It can be seen that the variations of the function values of X_i and Y_i in Table 5.1 reveal regular patterns, which allows us to derive very simple expressions for them. These regular patterns are the result of a proper scheme of code assignment of the operations. That is, the 16 operations are arranged in such an order that X_i depends only on s_1 and s_0 and Y_i depends only on s_3 and s_2. Thus, the truth table for X_i and Y_i in Table 5.1 can be reduced to Tables 5.2 and 5.3.

Table 5.2 Reduced truth table for $X_i(A_i, B_i)$ as functions of s_1 and s_0

Function Code		$X_i(A_i, B_i)$
s_1	s_0	
0	0	A_i
0	1	$A_i + B_i$
1	0	$A_i + \overline{B_i}$
1	1	1

Table 5.3 Reduced truth table for $Y_i(A_i, B_i)$ as functions of s_3 and s_2

Function Code		$Y_i(A_i, B_i)$
s_3	s_2	
0	0	0
0	1	$A_i \cdot \overline{B_i}$
1	0	$A_i \cdot B_i$
1	1	A_i

By the algebraic method, we can derive the simplest expressions for X_i and Y_i as follows:

$$X_i = A_i \overline{s_1} \cdot \overline{s_0} + 1 \cdot s_1 s_0 + \left(A_i + B_i\right) \cdot \overline{s_1} s_0 + \left(A_i + \overline{B_i}\right) \cdot s_1 \overline{s_0}$$

$$= A_i \overline{s_1 s_0} + s_1 s_0 + B_i \cdot \overline{s_1} s_0 + \overline{B_i} \cdot s_1 \overline{s_0}$$

$$= A_i + B_i \cdot s_0 + \overline{B_i} \cdot s_1$$

$$Y_i = 0 \cdot \overline{s_3} \cdot \overline{s_2} + A_i \cdot s_3 s_2 + \left(A_i \overline{B_i}\right) \cdot \overline{s_3} s_2 + \left(A_i B_i\right) \cdot s_3 \overline{s_2}$$ (5.16)

$$= A_i \cdot s_3 s_2 + A_i \overline{B_i} \cdot s_2 + A_i B_i \cdot s_3$$

$$= A_i \overline{B_i} \cdot s_2 + A_i B_i \cdot s_3$$

We can obtain the same result in an easier manner using a special form of Karnaugh map. The Karnaugh maps for $X_i(A_i, B_i)$ and $Y_i(A_i, B_i)$ are shown in Figure 5.7. They demonstrate a general case of the Karnaugh map in which each cell may contain an expression of the function rather than just the constant value 1 or 0. Any 2^k ($k = 1, 3, ...$) neighboring cells (including round wrapped neighborhood) forming a rectangle with the same expression can be combined into a prime implicant. If the expression in a cell can be decomposed into a SOP form, then any of its component product terms can be used to search for prime implicants. The final simplest expression thus obtained must cover the full expression originally given in that cell at least once. For example, in Figure 5.7, the final expression for X_i covers the components B_i and $\overline{B_i}$ of the original full expression $1 = B_i + \overline{B_i}$, so it can pick up A_i, but ignore $\overline{A_i}$ to derive the other terms.

After the preceding design process, the complete circuit of the SN74181 ALU can be drawn as shown in Figure 5.8. It includes four subcircuits:

- The input circuit to implement Expression (5.16).
- The carry look-ahead circuit of Figure 5.4.
- The output circuit of Figure 5.6 with its modifying part.
- A NOR gate to generate the "Zero" status Z, which equals "1" if result $= 0$, else "0".

The circuit of the look-ahead carry generator, SN74182, which was obtained in Figure 5.5 can be used with an SN74181 for expansion of the ALU to any larger size.

5.3.3 Analysis of the ALU for Arithmetic Operations

The next step in the analysis of the SN74181 ALU is to determine which arithmetic operations can be performed with the existing input circuit when $M = 0$. The general expression for the arithmetic operations to be done by the ALU when $M = 0$ was derived as $(X_i\,Y_i) \oplus C_{i-1}$ in Expression (5.14), where $\overline{X_i}$ and $\overline{Y_i}$ are the variables generated by the input circuit. As a special case, when $X_i = A_i + B_i$ and $Y_i = A_i \cdot B_i$, the above general operation $\left(X_i\overline{Y_i}\right) \oplus C_{i-1}$ turns into $A_i \oplus B_i \oplus C_{i-1}$ corresponding to

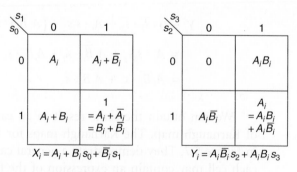

Figure 5.7   Using Karnaugh maps to obtain Expression (5.16)

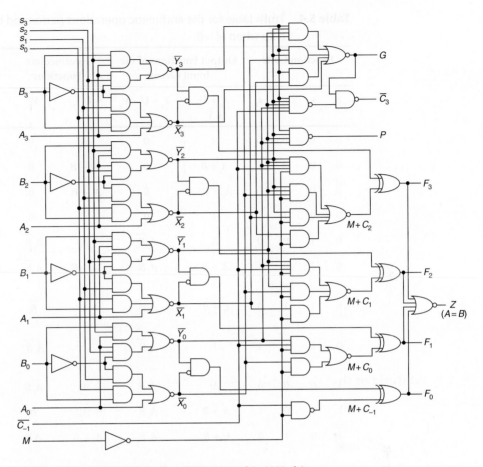

Figure 5.8 Logic circuit of an SN74181 4-bit ALU chip

the *add* operation of "A plus B plus C_{-1}" as indicated in Expression (5.14). For the other expressions of X_i and Y_i, the arithmetic operations performed will be different. If we can transform them into similar forms as

$$X_i = U_i + V_i$$
$$Y_i = U_i \cdot V_i \tag{5.17}$$

then, we can say that the ALU will perform the corresponding arithmetic operation as

$$F = U \text{ plus } V \text{ plus } C_{-1} \tag{5.18}$$

As a result of this transformation, the expressions of X_i, Y_i, U_i, and V_i together with the arithmetic operations performed are all listed in Table 5.4.

Table 5.4 Truth table for the arithmetic operations performed by an SN74181 ALU chip when $M = 0$

Function Code				Output Functions of the Input Circuit		Intermediate Functions		Arithmetic Operations
s_3	s_2	s_1	s_0	$X_i = U_i + V_i$	$Y_i = U_i \cdot V_i$	U_i	V_i	$F = U$ plus V plus C_{-1}
0	0	0	0	A_i	0	A_i	0	A plus C_{-1}
0	0	0	1	$A_i + B_i$	0	$A_i + B_i$	0	$(A + B)$ plus C_{-1}
0	0	1	0	$A_i + \overline{B_i}$	0	$A_i + \overline{B_i}$	0	$\left(A + \overline{B}\right)$ plus C_{-1}
0	0	1	1	1	0	1	0	$11 \cdots 1$ plus C_{-1}
0	1	0	0	A_i	$A_i \overline{B_i}$	A_i	$A_i \overline{B_i}$	A plus $A\overline{B}$ plus C_{-1}
0	1	0	1	$A_i + B_i$	$A_i \overline{B_i}$	$A_i + B_i$	$A_i \overline{B_i}$	$(A + B)$ plus $A\overline{B}$ plus C_{-1}
0	1	1	0	$A_i + \overline{B_i}$	$A_i \overline{B_i}$	A_i	$\overline{B_i}$	A minus B minus $\overline{C_{-1}}$
0	1	1	1	1	$A_i \overline{B_i}$	1	$A_i \overline{B_i}$	$A\overline{B}$ plus $11 \cdots 1$ plus C_{-1}
1	0	0	0	A_i	$A_i B_i$	A_i	$A_i B_i$	A plus AB plus C_{-1}
1	0	0	1	$A_i + B_i$	$A_i B_i$	A_i	B_i	A plus B plus C_{-1}
1	0	1	0	$A_i + \overline{B_i}$	$A_i B_i$	$A_i + \overline{B_i}$	$A_i B_i$	$\left(A + \overline{B}\right)$ plus AB plus C_{-1}
1	0	1	1	1	$A_i B_i$	1	$A_i B_i$	AB plus $11 \cdots 1$ plus C_{-1}
1	1	0	0	A_i	A_i	A_i	A_i	A plus A plus C_{-1}
1	1	0	1	$A_i + B_i$	A_i	$A_i + B_i$	A_i	$(A + B)$ plus A plus C_{-1}
1	1	1	0	$A_i + \overline{B_i}$	A_i	$A_i + \overline{B_i}$	A_i	$\left(A + \overline{B}\right)$ plus A plus C_{-1}
1	1	1	1	1	A_i	1	A_i	A plus $11 \cdots 1$ plus C_{-1}

Because the input circuit of an SN74181 was designed on the basis of a truth table of logic operations given in Table 5.1, not all of the 16 arithmetic operations defined in Table 5.4 are meaningful. There are several useful arithmetic operations that the SN74181 ALU performs when $M = 0$. They are listed as follows:

1. For $s_3s_2s_1s_0 = 1001$, $X_i = A_i + B_i$, $Y_i = A_iB_i$, we have addition: A *plus B plus* C_{-1}.

2. For $s_3s_2s_1s_0 = 0110$, $X_i = A_i + \overline{B_i}$, $Y_i = A_i\overline{B_i}$, we have A *plus* $\overline{B_i}$ *plus* C_{-1}, which is equivalent to A *minus B minus* $\overline{C_{-1}}$, since subtraction corresponds to the statement A *plus* $\overline{B}$ *plus* 1.

3. For $s_3s_2s_1s_0 = 0000$, $X_i = A_i$, $Y_i = 0$, we have increment: A *plus* C_{-1}.

4. For $s_3s_2s_1s_0 = 1111$, $X_i = 1$, $Y_i = A_i$, we have decrement: A *plus* $11\cdots1$ *plus* C_{-1}.

5. For $s_3s_2s_1s_0 = 0011$, $X_i = 1$, $Y_i = 0$, we have constant 0 or −1: $11\cdots1$ *plus* C_{-1}.

6. For $s_3s_2s_1s_0 = 1100$, $X_i = A_i$, $Y_i = A_i$, we have arithmetic left shift: A *plus A plus* C_{-1}.

5.4 METHODS FOR DESIGNING AN ALU

In this section, we will provide more examples of designing a customized ALU based on a user-specified function table. For convenience of comparison, all examples will design a 16-bit ALU implementing the same function table, but use different methods of design utilizing the functionality of an adder or a multiplexer in different ways.

5.4.1 Designing an ALU Using External Gates for Logic Operations

The first method of designing the ALU is to utilize only the *add* function and the *transfer* function of an adder, where the *transfer* function means to feed the data to the adder as one operand and set another operand and the carry-in signal to be "0". Then, the adder can simply transfer the input data to its output. Therefore, to execute logic operations, we can just connect external gates to one input of the adder and set the adder to the transfer mode. For example, if we want the adder to perform the logic operation of AND, we can simply connect AND gates to the input of the adder and let the other inputs be "0". Other logic operations such as OR, XOR, and NOT can be implemented in the same way. This is probably the simplest method of designing an ALU without special knowledge of the ALU organization, but it is applicable only for a simple function table that contains only a few logic operations to be implemented by external gates.

An alternative method of using external gates to design an ALU is the use of multiplexers at the output stage to collect the results of arithmetic and logic operations directly to the ALU output. The ALU's function code acts on the multiplexers' control input. All the external components, including the adder, should be connected to the inputs of the multiplexers. In this assignment, the adder performs only the arithmetic operations. Since the adder is more expensive than the simple logic gates, it must be shared by all arithmetic operations for delivering their results to the multiplexers. Therefore, this alternative method is preferable when the function table contains only a few arithmetic operations and the function table for designing the adder is small.

5.4.2 Designing an ALU Based on Standard ALU Chips

The ALU can be designed utilizing the standard ALU chips, such as the SN74181, to implement a user-specified function table. In this case, we choose the

Example 5.1   Design of a 16-bit ALU Using External Gates on an Adder

The ALU is to implement the function table given in the left-hand section of Table 5.5. The adder collects all the inputs from the external gates, so the input operands, A_{in}, B_{in}, and C_{-1}, should be synthesized as shown in the right-hand section of Table 5.5. Since most of the minterms of the expression for A_{in} are different and use external gates to implement, there is less potential of its simplification. Therefore, we simply implement the expressions for A_{in} and B_{in} by multiplexers. As for the variable C_{-1}, we derive its simplest expression below:

$$C_{-1} = \overline{f_2}(f_1 \oplus f_0) \tag{5.19}$$

The circuit diagram of the ALU is shown in Figure 5.9.

Table 5.5   Function table of an ALU for Example 5.1

f_2	f_1	f_0	Function	A_{in}	B_{in}	C_{-1}
0	0	0	OP1	OP1	0	0
0	0	1	OP2 − OP1	$\overline{OP1}$	OP2	1
0	1	0	OP1 − OP2	OP1	$\overline{OP2}$	1
0	1	1	OP1 + OP2	OP1	OP2	0
1	0	0	OP1 OR OP2	OP1 ∨ OP2	0	0
1	0	1	OP1 AND OP2	OP1 ∧ OP2	0	0
1	1	0	OP1 XOR OP2	OP1 ⊕ OP2	0	0
1	1	1	OP1 XNOR OP2	$\overline{OP1 \oplus OP2}$	0	0

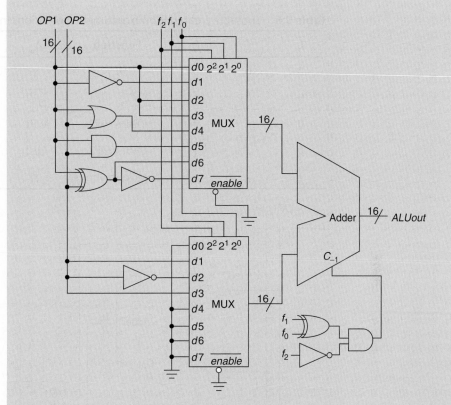

Figure 5.9   Circuit diagram of an ALU using external gates on an adder   ∎

Example 5.2   Design of a 16-bit ALU Using Multiplexers at the Output Stage

We assume the same function table as in Example 5.1, Table 5.5 (left-hand section). Since the logic operations are done by the external logic gates connected directly to the multiplexers, we need to create a small function table for the arithmetic operations only, as shown in Table 5.6. The simplest expressions can be derived from this table as follows:

$$A_{in} = \overline{f_1 \oplus OP1}$$
$$B_{in} = \overline{f_0 \oplus OP2} \qquad\qquad (5.20)$$
$$C_{-1} = f_1 \oplus f_0$$

The circuit diagram of the ALU is shown in Figure 5.10.

Table 5.6 Subtable created for the arithmetic operations in Example 5.2

f_2	f_1	f_0	Function	A_{in}	B_{in}	C_{-1}
0	0	0	OP1	x	x	x
0	0	1	OP2 − OP1	$\overline{OP1}$	OP2	1
0	1	0	OP1 − OP2	OP1	$\overline{OP2}$	1
0	1	1	OP1 + OP2	OP1	OP2	0
1	x	x	Logic operations	x	x	x

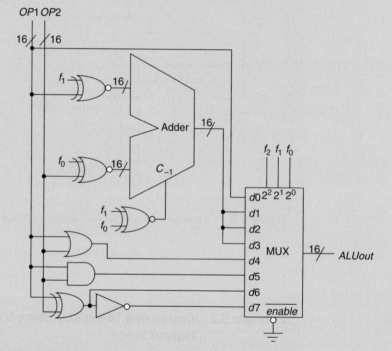

Figure 5.10 Circuit diagram of an ALU using a multiplexer at the output stage ∎

parameters $(M, s_3 - s_0)$ and the input operands $(A_3 - A_0, B_3 - B_0,$ and $\overline{C_{-1}})$ for the SN74181 to perform all the operations specified in the given function table. This will, in turn, require the corresponding logic circuits to be designed and connected to the inputs of the target ALU chips. This method is illustrated in Example 5.3.

Example 5.3 Design of a 16-Bit ALU Based on Four SN74181 Chips and One SN74182 Chip

This problem is to design an ALU with the same function table as Table 5.5. The function-select code, $f_2 f_1 f_0$, is defined to select from among eight different arithmetic logic operations. For each entry of the function table, we select a set of the above-stated parameters and input operands as shown in Table 5.7. The selection was made from the original function tables of SN74181 given in Tables 5.1 and 5.4. Some entries, for example, the first entry, may have more than one selection scheme. We should choose the scheme that yields the simplest expressions (e.g., the entry in parentheses is not chosen). To help derive these expressions, we draw the Karnaugh maps for $s_3 - s_0$ and $\overline{C_{-1}}$ in Figure 5.11 and derive them in Expression (5.21).

Table 5.7 Truth table of an ALU using SN74181 chips

f_2	f_1	f_0	M	s_3	s_2	s_1	s_0	A_{in}	B_{in}	$\overline{C_{-1}}$	Operation
0	0	0	0	0	0	0	0	$OP1$	x	1	$OP1$
(0	0	0	1	1	1	1	1	$OP1$	x	x	$OP1$)
0	0	1	0	0	1	1	0	$OP2$	$OP1$	0	$OP2 - OP1$
0	1	0	0	0	1	1	0	$OP1$	$OP2$	0	$OP1 - OP2$
0	1	1	0	1	0	0	1	$OP1$	$OP2$	1	$OP1 + OP2$
1	0	0	1	1	1	1	0	$OP1$	$OP2$	x	$OP1 \vee OP2$
1	0	1	1	1	0	1	1	$OP1$	$OP2$	x	$OP1 \wedge OP2$
1	1	0	1	0	1	1	0	$OP1$	$OP2$	x	$OP1 \oplus OP2$
1	1	1	1	1	0	0	1	$OP1$	$OP2$	x	$\overline{OP1 \oplus OP2}$

Figure 5.11 Karnaugh maps for deriving Expression (5.21) from Table 5.7

$$M = f_2$$
$$s_3 = f_1 f_0 + f_2 \overline{f_1}$$
$$s_2 = \overline{f_2} \cdot \overline{f_1} \cdot f_0 + f_2 \overline{f_0} + f_1 \overline{f_0} = \overline{f_2} \cdot \overline{f_1} \cdot f_0 + (f_2 + f_1) \overline{f_0}$$
$$s_1 = \overline{f_1} \cdot f_0 + f_2 \overline{f_0} + f_1 \overline{f_0} = \overline{f_1} \cdot f_0 + (f_2 + f_1) \overline{f_0}$$
$$\tag{5.21}$$

$$s_0 = f_1 f_0 + f_2 f_0 = (f_2 + f_1) f_0$$

$$A_{in} = OP1 \cdot \overline{\overline{f_2} \cdot \overline{f_1} \cdot f_0} + OP2 \cdot \overline{f_2} \cdot \overline{f_1} \cdot f_0$$

$$B_{in} = OP2 \cdot \overline{\overline{f_2} \cdot \overline{f_1} \cdot f_0} + OP1 \cdot \overline{f_2} \cdot \overline{f_1} \cdot f_0 \tag{5.21}$$

$$\overline{C_{-1}} = \overline{f_1 \oplus f_0}$$

Expression (5.21) is an example of designing multiple functions with the same set of independent variables. For maximal simplification, we need to make use of as many common terms as possible. In Expression (5.21), $f_2 + f_1, (f_2 + f_1)\overline{f_0}, \overline{f_2} \cdot \overline{f_1} \cdot f_0, \overline{f_2} \cdot \overline{f_1} \cdot f_0$ are all common terms.

The design of an ALU requires that status bits be generated. The SN74181 chip outputs only one carry signal out of the most-significant bit (MSB), and the carry signal into its MSB is not available, therefore the expression "*overflow* $= C_{14} \oplus C_{15}$" (which compares these two carry signals) can no longer be used for generating the overflow status. Instead, we can use the following expression by comparing three sign bits and one carry bit as follows [see Expression (3.21)]:

$$overflow = A_{in15} \oplus B_{in15} \oplus F_{15} \oplus C_{15} \tag{5.22}$$

The carry/borrow status, C, can be generated as follows:

$$carry / borrow = C_{15} \cdot add + \overline{C_{15}} \cdot (sub + inv\_sub)$$

$$= C_{15} \cdot f_2 \overline{f_1} \overline{f_0} + \overline{C_{15}} \cdot [\overline{f_2}(f_1 \oplus f_0)] \tag{5.23}$$

where

$$add = \overline{f_2} f_1 f_0$$

$$sub + inv\_sub = \overline{f_2}(f_1 \oplus f_0) \tag{5.24}$$

Since all the transfer and logic operations do not define *carry/borrow* status, we may use $sub + inv\_sub$ to replace *add* in the above expression and obtain

$$carry / borrow \ C = C_{15} \cdot \overline{sub + inv\_sub} + \overline{C_{15}} \cdot (sub + inv\_sub)$$

$$= C_{15} \oplus (sub + inv\_sub) \tag{5.25}$$

The other two status bits, N and Z, are simple to generate by the following formulae:

$$negative \ N = F_{15}$$

$$zero \ Z = (A = B)_{15-12}(A = B)_{11-8}(A = B)_{7-4}(A = B)_{3-0} \tag{5.26}$$

where $(A = B)$ equals $\overline{F_3 + F_2 + F_1 + F_0}$, that is, the output zero status of the SN74181 ALU chip.

Thus, we obtain the complete circuit of the designed ALU as shown in Figure 5.12.

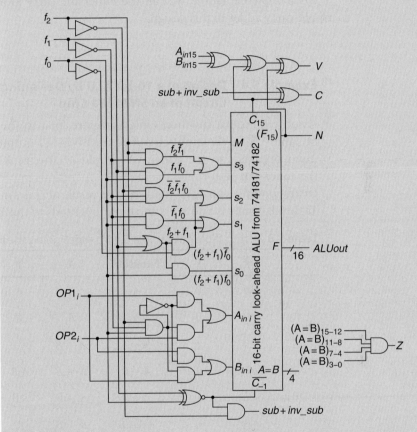

Figure 5.12   Logic diagram of a 16-bit ALU based on 74181/74182 chips

5.4.3 Redesigning the Input Circuit for the ALU

A new ALU can be designed using the same method as demonstrated for the design of the standard SN74181 ALU chip. The basic idea is that we can redesign the input circuit of the SN74181 in order to incorporate all the user-specified arithmetic logic operations in the standard circuit of an adder. This method is applicable for the case when we have a given function table whose logic and arithmetic operations are subsets of the operations listed in Tables 5.1 and 5.4. Then, we can synthesize the input circuit based on Expression (5.15) for the logic operations and use Expressions (5.17) and (5.18) for the arithmetic operations. These expressions are summarized below:

When $M = 1$, $F = \overline{X}_i + Y_i$.

When $M = 0$, $X_i = U_i + V_i$, $Y_i = U_iV_i$, $F = U$ plus V plus C_{-1}.

For implementation, we can use either the carry look-ahead adder or the ripple-carry adder in this design.

Example 5.4   Design of a 16-bit ALU by Designing the Input Circuit of an SN74181 Chip

Assume the same function table as before, that is, the left-hand section of Table 5.5. As the input circuit of the SN74181 outputs X_i and Y_i as the input operands to the adder, we should synthesize X_i and Y_i such that the adder can perform all the required operations in cooperation with the corresponding signals C_{-1} and M. The result of this synthesis is shown in Table 5.8, where A and B are the input operands to the ALU.

Table 5.8   Truth table of Example 5.4 for redesigning the input circuit

f_2	f_1	f_0	Function	X_i	Y_i	C_{-1}	M
0	0	0	A	1	A_i	x	1
(0	0	0	A	A_i	0	0	0)
0	0	1	$B - A$	$\overline{A}_i + B_i$	$\overline{A}_iB_i$	1	0
0	1	0	$A - B$	$A_i + \overline{B}_i$	$A_i\overline{B}_i$	1	0
0	1	1	$A + B$	$A_i + B_i$	A_iB_i	0	0
1	0	0	A OR B	$A_i + \overline{B}_i$	A_i	x	1
1	0	1	A AND B	1	A_iB_i	x	1
1	1	0	A XOR B	$A_i + \overline{B}_i$	$A_i\overline{B}_i$	x	1
1	1	1	A XNOR B	$A_i + B_i$	A_iB_i	x	1

For $f_2f_1f_0 = 000$, two possible choices for the dependent variables are listed in the truth table. The choice listed in parentheses is not as good as the other, so it is ignored. Moreover, since the truth table contains expressions rather than constant values for the functions X_i and Y_i, the simplification method can use a special form of Karnaugh maps as shown in Figure 5.13.

$f_2 f_1$ / f_0	00	01	11	10
0	$1\,(A_i\overline{B}_i + B_i)$	$\overline{A}_i + B_i$	$A_i + \overline{B}_i$	$A_i + \overline{B}_i$
1	$\overline{A}_i + B_i$	$A_i + B_i$	$A_i + B_i$	$1\,(B_i\overline{A}_i + A_i)$

X_i

$f_2 f_1$ / f_0	00	01	11	10
0	$A_i + A_i\overline{B}_i$	$A_i\overline{B}_i$	$A_i\overline{B}_i$	$A_i + A_i\overline{B}_i$
1	$\overline{A}_iB_i$	A_iB_i	A_iB_i	A_iB_i

Y_i

Figure 5.13 Karnaugh maps for Example 5.4 for redesigning the input circuit

The simplest expressions derived from Table 5.8 and Figure 5.13 are as follows:

$$X_i = A_i \cdot \overline{\overline{f_2} \cdot \overline{f_1}f_0} + \overline{A}_i \cdot \overline{f_1}f_0 + B_if_0 + \overline{B}_i \cdot \overline{f_0} + B_i\overline{f_2} \cdot \overline{f_1}$$

$$= A_if_2 + A_i \oplus (\overline{f_1}f_0) + \overline{B}_i \oplus f_0 + B_i\overline{f_2} + f_1$$

$$Y_i = A_i\overline{f_1} \cdot \overline{f_0} + A_i\overline{B}_i \cdot \overline{f_0} + A_iB_if_0(f_2 + f_1) + \overline{A}_iB_i\overline{f_2} \cdot \overline{f_1}f_0 \qquad \textbf{(5.27)}$$

$$= A_i\overline{f_0} \oplus (f_1B_i) + B_if_0(A_i \oplus \overline{f_2} + f_1)$$

$$M = f_2 + \overline{f_1} \cdot \overline{f_0} = f_2 + \overline{f_1 + f_0}$$

$$\overline{C}_{-1} = f_1f_0$$

The circuit diagram of the input circuit is shown in Figure 5.14.

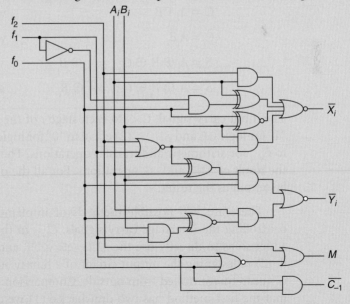

Figure 5.14 Circuit diagram of the redesigned input circuit for an ALU

In the above example, it is interesting to note that although Karnaugh maps give the simplest expressions in terms of f_2, f_1, and f_0 for X_i and Y_i (the first line of each expression) in Expression (4.27), algebraic transformation is still necessary to further simplify them to expressions with a minimum number of basic gates (the second line of each expression). Algebraic simplification takes advantages of the XOR, XNOR, NAND, and NOR gates to reduce the number of multi-input gates and inverters for the simplest implementation. As a result, the expressions contain only eight gates for X_i and six gates for Y_i, with only two inputs for most gates.

5.4.4 Designing an ALU Using the Internal Circuit of an Adder

The method presented in this section uses the internal circuit of an adder to implement common logic operations such as XOR, XNOR, AND, and OR. The XOR-based full adder circuit inherently provides these operations or gates. The principle of integrating the logic operations in the adder circuit is explained by the following basic expressions for a full adder:

$$S_i = (A_i \oplus B_i) \oplus C_{i-1}$$
$$C_i = (A_i + B_i)C_{i-1} + A_iB_i$$

(5.28)

We can generate the results of bitwise OR, AND, XOR, and XNOR operations for a bit i from the carry C_i and sum S_i under the corresponding conditions:

$$C_i = A_i + B_i \qquad\qquad \text{with } C_{i-1} = 1$$
$$C_i = A_iB_i \qquad\qquad \text{with } C_{i-1} = 0$$
$$S_i = A_i \oplus B_i \oplus C_{i-1} = A_i \oplus B_i \qquad\qquad \text{with } C_{i-1} = 0$$
$$S_i = A_i \oplus B_i \oplus C_{i-1} = \overline{A_i \oplus B_i} \qquad\qquad \text{with } C_{i-1} = 1$$

(5.29)

The input carry signal, C_{i-1}, to each stage i of the adder should be (1) equal to "1" for logic OR and XNOR, (2) equal to "0" for logic AND and XOR, and (3) equal to C_{i-1} for arithmetic and transfer operations. The output carry will be taken as the result of AND and OR operations. For all the other operations, the sum will be output as the result.

There are two possible methods of implementing these expressions: (1) controlling the interstage carry signals, C_{i-1}, in the internal circuit of a binary adder so as to directly use the AND, OR, XOR, and XNOR functions implied in it; (2) redesigning the output circuit of a binary adder so that the carry signals, C_{i-1}, can be controlled from outside. Comparison of these two methods reveals that the first method has two drawbacks: (1) we can use only the ripple-carry adder to provide the internal circuit with modifiable interstage carry signals; and (2) extra logic introduced to the carry signals, C_{i-1}, would make a longer critical path and thus, increase the carry propagation delay of the adder. Both of these drawbacks limit the first method to the design of slower ALUs. The second method can be used by redesigning the output circuit of the SN74181 chip with a carry look-ahead adder.

Example 5.5 **Design of a 16-bit ALU Using the Internal Gates of Full Adders**

This example will implement the same function table as shown in the left-hand section of Table 5.5. We will construct a 16-bit ALU on 16 full adders connected into a 16-bit ripple-carry adder through the controllable interstage carry signals, C_{i-1} for $i = -1, 0, 1, \ldots, 14$. The output carry signal of each full adder should be used as the result of logic operations.

The truth table for the inputs, A_{in} and B_{in}, to the adder, C_{in} to each full adder, and the output, $ALUout_{i}$, is derived as shown in Table 5.6. It can be seen that A_{in} is always $OP1$, except for "inverse subtract," which requires $A_{in} = \overline{OP1}$. The input B_{in} is equal to "0" for "transfer of $OP1$," $\overline{OP2}$ for subtract, and $OP2$ for the other operations. The input C_{in} and the output $ALUout$ are determined by the rules stated above in Expression (5.29). The input carry signal to the least significant bit of the adder is special, as listed in Table 5.9.

Table 5.9 Truth table for the synthesis of the ALU in Example 5.5

f_2	f_1	f_0	Function	A_{in}	B_{in}	C_{in} (not LSB)	C_{in} (LSB)	ALUout
0	0	0	OP1	OP1	0	C_{i-1}	0	S_i
0	0	1	OP2 − OP1	$\overline{OP1}$	OP2	C_{i-1}	1	S_i
0	1	0	OP1 − OP2	OP1	$\overline{OP2}$	C_{i-1}	1	S_i
0	1	1	OP1 + OP2	OP1	OP2	C_{i-1}	0	S_i
1	0	0	OP1 OR OP2	OP1	OP2	1	1	C_i
1	0	1	OP1 AND OP2	OP1	OP2	0	0	C_i
1	1	0	OP1 XOR OP2	OP1	OP2	0	0	S_i
1	1	1	OP1 XNOR OP2	OP1	OP2	1	1	S_i

From the truth table, we can derive the simplest expressions:

$$A_{in} = OP1 \oplus (\overline{f_2} \cdot \overline{f_1} \cdot f_0)$$
$$B_{in} = OP2 \cdot (f_2 + f_0) + \overline{OP2} \cdot \overline{f_2} \cdot f_1 \cdot \overline{f_0}$$
$$C_{in} = C_{i-1} \cdot \overline{f_2} + f_2 f_1 \oplus f_0 \quad \text{for all bits except the LSB}$$

$$C_{-1} = f_2 \oplus f_1 \oplus f_0 \quad \text{for the LSB}$$
$$ALUout_i = S_i(\overline{f_2} + f_1) + C_i f_2 \overline{f_1} \tag{5.30}$$

The circuit diagram corresponding to these expressions is drawn in Figure 5.15.

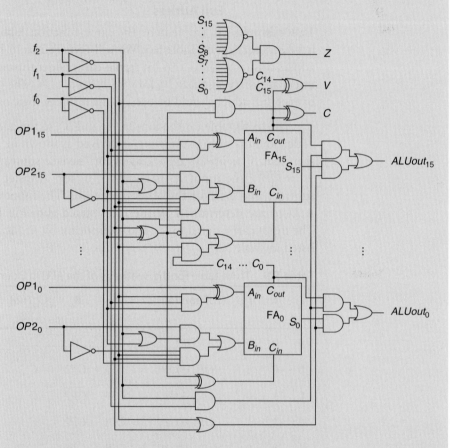

Figure 5.15 Logic diagram of a 16-bit ALU using the internal gates of an adder ∎

In Figure 5.15, the status bits are the same as in Figure 5.12 except that the overflow status is simpler to implement. Now, we have both carry signals C_{15} and C_{14} available for the following expression:

$$overflow = C_{15} \oplus C_{14} \tag{5.31}$$

5.4.5 Redesigning the Output Circuit of the Adder

In Example 5.5, we saw that the use of the internal circuit of an adder requires controlling the interstage carry signals of a ripple-carry adder. Thus, extra logic is introduced in the carry propagation path. For example, in Figure 5.15, the carry propagation path had its length increased by two gates per stage. This drawback limits the use of the method to the design of only low-speed ALUs. There exists an alternative method, also based on the principle of using the internal logic of an adder. In this method, we redesign the output circuit of the adder so that the carry propagation speed is not affected. From Figure 5.3, it can be seen that the output circuit of the adder receives the signals of $\overline{X}_i$ and $\overline{Y}_i$ for each bit i of the adder. We can use a function select code to implement logic operations. This function select code is abc, which coexists with the original control signal, M, as shown in Figure 5.16.

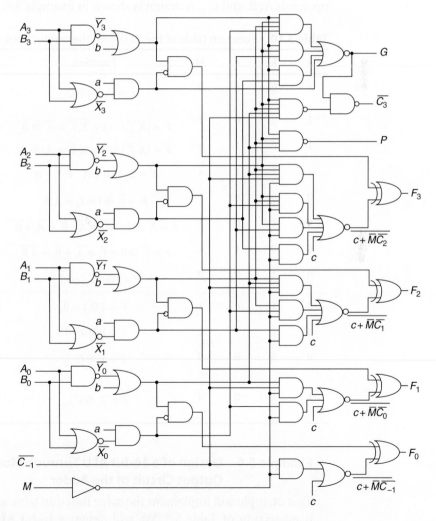

Figure 5.16 Circuit diagram of an ALU using the function select code $abcM$ for control

The expression for output F after inclusion of the four control signals—a, b, c, and M—becomes

$$F = [\overline{\overline{X_i \cdot a} \cdot \overline{(Y_i + b)}}] \oplus \overline{c + \overline{M} \cdot C_{i-1}}$$

$$= [(X_i + \overline{a})(\overline{Y_i} + b)] \oplus \overline{c + \overline{M} \cdot C_{i-1}} \quad \text{for } i = 0, 1, 2, 3 \qquad (5.32)$$

Thus, the function table of the ALU with the output controlled by a, b, c, and M is derived as shown in Table 5.10. It includes only a limited number of arithmetic and logic operations that can be performed with the simple input circuit shown in Figure 5.16. If we want to implement other operations, we can redesign the input circuit to modify the expressions for X_i and Y_i and/or modify the input operands A, B, and C_{-1}. A design is shown in Example 5.6.

Table 5.10 Function table of the ALU with the output controlled by a, b, c, and M

a	b	c	M	Function	Remarks
1	0	0	0	$F = (X_i \overline{Y_i}) \oplus C_{i-1}$	Arithmetic operation A plus B plus C_{-1}
1	0	0	1	$F = (X_i \overline{Y_i}) \oplus 1 = \overline{X_i \overline{Y_i}} = \overline{A_i \oplus B_i}$	Logic operation XNOR
1	0	1	x	$F = (X_i \overline{Y_i}) \oplus 0 = X_i \overline{Y_i} = A_i \oplus B_i$	Logic operation XOR
1	1	1	x	$F = X_i \oplus 0 = X_i = A_i + B_i$	Logic operation OR
0	0	0	1	$F = \overline{Y_i} \oplus 1 = Y_i = A_i B_i$	Logic operation AND
1	1	0	1	$F = X_i \oplus 1 = \overline{X_i} = \overline{A_i} \cdot \overline{B_i} = \overline{A_i + B_i}$	Logic operation NOR
0	0	1	x	$F = \overline{Y_i} \oplus 0 = \overline{Y_i} = \overline{A_i} + \overline{B_i} = \overline{A_i B_i}$	Logic operation NAND
0	1	0	0	$F = 1 \oplus C_{i-1} = \overline{C_{i-1}}$	Inverted input carry
0	1	0	1	$F = 1 \oplus 1 = 0$	Constant 0
0	1	1	x	$F = 1 \oplus 0 = 1$	Constant 1
0	0	0	0	$F = \overline{Y_i} \oplus C_{i-1}$	Mixed operation AB plus $11 \cdots 1$ plus C_{-1}
1	1	0	0	$F = X_i \oplus C_{i-1}$	Mixed operation $A + B$ plus C_{-1}

Example 5.6   Design of a 16-bit ALU Through Modification of the Output Circuit of the Adder

This example will implement the same function table as shown in the left-hand section of Table 5.5. We will design a 16-bit ALU on an extended carry look-ahead adder with the input and output circuits as shown in

Figure 5.16. The truth table for the inputs, A and B, to the adder and input carry, C_{-1}, is derived as shown in Table 5.11.

Table 5.11 Truth table for the ALU with a modified output circuit of an adder

f_2	f_1	f_0	a	b	c	M	A	B	$\overline{C_{-1}}$	Operation
0	0	0	1	0	0	0	$OP1$	0	0	$OP1$
0	0	1	1	0	0	0	$\overline{OP1}$	$OP2$	1	$OP2 - OP1$
0	1	0	1	0	0	0	$OP1$	$\overline{OP2}$	1	$OP1 - OP2$
0	1	1	1	0	0	0	$OP1$	$OP2$	0	$OP1 + OP2$
1	0	0	1	1	1	x	$OP1$	$OP2$	x	$OP1 \vee OP2$
1	0	1	0	0	0	1	$OP1$	$OP2$	x	$OP1 \wedge OP2$
1	1	0	1	0	1	x	$OP1$	$OP2$	x	$OP1 \oplus OP2$
1	1	1	1	0	0	1	$OP1$	$OP2$	x	$\overline{OP1 \oplus OP2}$

The simplest expressions can be derived from Table 5.11 as follows:

$$a = \overline{f_2 \overline{f_1} f_0}$$
$$b = f_2 \overline{f_1} \cdot \overline{f_0}$$
$$c = f_2 \overline{f_0}$$
$$M = f_2 \tag{5.33}$$
$$A = OP1 \oplus (\overline{f_2} \cdot \overline{f_1} f_0)$$
$$B = OP2 \cdot (f_2 + f_0) + \overline{OP2} \cdot \overline{f_2} f_1 \overline{f_0}$$
$$C_{-1} = \overline{f_2} \cdot \overline{f_1} f_0 + \overline{f_2} f_1 \overline{f_0}$$

The block diagram for the ALU, according to the above expressions, is drawn in Figure 5.17. The 16-bit adder should be built using a block carry look-ahead circuit like the SN74182 chip.

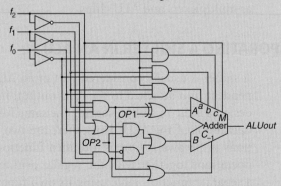

Figure 5.17 Block diagram of an ALU with the modified output circuit of an adder

Table 5.12 Comparison of the six methods of designing ALUs

Method	Example	Figure	Gates	Modules
MUX-adder	5.1	5.9	$6n + 3$	$2n$ MUXs; 1 adder
Adder-MUX	5.2	5.10	$6n + 1$	n MUXs; 1 adder
Design on an SN74181 chip	5.3	5.12	$6n + 16$	$n/4$ SN74181s
Design the input circuit	SN74181	5.8	$7n$	1 adder
Design the input circuit	5.4	5.14	$11n + 6$	1 adder
Use internal circuit of the adder	5.5	5.15	$10n + 8$	1 adder
Design the output circuit	5.6	5.17	$8n + 7$	1 adder

5.4.6 Comparison of Different Methods of Designing an ALU

We have used six different methods to design an ALU. We demonstrated the design procedures in six examples, Examples 5.1 to 5.6, to implement the same function table. Now, we can compare them from the viewpoint of hardware complexity. The results of the comparison are listed in Table 5.12. Also, for comparison, the table contains the minimum hardware used by the SN74181 ALU chip. Since the commercial SN74181 chip has been designed for a complete set of 16 logic operations arranged in an optimal order, it was constructed on a simplest possible input circuit, with a minimum number of $7n$ basic logic gates, where n is the word length, equal to 4 per chip. For the function table given in the examples, the method of redesigning the output circuit of the adder used by Example 5.6 seems to use the least amount of hardware, in addition to the n-bit adder. The methods of designing customized ALUs in Examples 5.1, 5.2, and 5.3 are all simple methods using little hardware added to off-the-shelf modules such as multiplexers and ALU chips.

5.5 INCORPORATING A SHIFTER IN AN ALU

A shifter is usually considered part of an ALU, but it is constructed as an independent unit attached to the ALU output. In some small, simple ALUs, we may design a built-in shifter, sharing the same function select codes with the regular operations of the ALU. Thus, there are two methods of specifying shift operations in hardware. One is a unified function table of the ALU specifying shift operations together with the regular arithmetic logic operations. The other is a separate function table using its own function select code for specifying shift operations.

The design of the SN74181 chip does not consider shift operations except the arithmetic operation "A plus A plus C_{-1}," equivalent to a one-bit arithmetic left shift when $C_{-1} = 0$. Usually the instruction set contains many other shift operations that require a special shifter be designed for their implementation. The operands of the shift operations can be provided by the CPU registers or memory. Many different types of shift instructions can be contained in the instruction set:

- *Left or right shift.*

- *Logic or arithmetic shift.* An arithmetic right shift requires sign-extension and an arithmetic left shift requires checking overflow (with the sign changed after shift), while the corresponding logic shift has zero-extension and no check for overflow.

- *Non-cyclic or cyclic shift.* A cyclic shift is also called *rotate*, i.e., the MSB of the bit pattern is shifted into the LSB position or vice versa, forming a closed cycle. We can use this type of rotate operation in a bit-serial adder (see Figure 9.8) to feed the full adder with serial binary code and, at the same time, keep the data unchanged after a complete sequence of add operations (with the number of rotates equal to the word length). We can also perform half the number of rotate operations to implement a swap operation.

- *Rotate with or without carry status involved.* The carry status (or any other one-bit flag) can be included or not included in the rotating loop. We can use the "rotate with carry status" operation to perform double-word shift in the following way: use the carry status to store the bit shifted out of the register during the first "rotate with carry" operation, and then shift this stored bit of carry status into another register using the second "rotate with carry" operation. Thus, the total effect is to logically connect two registers together through the carry status and perform a double-word shift operation in terms of two successive "rotate with carry" operations. This algorithm is depicted for the double-word right shift operation as shown in Figure 5.18.

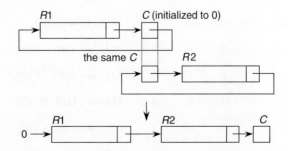

Figure 5.18   Two "rotate with carry" operations implement one double-word shift operation

5.5.1 Design of a Built-in Shifter in an ALU

From the applications in the later chapters, we will see that a "rotate with carry status" operation can be more general and powerful than the ordinary shift operations and, thus, better satisfy the requirements of such applications as multiply, divide, and double-word shift operations. Therefore, we choose "rotate left with carry" and "rotate right with carry" in Example 5.7 and Example 5.8, respectively, to illustrate how they can be designed. Example 5.7 will have the shifter built in the output circuit of the ALU, while Example 5.8 will have the shifter built in the input circuit of the ALU.

Example 5.7 Design of a 16-bit Simple ALU with a Built-in Shifter in the Output Circuit

With a shifter built in the ALU circuit, the function select code should be shared by all the operations of the ALU, including the rotate operations, as shown in the function table given in Table 5.13. The assignment of the function select code, $f_2 f_1 f_0$, to the arithmetic logic operations reveals a regular pattern that simplifies the design. These operations are evenly divided into four groups: transfer, arithmetic, logic, and shift, corresponding to the function codes $f_2 f_1 = 00, 01, 10, 11$ respectively. Because of the limited number of control codes, only XOR and AND are chosen for the minimum set of logic operations that can implement all the other logic operations by software. As explained above, the shift operations are of the type "rotate with carry." The argument of these operations must be the result generated by only one ALU operation selected from the function table. This is different from the general case, in which a separate shifter is attached to the output of the ALU, and the results of all ALU operations can be shifted. In Table 5.13, the "transfer of OP1" operation is selected for specifying the rotate operations.

Table 5.13 Function table of a simple ALU with a built-in shifter

f_2	f_1	f_0	Function	Explanation
0	0	0	ALU ← OP1	Transfer of operand 1
0	0	1	ALU ← OP2	Transfer of operand 2
0	1	0	ALU ← OP1 − OP2	Subtract
0	1	1	ALU ← OP1 + OP2	Add
1	0	0	ALU ← OP1 ⊕ OP2	Logical XOR
1	0	1	ALU ← OP1 ∧ OP2	Logical AND
1	1	0	C ← ALU = OP1	Rotate (of OP1) left with carry
1	1	1	ALU = OP1 → OP1	Rotate (of OP1) right with carry

At first, using the method of designing the ALU based on an SN74181 chip, we derive the truth table as shown in Table 5.14. We have a choice between two options. Option 1 involves designing "transfer $OP2$" as an arithmetic operation. Option 2 involves designing it as a logic operation.

Table 5.14 Truth table of a simple ALU with a built-in shifter

f_2	f_1	f_0	M	s_3	s_2	s_1	s_0	A_{in}	B_{in}	$\overline{C_{-1}}$	Operation
0	0	0	0	0	0	0	0	$OP1$	x	0	$OP1$
(0	0	0	1	1	1	1	1	$OP1$	x	x	$OP1$)
Option 1 0	1	0	1	0	0	1	0	$OP2$	0		$0 + OP2$
Option 2 0	1	1	1	0	1	0	x	$OP2$	x		$OP2$
0	1	0	0	0	1	1	0	$OP1$	$OP2$	1	$OP1 - OP2$
0	1	1	0	1	0	0	1	$OP1$	$OP2$	0	$OP1 + OP2$
1	0	0	1	0	1	1	0	$OP1$	$OP2$	x	$OP1 \oplus OP2$
1	0	1	1	1	0	1	1	$OP1$	$OP2$	x	$OP1 \wedge OP2$
1	1	0	0	0	0	0	0	$OP1$	x	0	$OP1$ after transfer by ALU
1	1	1	0	0	0	0	0	$OP1$	x	0	$OP1$ after transfer by ALU

We choose option 2 for our design because of its simpler result compared to option 1. From Table 5.14, we derive the simplest expressions for option 2 as follows:

$$A_{in} = OP1_i$$
$$B_{in} = OP2_i$$
$$C_{-1} = \overline{f_2} f_1 \overline{f_0}$$
$$M = s_1 = (f_2 + f_0)\overline{f_1}$$
$$s_3 = \overline{f_2 f_1} \cdot f_0 \tag{5.34}$$
$$s_2 = (f_2 \oplus f_1)\overline{f_0}$$
$$s_1 = s_2 + M$$
$$s_0 = (f_2 \oplus f_1)f_0$$

The circuit diagram for the implementation of Expression (5.34) with four SN74181 chips and one SN74182 chip is shown in Figure 5.19. So far, the design procedure is the same as stated in Example 5.3. The only additional procedure we need to state is the design of the shifter. Combinational shifters are usually built on multiplexers. In this case, since we have only two rotate operations, we can choose the minimum size 2×1 for the multiplexers. We can use the bit f_0 of the function select code as the control variable, and use $f_2 f_1 = 11$ as the condition on the $\overline{enable}$ input to distinguish the rotate operations from the others. The shifter is included in the output circuit of the ALU. Because of the involvement of the carry status, C, in the rotate operations, the MSB and LSB of the shifter require special treatment. The MSB receives C during rotate right, and the LSB receives C during rotate left. For the other bits, each bit i of the shifter receives F_{i-1} during rotate left and F_{i+1} during rotate right, where F_i is the output of the SN74181 chip at bit i corresponding to the operation "transfer of $OP1$." This relationship is implemented in the truth table shown in Table 5.14.

In the logic circuit of the ALU in Figure 5.19, part of the status register for storing the status bit C is shown as a flip-flop. It receives input from three different sources: the regular $carry/borrow$ status $C = C_{15} \oplus subtract$, F_{15} for rotate left, and F_0 for rotate right. It stores these inputs by way of a loading pulse, $lpStatus$, generated by the control unit for the general purpose of storing the status bits. The output of the flip-flop C is shifted into ALU_0 during rotate left and ALU_{15} during rotate right.

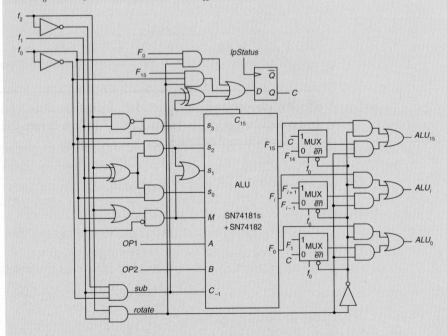

Figure 5.19   Circuit diagram of an ALU with a built-in shifter

Example 5.8 **Design of a 16-bit ALU with a Built-in Shifter in the Input Circuit**

As in Example 5.7, the shift operations specified in the function table of the ALU share the same function select code with the other ALU operations. The function table for this example is given in Table 5.15. Since multiplexers are the major components used for implementation of combinational shifters in general, the natural method we may choose for this design is the method stated in Section 5.4.1, which uses external gates for the logic operations through multiplexers. Besides the logic operations, we can implement shift operations on these input multiplexers of the ALU as well.

Table 5.15 Function table of a simple ALU with a built-in shifter

f_2	f_1	f_0	Function	Explanation
0	0	0	$ALU \leftarrow OP1 + C_{in}$	Transfer or increment
0	0	1	$ALU \leftarrow OP1 + OP2 + C_{in}$	Add without or with carry
0	1	0	$ALU \leftarrow OP1 - OP2 - C_{in}$	Subtract without or with borrow
0	1	1	$ALU \leftarrow OP2 - OP1 - C_{in}$	Reverse subtract without or with borrow
1	0	0	$ALU \leftarrow OP1 \oplus OP2$	Logical XOR
1	0	1	$ALU \leftarrow OP1 \wedge OP2$	Logical AND
1	1	0	$C \leftarrow OP1$	ROL : Rotate (of $OP1$) left with status C
1	1	1	$OP1 \rightarrow C$	ROR : Rotate (of $OP1$) right with status C

The entire ALU is built on a 16-bit adder. The truth table for its input parameters, A_i, B_i, and C_{-1} can be derived as shown in Table 5.16. We concentrate most of the input operands on the input A of the adder so that we can fully utilize the input multiplexers connected to this input, and then use only a few gates on the other inputs, B and C_{in}, of the adder for the simplest implementation of the ALU. For the rotate operations, we connect $OP1_{i-1}$ to bit i for left rotate and connect $OP1_{i+1}$ to bit i for right rotate. However, the inputs to bit 0 and bit 15 need special treatment. They should be status C connected to bit 0 for left rotate and to bit 15 for right rotate. Correspondingly, the output of bit 15 should be shifted into the flip-flop C for rotate left, and the output of bit 0 should be shifted into the flip-flop C for rotate right. The parameter C_{-1} of the adder is determined by the input C_{in} from the outside of the ALU. During add or forward operation, $C_{-1} = C_{in}$, while during subtract operation, $C_{-1} = 1 - C_{in} = \overline{C_{in}}$ because C_{-1} should be "1" even without C_{in}.

Table 5.16 Truth table for the design of the input parameters of the adder

f_2	f_1	f_0	A_{in}	B_{in}	C_{-1}	Remarks
0	0	0	$OP1_i$	0	C_{in}	
0	0	1	$OP1_i$	$OP2_i$	C_{in}	
0	1	0	$OP1_i$	$\overline{OP1_i}$	$1 - C_{in} = \overline{C_{in}}$	
0	1	1	$\overline{OP1_i}$	$OP2_i$	$1 - C_{in} = \overline{C_{in}}$	
1	0	0	$OP1_i \oplus OP2_i$	0	0	
1	0	1	$OP1_i \wedge OP2_i$	0	0	
1	1	0	C (for bit 0)	0	0	bit 15 to C
			$OP1_{i-1}$(for bit i)	0	0	
1	1	1	C (for bit 15)	0	0	bit 0 to C
			$OP1_{i+1}$(for bit i)	0	0	

The simplest logic expressions for the parameters B_i and C_{-1} of the adder not using multiplexers are derived as follows:

$$B_i = \overline{f_2} \cdot f_0 \cdot OP2_i + \overline{f_2} \cdot f_1 \cdot \overline{f_0} \cdot \overline{OP2_i}$$
$$C_{-1} = \overline{f_2} \cdot (f_1 \oplus C_{in}) \qquad (5.35)$$

Therefore, the logic diagram of the ALU is obtained as shown in Figure 5.20.

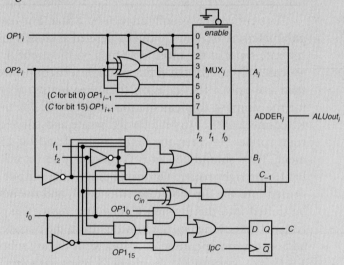

Figure 5.20 Logic diagram of an ALU with built-in shifter in its input circuit

5.5.2 Design of the Shifter as an Independent Unit

In most practical applications, a shifter is designed as an independent unit attached to the output of the ALU, so that the results of all the arithmetic logic operations of the ALU can be shifted (or just transferred without a shift) as needed. The shifter has its own function table, specifying various types of shift operations in terms of a common function select code. The shifter is constructed with multiplexers. So, in combination with the ALU, it actually plays the role of a common datapath to process and transfer information in the CPU. For generality, we will design a multifunction shifter in Example 5.9 in order to show the general principles of design.

Example 5.9   Design of a Multifunction Shifter as an Independent Unit

This example is the design of a multifunction shifter according to the function table given in Table 5.17. The table contains all the types of shift operations we studied at the beginning of Section 5.5. The meaning of each operation is explained in graphic form in Table 5.17. From these graphic forms, it is clear how the multiplexers should be connected to construct an n-bit shifter, as shown in Figure 5.21.

Table 5.17   Function table of a multifunction shifter for Example 5.9

h_2	h_1	h_0	Function	Meaning
0	0	0	ALU output with no shift	
0	0	1	ALU with 1-bit arithmetic shift right	→ALU→
0	1	0	ALU with 1-bit shift left	←ALU←0
0	1	1	ALU with 1-bit shift right	0→ALU→
1	0	0	ALU with 1-bit rotate left	←ALU←
1	0	1	ALU with 1-bit rotate right	→ALU→
1	1	0	ALU with 1-bit rotate left with C	←ALU←C←
1	1	1	ALU with 1-bit rotate right with C	→C→ALU→

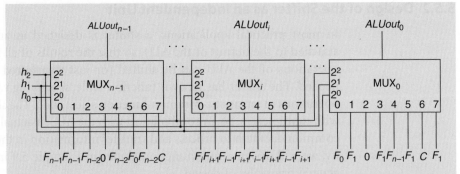

Figure 5.21 Block diagram of a shifter that implements the function table in Table 5.17

In Figure 5.21, it can be seen that the multiplexers for bit i, $i \neq n - 1$ or "0", have a regular pattern of inputs, which allows further simplification to reduce their sizes to 2×1 instead of 8×1. The simplification scheme is shown in Figure 5.22. The simplified multiplexers use h_0 as the control variable, while h_2 and h_1 are don't care variables for inputs 1 to 7. The input "0" should be controlled by h_2 and h_1 according to the following expression:

$$input\ ``0" = \overline{h_2} \cdot \overline{h_1} \cdot F_i + \overline{\overline{h_2} \cdot \overline{h_1}} \cdot F_{i-1} = \overline{h_2 + h_1} \cdot F_i + (h_2 + h_1) \cdot F_{i-1} \qquad (5.36)$$

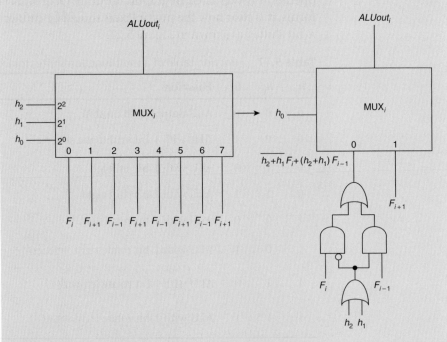

Figure 5.22 Simplified scheme for the MUXs for bit i of the shifter in Figure 5.21

5.5.3 Design of a Barrel Shifter

A shift operation is slow due to the sequential nature of execution. For a word length of 32 bits, the maximum shift amount specified by an instruction can be as large as 31 bits. If we use a serial shifter to execute this instruction, it may take 31 clock cycles to finish, which is intolerable. We need to design a fast shifter that can finish any number of shifts in just one cycle. Such a fast shifter is called a barrel shifter.

In principle, a barrel shifter is not difficult to design. For example, if the shift amount lies between 0 and 31, we can use a 32×1 multiplexer to shift any one of the 32 bits (including no shift) into a specific bit. Then, thirty-two 32×1 multiplexers are needed for shifting the entire word for any shift amount between 0 and 31. A conceptual view of this scheme for left shifting any bit between a_0 and a_{31} into $ALUout_0$ is shown in Figure 5.23. The 5-bit shift amount, $b_4 b_3 b_2 b_1 b_0$, is used as the control variable, selecting any one of the data bits from a_0 to a_{31} to be shifted into the destination bit a_0. The shift amount $b_4 b_3 b_2 b_1 b_0 =$ 00000 means no shift. Similar multiplexers are designed for the other destination bits a_1 to a_{31}.

The block diagram in Figure 5.23 is only a conceptual view of the barrel shifter in the sense that multiplexers of size 32×1 are not common. We can implement this concept using multiplexers of smaller size connected in multiple stages. As an example, we choose size 8×1 for the first stage and size 4×1 for the second stage to implement the size 32×1. The block diagram for the replacement of MUX_0 in Figure 5.23 is shown in Figure 5.24. It is only a very small part of a barrel shifter circuit. The complete circuit for a left rotate operation contains thirty-two 8×1 multiplexers, MUX_0 to MUX_{31} in the first stage, and thirty-two 4×1 multiplexers, MUX_0 to MUX_{31} in the second stage. These two sets of multiplexers are interconnected by the rule as shown in Table 5.18.

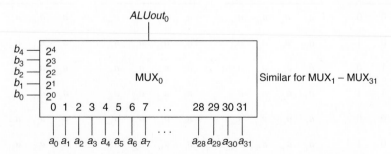

Figure 5.23   Conceptual view of the barrel shifter for a 32-bit left shift operation

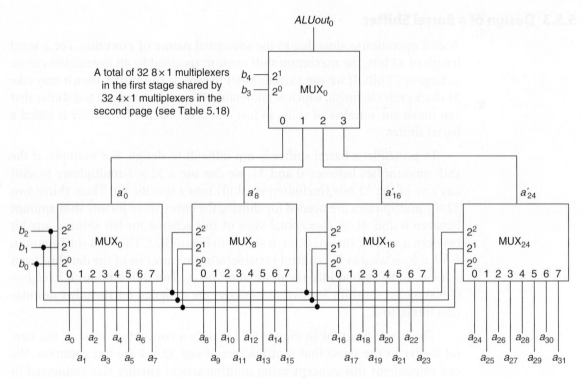

Figure 5.24 Circuit for bit 0 of the barrel shifter for left-shift operation

Table 5.18 Interconnections of multiplexers in a barrel shifter for a left rotate operation

$ALUout_0$					$ALUout_1$				$ALUout_2$				$ALUout_3$			
$b_4 b_3$		00	01	10	11	00	01	10	11	00	01	10	11	00	01	10	11
b_2	b_1	b_0	a'_0	a'_8	a'_{16}	a'_{24}	a'_1	a'_9	a'_{17}	a'_{25}	a'_2	a'_{10}	a'_{18}	a'_{26}	a'_3	a'_{11}	a'_{19}	a'_{27}
0	0	0	a_0	a_8	a_{16}	a_{24}	a_1	a_9	a_{17}	a_{25}	a_2	a_{10}	a_{18}	a_{26}	a_3	a_{11}	a_{19}	a_{27}
0	0	1	a_1	a_9	a_{17}	a_{25}	a_2	a_{10}	a_{18}	a_{26}	a_3	a_{11}	a_{19}	a_{27}	a_4	a_{12}	a_{20}	a_{28}
0	1	0	a_2	a_{10}	a_{18}	a_{26}	a_3	a_{11}	a_{19}	a_{27}	a_4	a_{12}	a_{20}	a_{28}	a_5	a_{13}	a_{21}	a_{29}
0	1	1	a_3	a_{11}	a_{19}	a_{27}	a_4	a_{12}	a_{20}	a_{28}	a_5	a_{13}	a_{21}	a_{29}	a_6	a_{14}	a_{22}	a_{30}
1	0	0	a_4	a_{12}	a_{20}	a_{28}	a_5	a_{13}	a_{21}	a_{29}	a_6	a_{14}	a_{22}	a_{30}	a_7	a_{15}	a_{23}	a_{31}
1	0	1	a_5	a_{13}	a_{21}	a_{29}	a_6	a_{14}	a_{22}	a_{30}	a_7	a_{15}	a_{23}	a_{31}	a_8	a_{16}	a_{24}	a_0
1	1	0	a_6	a_{14}	a_{22}	a_{30}	a_7	a_{15}	a_{23}	a_{31}	a_8	a_{16}	a_{24}	a_0	a_9	a_{17}	a_{25}	a_1
1	1	1	a_7	a_{15}	a_{23}	a_{31}	a_8	a_{16}	a_{24}	a_0	a_9	a_{17}	a_{25}	a_1	a_{10}	a_{18}	a_{26}	a_2

			$ALUout_4$				$ALUout_5$				$ALUout_6$				$ALUout_7$			
	b_4b_3		00	01	10	11	00	01	10	11	00	01	10	11	00	01	10	11
b_2	b_1	b_0	a'_4	a'_{12}	a'_{20}	a'_{28}	a'_5	a'_{13}	a'_{21}	a'_{29}	a'_6	a'_{14}	a'_{22}	a'_{30}	a'_7	a'_{15}	a'_{23}	a'_{31}
0	0	0	a_4	a_{12}	a_{20}	a_{28}	a_5	a_{13}	a_{21}	a_{29}	a_6	a_{14}	a_{22}	a_{30}	a_7	a_{15}	a_{23}	a_{31}
0	0	1	a_5	a_{13}	a_{21}	a_{29}	a_6	a_{14}	a_{22}	a_{30}	a_7	a_{15}	a_{23}	a_{31}	a_8	a_{16}	a_{24}	a_0
0	1	0	a_6	a_{14}	a_{22}	a_{30}	a_7	a_{15}	a_{23}	a_{31}	a_8	a_{16}	a_{24}	a_0	a_9	a_{17}	a_{25}	a_1
0	1	1	a_7	a_{15}	a_{23}	a_{31}	a_8	a_{16}	a_{24}	a_0	a_9	a_{17}	a_{25}	a_1	a_{10}	a_{18}	a_{26}	a_2
1	0	0	a_8	a_{16}	a_{24}	$-a_0$	a_9	a_{17}	a_{25}	a_1	a_{10}	a_{18}	a_{26}	a_2	a_{11}	a_{19}	a_{27}	a_3
1	0	1	a_9	a_{17}	a_{25}	$-a_1$	a_{10}	a_{18}	a_{26}	a_2	a_{11}	a_{19}	a_{27}	a_3	a_{12}	a_{20}	a_{28}	a_4
1	1	0	a_{10}	a_{18}	a_{26}	$-a_2$	a_{11}	a_{19}	a_{27}	a_3	a_{12}	a_{20}	a_{28}	a_4	a_{13}	a_{21}	a_{29}	a_5
1	1	1	a_{11}	a_{19}	a_{27}	$-a_2$	a_{12}	a_{20}	a_{28}	a_4	a_{13}	a_{21}	a_{29}	a_5	a_{14}	a_{22}	a_{30}	a_6

The tables for $ALUout_8$ to $ALUout_{27}$ are similar until the last row indicated below:

Table 5.18 (Continued)

			$ALUout_{28}$				$ALUout_{29}$				$ALUout_{30}$				$ALUout_{31}$			
	b_4b_3		00	01	10	11	00	01	10	11	00	01	10	11	00	01	10	11
b_2	b_1	b_0	a'_{28}	a'_4	a'_{12}	a'_{20}	a'_{29}	a'_5	a'_{13}	a'_{21}	a'_{30}	a'_6	a'_{14}	a'_{22}	a'_{31}	a'_7	a'_{15}	a'_{23}
0	0	0	a_{28}	a_4	a_{12}	a_{20}	a_{29}	a_5	a_{13}	a_{21}	a_{30}	a_6	a_{14}	a_{22}	a_{31}	a_7	a_{15}	a_{23}
0	0	1	a_{29}	a_5	a_{13}	a_{21}	a_{30}	a_6	a_{14}	a_{22}	a_{31}	a_7	a_{15}	a_{23}	a_0	a_8	a_{16}	a_{24}
0	1	0	a_{30}	a_6	a_{14}	a_{22}	a_{31}	a_7	a_{15}	a_{23}	a_0	a_8	a_{16}	a_{24}	a_1	a_9	a_{17}	a_{25}
0	1	1	a_{31}	a_7	a_{15}	a_{23}	a_0	a_8	a_{16}	a_{24}	a_1	a_9	a_{17}	a_{25}	a_2	a_{10}	a_{18}	a_{26}
1	0	0	a_0	a_8	a_{16}	a_{24}	a_1	a_9	a_{17}	a_{25}	a_2	a_{10}	a_{18}	a_{26}	a_3	a_{11}	a_{19}	a_{27}
1	0	1	a_1	a_9	a_{17}	a_{25}	a_2	a_{10}	a_{18}	a_{26}	a_3	a_{11}	a_{19}	a_{27}	a_4	a_{12}	a_{20}	a_{28}
1	1	0	a_2	a_{10}	a_{18}	a_{26}	a_3	a_{11}	a_{19}	a_{27}	a_4	a_{12}	a_{20}	a_{28}	a_5	a_{13}	a_{21}	a_{29}
1	1	1	a_3	a_{11}	a_{19}	a_{27}	a_4	a_{12}	a_{20}	a_{28}	a_5	a_{13}	a_{21}	a_{29}	a_6	a_{14}	a_{22}	a_{30}

Notes: 1. Every two horizontal underlined rows under $ALUout_i$ indicate the connections of four inputs: a'_i, $a'_{(i+8 \bmod 32)}$, $a'_{(i+16 \bmod 32)}$, and $a'_{(i+24 \bmod 32)}$.
2. Every vertical column under a'_i indicates the connections of the eight inputs a_i through $a_{(i+7 \bmod 32)}$.

SUMMARY

The von Neumann computer model was introduced in Section 5.1. In this model, the arithmetic logic unit (ALU) is a combinational circuit module at the center of the CPU of a computer and executes the basic arithmetic-logic operations required by the instruction set. The ALU can also be designed as a common datapath of the CPU for other operations that need to transfer data according to the RTL design model of the processor. The key requirements to the ALU design are speed, universality, and simplicity. Therefore, the fast carry look-ahead circuit is studied in Section 5.2. As a practical example of the ALU circuit, the design of the SN74181 chip is analyzed in Section 5.3 to derive a general design method based on a carry look-ahead adder. Then, many different design methods of the ALU are developed in Section 5.4, using the external gates of an adder through multiplexers (Section 5.4.1), using the internal gates of an adder (Section 5.4.4), using standard SN74181 chips (Section 5.4.2), redesigning the input circuit of the SN74181 adder (Section 5.4.3), and redesigning the output circuit of the SN74181 adder (Section 5.4.5). Finally, three methods of incorporating a shifter in the ALU are discussed in Section 5.5. They are: designing a built-in shifter in the ALU (Section 5.5.1), a single-bit independent shifter attached to the output of the ALU (Section 5.5.2), and a barrel shifter that shifts multiple bits in a single shift operation (Section 5.5.3).

EXERCISES

5.1 The SN74182 chip is a carry look-ahead generator, working with four SN74181 4-bit ALU chips to form a 16-bit carry look-ahead adder inside the ALU. The $G_{15}, P_{15}, G_{11}, P_{11}, G_7, P_7, G_3, P_3$ inputs are connected to the corresponding G and P outputs of the four SN74181 chips to be used.

(a) There are two possible schemes of connecting the carry-out signals of the SN74182 chip to the carry-in signals of the four SN74181 chips: (1) carry look-ahead inside each 4-bit group and ripple carry across different groups, and (2) carry look-ahead of all 16 bits. For each connection scheme, find the critical path from the input carry, C_{-1}, to the output carry, C_{15}, or to various high-order bits of the sum, and determine the worst-case time delay.

[Note: Assume one unit delay per gate. Also assume that both operands are available before the add operation begins, so you can neglect the delay in the input circuit.]

(b) How can SN74182 chips be cascaded to form one 64-bit ALU with sixteen SN74181 chips? Repeat Part (a) for this 64-bit case.

5.2 The carry look-ahead adder in the 74181 ALU was designed based on the *inverse* carry signals, $\overline{C_i}$ for $i = -1, 0, ..., 3$. This problem requires redesigning of a 4-bit carry look-ahead adder based on the *original* carry signals, C_i for $i = -1, 0, ..., 3$. The adder should include a *mode* signal, M, for distinguishing between arithmetic operations (when $M = 0$) and logic operations (when $M = 1$). Derive all the expressions for C_i, S_i, T_i, P, and G in terms of X_i, Y_i, C_{-1} and M, for $i = 3, ..., 0$. The circuit diagram is not required.

5.3 Assume that once the two operands $A = A_3 A_2 A_1 A_0$ and $B = B_3 B_2 B_1 B_0$ are present at the inputs of a 4-bit adder, the logic functions $X_i = A_i + B_i$ and $X_i = A_i B_i$ are available.

(a)   Write the formulae for look-ahead carry signals C_i ($i = 3, 2, 1, 0$) in terms of X_i, Y_i, and input carry C_{-1}.

(b)   What is the required maximum value of fan-in of logic gates for implementation of the expressions obtained in Part (a)?

(c)   What is the length (in terms of the number of gates) of the critical path traced from input carry C_{-1} up to the generation of the sum bits?

[Note. It is not required to draw any logic diagram for answering the questions in Parts (b) and (c). You can just inspect the logic expressions.]

5.4 Given the function select signals of the SN74181 ALU to be $s_3 s_2 s_1 s_0 = 0110$, write the logic expressions for the following logic variables in terms of A, B, and C_{-1} for the cases when $M = 0$ and $M = 1$:

$$X_3 - X_0, Y_3 - Y_0, T_3 - T_0, M + C_2 - M + C_{-1}, F_3 - F_0, C_3, G, P$$

5.5 (a)   Design a 4-bit ALU by designing an input circuit connected to (the inputs of) a 4-bit adder to supply proper operands A, B, and input carry C_{-1} for implementing the function table given in Table 5.19.

Table 5.19   Function table for Problem 5.5

f_2	f_1	f_0	Mnemonic	Operation	Explanation
0	0	0	ADD	$OP1 + OP2$	
0	0	1	SUBR	$OP2 - OP1$	R refers to $OP1$
0	1	0	SUBS	$OP1 - OP2$	S refers to $OP2$
0	1	1	OR	$OP1 \vee OP2$	
1	0	0	AND	$OP1 \wedge OP2$	
1	0	1	NOTRS	$\overline{OP1} \wedge OP2$	
1	1	0	XOR	$OP1 \oplus OP2$	
1	1	1	XNOR	$\overline{OP1 \oplus OP2}$	

where $f_2 f_1 f_0$ is a 3-bit function code for selecting among eight ALU operations. $OP1$ and $OP2$ are two 4-bit signed (for arithmetic operations) or unsigned (for logic operations) numbers on the inputs of the ALU.

Find the simplest expressions of A, B, and C_{-1} as functions of $OP1$, $OP2$, f_2, f_1, and f_0.

(b) Design the output circuit of the adder to produce the result, F, from the ALU plus the four statuses, N, Z, V, and C, to be stored in four flip-flops triggered by a common loading pulse called *lpStatus*.

5.6 Design a simple 4-bit ALU using a 4-bit adder with an attached shifter, so that it can perform the operations on operands $OP1$ and $OP2$ according to the function table given in Table 5.20. Since the adder and the shifter do not share the function select codes $f_2 f_1 f_0$ and $h_1 h_0$, the intermediate results S from the adder for all the arithmetic operations specified in the function table can be shifted or not shifted to produce the final result F at the output of the ALU.

Table 5.20 Function table of the ALU for Problem 5.6

h_1	h_0	f_2	f_1	f_0	Operation	Output
x	x	0	0	0	Transfer $OP1$	$S = OP1$
x	x	0	0	1	Negate $OP1$	$S = -OP1$
x	x	0	1	0	$OP1$ plus $OP2$	$S = OP1 + OP2$
x	x	0	1	1	$OP1$ minus $OP2$	$S = OP1 - OP2$
x	x	1	0	0	Output 0	$S = 0000$
x	x	1	0	1	Output -1	$S = 1111$
x	x	1	1	0	$OP1$ AND $OP2$	$S = OP1 \wedge OP2$
x	x	1	1	1	$OP1$ XOR $OP2$	$S = OP1 \oplus OP2$
0	0	x	x	x	No shift	$F = S_3 S_2 S_1 S_0$
0	1	x	x	x	Arithmetic right shift 1 bit	$F = S_3 S_3 S_2 S_1$
1	0	x	x	x	Logical left shift 1 bit	$F = S_2 S_1 S_0 0$
1	1	x	x	x	Logical right shift 1 bit	$F = 0 S_3 S_2 S_1$

(a) Let the inputs of the adder be A, B, and C_{-1}. Write the truth table for them.

(b) Write the simplest expressions for the variables A, B, and C_{-1}.

(c) Draw the circuit diagram showing how to feed these variables to the adder and to connect the adder to the shifter.

5.7 Design a simple ALU using a 4-bit adder with an embedded shifter so that it can perform the operations on operands $OP1$ and $OP2$ according to the function table given in Table 5.21. Since the adder and the shifter share the function select code $f_2 f_1 f_0$, the shift operations can have only $OP1$ involved and work together with the arithmetic operations to produce the unified output result from the ALU.

Table 5.21   Function table of the ALU for Problem 5.7

f_2	f_1	f_0	Operation	Output
0	0	0	Transfer $OP1$	$F = OP1$
0	0	1	Negate $OP1$	$F = -OP1$
0	1	0	$OP1$ plus $OP2$	$F = OP1 + OP2$
0	1	1	$OP1$ minus $OP2$	$F = OP1 - OP2$
1	0	0	Output 0	$F = 0000$
1	0	1	Output -1	$F = 1111$
1	1	0	Logical left shift $OP1$ 1 bit	$F = OP1_2 OP1_1 OP1_0 0$
1	1	1	Logical right shift $OP1$ 1 bit	$F = 0\ OP1_3 OP1_2 OP1_1$

(a)   Write the truth table for implementation of the given function table.

(b)   Write the simplest expressions for the variables involved.

(c)   Draw the circuit diagram of the ALU.

5.8 Design a 4-bit ALU using an SN74181 ALU chip according to the function table given in Table 5.22.

Table 5.22   Function table of the ALU for Problem 5.8

f_2	f_1	f_0	Function of the ALU	Meaning
0	0	0	$OP1$ plus C_{in}	Transfer or increment
0	0	1	$OP1$ plus $OP2$ plus C_{in}	Add without or with a carry
0	1	0	$OP1$ minus $OP2$ minus C_{in}	Subtract without or with a borrow
0	1	1	$OP2$ minus $OP1$ minus C_{in}	(In)reverse subtract without or with a borrow
1	0	0	$OP1$ minus 1	Decrement by 1
1	0	1	$OP1 \wedge OP2$	$OP1$ AND $OP2$
1	1	0	$OP1 \vee OP2$	$OP1$ OR $OP2$
1	1	1	$OP1 \oplus OP2$	$OP1$ XOR $OP2$

(a) Design a truth table such that it will allow the parameters of the SN74181 chip to be chosen in the best way to allow the simplest expressions to be derived in Part (b).

(b) Derive the simplest expressions for all the dependent variables in the truth table. Your expressions must be simplified for optimal implementation satisfying the following conditions:

- Share as many common terms as possible.
- Use only two-input basic gates selected from AND, OR, NAND, NOR, XOR, and XNOR without inverted inputs.
- Only two inverted variables $\overline{f_1}$ and $\overline{f_0}$ are given, while all the other inverted variables, $\overline{f_2}, \overline{OP1}, \overline{OP2},$ and $\overline{C_{in}}$, are not available, so you should not use them.
- The total number of gates used by all the expressions must be minimum, not exceeding $8n + 11$, where n is the word length.

5.9 Repeat Problem 5.8 with the function table given in Table 5.23.

Table 5.23 Function table for Problem 5.9

Function Code			Operation	Output F
f_2	f_1	f_0		
0	0	0	Forward	$OP1$
0	0	1	Reverse subtract	$OP2 - OP1$
0	1	0	Subtract	$OP1 - OP2$
0	1	1	Add	$OP1 + OP2$
1	0	0	XOR	$OP1_i \oplus OP2_i$
1	0	1	AND	$OP1_i \wedge OP2_i$
1	1	0	OR	$OP1_i \vee OP2_i$
1	1	1	XNOR	$\overline{OP1_i \oplus OP2_i}$

5.10 Design a 4-bit ALU to implement the function table given in Table 5.24.

Table 5.24 Function table for Problem 5.10

M	s_1	s_0	Operation
0	0	0	$A + B + C_{-1}$
0	0	1	$A - B - \overline{C_{-1}}$
0	1	0	$(A \vee B) + C_{-1}$
0	1	1	$A\overline{B} + 1111 + C_{-1}$
1	0	0	$\overline{A \oplus B}$
1	0	1	$A \oplus B$
1	1	0	$\overline{A} \wedge \overline{B}$
1	1	1	$A \wedge \overline{B}$

Use a simple method that chooses the same functions from the function table of the SN74181 ALU chip. Then, you can design a simplified input circuit for it so that the same signal M in the ALU can be used to distinguish between logic operations and arithmetic operations.

(a) Write the truth table and derive the simplest logic expressions for the input circuit.

(b) Complete the entire circuit of the ALU.

(c) The above table contains four multifunctional arithmetic operations. List all the possible operations that can be implemented by the function "$(A \vee B)$ plus C_{-1}" and "$A\overline{B}$ plus 1111 plus C_{-1}" by choosing different constant values of 0 or 1 for the parameters C_{-1}, A_i, B_i, for $i = 0$ to 3.

5.11 Given the function table of a 4-bit ALU as given in Table 5.25.

Table 5.25 Function table for Problem 5.11

Function Code			Operation	Output F
f_2	f_1	f_0		
0	0	0	Clear	0000
0	0	1	Reverse subtract	$OP2 - OP1$
0	1	0	AND	$OP1 \wedge OP2$
0	1	1	Add	$OP1 + OP2$
1	0	0	Subtract	$OP1 - OP2$
1	0	1	OR	$OP1 \vee OP2$
1	1	0	XOR	$OP1 \oplus OP2$
1	1	1	Preset	1111

Design this ALU using a standard SN74181 ALU chip.

(a) Write the truth table.

(b) Derive the simplest expressions for all the input parameters of the SN74181 chip.

5.12 Given the function table as in Table 5.26.

Table 5.26 Function table for Problem 5.12

Function Code			Operation	Output F
f_2	f_1	f_0		
0	0	0	Clear	0000
0	0	1	Reverse subtract	$B - A$
0	1	0	AND	$A \wedge B$
0	1	1	Add	$A + B$
1	0	0	Subtract	$A - B$
1	0	1	OR	$A \vee B$
1	1	0	XOR	$A \oplus B$
1	1	1	Preset	1111

Design a 4-bit ALU using the same method as we have learned for designing the SN74181 ALU chip. The basic idea of this method is to use the same adder circuit and output circuit as in the SN74181 chip, but synthesize a different input circuit. This input circuit should receive A and B as the input operands for all the cases of $f_2f_1f_0 = 000$ to 111. The basic requirement is that the input circuit should produce its output variables with simplest implementation. This problem requires only the following two steps:

(a) Write a truth table for the input circuit. Besides the other variables, your truth table should include signals X_i and Y_i rather than $\overline{X_i}$ and $\overline{Y_i}$. The simplification of the expressions should also be based on X_i and Y_i rather than $\overline{X_i}$ and $\overline{Y_i}$. This will ensure the simplest results satisfying the requirement of this problem.

(b) Use Karnaugh maps to derive the simplest expressions for all the output variables of the input circuit.

5.13 Design a 4-bit ALU whose function table is given in Table 5.27.

Table 5.27 Function table of the ALU for Problem 5.13.

Function Code			Operation	Output F
s_2	s_1	s_0		
0	0	0	Forward	A
0	0	1	Reverse subtract	$B - A$
0	1	0	Subtract	$A - B$
0	1	1	Add	$A + B$
1	0	0	XOR	$A_i \oplus B_i$
1	0	1	AND	$A_i \wedge B_i$
1	1	0	OR	$A_i \vee B_i$
1	1	1	XNOR	$\overline{A_i \oplus B_i}$

This problem requires you to design an ALU similar to the SN74181 ALU chip, but with its input circuit to be redesigned, while keeping its carry look-ahead adder and output circuit unchanged. Give the detailed design process including:

(a) Write the truth table for the variables X_i, Y_i, $\overline{C_{-1}}$, and M.

(b) Draw the Karnaugh maps for X_i and Y_i.

(c) Derive the simplest expressions for X_i, Y_i, C_{-1}, and M.

(d) Draw the input circuit for $\overline{X_i}$, $\overline{Y_i}$, C_{-1}, and M using a minimum number of basic gates (AND, OR, NOT, NAND, NOR, XOR, and XNOR).

5.14 Design a 4-bit ALU based on a 4-bit *ripple-carry* adder using the *internal* logic of the adder to implement the logic operations of the ALU. The function table of the ALU is given in Table 5.28.

Table 5.28 Function table for Problem 5.14

Function Code			Operation	Output F
M	s_1	s_0		
0	0	0	Add	$OP1 + OP2$
0	0	1	Subtract	$OP1 - OP2$
0	1	0	Reverse subtract	$OP2 - OP1$
0	1	1	Decrement	$OP1 - 1$
1	0	0	OR	$OP1_i \vee OP2_i$
1	0	1	XOR	$OP1_i \oplus OP2_i$
1	1	0	AND	$OP1_i \wedge OP2_i$
1	1	1	XNOR	$\overline{OP1_i \oplus OP2_i}$

Give the detailed design procedure including:

(a) Propose a general circuit diagram of the ALU that can most conveniently realize the above-stated idea of using the internal logic circuits of the adder to implement the logic operations of the ALU when $M = 1$. The circuit diagram should use the standard XOR-based full-adder circuit [see Figure 3.11(a)] with necessary control signals introduced for configuring the ALU to perform different operations required by the above-given function table.

(b) Derive the simplest expressions for the control signals introduced in Part (a) using a minimum number of gates selected from two-input AND, OR, NAND, NOR, XOR, XNOR gates and inverters.

(c) Draw the complete circuit diagram of the ALU from the result of design in Parts (a) and (b).

5.15 Design a 16-bit ALU that contains a shifter built in its input circuit for implementation of the rotate operations in its function table given in Table 5.29.

Table 5.29 Function table of the ALU for Problem 5.15

f_2	f_1	f_0	Function	Explanation
0	0	0	ALU ◄— $OP1 + C_{in}$	Transfer or increment
0	0	1	ALU ◄— $OP1 + OP2 + C_{in}$	Add without or with carry
0	1	0	ALU ◄— $OP1 - OP2 - C_{in}$	Subtract without or with borrow
0	1	1	ALU ◄— $OP2 - OP1 - C_{in}$	Reverse subtract without or with borrow
1	0	0	ALU ◄— $OP1 \oplus OP2$	Logical XOR
1	0	1	ALU ◄— $OP1 \wedge OP2$	Logical AND
1	1	0	⌐C ◄— $OP1$↰	ROL : Rotate (of $OP1$) left with status C
1	1	1	↱$OP1$ ► C⌐	ROR : Rotate (of $OP1$) right with status C

It is required that your design use a 16-bit adder with a set of multiplexers connected to its input A so that the multiplexers implement not only shift functions, but also logic functions using external gates.

Give the detailed procedure of design:

(a) The truth table for the parameters, A_i, B_i, and C_{-1}, of the adder.

(b) The simplest logic expressions for the parameters B_i and C_{-1} of the adder not using multiplexers.

(c) The circuits of the multiplexers (if similar, draw only one circuit for bit i, if different, show the difference).

(d) The circuit of the flip-flop C.

5.16 A fully functional logic unit can be designed based on the functional characteristics of a JK flip-flop. The *internal* function performed by a JK flip-flop with inputs J and K, current state $Q(t)$, and next state $Q(t+1)$ can be described by its characteristic equation as shown in Expression (4.4). Suppose we have a logic variable A stored in a JK flip-flop so that $Q(t) = A$. By choosing J and K as a function of the logic variable B, we can generate $Q(t+1)$ as a logic function $F(A, B)$ to be saved and used as the output of the logic unit. For example, if $J = 0$, $K = B$, then $F = A \wedge B$; if $J = B$, $K = 0$, then $F = A \vee B$.

Given the function table in Table 5.30, design a 4-bit logic unit based on JK flip-flops to implement this table.

Table 5.30   Function table of a logic unit on a JK flip-flop for Problem 5.16.

s_3	s_2	s_1	s_0	Logic Operation $F(A, B)$
0	0	0	0	$\overline{A}$
0	0	0	1	$\overline{A} \wedge \overline{B}$
0	0	1	0	$\overline{A} \wedge B$
0	0	1	1	0
0	1	0	0	$\overline{A} \vee \overline{B}$
0	1	0	1	$\overline{B}$
0	1	1	0	$A \oplus B$
0	1	1	1	$A \wedge \overline{B}$
1	0	0	0	$\overline{A} \vee B$
1	0	0	1	$\overline{A \oplus B}$
1	0	1	0	B
1	0	1	1	$A \wedge B$
1	1	0	0	1
1	1	0	1	$A \vee \overline{B}$
1	1	1	0	$A \vee B$
1	1	1	1	A

(a)   Derive the truth table for the J and K signals.

(b)   Derive the simplest expressions for the J and K signals.

(c)   Design the circuit of the register using JK flip-flops, which can be loaded with the logical data A and perform all the 16 logic operations on the external logical data B and internal data A according to Table 5.30 under the control of the 4-bit function code s_3, s_2, s_1, and s_0.

6

Complex Arithmetic Operations

The arithmetic logic unit contained in the CPU provides the hardware to perform basic arithmetic logic operations. Utilizing these basic operations, complex operations can be realized by various methods: (1) software at assembly language level, (2) hardware with sequential control, (3) firmware at the microprogram level, and (4) special coprocessors with a pipelined organization. In this chapter, we will describe three complex operations: fixed-point multiplication, fixed-point division, and floating-point operations (which require a floating-point data representation). For each operation, we will provide the algorithms for both single-precision and double-precision operations, and show how these algorithms can be implemented by sequential hardware.

6.1 SINGLE-PRECISION MULTIPLICATION

This section discusses the basic algorithm for two's complement multiplication and also how the Booth algorithm and bit pairwise multiplication can be used for fast multiplication.

6.1.1 Basic Algorithm for Two's Complement Multiplication

Given two n-bit single-word operands, the multiplicand M and the multiplier Y, the CPU is required to calculate a double-word product, $P = M \cdot Y$. Assume that P, M, and Y are all signed numbers in two's complement representation. The most basic technique for multiplication in hardware follows the *add-shift* algorithm, which decomposes the multiplication process into a number of iterations, each performing a pair of conditional add and shift right operations. This algorithm can be most simply implemented using three registers, as shown in Figure 6.1.

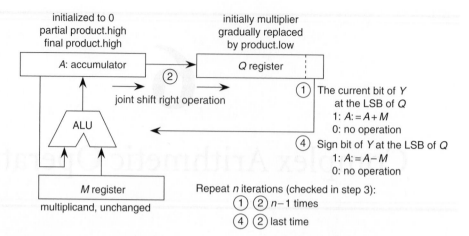

Figure 6.1 Schematic diagram of multiplication hardware consisting of three registers

The n-bit multiplicand is stored in the M register, which provides a fixed operand for each add operation and, therefore, has its contents unchanged throughout the entire process of multiplication. The n-bit multiplier is stored in a shift register called the Q register before the multiplication begins. The third register is the accumulator, A, which is initialized to zero. Because the accumulator is always the destination register of the add operation, it stores the new higher-order partial product created by the adder during each iteration if the current multiplier bit is "1". The accumulator A is concatenated with the Q register to form a $2n$-bit joint shift-right register, so that the register contents can be shifted together to the right during each iteration. As a result, the multiplier in the Q register will be gradually replaced in successive iterations by the lower-order bits of the partial product in the accumulator. Finally, when the multiplication finishes, the accumulator will contain the high-order final product, and the Q register will contain the low-order final product.

The two's complement multiplication algorithm consists of the following steps.

Initial condition: The initial data allocation places the n-bit multiplicand in the M register without change, the n-bit multiplier in the Q register, and "0" in the n-bit accumulator. When the multiplication proceeds during each iteration, the result of the addition is stored in the accumulator and then shifted one bit to the right, jointly with the multiplier in the Q register.

Step 1. The LSB of the multiplier is examined: If it is "1", the multiplicand is added to the partial product to generate a new partial product;

otherwise, the partial product remains unaltered. This step is indicated by ① in Figure 6.1.

Step 2. The accumulator and the Q register are interconnected as a double-length shift register and jointly perform a "shift right 1 bit" operation. During the right shift of the accumulator, the correct sign of the partial product should be shifted into the most significant bit (MSB) of the accumulator in the following way. If there is no overflow, the MSB of the accumulator should be repeated by the sign extension rule. However, if an overflow occurs, the MSB of the accumulator is no longer the correct sign of the partial product and is changed to become the significant bit of the numerical part. Therefore, we should shift in the inverse of the MSB of the partial product. This can be implemented with an XOR of the MSB of the partial product and the overflow status, V. If $V = 0$, the sign of the partial product is shifted in without change; if $V = 1$, the inverse sign of the partial product is shifted in. This step is indicated by ② in Figure 6.1.

Step 3. Check the number of iterations. If it has reached $n - 1$, go to Step 4; otherwise, go back to Step 1 for the next iteration.

Step 4. Examine the last bit (which is the sign bit) of the multiplier in the Q register. If it is "1", subtract the multiplicand from the partial product; otherwise, the partial product is unchanged. This step is indicated by ④ in Figure 6.1.

Step 5. Jointly shift the partial product and the Q register one bit right. After this step, all n bits of the multiplier have been shifted out of the Q register, so the contents of the accumulator and the Q register will be a double-length final product, with the upper half in the accumulator and the lower half in the Q register.

Considering that the two's complement representation of a number is evaluated by taking a negative weight for its sign bit [see Expression (2.14)], we can confirm the utility of the above-mentioned algorithm by the following expression:

$$M \cdot Y = M \cdot (-2^{n-1}y_{n-1} + 2^{n-2}y_{n-2} + \ldots + 2^1 y_1 + 2^0 y_0)$$
$$= 2^n \{(((((0 + y_0 \cdot M)/2 + y_1 \cdot M)/2 + \ldots)/2 + y_{n-2} \cdot M)/2 - y_{n-1} \cdot M)/2\} \quad (6.1)$$

Comparing this expression with the algorithm, we can see that $y_i \cdot M$ for $0 \leq i \leq n - 2$ corresponds to Step 1; division by "2" corresponds to Step 2; the first $n - 1$ terms with y_0 to y_{n-2} correspond to Step 3; the final subtraction of $y_{n-1} \cdot M$ corresponds to Step 4; the final division by "2" corresponds to Step 5; and finally, multiplication by $2n$ corresponds to the double-length product having its upper half in the accumulator.

Example 6.1 Numerical Examples of Multiplication in Hardware Using Two's Complement Representation

Given $M = 1011$ and $Y = 0111$, the calculation process is shown in Figure 6.2(a). This example shows different cases of sign extension and sign correction in shift right operations. A second example shown in Figure 6.2(b) with $M = 0111$ and $Y = 1011$ shows the last step of subtraction for the negative sign of the multiplier.

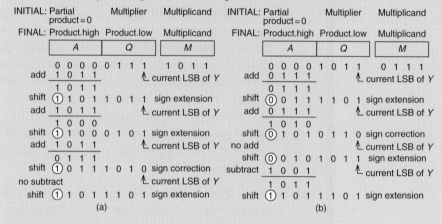

Figure 6.2 Numerical examples of multiplication in hardware

The correctness of the calculation processes in Figure 6.2 for Example 6.1 can be checked by a hand calculation according to Expression (6.1). However, our regular hand calculation multiplies only the magnitudes of two numbers; thus, there are two differences between hand multiplication and computer multiplication:

- If the partial products are negative, they should be sign-extended to full word length before being added together.

- If the multiplier is negative, the last partial product should be negated, that is, it should be subtracted from the sum of the other partial products.

The hand calculation simulation corresponding to the multiplication process for this example is shown in Figure 6.3.

6.1.2 Fast Multiplication

The basic multiplication algorithm stated above is a sequential process written as a loop consisting of n iterations, where n is the word length. If every iteration is done in the same way with an addition and a shift, the algorithm would be very slow, requiring an amount of time directly proportional to the word length. However, not every iteration requires an addition. It requires an addition only if

```
         1011                     0111
   ×     0111               ×     1011
   + 11111011               + 00000111
   + 1111011                + 0000111
   + 111011                 + 000000
   + 00000                  + 11001 (two's complement of 0111)
     11011101                 11011101
       (a)                       (b)
```

Figure 6.3 Hand calculation corresponding to the multiplication processes in Figure 6.2

the current running bit of the multiplier is "1". The multiplication time is data-dependent, varying with the number of "1" bits in the multiplier. This fact provides the potential for speeding up the multiplication process by recoding the multiplier to reduce the number of "1" bits. Two improvements of the above regular algorithm are as follows.

1. The Booth Algorithm

A fast multiplication algorithm called the *Booth algorithm* is based on the fact that the time required for multiplication is dependent on the bits of value "1" in the multiplier's binary code. The algorithm tends to reduce this time by replacing "1" bits with "0" bits whenever possible. Look at a binary pattern example of a multiplier, "0111111000". This pattern has a section of consecutive "1" bits preceded with and followed by at least one "0" bit on each side, as shown in Figure 6.4. If we add "1" to the value represented by the sequence "011…1", we will get a pattern "100…0" with all the 1s changed to all 0s and the leading bit changed from "0" to "1". To specify the value of the original pattern, we should change the vending "1" bit of the pattern into "−1". This process is shown in the upper half of Figure 6.4. It gives rise to the idea of recoding the multiplier in sequences of "0" bits interleaved with "+1" bit and "−1" bit according to the following rule:

Rule 6.1: Starting from the LSB of the multiplier, examine each bit together with its previous bit (i.e., the lower order bit). For the LSB, take a default "0" as its previous bit. If the bit pair is "10", recode the examined bit as "−1"; if the bit pair is "01", recode the examined bit as "+1"; otherwise, for the bit pairs of "00" and "11", recode the examined bit as "0".

Rule 6.1 is shown in the lower half of Figure 6.4. It should be noted that the above rule applies only to the numerical part of the multiplier. The rule for the sign bit of the multiplier in two's complement multiplication is analyzed in Figure 6.5. It depends on the MSB of the numerical part of the multiplier code. If it is "0", it has no effect on the sign bit, so the sign bit will be examined with a

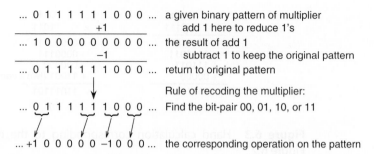

Figure 6.4 Analysis of the Booth algorithm for the numerical part of the multiplier code

bit pair of either "00" or "10" treated in the same way as in the normal algorithm, that is, recorded as "0" or "−1", respectively. If the MSB of the numerical part of the multiplier is "1", the sequence should be preceded with a leading "0", so an extra "1" should be added to the sign bit. The bit pair "01" and "11", examined at the sign bit, will be recorded as "+1" and "−1 + 1" = "0", respectively. Comparing Figures 6.4 and 6.5, we can see that the rules for the numerical bits and the sign bit are exactly the same, and are summarized as follows:

> **Rule 6.2:** If bit pair = 01, add M;
> if bit pair = 10, subtract M;
> otherwise, if bit pair = 00 or 11, no add.

Therefore, the Booth algorithm has all its n iterations performing the same operations with no difference between the numerical part and the sign bit of the multiplier code. This is another advantage of the Booth algorithm.

Therefore, the Booth algorithm for two's complement multiplication can be derived as follows:

> **Initial condition:** Similar to the normal algorithm on three-register hardware, the initial data allocation places the n-bit multiplicand in the M register without change, the n-bit multiplier in the Q register, and "0" in the n-bit accumulator. When the multiplication proceeds during each iteration, the result of the addition is stored in the accumulator, and then shifted one bit to the right jointly with the multiplier in the Q register. The only difference from the normal algorithm is that the Booth algorithm needs an additional flip-flop attached to the LSB of the Q register and initialized to "0", so that a bit pair of the multiplier can be examined during each iteration.

Step 1. The LSB of the multiplier is examined together with the attached bit from the previous (lower order) iteration. If the bit pair is "10", the multiplicand is subtracted from the partial product. If the bit pair is "01", the multiplicand is added to the partial product. Otherwise, if the bit pair is "00" or "11", the partial product is unaltered. For the first iteration, when the LSB of the multiplier is examined, a default "0" bit is considered to be attached to it, so the bit pair could be either "10" or "00", and treated as above.

Step 2. The accumulator and the Q register are interconnected as a double-length shift register and jointly perform a "shift right 1 bit" operation. During the right shift of the accumulator, the correct sign of the partial product should be shifted into the MSB of the accumulator. As in the normal algorithm, the sign should be calculated as $A_{n-1} \oplus V$, where A_{n-1} is the sign bit of the partial product in the accumulator.

Step 3. Check the number of iterations. If it has not reached n, go back to Step 1 for the next iteration. Otherwise, the multiplication is completed. All n bits of the multiplier have been shifted out of the Q register, so the contents of the accumulator and the Q register will be the $2n$-bit final product, with the upper half in the accumulator and the lower half in the Q register.

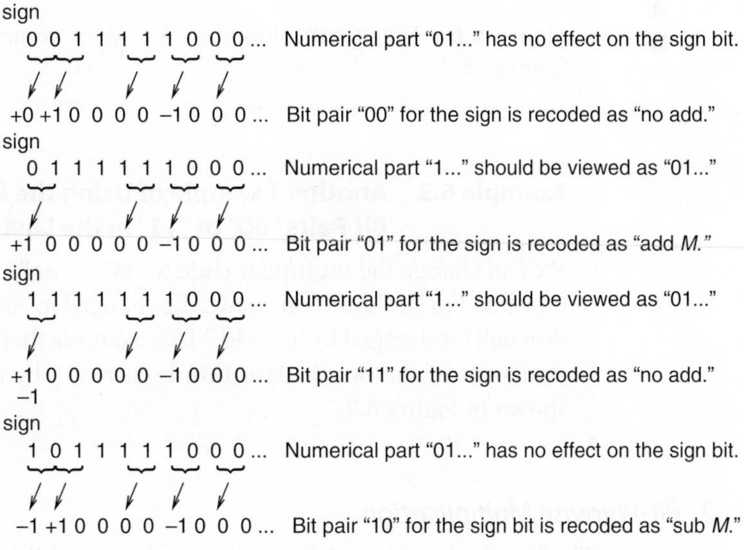

sign
0 0 1 1 1 1 1 0 0 0 ...   Numerical part "01..." has no effect on the sign bit.

+0 +1 0 0 0 0 −1 0 0 0 ...   Bit pair "00" for the sign is recoded as "no add."
sign
0 1 1 1 1 1 1 0 0 0 ...   Numerical part "1..." should be viewed as "01..."

+1 0 0 0 0 0 −1 0 0 0 ...   Bit pair "01" for the sign is recoded as "add *M*."
sign
1 1 1 1 1 1 1 0 0 0 ...   Numerical part "1..." should be viewed as "01..."

+1 0 0 0 0 0 −1 0 0 0 ...   Bit pair "11" for the sign is recoded as "no add."
−1
sign
1 0 1 1 1 1 1 0 0 0 ...   Numerical part "01..." has no effect on the sign bit.

−1 +1 0 0 0 0 −1 0 0 0 ...   Bit pair "10" for the sign bit is recoded as "sub *M*."

Figure 6.5   Analysis of the Booth algorithm for the sign of the multiplier code

Thus, we can see that the Booth algorithm for two's complement multiplication is simpler than the normal algorithm, except for Step 1. Its execution time is data-dependent. In the best case, when the multiplier code contains a long sequence of consecutive 1s or 0s, it saves considerable time for repeated additions, but in the worst case of "010101…" or "101010…", it will take even more time than the normal algorithm, since the total addition time is doubled.

Example 6.2 Solving the Same Numerical Example as in Example 6.1 Using the Booth Algorithm

The multiplication process is shown in Figure 6.6. The Q register needs an additional bit beyond the LSB and initializes it to "0" so that a bit pair can be examined during each iteration. The last iteration examines bit pairs of "01" or "10." The result is the same as in Example 6.1.

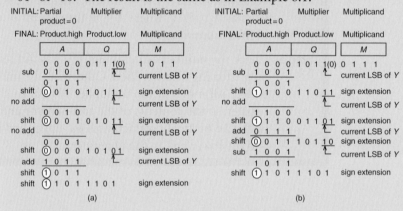

Figure 6.6 The Booth algorithm for two's complement multiplication in Example 6.2

Example 6.3 Another Example of Using the Booth Algorithm with Bit Pairs "00" or "11" in the Last Iteration

We can change the multiplier code to "00…" or "11…" so that the bit pairs examined in the last iteration will be changed to "00" or "11" and the operation will be changed to "no add." This example further shows that the above statement of the Booth algorithm is correct. The multiplication process is shown in Figure 6.7.

2. Bit-Pairwise Multiplication

The Booth algorithm reduces the number of additions, but not the number of shift operations, in the multiplication process. Another method may be used to

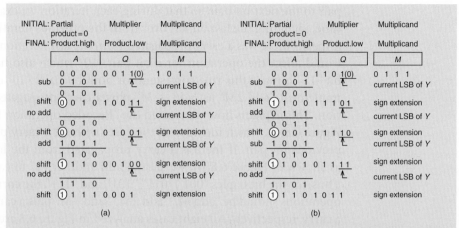

Figure 6.7 The Booth algorithm for two's complement multiplication in Example 6.3

further reduce the multiplication time by reducing the number of shift operations. The idea is to examine the binary code of the multiplier two bits at a time, so that the loop process of multiplication repeats only $n/2$ iterations. Thus, this process can be called bit-pairwise multiplication. The algorithm of bit-pairwise multiplication also relies on multiplier recoding, but it is different from the Booth algorithm in the use of bit-pair recoding, that is, recoding two bits of the multiplier at a time.

The algorithm for bit-pairwise multiplication is based on repeatedly running add-shift cycles. However, these cycles are controlled by a complicated rule with a suitably recoded multiplier code. To derive the rule of control, we should analyze all possible cases of multiplier bit pairs to find the corresponding required operations to be performed on the multiplicand and partial products. The analysis should be made on both the numerical part and the sign part of the multiplier according to their different requirements to the two's complement multiplication. Using this analysis, we derive Tables 6.2 and 6.3, for the numerical part and the sign part, respectively. To simplify Table 6.2, we have created Figure 6.8, in which two special multiplier patterns are designed that contain all the possible bit pairs "00", "01", "10", and "11". In each iteration of multiplication, when these bit pairs are examined, (1) the lower-order bit being "1" indicates the addition of the multiplicand, M, to the current partial product, and (2) the higher-order bit being "1" indicates the addition of $2M$ to the partial product. For example, the operations for bit pairs "00", "01", "10", and "11" are "add 0," "add M," "add $2M$," and "add $3M$," respectively. Because "add $3M$" cannot be implemented in just one operation, it should be replaced by "add $-M$" plus a carry (i.e., "add $4M$") propagated to the next iteration. How do we propagate this carry signal to the next bit pair? We do this by attaching the higher-order bit "1" of the current bit pair to the next bit pair, so that during each iteration we examine three bits at a time, including the last bit left over from the previous iteration. If this bit is "1", it means there was a carry propagated from the last iteration. However, this rule would affect the operation for a bit pair "10" which also has the higher-order bit "1". To make this rule consistent for both bit pairs "10" and "11", we should implement "add 2M" as "add −2M" plus a carry propagated to the next iteration. This explains how we created the "Recoded operation for each bit pair" in Figure 6.8(a), which includes all the cases without a carry propagated from the previous bit pair. If there is a carry propagated from the lower-order bit pair, as shown in Figure 6.8(b), we should add another "1" to each case in Part (a). Thus, for the bit triples "001", "011", "101", and "111", the corresponding recoded operations should be "add M," "add 2M," "add −M" plus a carry, and "add 0" plus a carry, respectively. All eight cases analyzed in Figure 6.8 are listed in Table 6.1.

A similar method of analysis can be applied to bit-pair recoding with the higher-order bit containing the sign bit of the multiplier. According to the algorithm for two's complement multiplication, if this bit equals "1", it is evaluated as "add −2M." Therefore, the operations for the triples "100", "101", "110", and "111" are "add −2M," "add −M," "add −M," and "add 0," respectively. Since there is no need to propagate the carry to the next iteration, all these operations are implemented in just one operation, as listed in Table 6.2.

Comparing Tables 6.1 and 6.2, we can see that they have the same recoded operations for the same bit triples, the only difference being the carry-out signals. They are generated from the highest bit of the bit triples in Table 6.1. None are generated for the bit triples in Table 6.2. Therefore, the sign bit of the multiplier can be treated in the same way as the numerical bits, which simplifies the algorithm.

Table 6.1 Recoding bit pairs of Y for the numerical part

Bit Pair of Y		Carry-in (= +1)	Operation	Recoded Bit Pair of Y		Carry-out (= +4)
0	0	0	no add	0	0	0
0	1	0	add M	0	+1	0
1	0	0	add $2M$	0	−2	1
1	1	0	add $3M$	0	−1	1
0	0	1	add M	0	+1	0
0	1	1	add $2M$	0	+2	0
1	0	1	add $3M$	0	−1	1
1	1	1	add $4M$	0	0	1

(a) Bit pairs without a carry propagated from the lower-order bit pair:

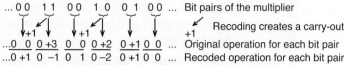

(b) Bit pairs with a carry propagated from the lower-order bit pair:

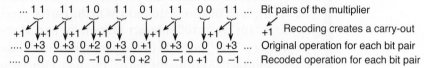

Figure 6.8 Interpretation of the recoding scheme in Table 6.1

Table 6.2 Recoding bit pairs of Y for the sign bit

Bit Pair of Y	Carry-in (= +1)	Operation	Recoded Bit Pair of Y		Carry-out (= +4)
0	0	no add	0	0	0
0	1	add M	0	+1	0
1	0	sub 2M	0	−2	0
1	1	sub M	0	−1	0
0	0	add M	0	+1	0
0	1	add 2M	0	+2	0
1	0	sub M	0	−1	0
1	1	no add	0	0	0

The bit-pairwise algorithm for two's complement multiplication can be derived as follows.

Initial condition: As with the Booth algorithm on three-register hardware, with the exception that the accumulator and the adder/subtractor must be of size $(n + 1)$ bits in order to accommodate the $(n + 1)$-bit 2M. The initial data allocation places the n-bit multiplicand in the M register with no change, the n-bit multiplier in the Q register, and "0" in the $(n + 1)$-bit accumulator. When the multiplication proceeds during each iteration, the result of addition is stored in the accumulator, and then shifted two bits to the right jointly with the multiplier in the Q register. As in the Booth algorithm, an additional flip-flop needs to be attached to the LSB of the Q register and initialized to "0" so that the last three bits of the multiplier can be examined during each iteration.

Step 1. The two LSBs of the multiplier are examined together with the attached bit from the previous (lower-order) iteration: If the bit triple is "001" or "010", add M to the partial product. If the bit triple is "101" or "110", subtract M from the partial product. If the bit triple is "011", add $2M$ to the partial product. If the bit triple is "100", subtract $2M$ from the partial product. Otherwise, if the bit triple is "000" or "111", the partial product is unaltered. For the first iteration, when the two LSBs of the multiplier are examined, a default "0" bit is considered to be attached to it, so the bit triple can be only "000", "100", "010", or "110", treated in the same way as above.

Step 2. The extended accumulator and the Q register with attached bit are interconnected as a $(2n + 2)$-bit shift register and jointly perform a "shift right 2 bits" operation. During the right shift of the accumulator, the correct sign of the partial product should be shifted into the MSBs of the accumulator. As in the normal algorithm, it should be calculated as $A_n \oplus V$, where A_n is the extended sign bit of the partial product in the accumulator.

Step 3. Check the number of iterations. If it has not reached $n/2$, go back to Step 1, otherwise the operation is finished, so the contents of the accumulator and the Q register will be the double-word final product, with the upper half (with the extended bit discarded) in the accumulator and the lower half (without attached bit) in the Q register. Here, we assume that n is even, otherwise both operands should be sign-extended to $(n + 1)$ bits, and the hardware should also be extended.

Thus, we can see that the bit-pairwise algorithm for multiplication is even simpler than the normal algorithm, except for Step 1, in the sense that all the iterations, including the last one for treating the sign bit of the multiplier, are the same. Moreover, it reduces the total number of iterations by half.

Example 6.4 **Numerical Example of Bit-Pairwise Multiplication**

$$M = 10110110, \ Y = 11100110$$
$$M \cdot Y = 0000011110000100$$

The multiplication process is shown in Figure 6.9. The result can be checked by hand multiplication in decimal as follows: $(1924)_{10} = (-72)_{10} \cdot (-26)_{10}$

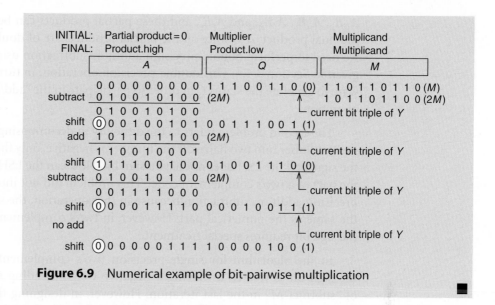

Figure 6.9   Numerical example of bit-pairwise multiplication

6.2   DOUBLE-PRECISION MULTIPLICATION

In terms of double-precision multiplication, there are special requirements for such an operation. This section will also cover algorithms we use for double-precision multiplication of positive numbers and two's complement numbers.

6.2.1   Special Requirement for the Algorithm

Suppose we have a word length of 32 bits in single-precision arithmetic. Then, double-precision multiplication should involve multiplying two 64-bit numbers to obtain a 128-bit product. If this multiplication can be implemented on 64-bit hardware, the algorithm would be the same as we have stated above. However, we have a different requirement in this section, which is to implement double-word multiplication on a single-word datapath. This can be done by generating single-precision results by hardware and then processing these intermediate results using a programming method. To do this, we need to develop an algorithm for double-precision multiplication based on single-precision partial products.

Let us look at the problems we face and some possible solutions.

The first problem is related to the required hardware support. The basic idea of double-precision multiplication is to decompose each of the double-word operands, A and B, into two parts—the most-significant half (MSH), A_H and B_H, and the least-significant half (LSH), A_L and B_L. Then, the parts of A and the parts of B can be cross-multiplied to generate four partial products,

$A_H B_H$, $A_H B_L$, $A_L B_H$, and $A_L B_L$, and these partial products can be assembled into the final product, AB. Since all the partial products are of double-word length, we need to perform double-precision addition/subtraction using the algorithm given in Section 3.4.4. This double-precision operation, in turn, requires hardware to generate the status C in order to participate in the "add/subtract with C" operation.

The second problem refers to the difficulty in decomposing a two's complement number into two halves. If the number is negative, only the MSH can carry the sign, and the LSH does not have a sign bit. How can the LSH identify itself as the part of a two's complement code? This problem did not interfere in double-precision addition/subtraction because in that operation, the sign bit is treated the same as the numerical part. However, in two's complement multiplication, the sign bit requires special treatment.

In the algorithm for single-precision two's complement multiplication, the sign bit is treated as having a negative weight, leading to the operation of "subtract M" in the last iteration. However, in designing the algorithm for double-precision multiplication, such a simple method for handling the sign bit is no longer applicable to the LSHs of the operands, which do not have sign bits. There are two possible methods to solve this problem. The first method is to multiply only positive numbers and, if needed, require number conversion before and after the multiplication. Before multiplication, any negative number should be converted into its absolute value, and after multiplication, if the two operands have different signs, the result should be converted to the negative value. In spite of its simplicity, this method has a drawback in that it cannot handle the special case of the most negative number in two's complement representation.

The second method is to use the two's complement codes of the two operands and multiply them by the same procedure as in the first method. However, at the end of the algorithm, we must use the original sign bits to correct the result if any one (or both) of them is negative. We will look at these two methods in more detail in the following two sections.

6.2.2 Algorithm for Double-Precision Multiplication of Positive Numbers

The basis for the following multiplication algorithm is the decomposition of the 64-bit multiplicand and the 64-bit multiplier into two 32-bit halves: a MSH and a LSH. Thus, the two halves of the multiplicand and the two halves of the multiplier are cross-multiplied to generate four 64-bit partial products, which are then added together with the proper alignment to obtain the final product in two 64-bit words. Therefore, each basic multiply operation multiplies only two 32-bit operands, avoiding the necessity of jointly shifting two 64-bit words.

The algorithm for double-precision multiplication is described in the following steps:

Step 1. Find the sign of the product by XORing the multiplicand and the multiplier. Save it for use in the last step.

Step 2. Convert the multiplicand and the multiplier into absolute values. Denote them as M and Y, respectively.

Step 3. Partition each of M and Y into two halves: M_H, M_L, and Y_H, Y_L, each of 32 bits.

Step 4. Calculate the 64-bit products $M_H \cdot Y_H$, $M_H \cdot Y_L$, $M_L \cdot Y_H$, and $M_L \cdot Y_L$.

Step 5. Perform the following calculation to find two 64-bit halves of the 128-bit final product, P_H and P_L.

$$P_H P_L = 2^{64}(M_H \cdot Y_H) + 2^{32}(M_H \cdot Y_L + M_L \cdot Y_H) + M_L \cdot Y_L \tag{6.2}$$

Step 6. If the sign of the product obtained in Step 1 is negative, convert the product $P_H P_L$ into a negative value.

The detailed steps for basic single-precision multiplication is the same as described in the last section, so it is not included in the above algorithm.

Now we need to analyze Step 5 in more detail. The major problem is to correctly order the addition of the four partial products so that the carry signals can be propagated from the lower-order part to the higher-order part without losing them. The required add operations are given in Expression (6.2), and the alignment of the four partial products is depicted in Figure 6.10. To find the worst case for carry propagation from the addition of lower-order parts to the addition of higher-order parts, we look at the multiplication of two maximum values of M and Y. For the convenience of analysis, without losing generality, we take a reduced double-word size of 8 bits as an example. The maximum positive double-words M and Y are given as 01111111, each of which can be decomposed into a single-word higher-order part "0111" and a lower-order part "1111". The maximum values of the four partial products are calculated as follows:

$$\max M_H = 0111$$
$$\max M_L = 1111$$
$$\max Y_H = 0111$$
$$\max Y_L = 1111$$
$$\max M_H \cdot Y_H = \underline{0011}0001$$
$$\max M_H \cdot Y_L = 01101001$$
$$\max M_L \cdot Y_H = 01101001$$
$$\max M_L \cdot Y_L = 1110\underline{0001}$$

The calculation correspondiing to Expression (6.2) indicates that the two underscored parts, the higher-order part, 0011, of $M_H \cdot Y_L$ and the lower-order part, 0001, of $M_L \cdot Y_L$ will not be changed in the final product. The addition of the other six parts (each of four bits, not underscored) consists of four steps—two steps among the three lower-order parts and two steps among the three higher-order parts. The calculation in this example indicates that each of the two steps involving the lower-order parts can create carry signals, and the two steps involving the higher-order parts must incorporate these carry signals into their add operations. Therefore, the two steps with lower-order parts and the two steps with higher-order parts must be correctly interleaved with each other, and the ordering of the two steps with lower-order parts or higher-order parts between themselves is immaterial. The following calculation shows two of the nine possible interleaving sequences:

$$a = (\max M_H \cdot Y_L)_L + (\max M_L \cdot Y_H)_L = 1001 + 1001 = 0010 \text{ with a carry "1"}$$
$$b = (\max M_H \cdot Y_L)_H + (\max M_L \cdot Y_H)_H + \text{carry} = 0110 + 0110 + 1 = 1101$$
$$c = a + (\max M_L \cdot Y_L)_H = 0010 + 1110 = 0000 \text{ with a carry "1"}$$
$$d = b + (\max M_H \cdot Y_H)_L + \text{carry} = 1101 + 0001 + 1 = 1111$$

Thus,

$$\max P_H P_L = (\max M_H \cdot Y_H)_H \#\# d \#\# c \#\# (\max M_L \cdot Y_L)_L = 0011\ 1111\ 0000\ 0001$$

where ## denotes concatenation of two components.

$$a' = (\max M_L \cdot Y_H)_L + (\max M_L \cdot Y_L)_H = 1001 + 1110 = 0111 \text{ with a carry "1"}$$
$$b' = (\max M_H \cdot Y_H)_L + (\max M_H \cdot Y_L)_H + \text{carry} = 0001 + 0110 + 1 = 1000$$
$$c = a' + (\max M_H \cdot Y_L)_L = 0111 + 1001 = 0000 \text{ with a carry "1"}$$
$$d = b' + (\max M_L \cdot Y_H)_L + \text{carry} = 1000 + 0110 + 1 = 1111$$

Thus,

$$\max P_H P_L = (\max M_H \cdot Y_H)_H \#\# d \#\# c \#\# (\max M_L \cdot Y_L)_L = 0011\ 1111\ 0000\ 0001$$

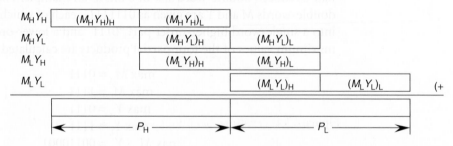

Figure 6.10 Summation of four partial products to obtain a double-length product

To avoid the uncertainty of the interleaving sequence in the above calculation, we can derive a formal algorithm for summation using Expression (6.2) in terms of just two successive double-word add operations as follows:

> **Step 1.** Perform a double-word add operation $M_H Y_L + M_L Y_H$.
>
> **Step 2.** Form a double word by concatenating $(M_H Y_H)_L$ and $(M_L Y_L)_H$, and add this double word to the result in Step 1.
>
> **(Step 2'.** If Step 1 or Step 2 produces a carry, add it to $(M_H Y_H)_H$.)
>
> **Step 3.** The higher-order final product, P_H, is obtained by concatenating $(M_H Y_H)_H$ and the higher-order part of the result in Step 2.
>
> **Step 4.** The lower-order final product, P_L, is obtained by concatenating the lower-order part of the result in Step 2 and $(M_L Y_L)_L$.

Step 2', in parentheses, is optional, and is used in the next section for handling cases with two's complement numbers, M and Y. The execution of this algorithm for the numerical data of the above example is shown in Figure 6.11.

6.2.3 Algorithm for Double-Precision Multiplication of Two's Complement Numbers

The above algorithm for double-precision multiplication for positive numbers can be applied to double-precision two's complement multiplication, with an additional correction step at the end of the process. The basic idea is based

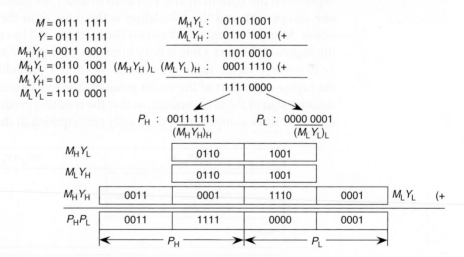

Figure 6.11 Example of adding four partial products with the proper alignment

on a formula for the evaluation of a two's complement number by assuming a negative weight for the sign bit. For example, we have two $2n$-bit numbers, M and Y, both in two's complement representation:

$$M = s_M \, m_{2n-2} m_{2n-3} \cdots m_1 m_0$$
$$Y = s_Y \, y_{2n-2} y_{2n-3} \cdots y_1 y_0$$

where $2n$ is the double-word length related to the single-word length n. Then, their values can be evaluated as

$$M = -2^{2n}s_M + \text{value of } m_A m_{2n-2} m_{2n-3} \cdots m_1 m_0 = -2^{2n}s_M + M_{ext} \qquad (6.3)$$

$$Y = -2^{2n}s_Y + \text{value of } s_Y y_{2n-2} y_{2n-3} \cdots y_1 y_0 = -2^{2n}s_Y + Y_{ext} \qquad (6.4)$$

Hence, both numbers are sign-extended to $(2n+1)$ bits, so that each sign bit has a negative weight equal to -2^{2n}, which better matches the double-word length $2n$ when it is used in the last step of the algorithm to correct the $2n$-bit final product. The extended numerical parts, M_{ext} and Y_{ext}, are the same numbers that were originally specified.

Now, both extended numerical parts, $M_{ext} = s_M m_{2n-2} m_{2n-3} \cdots m_1 m_0$ and $Y_{ext} = s_Y y_{2n-2} y_{2n-3} \cdots y_1 y_0$, of the numbers, M and Y in the above Expressions (6.3) and (6.4), are of double-word length, $2n$, and have only positive weights for all bits. Therefore, they can be multiplied using the algorithm for double-precision multiplication for positive numbers stated in the previous section. Their product, $M_{ext} \cdot Y_{ext}$, will be corrected according to the following formula:

$$M \cdot Y = -2^{4n}s_M \cdot s_Y - 2^{2n}s_M Y_{ext} - 2^{2n}s_Y M_{ext} + A_{ext} \cdot B_{ext} \qquad (6.5)$$

This is another case of summation of four components with proper alignment as shown in Figure 6.12. The number of components involved in the summation depends on the signs of M and Y. If both M and Y are positive, then there is only one component, and the calculation is the same as in the last section. If only one of M and Y is negative, then two components will be subtracted to generate the higher-order part. Only if both numbers are negative will four components be considered in the summation. Both M_{ext} and Y_{ext} should be subtracted from the higher-order part of the $4n$-bit product. The fourth component discards the negative sign of the final product, so that the resulting product is positive. Therefore, only three components are actually participating in the summation.

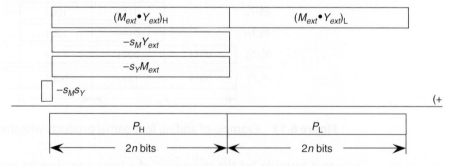

Figure 6.12   Summation of the terms according to Expression (6.5)

After the above analysis, we can now formulate the algorithm for double-precision multiplication of two's complement numbers as follows:

Step 1. Look at the two given double-word numbers, M and Y, as positive numbers and multiply them using the algorithm in the last section to get a positive quadruple-word product.

Step 2. If M is negative, subtract Y from the higher-order part of the product obtained above, else skip this step.

Step 3. If Y is negative, subtract M from the higher-order part of the product obtained above, else skip this step.

Step 4. If both M and Y are negative, discard "1" from the bit position $2n$ in the resulting product.

We will use a reduced double-word length of $2n = 8$ to test the algorithm for double-precision two's complement multiplication in the following examples.

Example 6.5   The Worst Case for Carry Propagation in Double-Precision Multiplication

Given $M = 11111111$, $Y = 11111111$.

Step 1. Multiply M and Y to get the positive $4n$-bit product:
$$M_H = M_L = 1111$$
$$Y_H = Y_L = 1111$$
$$M_H \cdot Y_H = M_H \cdot Y_L = M_L \cdot Y_H = M_L \cdot Y_L = 11100001$$
$$M_H \cdot Y_L + M_L \cdot Y_H = 11000010, \text{ with a carry "1"}$$
$$[(M_H \cdot Y_H)_L \# (M_L \cdot Y_L)_H] + (M_H \cdot Y_L + M_L \cdot Y_H)$$
$$= 00011110 + 11000010 = 11100000$$
$$(M_H \cdot Y_H)_H + \text{carry} = 1110 + 0001 = 1111$$
$$M_{ext} \cdot Y_{ext} = 1111111000000001$$

Step 2. Since M is negative,
$$(M_{ext} \cdot Y_{ext})_H - Y_{ext} = 11111110 - 11111111 = 11111111$$

Step 3. Since Y is negative,
$$(M_{ext} \cdot Y_{ext})_H - Y_{ext} - M_{ext} = 11111111 - 11111111 = (1)00000000$$

Step 4. Since both M and Y are negative, discard the bit "1" from bit $4n$.

Therefore, the final result is 0000000000000001, as expected. ∎

Example 6.6   Same Data as in Example 6.5, But with Negative Signs

Given $M = 10000001$, $Y = 10000001$.

Step 1. Multiply M and Y to get the positive $4n$-bit product:
$$M_H = Y_H = 1000$$
$$M_L = Y_L = 0001$$

$$M_H \cdot Y_H = 01000000$$
$$M_H \cdot Y_L = M_L \cdot Y_H = 00001000$$
$$M_L \cdot Y_L = 00000001$$
$$M_H \cdot Y_L + M_L \cdot Y_H = 00010000$$
$$[(M_H \cdot Y_H)_L \#\#(M_L \cdot Y_L)_H] + (M_H \cdot Y_L + M_L \cdot Y_H)$$
$$= 00000000 + 00010000 = 00010000$$
$$M_{ext} \cdot Y_{ext} = 0100000100000001$$

Step 2. Since M is negative,
$$(M_{ext} \cdot Y_{ext})_H - Y_{ext} = 01000001 - 10000001 = 11000000$$

Step 3. Since Y is negative,
$$(M_{ext} \cdot Y_{ext})_H - Y_{ext} - M_{ext} = 11000000 - 10000001 = (1)00111111$$

Step 4. Since both M and Y are negative, discard the bit "1" from bit position $4n$.

Therefore, the final result is 0011111100000001, the same as the result obtained in the last section for positive M and positive Y. ∎

6.3   SINGLE-PRECISION DIVISION

Suppose there are two operands, a $2n$-bit dividend D and an n-bit divisor Y. We assume that D and Y are both unsigned fractional numbers (for example, D and Y can be the fractional parts of two floating-point numbers). For simplicity, we will look at the algorithm for fixed-point unsigned division, which is more straightforward to understand. If any operand is negative, we convert it into positive and treat the sign bit and the magnitude (as an unsigned number) separately. The sign of the quotient is the XOR of the sign of D and the sign of Y. If it is negative, then, after execution of the algorithm of division, the result of dividing the magnitudes can be maintained as unsigned for the sign-magnitude representation or converted into a two's complement representation. The sign of the remainder is the same as that of the dividend. For fixed-point division of fractions, if $D \geq Y$, the quotient will have an integer part, which is considered as overflow. Another case of overflow occurs when $Y = 0$. The normal case of division with $D < Y$ and $Y \neq 0$ calculates an n-bit quotient Q and an n-bit remainder R satisfying the following relation:

$$D = Y \cdot Q + 2^{-n}R \tag{6.6}$$

The algorithm must be modified if it is to be applied to integer division because the n-bit integer quotient cannot match the $2n$-bit integer dividend D. An algorithm for integer division will be presented in Section 6.4.3.

The basic technique for division in hardware is the use of the *subtract-shift algorithm*. First, subtract the divisor from the dividend. If the first partial remainder < 0, then $D < Y$ and $Y \neq 0$, so division can be continued with n subtract/shift iterations. During each iteration, subtract the divisor from the partial remainder. The new partial remainder may be positive or negative. Handling a negative partial remainder is a special problem that needs to be considered. If the partial remainder is positive, it can be used in the next iteration to continue the division. If it is negative, the new partial remainder loses its original value due to an apparently unnecessary subtraction, and therefore, this condition requires special treatment. Two methods can be used to proceed with the division. One method is called the *restoring algorithm*, which restores the original partial remainder each time the subtraction results in a negative partial remainder. The other method is called the *nonrestoring algorithm*, which does not require a restoration and continues the algorithm in a modified manner using the existing negative partial remainder. The operating principle of both algorithms, in the subtract-shift looping structure, is basically the same. The only difference is the treatment of the negative partial remainder during each iteration. Therefore, we will study restoring division and nonrestoring division simultaneously in a common algorithm.

For *restoring division*, if the new partial remainder is negative, we cancel the subtraction and restore the previous partial remainder. That is, we add the divisor back in order to restore the partial remainder to the value that existed before the subtraction. The restored partial remainder will then be shifted left 1 bit and followed by a *subtraction* of the divisor during the next iteration. For *nonrestoring division*, the negative partial remainder is not restored, but will be directly shifted left 1 bit and followed by an *addition* of the divisor during the next iteration. This difference will be reflected in the following derivation of a common algorithm for both restoring division and nonrestoring division.

As for multiplication, we will describe the algorithm for division on a three-register hardware structure, as shown in Figure 6.13. It contains three n-bit registers for $2n$-bit by n-bit division. The divisor is stored in the Y register, which provides a fixed operand for each subtract/add operation, and therefore, has its contents unchanged during the process of division. The accumulator and the Q register initially store the MSH and the LSH of the dividend, respectively. They are interconnected as a $2n$-bit shift register and jointly perform a "shift left 1 bit" operation during each iteration. A separate flip-flop, Q_{-1}, used for control, stores the new quotient bit to be entered into the Q register during the left shift operation of A and Q. As division proceeds, the contents of the accumulator and the Q register will be replaced by the partial remainder and partial quotient, respectively. After n iterations and the set-up and finish-up steps of division, we will have the final quotient Q in the Q register and the final remainder R in the accumulator.

The subtract-shift algorithm of division consists of $n + 1$ iterations of basic "subtract and shift" operations. The first iteration is special—it creates the integer bit of the quotient only for the purpose of checking for overflow. Its subtract operation of "dividend minus divisor" can be isolated from the loop. Thus, we

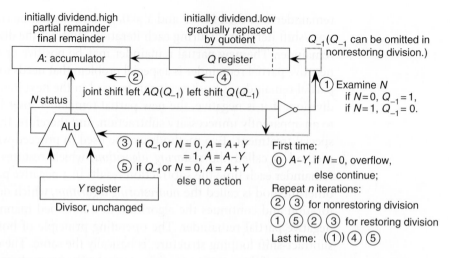

Figure 6.13 Schematic diagram of hardware for division using three registers

can reorganize the loop as *n* iterations that create the *n* fractional bits of the quotient. Each iteration of this remodeled loop can be described as *basic shift and subtract* operations consisting of the following steps:

Step 1. This is a preliminary step that is required only for the restoring algorithm. The current remainder was created in the previous iteration by subtracting the divisor from the previous partial remainder. Therefore, the current iteration for the nonrestoring algorithm should start from the left shift operation, disregarding the sign of the current partial remainder. However, in the restoring algorithm, if the current partial remainder is negative, we should do an additional operation to restore the previous partial remainder by adding the divisor back to the current partial remainder. Furthermore, since the negative sign of the current partial remainder will disappear after the restoration, it should be saved in a flip-flop, Q_{-1}, as the new quotient bit, which will be shifted into the Q register in Step 2.

Step 2. In both the restoring and nonrestoring algorithms, we can do the "shift left 1 bit" operation on the restored or nonrestored partial remainder, respectively. This performs the "joint shift left 1 bit" operation on the accumulator and the Q register, which is equivalent to multiplying the partial remainder by "2" and moving, at the same time, the new quotient bit into the LSB of the Q register.

Step 3. After the shift operation, in the restoring algorithm, we can subtract the divisor from the current partial remainder. In the nonrestoring algorithm, we should either subtract the divisor from the positive partial remainder or add the divisor to the negative partial remainder.

These three steps are indicated by ①, ②, and ③ in Figure 6.13.

The *subtract/add-shift algorithm* for nonrestoring/restoring division consists of the following steps:

Step 1. We do a special start-up step of subtracting the divisor Y from the MSH of the dividend D. If the first partial remainder is positive (or "0"), the quotient bit is "1", corresponding to an integer bit. Therefore, the algorithm sets the overflow flag and terminates. If the remainder is negative, the quotient bit is "0", and the division will proceed. This step corresponds to microstep ⓪ in Figure 6.13.

Step 2. Repeat the above-mentioned basic "shift and subtract" cycle n times.

Step 3. Perform a special finish-up step. After performing the subtract/add operation and determining the last quotient bit, we need to shift left 1 bit only for the Q register. The remainder in the accumulator is not shifted. In doing this, we shift the first quotient bit (the integer bit 0) out of the Q register, and the final quotient is placed correctly in the Q register. If the last quotient bit obtained in the last iteration of Step 2 was "0", resulting in a negative remainder in the accumulator, we should restore the remainder by adding back the divisor. If the last quotient bit was "1", the correct final remainder is already in the accumulator and needs no restoration. This final step corresponds to microsteps ①, ④, and ⑤ in Figure 6.13, where microstep ① is optional. It is used only for restoring division.

The correctness of this treatment can be shown as follows:

(a) For restoring division:

Let R_{i-1} be the partial remainder from the previous iteration $i - 1$. Then, if in iteration i we have $R_i = R_{i-1} - Y < 0$, the remainder R_{i-1} should be restored, and in the next iteration, we will shift the restored remainder R_{i-1} left 1 bit followed by a subtraction of Y. Thus, we obtain the new partial remainder in iteration $i + 1$ equal to $2R_{i-1} - Y$.

(b) For nonrestoring division:

If the new remainder R_i in the ith iteration equals $R_{i-1} - Y$ and is less than 0, it is not restored, and in the next iteration $i + 1$, it will be shifted left 1 bit, followed by an addition of Y, that is, we have the new remainder in iteration $(i + 1)$ equal to $2 \cdot (R_{i-1} - Y) + Y = 2 \cdot R_{i-1} - Y$, the same as for the restoring division.

Example 6.7 **Numerical Example Comparing the Nonrestoring and Restoring Algorithms**

$$D = 00100001, Y = 0110.$$

Numerical examples of the restoring and nonrestoring algorithms are shown in Figure 6.14. It can be seen that all the values of the partial remainders for the nonrestoring algorithm are the same as the corresponding values for the restoring algorithm, as indicated by the bold digits in Figure 6.14(a) and Figure 6.14(b). The result obtained by each algorithm is equivalent to $Q = 0101$ and $R = 0011$. These values can be checked by the following equation:

$$\begin{aligned} Y \times Q + 2^{-4} R &= 0110 \times 0101 + 00000011 \\ &= 00011110 + 00000011 \\ &= 00100001 = D \end{aligned}$$

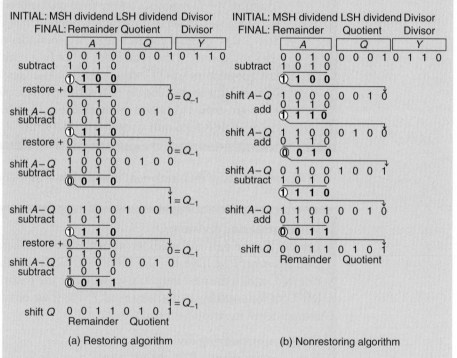

(a) Restoring algorithm   (b) Nonrestoring algorithm

Figure 6.14   Numerical examples of nonrestoring vs. restoring division

Example 6.8 Another Numerical Example of Nonrestoring Division

$D = 11011001$ and $Y = 0110$, both in two's complement representation.

Before division, D as a negative dividend should be converted into a positive number, 00100001. The process of dividing $D = 00100111$ by $Y = 0110$ is shown in Figure 6.15. This example is different from the last example in that a negative partial remainder 1110 is generated in the last iteration. It is the final remainder and must be restored to its positive value 0011. However, according to the rule for determining the signs of Q and R, we know that Q should be negative since D and Y are of different signs, and R should be negative, with the same sign as D. Therefore, the final result, in two's complement representation, is $Q = 1011$ and $R = 1101$. These values can be checked with the following equation:

$$Y \times Q + 2^{-4} R = 0110 \times 1010 + 11111101$$
$$= 11011100 + 11111101$$
$$= 11011001 = D$$

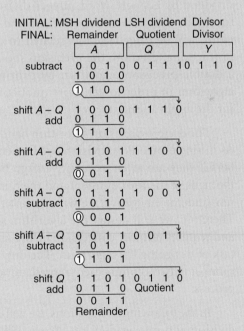

Figure 6.15 Numerical example of a hardware nonrestoring division

6.4   DOUBLE-PRECISION DIVISION

For double-precision division, there are also special requirements. Here, we will cover algorithms used for double-precision division of fractional numbers and integer numbers.

6.4.1 Special Requirements of the Algorithm

The algorithms for division that we have studied so far have limited precision because in the case of fractional numbers, dividing a double-word dividend by a single-word divisor results in a single-word quotient. Therefore, they are classified as algorithms for single-precision division, despite the use of double-word dividends. When we divide a double-word dividend by a single-word divisor, we could require higher precision when obtaining a double-word quotient with a single-word remainder. If we look at the case of integer division with a double-word dividend and a single-word divisor, the maximum quotient must be obtained as a double-word integer. In the extreme case, if the value of the divisor equals "1", the quotient will equal the double-word dividend. Therefore, the algorithm we studied in Section 6.3 is not applicable for the division of integer numbers. If we want to divide a double-word integer dividend by a single-word integer divisor, we must develop a new algorithm to obtain a double-word quotient and a single-word remainder. This algorithm will be categorized as related to double-precision division. In the case of fractional division, the precision should be unlimited. We can also develop a double-precision algorithm by continuously applying the single-precision algorithm in order to get more quotient bits to satisfy the required precision for the application.

The double-precision algorithm handles the division of two signed numbers. As in single-precision division, we first convert the numbers into positive numbers if they are given as negative. Sign bits are treated separately to determine the signs of the final quotient and the final remainder. If the quotient and/or the remainder are negative, we will convert them into two's complement numbers. Therefore, we will design the algorithm so that it divides two positive numbers and requires number conversion before and after the division. This simplifies the task of designing the algorithm. The only limitation is that the smallest negative number in two's complement representation cannot be handled in the conversion process.

In the following two sections, we will consider algorithms for both fractional division and integer division. As we will see, these two algorithms for double-precision division are significantly different. The reason is that they must be developed on the basis of different single-precision algorithms. The single-precision integer divide algorithm can have only a single-precision dividend for producing a single-word quotient, but its fractional counterpart can have a double-precision dividend for producing a single-word quotient, as we had shown in Section 6.3.

6.4.2 Algorithm for Double-Precision Division of Fractional Numbers

From the above discussion, we can see that the double-precision divide operation is specified by the following general expression:

$$\frac{Dividend}{Divisor} = Quotient + 2^{-2n}\frac{Remainder}{Divisor} \tag{6.7}$$

where n is the single word length. For both fractional and integer divisions, both the dividend and quotient are $2n$ bits, and the divisor and remainder are n bits.

For fractional division, we already have an algorithm for dividing a double-word dividend by a single-word divisor, presented in Section 6.3. We will derive a new double-precision algorithm to implement Expression (6.7) by applying the basic algorithm for single-precision division repeatedly.

Suppose we have a 64-bit dividend, D, consisting of a MSH, D_H, and a LSH, D_L, so that

$$D = D_H + 2^{-32}D_L \tag{6.8}$$

The divisor, Y, has 32 bits. The quotient should have 64 bits, as follows:

$$Q = Q_H + 2^{-32}Q_L \tag{6.9}$$

From the basic equation for single-precision division in Expression (6.7), we have the process:

$$\frac{D}{Y} = \frac{D_H + 2^{-32}D_L}{Y} = Q1 + 2^{-32}\frac{Rem1}{Y}$$

$$= Q1 + 2^{-32}(Q2 + 2^{-32}\frac{Rem2}{Y})$$

$$= Q1 + 2^{-32}Q2 + 2^{-64}\frac{Rem2}{Y} \tag{6.10}$$

$Q1$ and $Rem1$ results from dividing D by Y. $Q2$ and $Rem2$ result from dividing $Rem1$ by Y. Thus, two successive single-precision divide operations are required.

We obtain the double-word quotient, Q, and the single-word remainder, Rem, as follows:

$$\left.\begin{array}{l} Q_{\text{H}} = Q1 \\ Q_{\text{L}} = Q2 \\ Rem = Rem2 \end{array}\right\} \tag{6.11}$$

Expression (6.11) shows that the entire process of double-precision division consists of two basic divide subprocesses, leading to the following steps:

Step 1. Divide double-word D by single-word Y to get $Q1$ and $Rem1$.

Step 2. Divide single-word $Rem1$ by Y to get $Q2$ and $Rem2$.

Step 3. Single-word $Q1$ concatenated with single-word $Q2$ will give the double-word quotient, and $Rem2$ will be the remainder.

Example 6.9   Numerical Example of Double-Precision Fractional Division

$$\begin{array}{cccc} & D_{\text{H}} & D_{\text{L}} & Y \\ \text{Divide} & 0011 & 0111 & \text{by} \quad 0111 \end{array}$$

First Division:

$$\begin{array}{cccc} & D_{\text{H}} & D_{\text{L}} & Y \\ \text{Divide} & 0011 & 0111 & \text{by} \quad 0111 \end{array}$$
Result: $Q1 = 0111$, $Rem1 = 0110$

Second Division:
Use $Rem1 = 0110\ 0000$ as the new dividend and divide it by Y.

$$\begin{array}{cccc} & D_{\text{H}} & D_{\text{L}} & Y \\ \text{Divide} & 0110 & 0000 & \text{by} \quad 0111 \end{array}$$
Result: $Q2 = 1101$, $Rem2 = 0101$

Final result:
$Q_{\text{H}} = 0111$, $Q_{\text{L}} = 1101$, $Rem = 0101$

Check:

$$\begin{array}{cccc} & Q_{\text{H}} & Q_{\text{L}} & Y \\ \text{Multiply} & 0111 & 1101 & \text{by} \quad 0111 \end{array}$$
Product: $0011\ 0110\ 1011$
Add $Rem = 0000\ 0000\ 0101$
Result: $0011\ 0111 = D$ Correct!

■

6.4.3 Algorithm for Double-Precision Division of Integer Numbers

Integer division is different from fractional division in two ways: (1) the integer quotient must have the same word length as the dividend, and (2) the remainder has the same order as the dividend. Therefore, the basic equation connecting the quotient and remainder with the dividend and quotient is different from Expression (6.6). It should be in the following form:

$$D = Q \cdot Y + R \tag{6.12}$$

Example 6.10 Applying the Basic Algorithm of Single-Precision Integer Division

$$D = 0111, \quad Y = 0011$$

Using the same basic algorithm for fractional numbers, but replacing the lower-order half of the dividend with the given integer number D and the higher-order half with "0", we have the operation of dividing 0000 0111 by 0011 and the result $Q = 0010$ and $R = 0001$. Checking with Expression (6.12), we have

$$0010 \cdot 0011 + 0001 = 0110 + 0001 = 0111,$$

or we can check the result by hand in decimal:

$$D = 7, Y = 3, Q = 2, R = 1, D = 3 \cdot 2 + 1 = 7.$$

The process of division is shown in Figure 6.16.

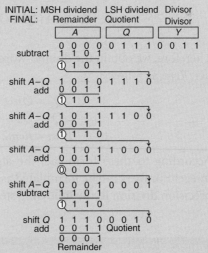

Figure 6.16 Numerical example of integer division

Therefore, the algorithm for double-precision division for integer numbers should be developed based on the basic algorithm for dividing a single-word integer dividend by a single-word integer divisor. This basic algorithm can be the same as its counterpart for fractional numbers we derived before in Section 6.3, except that the double-word dividend in that algorithm should have its lower-order half replaced by the given single-word integer and its higher-order half initialized to "0". The following example shows this basic algorithm applied to integer numbers.

Now we can derive the algorithm for double-precision division for integer numbers in the same manner as for fractional numbers, but change Expressions (6.8) to (6.11) to the following:

$$D = 2^{32}D_H + D_L \tag{6.13}$$

$$Q = 2^{32}Q_H + Q_L \tag{6.14}$$

$$
\begin{aligned}
\frac{D}{Y} &= \frac{D_H 2^{32} + D_L}{Y} = 2^{32}\frac{D_H}{Y} + \frac{D_L}{Y} \\
&= 2^{32}(Q1 + \frac{Rem1}{Y}) + (Q3 + \frac{Rem3}{Y}) \\
&= 2^{32}Q1 + \frac{2^{32} Rem1}{Y} + (Q3 + \frac{Rem3}{Y}) \\
&= 2^{32}Q1 + (Q2 + \frac{Rem2}{Y}) + (Q3 + \frac{Rem3}{Y}) \\
&= 2^{32}Q1 + (Q2 + Q3) + \frac{Rem2 + Rem3}{Y}
\end{aligned}
\tag{6.15}
$$

Therefore, we obtain the double-word quotient, Q, and the single-word remainder, Rem, as follows:

$$
\left.
\begin{aligned}
Q_H &= Q1 \\
Q_L &= Q2 + Q3 \\
Rem &= Rem2 + Rem3
\end{aligned}
\right\}
\tag{6.16}
$$

According to these formulae, the algorithm for double-precision division of integer numbers can be formulated as a sequence of three subprocesses of single-precision division in the following steps:

Step 1. Place the single-word D_H in the position of the lower-order half and divide it by single-word Y to get $Q1$ and $Rem1$.

Step 2. Place the single-word $Rem1$ in the position of the higher-order half and divide it by single-word Y to get $Q2$ and $Rem2$.

> **Step 3.** Place the single-word D_L in the position of the lower-order half and divide it by single-word Y to get $Q3$ and *Rem3*.
>
> **Step 4.** The single-word $Q1$ concatenated with the single-word $Q2 + Q3$ will give the double-word quotient, and the single-word $Rem2 + Rem3$ will be the remainder.

The following numerical example will show the implementation of this algorithm.

Example 6.11   **Numerical Example of Double-Precision Integer Division**

Suppose the single word length is $n = 4$. We are given 8-bit integer $D = 0111\ 0111$, and the 4-bit divisor is $Y = 0011$. Each of the following steps of the algorithm is accompanied by the corresponding hand calculation in decimal for verification.

$$\begin{array}{cccc} & D_H & D_L & Y \\ \text{Divide} & 0111 & 0111 & \text{by} & 0011 \end{array} \Rightarrow D = 7 \cdot 2^4 + 7 = 119, Y = 3$$

First division:

$$\begin{array}{ccc} & D_H & Y \\ \text{Divide} & 0000\ 0111 & \text{by} & 0011 \end{array} \Rightarrow 7 \cdot 2^4 = 112, 2^4(7/3) = 2^4(2 + 1/3)$$

Result: quotient $Q1 = 0010$, save it as Q_H
          remainder *Rem1*: 0001, leave *Rem1* for second division.

Second division:

$$\begin{array}{ccc} & Rem1 & Y \\ \text{Divide} & 0001\ 0000 & \text{by} & 0011 \end{array} \Rightarrow 1 \cdot 2^4 = 16, 16/3 = 5 + 1/3$$

Result: quotient $Q2 = 0101$, save it as part of Q_L
          remainder *Rem2*: 0001, save it as part of the remainder.

Third division:

$$\begin{array}{cc} D_L & Y \\ \text{Divide} \quad 0000\ 0111 & \text{by} \quad 0011 \end{array} \Rightarrow 7/3 = 2 + 1/3$$

Result: quotient $Q3 = 0010$, add it to $Q2$, so $Q_L = 0111$ or $5 + 2 = 7$
          remainder *Rem3*: 0001, add it to *Rem2*, so $Rem = 0010$ or $1 + 1 = 2$

Final result:

$$Q = 0010\ 0111, Rem = 0010$$

Check in binary format:

$$Q \cdot Y + Rem = 0010\ 0111 \cdot 0011 + 0010 = 01110101 + 0010$$
$$= 01110111 = D$$

Check in decimal format:
$$Q_H = 2, Q_L = 7, Rem = 2$$
$$Q = 2 \cdot 2^4 + 7 = 32 + 7 = 39, Rem = 2$$
$$119/3 = 39 + 2/3$$
$$119 = 39 \cdot 3 + 2 = 117 + 2 \quad \text{Correct!}$$

∎

6.5 FLOATING-POINT OPERATIONS

Besides operations on single-precision and double-precision numbers, floating-point numbers requires different algorithms for representation and mathematical operations. In addition, this section also discusses the full algorithm for floating-point addition/subtraction and how sequential logic can be used in such operations.

6.5.1 Representation of Floating-Point Numbers

Floating-point numbers are not unfamiliar to us. We see them displayed as a result of calculations with real numbers when we use scientific calculators or run high-level language programs on computers. The floating-point representation of real numbers is sometimes called scientific notation. It consists of two parts: the mantissa or fraction, m, and the exponent, e, so that the value of the represented number equals

$$N_{fp} = mr^e \tag{6.17}$$

where r is the radix or base of the number system to represent the mantissa. For example, the real number 0.1 in decimal can be represented in different forms using different radix values, r, as shown below:

$$(0.1)_{10} = (0.000110011001100\ldots)_2 = 0.110011001100 \cdot 2^{-3}$$
$$= (0.063146314\ldots)_8 = (0.63146314\ldots)_8 \cdot 8^{-1}$$
$$= (0.1919\ldots)_{16} = (0.1919\ldots)_{16} \cdot 16^0 \tag{6.18}$$

From this example, we can ascertain some of the important properties of the floating-point number representation:

1. m and e can be represented in different number systems with different radix values. Usually, the mantissa, m, is a fractional number that is represented in sign-magnitude format, which is convenient for multiplication, division, and shift operations during addition/subtraction (for exponent equalization). The exponent, e, is an integer using two's complement representation (or a variant), which is more convenient for addition/subtraction of exponents. Inside the computer, both m and e

are represented in binary, and the radix value 2, 8, or 16 is implicit and invisible to the computer hardware.

2. With a given value of the radix r, a floating-point number can have different representations by shifting the mantissa and adjusting the exponent correspondingly. For example, if we shift the mantissa left (or right) k positions, we should decrease (or increase) the exponent by k. To avoid indeterminacy or redundancy, we use the normalized floating-point number representation, which specifies that the MSD of the mantissa be nonzero when representing any nonzero floating-point number. All the floating-point numbers in Expression (6.18) are in normalized form. This rule is only for the sign-magnitude representation. For the r's-complement representation of m, the MSD of its numerical part should be different from the sign bit. The normalized floating-point numbers ensure maximum accuracy of representation. Therefore, algorithms for floating-point operations usually process normalized numbers at the start, and the final result is converted into normalized form with a normalization step.

3. A normalized floating-point number, as defined above, does not include "0". Two cases are treated as "0": (1) the mantissa equals "0" or (2) the exponent equals the minimum value (i.e., most negative). For the sake of consistency, we consider a number of all 0s, including the exponent, as "machine zero." Machine zero has zero mantissa and a minimum exponent at the same time. Therefore, we should modify the two's complement representation of the exponent to a biased code or excess-2^q code, where q is the number of exponent bits (excluding the sign bit). An example of excess-2^3 code is shown in Table 6.3. It can be seen that the minimum of the excess-2^3 code is "0000". To be consistent with the format of machine zero, algorithms for floating-point operations should contain a special step to treat a "0" result.

4. Unlike fixed-point numbers, floating-point numbers suffer from representation error as well as calculation error. Strictly speaking, the associative law and distributive law that are true for fixed-point calculation are no longer true for floating-point calculations. We must carefully choose a method of *rounding* and include it in algorithms for floating-point operations.

As a practical example, we give the IEEE-754 standard for the 32-bit single-precision floating-point format as follows:

1 bit	8 bits	23 bits
s	e	m

sign of m exponent   mantissa with implied leading 1

Table 6.3 Excess-2^3 code vs. 4-bit two's complement code

Decimal Number	Two's Complement Code	Excess-2^3 Code
+7	0111	1111
+6	0110	1110
+5	0101	1101
+4	0100	1100
+3	0011	1011
+2	0010	1010
+1	0001	1001
0	0000	1000
−1	1111	0111
−2	1110	0110
−3	1101	0101
−4	1100	0100
−5	1011	0011
−6	1010	0010
−7	1001	0001
−8	1000	0000

The sign bit s and the 23-bit mantissa m form a 25-bit sign-magnitude fraction, including an implicit leading bit "1" to the left of the binary point. The actual magnitude of the complete mantissa is $1.m$. The implicit bit "1" is hidden when the number is stored in memory or the register set, and recovered when the number is brought into the ALU.

The exponent e is represented in excess-127 code. Since the bias value is 127 instead of 2^7 as we used before, the range of valid exponents is from −126 (code 00000001) up to +127 (code 11111110). The maximum code "11111111" and the minimum code "00000000" are reserved to indicate exceptional conditions. The meaning of normal and exceptional biased exponents is listed in Table 6.4.

The normal range for the exponent, e, is −126 to +127 (approximately $10^{\pm 38}$ in decimal), while the range of mantissa for normalized numbers is $\pm 1.00\ldots 0$ to $\pm 1.11\ldots 1$ (approximately 7 to 8 decimal digits).

Table 6.4 Evaluating biased exponents of an IEEE-754 standard floating-point operand

Biased Exponent e		Value of e in Decimal	Mantissa m	Meaning
Binary	**Decimal**			
00000000	$0 = -127 + 127$	-127	0	$\pm$ zero
00000000	$0 = -127 + 127$	-127	$\neq 0$	denormalized
00000001	$1 = -126 + 127$	-126	$\times$	normalized
...	...	...	$\times$	normalized
01111110	$126 = -1 + 127$	-1	$\times$	normalized
01111111	$127 = 0 + 127$	0	$\times$	normalized
10000000	$128 = 1 + 127$	1	$\times$	normalized
...	...	...	$\times$	normalized
11111110	$254 = 127 + 127$	127	$\times$	normalized
11111111	$255 = 128 + 127$	128	$\times$	$\pm$ infinity
11111111	$255 = 128 + 127$	128	$\neq 0$	not a number (NaN)

The exceptional cases shown in Table 6.4 are explained as follows:

- When $e = 00000000$ and $m = 0$, the number represents plus or minus zero.
- When $e = 00000000$ and $m \neq 0$, the magnitude of the number is less than the minimum value that is represented in the normalized format, so it is said to be "denormalized."
- When $e = 11111111$ and $m = 0$, the number represents plus or minus infinity.
- When $e = 11111111$ and $m \neq 0$, the representation is considered to be "not a number (NaN)," which is used to signify invalid operations, such as zero multiplied by infinity.

To provide more precision and range of representation for floating-point numbers, the IEEE-754 standard also specifies a double-precision format as shown below:

1 bit	11 bits	52 bits
s	e	m

sign of m exponent mantissa with implied leading 1

The 11-bit exponent is expressed in excess-1023 code with a biased value of 1023. The range of the valid exponent is from -1022 (code 00000000001) to

+1023 (code 11111111110). The maximum code "11111111111" and minimum code "00000000000" are reserved to indicate exceptional conditions. We can create a table similar to Table 6.4 to interpret the meaning and range of the normal and exceptional biased exponents for the double-precision IEEE format. Specifically, the normal range for exponents, −1022 to +1023, corresponds approximately to the range $10^{\pm 308}$ in decimal, while the range of mantissa for normalized numbers between ±1.00...0 (52 zeros) and ±1.11...1 (52 ones after binary point) corresponds approximately to 16 to 17 decimal digits.

Example 6.12   Numerical Example of a Conversion of an Integer to a Floating-Point Number

Given a decimal number 45.828125, represent it as a normalized single-precision floating-point number in IEEE single-precision standard format.

1. Using the weights of both integer and fractional binary digits, we find the binary code of the mantissa before normalization = 101101.110101
2. Shift the binary point left 5 bits, until we get a most significant integer bit "1," and increase the exponent correspondingly. Thus, we get the exponent in two's complement representation = 00000101 after normalization. Transform it into excess-127 representation = 10000100.
3. IEEE standard format in binary representation = 010000100 011011101010...
4. IEEE format in hexadecimal representation: 42375000

■

6.5.2 Algorithms for Floating-Point Operations

The four basic arithmetic operations on two floating-point operands, $A = m_a 2^{e_a}$ and $B = m_b 2^{e_b}$ (both m_a and m_b are the mantissa, including the sign) are performed according to the following expressions:

- Floating-point addition/subtraction

$$
\left.
\begin{aligned}
A \pm B &= m_a 2^{e_a} \pm m_b 2^{e_b} \\
&= (m_a \pm m_b 2^{e_b - e_a}) \cdot 2^{e_a} && \text{if } e_a > e_b \\
A \pm B &= m_a 2^{e_a} \pm m_b 2^{e_b} \\
&= (m_a \pm m_b) \cdot 2^{e_a} \text{ or } (m_a \pm m_b) \cdot 2^{e_b} && \text{if } e_a = e_b \\
A \pm B &= m_a 2^{e_a} \pm m_b 2^{e_b} \\
&= (m_a 2^{e_a - e_b} \pm m_b) \cdot 2^{e_b} && \text{if } e_a < e_b
\end{aligned}
\right\}
\quad (6.19)
$$

- Floating-point multiplication

$$A \times B = m_a 2^{e_a} \times m_b 2^{e_b} = (m_a \times m_b) 2^{e_a + e_b} \qquad (6.20)$$

- Floating-point division

$$A \div B = m_a 2^{e_a} \div m_b 2^{e_b} = (m_a \div m_b) 2^{e_a - e_b} \qquad (6.21)$$

From the above expressions, some common principles can be summarized:

1. The exponent and mantissa are treated separately. The exponents need only addition/subtraction. The mantissa needs fixed-point addition/subtraction, multiplication, and division. The results of the two parts are combined together as the floating-point result.

2. The operations are usually defined as normalized operations. The initial operands are always normalized, and the result should also be normalized by shifting the mantissa and adjusting the exponent correspondingly. Left normalization is needed for removing the leading zeros from the mantissa, and right normalization is needed if the operation on the mantissa has caused overflow. The final result has an overflow only when the exponent part has an overflow after right normalization.

3. Floating-point addition/subtraction is more complicated than its fixed-point counterpart. It requires exponent equalization before the two mantissa can perform addition/subtraction. A compare operation is needed by the exponents, and a right shift operation is needed by the mantissa. Detailed implementation of the floating-point addition/subtraction will be described next.

6.5.3 A Complete Algorithm for Floating-Point Addition/Subtraction

From Expression (6.19), we can derive the following steps for floating-point addition/ subtraction:

Step 1. Exponent equalization

$m_b 2^{e_b - e_a}$ if $e_a > e_b$ or $m_a 2^{e_a - e_b}$ if $e_a < e_b$ or no shift if $e_a = e_b$

1.1 Compare the exponents, e_a and e_b, by subtraction.

1.2 Check the difference, and shift right the mantissa of the number with the smaller exponent, that is, if $e_a > e_b$, shift m_b; if $e_a < e_b$, shift m_a; if $e_a = e_b$, no shift.
The number of bits shifted equals the absolute value of the difference between e_a and e_b. Retain some bits shifted out of the LSB as *guard bits* to be used in Step 4.

1.3 Retain the larger exponent, e_a if $e_a > e_b$ or e_b if $e_a < e_b$, as the exponent of the result.

Step 2. Fixed-point addition/subtraction of the mantissa after exponent equalization

$$m_a \pm m_b 2^{e_b - e_a} \text{ if } e_a > e_b \text{ or } m_a 2^{e_a - e_b} \pm m_b \text{ if } e_a < e_b \text{ or } m_a \pm m_b \text{ if } e_a = e_b$$

Step 3. Left normalization or right normalization

Left normalization is done if there are leading zero(s) in the MSD of the result, or right normalization if there was overflow in Step 2. The number of bits to be shifted left is equal to the number of leading 0s. The number of bits to be shifted right is, at most, one. Decrease or increase the exponent retained in Step 1.3 by the number of bits shifted on the mantissa.

Step 4. Rounding

Many different rounding methods are utilized. Most commonly, if the highest bit of the guard bits is "0", truncate it, otherwise, round and add "1" to the resulted mantissa.

Step 5. Renormalization

A right normalization is needed if the rounding operation in Step 4 caused the mantissa to have an overflow.

Step 6. Check the result exponent for overflow or check for zero result

The result has an overflow only if the exponent has an overflow. The result is set to machine zero if either the mantissa is zero or the exponent is the most negative value.

The following are some numerical examples used to demonstrate the different cases which should be treated in the above algorithm. Each mantissa is provided in binary and in sign-magnitude format, and the underlined bits are the sign bits. Each exponent is provided in decimal.

Example 6.13   Floating-Point Addition/Subtraction (I)

$A + B = \underline{0}101.2^2 + \underline{0}110.2^3$ (both are normalized numbers)

$\quad = \underline{0}0101.2^3 + \underline{0}110.2^3$ (after exponent equalization)

$\quad = \underline{1}0001.2^3$ (after mantissa addition)

$\quad = \underline{0}10001.2^4$ (after right normalization)

$\quad = \underline{0}100.2^4$ (after truncation) (could be an overflow if the exponent has only 3 bits)

∎

> ### Example 6.14   Floating-Point Addition/Subtraction (II)
>
> $A - B = \underline{0}101.2^2 - \underline{0}110.2^3$ (both are normalized numbers)
>
> $= \underline{0}0101.2^3 - \underline{0}110.2^3$ (after exponent equalization)
>
> $= \underline{1}0111.2^3$ (after mantissa subtraction)
>
> $= \underline{1}111.2^2$ (after left normalization) (a case showing that the guard bits are useful)
>
> $= \underline{1}111.2^2$ (rounding has no effect)
>
> ■

> ### Example 6.15   Floating-Point Addition/Subtraction (III)
>
> $A + B = \underline{0}101.2^2 + \underline{0}101.2^3$ (both are normalized numbers)
>
> $= \underline{0}0101.2^3 + \underline{0}101.2^3$ (after exponent equalization)
>
> $= \underline{0}1111.2^3$ (after mantissa addition)
>
> $= \underline{0}1111.2^3$ (no left or right normalization)
>
> $= \underline{1}000.2^3$ (after rounding)
>
> $= \underline{0}100.2^4$ (after renormalization) (could be an overflow for 3-bit exponent)
>
> ■

6.5.4 Implementation of Floating-Point Addition/Subtraction by Sequential Logic

There are many methods for implementing floating-point addition/subtraction. The fastest method uses combinational logic to construct a multi-stage pipeline. Each stage implements a step of the above algorithm, and all the stages perform the floating-point addition/subtraction in an interleaved fashion. The slowest method uses software at the machine-language level to program the floating-point operation as a subroutine. The method with intermediate speed uses sequential logic or microcode to implement the sequence of microoperations stated in the above algorithm.

The three-register structure of a sequential floating-point adder and the sequence of microoperations reflecting the above-mentioned algorithm are shown in Figure 6.17. The microoperations represented with the circled numbers in the figure have the following meaning:

1. Calculate $e_a - e_b$ and store it in a counter C_d, which is used to control the number of bits to be shifted jointly in A and Q. Send e_b to A as the result exponent if $e_a < e_b$, so that A always holds the larger exponent of e_a and e_b.

2. Exchange m_a and m_b between A and D if $e_a > e_b$ so that the mantissa of the number with the smaller exponent is placed in A for exponent equalization. Then, shift m_a (if $e_a < e_b$) or m_b (if $e_a > e_b$) in A and Q jointly under the control of the counter C_d.

3. Exchange m_a and m_b back if $e_a > e_b$ so as to restore m_a and m_b to the original position. Then add/subtract mantissa together with the guard bits.

4. Left/right normalization in A and Q jointly. Use ALU_e to decrease/increase the result exponent (e_a if $e_a \geq e_b$ or e_b if $e_a < e_b$) in A.

5. Other steps of rounding and renormalization are not shown in Figure 6.17.

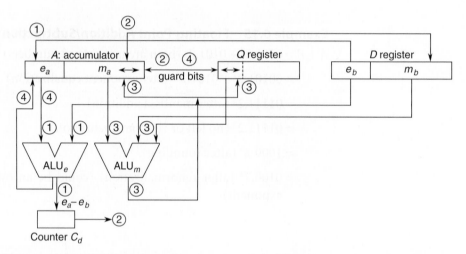

Figure 6.17 Implementation of floating-point addition/subtraction by sequential logic

SUMMARY

Complex arithmetic operations such as multiplication, division, and floating-point operations are usually not included in the list of basic arithmetic logic operations designed in the simple circuit of the ALU. The method based on hardware with sequential control is discussed in this chapter. It is faster than the method of software at assembly-language level and simpler than the method of combinational hardware. It is different from the method of firmware at the microprogram level and can be used in the hardwired control of the CPU. The algorithm of single-precision two's complement multiplication based on three registers, an ALU, and sequential control is derived in Section 6.1.1, followed by the fast multiplication algorithms (the Booth and the bit-pairwise algorithms) in Section 6.1.2, with the same data representation and hardware condition. Based on the single-precision algorithms in Section 6.1, the algorithm of double-precision multiplication of two's complement numbers is then developed in Section 6.2. Similarly, the algorithms of division on single-precision and double-precision numbers (integer or fraction) are derived in Section 6.3 and Section 6.4, respectively. Finally, the algorithms for floating-point operations are derived in Section 6.5 with emphasis on floating-point addition/subtraction. The floating point numbers can be represented either in a general format or in IEEE-754 standard single-precision or double-precision format.

EXERCISES

6.1 (a) Demonstrate the step-by-step procedure of the multiplication algorithm stated in Section 6.1.1, using the example data $M = 1001$ and $Y = 1011$, both being two's complement signed integers.

(b) Using the above example data and performing hand calculation of $M \times Y$ directly on two's complement numbers, check the correctness of the result obtained in Part (a).

6.2 Given multiplicand $M = 1101$ and multiplier $Y = 1011$, both being signed integers in two's complement representation. Using the format of Figure 6.2, demonstrate the step-by-step results of implementation of the hardware multiplication $M \times Y$ by the direct two's complement multiplication algorithm. Check your result by performing the calculation by hand, and also directly in two's complement notation.

6.3 (a) Given multiplicand $M = 10110010$ and multiplier $Y = 10011101$, both being signed integers in two's complement representation. Using the format of Figure 6.6, demonstrate the step-by-step results of implementation of the hardware multiplication $M \times Y$ by the Booth algorithm for two's complement multiplication. Check your result by performing the calculation by hand, also directly in two's complement notation.

(b) Repeat Part (a) by exchanging the positions of the multiplicand and the multiplier.

6.4 (a) Given multiplicand $M = 10110010$ and multiplier $Y = 10011101$, both being signed integers in two's complement representation. Using the format of Figure 6.10, demonstrate the step-by-step results of implementation of the hardware multiplication $M \times Y$ by the bit-pairwise algorithm for two's complement multiplication. Check your result by performing the calculation by hand, also directly in two's complement notation.

(b) Repeat Part (a) by exchanging the positions of the multiplicand and the multiplier.

6.5 (a) Given multiplicand $M = 10110010$ and multiplier $Y = 10011101$, both being signed integers in two's complement representation. Demonstrate the step-by-step results of implementation of the hardware multiplication $M \times Y$ by the algorithm for double-precision multiplication of two's complement numbers in Section 6.2.3. Assume 4-bit single-word length for execution of the algorithm. Check your result by performing the calculation by hand, also in two's complement notation.

(b) Repeat Part (a) by exchanging the positions of the multiplicand and the multiplier.

6.6 Given dividend $D = 11010011$ and divisor $Y = 0111$, both being signed fractional numbers in two's complement representation.

(a) Converting the numbers into positive if necessary and using the format of Figure 6.14, demonstrate the step-by-step results of implementation of the hardware division $|D| / |Y|$ by the nonrestoring division algorithm versus the restoring division algorithm.

(b) Since the two given operands are signed numbers, we need additional steps to determine the sign of the quotient and transform the final results into two's complement representations accordingly. Describe these steps to obtain a complete algorithm of two's complement division. Using your algorithm to find the final results of D/V for the values of D and V given above. Check the correctness of your answer directly in two's complement representation by Expression (6.6): $D = Y \cdot Q + 2^{-n}R$.

6.7 Given dividend $D = 11010011$ and divisor $Y = 0111$, both being signed fractional numbers in two's complement representation.

(a) Using the algorithm for double-precision division of fractional numbers stated in Section 6.4.2, demonstrate the step-by-step results of implementation of the division $|D| / |Y|$. Assume 4-bit single-word length for execution of the algorithm.

(b) Determine the final results of the above calculation in terms of the quotient and remainder of D/V with their correct signs, and then check their correctness using Expression (6.7).

6.8 Given dividend $D = 11010011$ and divisor $Y = 0111$, both being signed integer numbers in two's complement representation.

(a) Using the algorithm for double-precision division of integer numbers stated in Section 6.4.3, demonstrate the step-by-step results of implementation of the division $|D| / |Y|$. Assume 4-bit single-word length for execution of the algorithm.

(b) Determine the final results of the above calculation in terms of the quotient and remainder of D/V with their correct signs, and then check the correctness of them by Expression (6.12).

6.9 Represent all 16 decimal numbers in the range

$$1\frac{3}{4}, \ 1\frac{1}{2}, \ 1\frac{1}{4}, \ ..., \ 0, \ ..., \ -1\frac{1}{2}, \ -1\frac{3}{4}, \ -2$$

(a) using two's complement representation;

(b) using excess-2 representation;

(c) using 32-bit IEEE-754 standard floating-point representation (Give your result for this part in hexadecimal form).

6.10 A binary floating-point number system has 5 bits for a biased exponent.

(a) What should be the constant used for the bias such that machine zero can be represented as all zeros? Write a table listing all the biased representations of the exponents from the largest to the smallest and their corresponding ordinary two's complement representations in another column.

(b) Derive the rules of directly adding or subtracting two biased exponents to obtain a biased-exponent result, including the rule of detection of overflow.

6.11 Suppose a floating-point number system has a data format as shown in Figure 6.18. It uses radix-2 sign-magnitude representation for the mantissa, with 1 bit for the sign, s, and 12 bits for the magnitude, m. The 3-bit exponent, e, uses excess-4 code. Assume that the normalized number has no hidden bit.

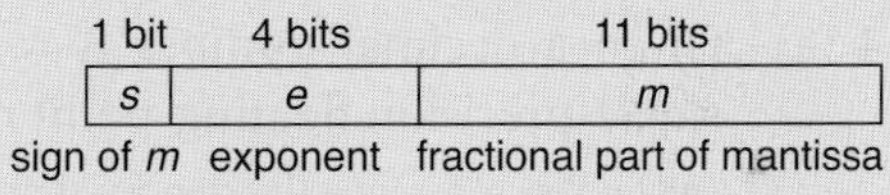

1 bit	4 bits	11 bits
s	e	m
sign of m	exponent	fractional part of mantissa

Figure 6.18 Floating-point number format for Problem 6.11

(a) What is the largest normalized number? What is the smallest positive normalized number? Write each of these two numbers in binary (write mantissa in hexadecimal) and in decimal floating-point formats.

(b) Given four floating-point numbers in the above system, written in hexadecimal (the radix is still 2). Find the normalized result of the following calculations:

$$N1 + N2 = \underline{0}.86D \times 2^2 + \underline{0}.F8A \times 2^3$$
$$N3 + N4 = \underline{1}.86F \times 2^{-3} + \underline{0}.84D \times 2^{-1}$$

[Note: Underlined digit denotes the sign bit.]

Strictly follow the detailed steps of the algorithm and give the name of the operation performed and the intermediate result obtained at every step.

(c) Convert the given numbers and the result of the calculation in Part (b) into fixed-point decimal numbers, and check the correctness of the calculation.

6.12 Assume that a floating-point system uses 16 as the radix r. Perform the following arithmetic operations and write the results in normalized form. Give the detailed steps and the intermediate result at every step.

(a) $0.(F8EB)_{16} \times 16^3 + 0.(95A4)_{16} \times 16^2$

(b) $0.(1845)_{16} \times 16^2 - 0.(F5A1)_{16} \times 16^3$

6.13 (a) Convert the following decimal numbers to IEEE-754 standard single-precision floating-point numbers. Report the results as hexadecimal values.

(i) 23.5625

(ii) −42.8125

(b) Convert the following IEEE single-precision floating-point numbers to their decimal values.

(i) $(3F780000)_{16}$

(ii) $(C5B40000)_{16}$

(c) Calculate the values that can be represented in the IEEE-754 standard single-precision format, considering:

(i) largest positive normalized (values) number

(ii) smallest nonzero positive normalized number

(iii) smallest nonzero positive denormalized number

Report your answer in binary as well as decimal scientific notations.

6.14 (a) Given a decimal number $A = 45.828125$, represent it as a normalized single-precision floating-point number in IEEE-754 standard format.

[Note: You must give the step-by-step procedure of number transformation with all the intermediate results and finally write the end result in eight hexadecimal digits.]

(b) Perform the operation of floating-point multiplication to obtain the normalized result of A^2 in the IEEE-754 standard single-precision format. Write the result in a hexadecimal code.

(c) Represent the result in Part (b) in the IEEE-754 standard double-precision format. Write the result in a hexadecimal code.

6.15 In this problem, we will use a 16-bit word to imitate the 32-bit IEEE-standard representation of floating-point numbers. We will use a similar format of representation with a *hidden bit* defined in the same way as in the IEEE-754 standard, but with different field lengths as shown in Figure 6.19.

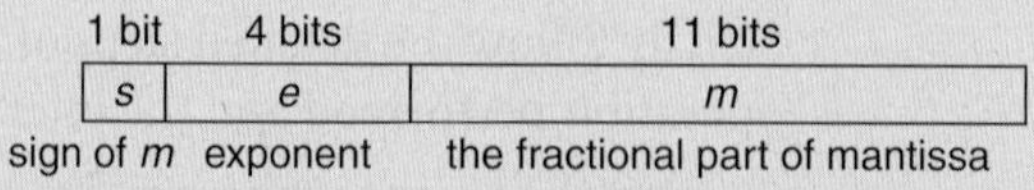

Figure 6.19   The floating-point number format for Problem 6.15

(a) Write a table of biased exponents from 0000 to 1111 to show their correspondence to the decimal values of e, the two's complement representations of e, and the meanings of e when used with different m's to represent different ranges of floating-point numbers.

[Note: The table should be complete, including all the cases of the floating-point numbers that are defined in the IEEE-754 standard.]

(b) Now given two floating-point numbers in the above standard format, written in hexadecimal:

$$X = 36E7, Y = BA6D$$

Show the step-by-step process of performing the operations of $X + Y$ and $X - Y$ in a computer. Write a short comment for each step indicating the operation performed. Obtain the final result in the given standard format, written in hexadecimal.

6.16 For convenience of manual calculation, this problem introduces a floating-point number representation similar to the single-precision IEEE-754 format in all aspects except that its mantissa field is reduced from 23 bits to 11 bits, as shown in Figure 6.20.

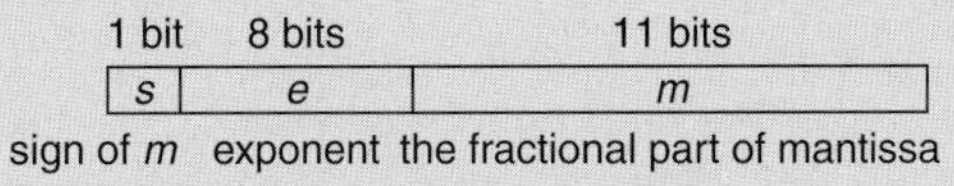

Figure 6.20 Floating-point number format for Problem 6.16

(a) Given two signed decimal fixed-point numbers X and Y as follows:

$$X = +103.28125$$
$$Y = +175.8125$$

Convert them into equivalent floating-point numbers in the above modified IEEE-754 format. You should give the detailed step-by-step procedure of data conversion showing all the intermediate results. Your final result must be in the modified IEEE-754 format as depicted in Figure 6.20.

(b) Using the two floating-point numbers in the modified IEEE-754 format obtained above in Part (a), perform add and subtract operations

$$X + Y \text{ and } X - Y$$

following the formal algorithm of floating-point calculation performed in a computer.

You must give the detailed steps of the calculation, showing the name of the operation and the intermediate result at every step. The final result should be represented in the above-given modified IEEE-754 format.

7

Instruction Set Architecture

Instruction set architecture is an important component of computer architecture. The design of the instruction set is the basis for the design of the CPU. The *instruction format*, the *addressing modes*, and the *instruction set* are important aspects of the instruction set architecture. The instruction format has a strong impact on the basic organization of the CPU. An instruction word consists of several fields. The *operation code* field specifies the operations implemented by the CPU in the instruction set of a computer. The basic arithmetic and logic operations in the instruction set are directly performed by the ALU. Complex operations such as multiplication, division, and floating-point operations can be implemented in different ways, either directly by hardware in the CPU or indirectly by software or coprocessors. The *address* fields and the associated addressing modes in an instruction have a significant influence on the organization of the CPU and determine the number and type of registers. Therefore, CPU organization should be determined with careful consideration of the instruction set architecture based on the requirements of the target applications and the desired performance of the computer. In the following discussion, we will study different instruction formats and addressing modes, and see how they affect the different styles of instruction set designs. For each major topic, we will provide some practical examples as case studies.

7.1 THE INSTRUCTION FORMAT

The instruction format represents the machine instruction in a binary format. It provides a language interface for the system software that transforms an assembly-language program into machine code as its executable image to be stored in memory and executed in a computer. Therefore, the instruction format determines both the external view of a computer seen by the programmers' developing system software and the internal view of the CPU seen by computer architects implementing the instruction set and designing the control unit.

The instruction format is determined by the machine code representation of the instruction set of a computer. To specify a computer operation, the instruction format must contain, implicitly or explicitly, three necessary parts:

- The operation to be performed, encoded in binary bits called the *operation code* (Opcode).

- The information about the locations of source and destination operands in memory and/or in registers (these locations are specified as the *addresses* with various *addressing modes*).

- The data types of the operands.

The instruction format can contain other optional fields, such as:

- The *immediate data* or *displacement* field, for specifying operand or address information in the instruction code.

- The fields specifying additional information for control purposes.

The operation code and the addresses are the two most important parts of a machine instruction. The operation code field determines the functionality of a computer in software, and the address fields play the major role in determining the structure of a computer in hardware. Now, we will see how the address fields of an instruction format determine the machine structure. An instruction set contains many different types of instructions. The basic operation type that uses the full set of three operand addresses is called a *binary operation*. A binary operation is an operation involving two source operands and one destination (result) operand. Each operand can be located either in memory or in a register. In an instruction for a binary operation, we typically require that two source addresses for fetching two operands and one destination address for storing the result are explicitly specified. This defines the *three-address instruction format*, in which all three addresses are independent and explicitly specified in the instruction. However, due to the limited length of an instruction, it is not easy to accommodate all three memory addresses (some may use a direct memory address) in an instruction format.

We have two methods to overcome this difficulty. One method is to specify only one address for an operand in memory, and the remaining addresses are specified for the operands in CPU registers or general-purpose registers, for which the register numbers can be specified explicitly in the instruction format. The other method is to make one, two, or three addresses of the operands implicit in the instruction format. The implicit addresses can be specified to special-purpose registers, whose names are implicit in the operation code of the instruction format. Use of the first method creates, besides the traditional memory-memory (M-M) machine, the architectures of the memory-register (M-R) machines and the register-register (R-R) machines. Use of the second method creates the architectures of two-address, one-address, and zero-address machines.

To obtain the two-address instruction format, we modify the three-address instruction format by always combining one of the source addresses with the destination address and leave another source address independent in the instruction format. This creates the *two-address instruction format*. Depending on which source address, that is, the first source or the second source, is combined with the destination, there are two options for the two-address instruction format. The two-address format saves one address field and provides the possibility of specifying one memory address to the source/destination operand and a register address to another source operand. Thus, the two-address format improves the code compactness as compared to the three-address format. However, the two-address format loses some programming flexibility because after executing each instruction, one of the source operands must be overwritten by the result of the operation. If we need to keep this operand unchanged after the operation, we must copy its value into a third register and use this third register to participate in the operation. Therefore, "Copy Register" and "Copy Immediate" instructions are useful in the two-address instruction set. The former copies the content of the source register into a destination register, while the latter copies a source of immediate data specified in the instruction code into a destination register. Without this "Copy Immediate" instruction, it would be impossible to initialize a register without going through memory.

Both the three-address instruction format and the two-address instruction format belong, in principle, to the same class since they lead to the same CPU organization. Both of them do not need an implied register to specify an implied operand. Both of them may use general-purpose registers to specify one or both operands in the address fields. Therefore, both the three-address and two-address instruction formats correspond to a CPU organization based on a *general-purpose register set*. The registers are called general purpose because they can be used for storing data or addresses and can play different roles by supplying or storing information in different steps of the instruction execution. They are also called *programmable registers* in the sense that the registers are visible to assembly-language programmers. A computer based on this CPU organization is called a *general-purpose register machine*. For this class of machines, if both source operands can be in memory, we have a M-M machine. If one source operand can be in memory and the other is in a register, we have a M-R machine. If both source operands are in registers, we have a R-R machine.

Specifying the source/destination address to be a special-purpose register called an accumulator can further reduce the number of address fields of a two-address instruction format. The instruction format has only one address field, usually containing a memory address. A binary operation always takes the first source operand from the accumulator and the second operand from the memory address specified in the instruction code and, after operation, stores the result in the accumulator. Thus, we obtain the *one-address instruction format*. The computer with a CPU organization supporting the one-address instruction format is called an *accumulator-based machine*.

If we eliminate both address fields in a two-address instruction format and make them implicit, then we have the *zero-address instruction format*. All the source operands and the destination operand are implied in a processor stack, with the two top-of-stack elements providing the two source operands and the top-of-stack location storing the destination operand. An instruction with a binary operation pops the two top-of-stack elements out of the stack, performs the operation, and then pushes the result back to the new top-of-stack location. A computer with a CPU organization supporting this zero-address instruction format is called a *stack machine*.

Example 7.1   Comparison of Instruction Formats with Different Numbers of Addresses

Write short assembly language codes for calculating $Z = |X|$, where X is an arbitrary number in two's complement representation stored in memory at address mX, and Z is the result to be stored in memory location addressed by mZ.

The Algorithm

Load X into a register. Test X. If X is positive, then X is the result, else subtract X from 0 to get $-X$. If $-X$ is positive, then $-X$ is the result, else both X and $-X$ must be 10...00, which is an overflow error. Store the result in memory at address mZ.

1. Three-Address Instruction Format

```
        LOAD  R1, mX          ; Load from memory: R1 ← mem[mX]=X

        BGE   R1, L1           ; Branch greater than or equal: if (R1)≥0,
                                 branch to L1

        SUB   R2, R2, R2       ; Subtract: clear R2 by subtracting R2 by itself

        SUB   R3, R2, R1       ; Subtract: R3←(R2)−(R1)=0−X

        BLT   R3, L2           ; Branch less than: if (R3)=−X is still negative,
                                 branch to L2, i.e., the result equals 10...00, an
                                 overflow error!

    L1: STORE mZ, R3           ; Store into memory: mem[mZ]←(R3)

        EXIT                   ; Exit to system

    L2: ...                    ; Trap to system for error handling
```

2. Two-Address Instruction Format

```
    LOAD R1, mX     ; Load from memory: R1←mem[mX]=X
    BGE R1, L1      ; Branch greater than or equal: if (R1)≥0,
                      branch to L1
    SUB R3, R3      ; Subtract: R3←(R3)−(R3)=0
    SUB R3, R1      ; Subtract: R3←(R3)−(R1)=0−X
    BLT R3, L2      ; Branch less than: if (R3)=−X is still negative, branch
                      to L2, i.e., the result equals 10...00, an overflow error!
L1: STORE mZ, R3    ; Store into memory: mem[mZ]←(R3)
    EXIT            ; Exit to system
L2: ...             ; Trap to system for error handling
```

3. One-Address Instruction Format

```
    LDA  mX         ; Load accumulator: A←mem[mX]=X
    BGE  L1         ; Branch greater than or equal: if (A)≥0, branch to L1
    CLRA            ; Clear accumulator: A←0
    SUBA mX         ; subtract accumulator: A←(A)−mem[mX]=0−X
    BLT  L2         ; Branch less than: if (A)=−X is still negative, branch to
                      L2, i.e., the result equals 10...00, an overflow error!
L1: STA  mZ         ; Store from accumulator: mem[mZ]←(A)
    EXIT            ; Exit to system
L2: ...             ; Trap to system for error handling
```

4. Zero-Address Instruction Format

In the following code, assume that the stack is originally empty. After the execution of the program, the stack must return to its original state, as shown in Figure 7.1. This is obtained by adding a POP instruction into the program so as to delete the unused result in the stack after a taken branch instruction BLT **L2**.

```
    LOAD mX         ; Push mem[mX]=X onto stack
    DUP             ; Duplicate: copy top word, X, on stack and push it onto
                      stack
    BGE L1          ; Branch greater than or equal: pop top word, X, from
                      stack and branch to L1 if it is ≥ 0
    LOAD #0         ; Push constant 0 onto stack
    SWAP            ; Swap the two top words on the stack
```

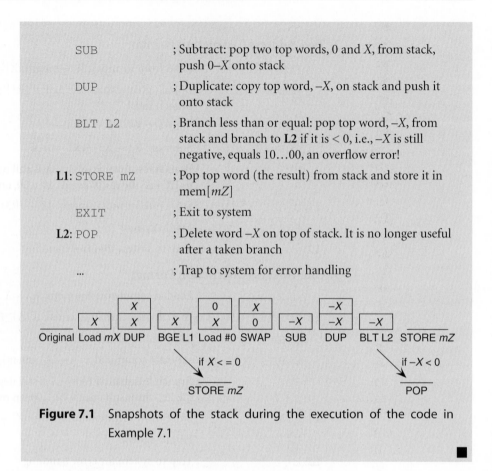

```
        SUB             ; Subtract: pop two top words, 0 and X, from stack,
                          push 0–X onto stack

        DUP             ; Duplicate: copy top word, –X, on stack and push it
                          onto stack

        BLT L2          ; Branch less than or equal: pop top word, –X, from
                          stack and branch to L2 if it is < 0, i.e., –X is still
                          negative, equals 10…00, an overflow error!

L1: STORE mZ            ; Pop top word (the result) from stack and store it in
                          mem[mZ]

        EXIT            ; Exit to system

L2: POP                ; Delete word –X on top of stack. It is no longer useful
                          after a taken branch

        …               ; Trap to system for error handling
```

Figure 7.1 Snapshots of the stack during the execution of the code in Example 7.1

Comparing the above four short codes, we can see that the three-address and two-address instruction formats take full advantage of general-purpose registers to reduce memory traffic. The one-address and zero-address instruction formats usually have smaller code size, but heavier memory traffic.

7.2 THE ADDRESSING MODES

By using different methods for specifying addresses, the instruction set can support various addressing modes. For example, when we assign a register number to an address field of an instruction, it does not mean that the data-operand is in that register. The register may just contain a pointer to a memory location where the data is stored. Therefore, it is the addressing mode that plays an important role for determining the exact location of the source or destination operand. A large variety of addressing modes have been adopted in different computer families. We classify them according to where the operand is actually located. The operand to be addressed can be (1) in the instruction code, (2) in a register, (3) in a memory location or (4) in a location inside the assembly-language program code. Therefore, there are four classes of addressing modes, as follows:

7.2.1 Specifying the Operand in the Instruction Code

The only addressing mode belonging to this class is the *immediate addressing mode*. By this addressing mode, the instruction can directly specify data in its instruction code, rather than through a register. It provides the simplest way to assign a value to an operand that can immediately participate in an operation or initialize a register. The problem is that the length of the immediate field in the instruction format is limited by the instruction length. A short immediate data in this field is usually a signed number, which must be sign-extended to the full word length in order to match the length of the register. The immediate addressing mode is shown in Figure 7.2.

add	Rd	Rs1	imm

e.g., add Rd, Rs1, #imm ; Rd ← (Rs1) + sign-extended imm

Figure 7.2 Immediate addressing mode: specifying the operand in the instruction code

7.2.2 Specifying the Operand in a Register

The only addressing mode belonging to this class is the *register direct addressing mode*. By this addressing mode, the instruction specifies a register number in an address field and the content of the specified register is an operand, that is, the register number is a pointer that directly points to the operand in that register. This is the most frequently used addressing mode in a general-purpose register machine. In this mode, each address field of the instruction format needs only n bits for specifying a register operand from 2^n general-purpose registers. The register direct addressing mode is shown in Figure 7.3.

add	Rd	Rs1	Rs2

e.g., add Rd, Rs1, Rs2 ; Rd ← (Rs1) + (Rs2)

Figure 7.3 Register direct addressing mode: specifying the operand in a register

7.2.3 Specifying the Operand in Memory

Memory operands have the most advanced addressing modes because the global variables, especially large data arrays, in a high-level language program are assumed to be located in memory. In fact, many of the addressing modes for specifying operands in memory are designed to facilitate access of a data array in the successive iterations of a loop program.

1. Memory Direct Addressing Mode

The direct way of specifying a memory address is to specify it as an immediate number in the immediate field of the instruction format. This addressing mode of specifying a memory address in an instruction code is called the *memory direct addressing mode*. The problem with using this addressing mode is that the instruction length has a limited number of bits. This is not compatible with the fact that a full memory address in a contemporary computer can be very long, due to very large and scalable memory capacity. Using this addressing mode, we can specify only a short memory address. To extend this short address to a full address, we have several methods: (1) use it as an absolute address in a default memory area, for example, in the system area or in the area of memory-mapped I/O; (2) use it within a specific memory area specified by a base register; (3) assign a memory address through a label in a program code, such as a PC-relative address, since a label is associated with the program in which it appears. The memory direct addressing mode is shown in Figure 7.4.

2. Register Indirect or Register Deferred Addressing Mode

The simplest way to solve the problem of limited address length in the memory direct addressing mode is to specify the memory address in a register. This defines the *register indirect* or *register deferred addressing mode*, in which the register content is pointing to a memory location where the operand can be accessed. The general-purpose register is used in this mode as an address register. The advantage of using an address register is that a complete memory address can be assigned in a short address field of an instruction format. Thus, the address length is limited only by the word length. Another advantage of this addressing mode is its flexibility since the memory address in the address register can be modified easily in an instruction. This simple addressing mode can be used to develop more sophisticated addressing modes for efficient access of data arrays. The register indirect or deferred addressing mode is shown in Figure 7.5.

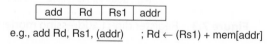

| add | Rd | Rs1 | addr |

e.g., add Rd, Rs1, (addr)   ; Rd ← (Rs1) + mem[addr]

Figure 7.4   Memory direct addressing mode: specifying the memory address in the instruction code

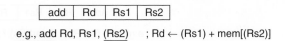

e.g., add Rd, Rs1, (Rs2)   ; Rd ← (Rs1) + mem[(Rs2)]

Figure 7.5 Register indirect or deferred addressing mode: specifying the memory address in a register

3. Memory Indirect or Memory Deferred Addressing Mode

Sometimes, we need to access a subroutine stored in a fixed memory area with its starting address stored in a jumping table in memory. If we specify the index of the corresponding jumping table entry in a register, then through this register we can access the memory location where the starting address of the subroutine is located, and through this memory location further enter the required subroutine. This multilevel indirect addressing is called *memory indirect* or *memory deferred addressing mode*. In principle, the number of levels of memory indirect addressing is not limited to two. We set an indirect bit in each intermediate level to "1" so that memory indirect addressing may continue any required number of times, until a level with an indirect bit equal to "0" is reached. The memory indirect or deferred addressing mode is shown in Figure 7.6.

4. Displacement Addressing Mode

We need to have an addressing mode to facilitate the writing of position-independent assembly-language programs, in which no absolute memory addresses are allowed. During the execution of a program in the environment

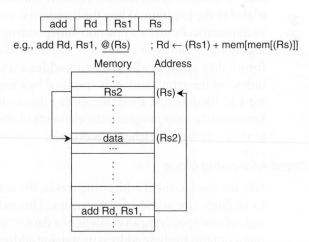

Figure 7.6 Memory indirect or deferred addressing mode: specifying the memory address in a register with multi-level indirect pointers

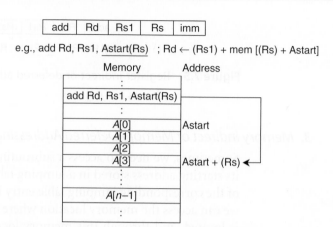

Figure 7.7 An example of the displacement addressing mode: specifying the memory address in a register plus a displacement in the *imm*

of a multitasking operating system, the executable image of the program has to migrate frequently in memory space and its absolute addresses should be assigned by the system. One method of writing a position-independent program is to specify all memory addresses relative to a starting position. An addressing mode satisfying this condition is the *displacement addressing mode,* in which the instruction format has an extra immediate field to specify a *displacement* value in addition to the regular address field for specifying an address register. Then, the effective address of a memory operand equals the sum of the displacement and the content of the address register. This displacement should be specified as a label in the program. When the program is assembled later by the system, it will be automatically given a position-independent value. The displacement addressing mode is shown in Figure 7.7. The second source operand, $A[i]$, is accessed from a data array, A, whose starting address is assigned by a label, *Astart*, and the index i of the array element is specified by a register, Rs, whose content equals $4i$ for a 32-bit data size. By incrementing the content of the register Rs by 4 in each iteration of a loop program, the elements of the data array, A, starting from $i = 0$ to $i = n - 1$, can be fetched successively.

5. Indexed Addressing Mode

Like the displacement addressing mode, the *indexed addressing mode* is designed to facilitate the access of data arrays. The indexed addressing mode uses two registers for specifying an element of a data array. One register, called the *base register,* contains the base address or starting address of the data array. The other register, called the *index register,* contains the index of the element of the data array, which is to be fetched. Adding the contents of these two registers will give the effective address for fetching the required element. During the execution of a

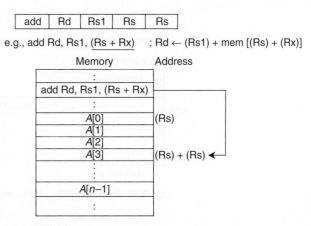

Figure 7.8 Indexed addressing mode: specifying a base address and an index value in two registers

loop program accessing successively the data elements of this array, an instruction within the loop should increment or decrement the content of the index register in each iteration. The indexed addressing mode is shown in Figure 7.8. Compared with Figure 7.7, the base register content (Rs) replaces the displacement.

6. Autoincrement and Autodecrement Addressing Modes

There are two addressing modes that are specially designed for stack operations with a stack implemented in memory. They are called the *autoincrement addressing mode* and the *autodecrement addressing mode*. A special register called the *stack pointer register* (SP) is specified in the address field of the instruction format. It contains the stack pointer, which is always pointing to the current top-of-stack location. The examples of using the autodecrement addressing mode and the autoincrement addressing mode for execution of the PUSH and POP operations respectively are as follows:

Autodecrement Addressing Mode	**Autoincrement Addressing Mode**
PUSH: store -(SP), Rs SP ← (SP) - d; mem[(SP)] ← (Rs); *where d is the data size in bytes*	POP: load Rd, (SP)+ Rd ← mem[(SP)]; SP ← (SP) + d; *where d is the data size in bytes*

These operations are depicted in Figure 7.9.

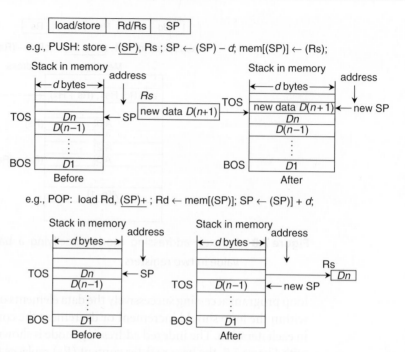

Figure 7.9 Autodecrement and autoincrement addressing modes: specifying a register, especially a stack-pointer register in the address field

7. Scaled Addressing Mode

By combining the displacement addressing mode and the index addressing mode, we can get a universal addressing mode, which is called the *scaled addressing mode*. It has three parameters to be specified: an immediate number, *imm*, used as the displacement for the position-independent code, and two registers, Rs and Rx, used for the indexed addressing mode. The effective memory address is

$$\text{effective memory address} = imm + (\text{Rs}) + (\text{Rx}) \cdot d \qquad (7.1)$$

where d is the operand length in bytes. Multiplying (Rx) by d means (Rx) can be simply incremented or decremented by "1" in each iteration by an instruction in the loop program, and the exact modified value of the index in each iteration will be taken care of automatically by the addressing mode. The scaled addressing mode is shown in Figure 7.10.

7.2.4 Specifying a Location Inside the Assembly-Language Program Code

The category of addressing mode belonging to this class is the *PC-relative addressing mode*. It is primarily used in branch and jump instructions. The destination

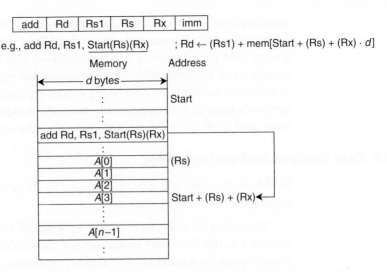

Figure 7.10 Scaled addressing mode: specifying the memory address in two registers plus a displacement in the *imm*

or target address for a branch or jump instruction is specified as a label inside an assembly-language program code. Each label is attached to an instruction so that its value equals the address of that instruction when the program code is loaded into memory. During assembly of the program, a label can be easily converted into an offset relative to the value of the program counter. Therefore, using this addressing mode, a destination address can be calculated pointing to a prespecified instruction for the purpose of branch control. The PC-relative addressing mode is shown in Figure 7.11.

Branch and jump instructions are examples of how to specify an addressing mode by implying it in the operation code of an instruction. Whenever we encounter a branch or jump instruction, we know that the addressing mode is automatically a PC-relative one. Another example is to imply the immediate addressing mode in the operation code "addi," where "i" means an add operation with one operand using the immediate addressing mode. There are two other methods of specifying the addressing modes. In one method, extra bits are

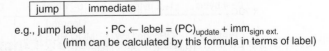

Figure 7.11 The PC-relative addressing mode: specifying the operand in a location inside the assembly-language program code

associated with each address field in the instruction format in order to specify its addressing mode. For example, the early PDP-11 minicomputer instruction used a 6-bit field for addressing each operand—3 bits of which specified a register number, and the remaining 3 bits specified one out of eight addressing modes. In the other method, the addressing modes are implied in the mnemonics of the operands used in writing assembly-language programs. These mnemonics have been used in all the above figures for writing the example instructions.

7.2.5 Case Study of Addressing Modes

In this section, we will give an example to show how the Pentium® computer implements addressing modes.

According to the classification scheme of the CPU structures stated in Section 7.1, the Pentium® computer is a two-address M-R machine based on a general-purpose register set. For a binary operation, one operand is always specified in a register, and the other operand can be fetched either from memory or from a register. To specify the address of the operand, which always comes from a register, we use the 3-bit REG (register) field in the above instruction format to select a register number among eight general-purpose registers according to Table 7.1. Another 1-bit flag, D (destination), in the instruction format specifies whether the REG is a destination (if D = 1) or a source (if D = 0). Since the Pentium® computer must satisfy the requirement of binary compatibility, it specifies registers of different sizes (8, 16, and 32 bits) by using a 1-bit flag, W (word), to distinguish between a 16-bit word (if W = 1) and an 8-bit byte (if W = 0), and also using the prefixes field which contains information about the *operand size override* and *address size override*, to switch between 16 bits and 32 bits.

Example 7.2   Case Study: The Pentium® Instruction Format and Addressing Modes

The Pentium® computer has a highly irregular instruction format due to the requirement of maintaining binary compatibility with the earlier members of the Pentium® family. Its basic CPU register set has remained unchanged since the 80386 microprocessor. The instruction format has a variable length from 1 to 16 bytes, divided into six fields, as shown in Figure 7.12.

0–4 bytes	1–2 bytes	0–1 byte	0–1 byte	0,1,2,4 bytes	0,1,2,4 bytes
Prefixes	OPcode D W Bits 6 1	Operand MOD REG R/M Bits 2 3	S I B Bits 2 3	Displacement	Immediate

Figure 7.12   Instruction format of the Pentium® computer

Table 7.1 Selecting the Intel 80x86/Pentium® CPU registers using the REG and W fields

REG	W = 0 (byte)	W = 1 (word)	32-bit Register	Remarks
000	AL	AX = AH AL	EAX	Accumulator
001	CL	CX = CH CL	ECX	Count register
010	DL	DX = DH DL	EDX	Data register
011	BL	BX = BH BL	EBX	Base register
100	AH	SP (address)	ESP	Stack pointer register
101	CH	BP (address)	EBP	Stack base pointer register
110	DH	SI (index)	ESI	Source index register
111	BH	DI (index)	EDI	Destination index register

Note: For some instructions, REG can be used to extend the Opcode information.

From Table 7.1, it can be seen that although the Pentium® computer is a general-purpose register machine, it still retains some similarity to the original Intel 8080 register structure. The special names given to the registers (e.g., 32-bit registers use prefix "E" to denote "extended") are of interest only for assembly-language programmers and compiler writers. For example, EAX (the accumulator) and EDX (the data register) are frequently involved with multiply-divide instructions and input/output data transfers. EBX (the base register) and ECX (the count register) can hold the base address of a data array and the count of iterations of a loop program, respectively. There are several groups of registers not specified by the REG field in Table 7.1. They include an instruction pointer, EIP (program counter PC); a status register, EFlags; eight 64-bit floating-point registers, FP0–FP7; six segment registers (one for the code segment, CS, one for the stack segment, SS, and four for data segments, DS, ES, FS, and GS); the registers for MMU (memory management unit); and newer MMX (multimedia extension) registers, MM0–MM7.

Now, we will look at how to specify another operand that can be either in memory or in a register. Various addressing modes can be specified by using the R/M (register/memory) field, the MOD (mode) field, the SIB (scale, index, base) fields, the displacement field, and the prefix field. The 3-bit R/M field and the 2-bit MOD field can specify $2^5 = 32$ combinations, as listed in Table 7.2. They cover all the different memory and register addressing modes we have specified in this section. In particular, when MOD = 01

Table 7.2   Pentium-II® addressing modes for an operand in either memory or a register

Access Mode		Displacement	Addressing Mode	Register Direct
R/M	MOD = 00	MOD = 01	MOD = 10	MOD = 11
000	(EAX) — register indirect	d8(EAX)	d16/d32(EAX)	EAX, AX, AL
001	(ECX) — register indirect	d8(ECX)	d16/d32(ECX)	ECX, CX, CL
010	(EDX) — register indirect	d8(EDX)	d16/d32(EDX)	EDX, DX, DL
011	(EBX) — register indirect	d8(EBX)	d16/d32(EBX)	EBX, BX, BL
100	SIB — scaled addressing mode	SIB with d8	SIB with d16/d32	ESP, SP, AH
101	memory direct addressing mode	d8(EBP)	d16/d32(EBP)	EBP, BP, CH
110	(ESI) — register indirect	d8(ESI)	d16/d32(ESI)	ESI, SI, DH
111	(EDI) — register indirect	d8(EDI)	d16/d32(EDI)	EDI, DI, BH

and 10, a register is added to a displacement of different sizes (sign-extended if necessary) to form an effective address. MOD = 11 gives a choice of registers of different sizes (32, 16, or 8 bits), depending on the W flag and the prefix information, in a similar way as specified in Table 7.1. When MOD = 00, the table is not entirely regular, and two exceptions are introduced to make room for the scaled addressing mode (if R/M = 100) and the memory direct addressing mode (if R/M = 101). Thus, indirect addressing through the registers EBP and ESP is excluded. Instead, we have the possibility of specifying the most flexible addressing mode—the scaled addressing mode—using the SIB field. To form an effective address, EA, calculated by Expression (7.1), the SIB byte specifies (1) a scale factor, $d = 1, 2,$ or 4, (2) an index register, Rx, (3) a base register, Rs, and (4) an 8-bit, 16-bit, or 32-bit displacement value from the displacement field. This addressing mode can most efficiently access an array element in a single instruction (see Figure 7.11). Almost all the registers can be used as either a base or an index. ∎

7.3   INSTRUCTION SET DESIGN

We have studied the instruction format and addressing modes of a computer. In this section, we will study another important issue of instruction set architecture—the instruction set design. The instruction set determines the functionality of a computer, so it is natural to say that the instruction set of a computer is application dependent since the ultimate goal of designing an instruction set is to satisfy the users' requirements. For a general-purpose computer, the basic operation repertoire of an instruction set is more or less standard and similar from machine to machine. A computer may require only a few specific instructions in order to satisfy the requirements of a particular application. Instruction set design is very complex, affecting many aspects of the computer design. Therefore, instruction set design is concentrated on factors concerning the general characteristics of a computer system. These factors are:

- *Programmer requirements.* Since the instruction set is the hardware-software interface for compiler writers and assembly-language programmers, programming convenience and efficiency must be considered when designing the instruction set.

- *Implementation technology.* Since the instruction set provides a basis for the hardware designers to implement the CPU and the control unit of a computer, the implementation technology must be considered in designing the instruction set. For example, pipelining is the prevailing technology for implementing high-performance processors; hence, the instruction set should be designed for facilitating a pipeline implementation.

- *Overall performance of the computer.* From the performance model introduced in Chapter 1, Expression (1.1), and Example 1.1, we know that the CPU execution time of a program is the real performance measure of a computer. This time, in turn, depends on the average time of execution of each type of instruction expressed as CPI_{ave} (average cycles per instruction) and the clock frequency. To optimize this performance, the most commonly used instruction types should be executed as fast as possible, while the most time-consuming (but least frequently used) instruction types should be removed from the instruction set and implemented by software. This is a problem of trade-offs between hardware and software that computer architects constantly face when designing an instruction set.

- *Backward compatibility in the computer family.* This is actually a constraint rather than a favorable factor in designing the instruction set. The Pentium® family is a typical example. The restriction of backward compatibility has made its instruction set design very difficult and complex.

The operations of an instruction set are encoded in binary, forming an Opcode field. For simplicity of designing the control unit, the Opcode bits are assigned to the operations in groups. Each group contains the same type of operations that require the same or similar control signals and, therefore, are assigned successive binary codes with as many common bits as possible. The basic operations that are similar from machine to machine can be approximately divided into the following categories.

7.3.1 Data Movement Instructions

Data can be located either in memory or in a register, and it can also be immediate data specified in the instruction code. Therefore, data movement instructions are divided into subgroups. Moving data between two registers is called COPY or DUPLICATE or simply MOVE, since the source register still keeps the original data unaltered. Moving immediate data into a register is called COPYI (copy immediate). With a three-address instruction format, these instructions may be unnecessary because they can be replaced by ADD or ADDI (add immediate) instructions provided that the general-purpose register set can have a register (usually R0) defined as constant zero and use it as one of the source registers. However, all computers must have instructions to move data between memory and the CPU registers. These instructions are called LOAD and STORE in general-purpose register machines, LDA (load accumulator) and STA (store accumulator) in accumulator-based machines, and PUSH (load stack) and POP (store stack) in stack machines. Immediate data cannot be a destination, but it can be stored in memory through a register. These memory-related data movement instructions have significant importance in the instruction set design because of the large variety of memory addressing modes and data types involved. Two methods can be used to include information about data types in the instruction format. One method uses individual bits as flags to distinguish among different data types. For example, the W flag in the Pentium® instruction format distinguishes between a word (W = 1) and a byte (W = 0). Another method uses different Opcodes with different LOAD/STORE instructions handling different data types. For example, we may have different LOAD/STORE instructions such as LB/SB (load/store byte), LH/SH (load/store half word), LW/SW (load/store word), and LD/SD (load/store double word).

Implementation of the load/store instructions to access memory operands of different data sizes must solve two problems: the memory byte ordering problem and the memory alignment problem. Both problems are caused by a memory organization that uses byte addressing (i.e., gives each byte a distinct address), but accesses 1, 2, 4 or 8 bytes at a time. The ordering of bytes of a 16-bit half word, a 32-bit word, or a 64-bit double word in successive memory locations is a problem. As shown in Figure 7.13, there are two possible choices of byte ordering in a 32-bit memory. The *big-endian memory* allocates the MSB of a 32-bit word at the *byte address..xx00*. The *little-endian memory* allocates the LSB of a 32-bit word at the *byte address..xx00*. Both memories use the address..xx00 to represent the memory address of the entire 32-bit word. When accessing a single byte, using the address ..xx00, the big-endian scheme will address the leftmost byte (MSB) of the word and the little-endian scheme will address the rightmost byte (LSB) of the word. In practice, IBM systems, Motorola 680x0, Sun SPARC®, and most RISC machines are big-endian machines, whereas the Intel 80x86, Pentium®, and VAX are little-endian machines. The lack of a standard for byte ordering may cause a problem when data is exchanged between the two different groups of machines.

The memory alignment problem concerns how to address a multibyte memory object. If we must keep the right boundary and use an address with

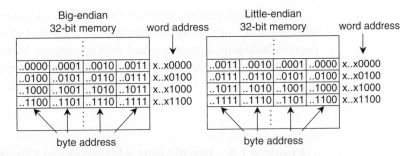

Figure 7.13 Big-endian memory vs. little-endian memory

the two LSBs equal to "00" to access a 32-bit word, the access is called *aligned*. Otherwise, if a word can be accessed using any address from ..xx00 to ..xx11, the access is called *misaligned*. Similarly, the aligned access of a 16-bit half word must use a memory address ..xxx0, and the aligned access of a 64-bit double word must use a memory address ..x000. Memory is typically aligned in order to limit the access of any memory object of single word length in a single memory reference. Violation of the aligned access of a memory object will cause an address error.

Before applying load/store instructions to different data types, we have to solve another data alignment problem. Alignment of bytes or half words in a register may require different treatments depending on the instruction. A LOAD instruction may require loading a byte or a half word into the least significant byte or half word, with the upper portion of the register unaltered (for characters), or sign-extended (for arithmetic data), or zero-extended (for logic data). If the instruction requires loading the data into different portions of the register as specified by the instruction code, it may need the hardware support of an alignment network. The STORE instructions, on the other hand, are simpler because they affect only the addressed bytes in memory.

7.3.2 Arithmetic-Logic Instructions

Most computers provide basic arithmetic instructions, such as ADD, SUB (subtract), MUL (multiply), and DIV (divide) on integers. These operations can have many variants. For example, the operands can be signed or unsigned, can be floating-point numbers (for scientific calculations), or can even be decimal numbers (for business data processing). ADD and SUB can have immediate options denoted as ADDI and SUBI, respectively, with the immediate data sign-extended to necessary data size. To facilitate double-precision arithmetic calculation, ADDC and SUBC (add/subtract with carry/borrow) may be found necessary, and MULT and DIV may need to keep a double-precision product and a remainder, respectively. A unary operation NEG (negate) may be useful for inverting the sign of an operand; however, a reverse subtract operation may replace it.

Most computers also provide a variety of logic instructions that manipulate individual bits of operands. Operations performed by this category of instructions include logic operations and shift operations. Various shift operations have been studied in Section 5.5. Logic operations will be explained in greater detail in this section. Operands of logic operations are logic variables represented as

---

Example 7.3　Use of Logic Instructions in a Program

Write an assembly-language program in a fictitious three-address instruction format for a bit-pattern search problem. Assume an arbitrary bit string of 32 bits in the register R1 and a shorter bit pattern in the five LSBs of the register R2 with all the remaining 27 bits equal to "0". The program should search the entire bit string in R1 and find all the substrings that match the given bit pattern in R2. The result should be stored in register R3, recording the starting bit numbers of these matching substrings. Each time a matching substring starting from bit #i to bit #$(i-4)$ in R1 is found, bit #i of the result register R3 should be set to "1", where $4 \leq i \leq 31$, increasing from right to left. For example, (R1) = …110111011011 contains (R2) = 11011 at $i = 4$, 7, 11, …, and the result in R3 should be …100010010000.

A short program for this example is written as follows:

```
          ADDI  R3, R0, #0     ; initialize R3 to 0 for storing the future
                                 result
          ADDI  R4, R0, #31    ; initialize mask1 = 00...011111 in R4
          ADDI  R5, R0, #16    ; initialize mask2 = 00...010000 in R5
    LOOP: AND   R6, R1, R4     ; (R1) AND (R4) to extract a 5-bit portion
                                 of R1 in R6
          XOR   R6, R6, R2     ; (R6) ⊕ (R2) to test if (R6) = (R2). If
                                 match, (R6) = 00...0
          BNEZ  R6, SKIP       ; If no match, skip to continue
          OR    R3, R3, R5     ; else, (R3) OR (R5) to set the starting bit#
                                 to "1" in R3
    SKIP: SLI   R4, R4, #1     ; logic shift mask1 in R4 left on bit
          SLI   R2, R2, #1     ; logic shift the bit pattern in R2 left
                                 one bit
          SLI   R5, R5, #1     ; logic shift mask2 in R5 left on bit
          BNEZ  R5, LOOP       ; loop if mask2 ≠ 0
          EXIT                 ; else exit
```

bit strings; therefore, logic operations are *bitwise operations*, that is, all the bits perform the same logic operation independently of one another. An instruction set should provide, at least, a minimum set of basic logic operations, such that any logic relationship can be expressed in terms of these basic logic operations. This property is called the *logic completeness* of logic operations. For example, {AND, OR, NOT}, {NAND}, {NOR}, {XOR, AND}, and {XOR, OR} are all the minimum sets that satisfy the requirement of logic completeness. Because AND and OR are used frequently in programs that manipulate bits, they should be included directly as basic logic operations in the instruction set. Thus, either NOT or XOR can be selected as the third logic operation to make the set of logic operations logically complete. XOR is obviously a better choice than NOT because it is more useful than the NOT operation. Since logic instructions are often used with immediate operands, separate immediate logic instructions ANDI, ORI, and XORI can be included in the instruction set.

The program in Example 7.3 uses AND, OR, and XOR instructions. With a *mask* as the second operand, the AND operation is used for extracting a portion of the first operand at the position where the corresponding bits of the mask equal "1". The AND operation also clears the remaining bits of the first operand to "0" at the position where the corresponding bits of the mask equal "0". The XOR operation is used for comparing two operands to test for their equality. If the two operands are identical, all the bits of the result must be "0". With a mask as the second operand, the OR operation is used for setting the bits of the first operand to "1" at the position where the corresponding bits of the mask equal "1". Therefore, some computers have the *BitTest* and *BitClear* instructions implemented with an AND operation, the *BitSet* instruction implemented with an OR operation, and the *BitEqual* instruction implemented with an XOR operation.

7.3.3 Control Instructions

Control instructions implement the high-level language constructs "if…then… else," "while…do," "case," and "goto" at the assembly-language level. They are further divided into two sub-categories: BRANCH and JUMP. Conditional branch instructions implement the decision-making statements associated with certain conditions, which are generated either by normal arithmetic instructions as *condition codes* (e.g., N, V, Z, and C stated in Section 3.4.2) or by COMPARE instructions specially designed for being used jointly with branch instructions. Therefore, COMPARE instructions are also classified in the category of control instructions. Two implementations of COMPARE are possible: either as a separate instruction from the BRANCH instruction to implement various conditional operators, such as ≥, >, ≤. <. =, and ≠, or as a joint instruction "COMPARE & BRANCH" which generates a conditional operator and uses it immediately to branch in a single instruction. The former implementation is more flexible and faster in execution, but some means must be taken to ensure that the branch condition is not overwritten by any intervening instructions before it is used by a later branch instruction. The latter implementation can be used without worrying about the branch condition being overwritten, but the execution of the joint instruction may take longer. An example of the separate COMPARE instruction is the Sxx instruction, which means "Set with the condition xx," where "xx" denotes GE (≥ 0), GT (>0), LE (≤ 0), LT ($<$), EQ ($=0$) or NE ($\neq 0$). A specified destination register is set to "1" if the condition of the comparison is true, and reset to "0" if otherwise. An example of the joint COMPARE & BRANCH instruction is the Bxx instruction, which means "Branch if xx," where xx has the same meaning as in the Sxx instruction.

If the BRANCH instruction has a condition which is always TRUE, this is equivalent to a JUMP instruction. The difference is that BRANCH usually uses the PC-relative addressing mode, whereas JUMP can use the memory direct addressing mode. Besides these two instructions, the JUMP instructions include many other variants for transferring program control, namely TRAP, CALL, J&L (Jump & Link), RFS (return from subroutine), RETURN, JR (Jump register), as well as the unconditional BRANCH. The TRAP instruction is used as a *system call* to the operating system or during a software interrupt for transferring control to an *interrupt service routine*. The TRAP instruction first saves the process context, including the program counter (PC) and the status register (SR) into the system stack, and then transfers to a system routine through a parameter (usually an index to a jumping table) specified in the TRAP instruction format. When the system routine is finished, it will execute a RFS instruction to access the saved context from the stack and return the control to the user program. This bidirectional process is therefore called context switching. A similar process can be written in an assembly-language program to call a subroutine by a CALL instruction (with a label pointing to the subroutine as the parameter) and return to the main program by a RETURN instruction, both through the processor stack. However, a stack is not the only way context switching can be implemented. In a RISC computer, in order to avoid time-consuming stack operations unsuitable for a pipeline organization, context switching is usually executed through a general-purpose, fixed register. The corresponding instructions are, thus, called the Jump & Link (saving the return address in a link register before jumping) and Jump Register (jumping by taking the return address from the link register).

The Pentium® computer has a special subset of instructions that perform vector operations in a single instruction stream, multiple data stream (SIMD) fashion. A single instruction stream can perform the same sequence of operations on multiple data elements in parallel. In particular, the Pentium® MMX (Multi-Media Extension) instructions focus on enhancing the performance of multimedia programs that process video and audio images. These instructions are designed for the parallel processing of large data arrays of *packed data types*. Each packed data operand is composed of either 8 bytes (B) or four 16-bit words (W)

Example 7.4 Case Study: The Pentium® Instruction Types

A Pentium® computer has a complex instruction set with a large variety of instruction types. Examples of integer instruction types are listed as follows:

- **Data Movement.** Move (MOV) or exchange (XCHG) data between registers or between register and memory, PUSH/POP, load effective address (LEA), conditional move (CMOV).
- **Arithmetic.** ADD, SUB, add with carry (ADC), subtract with borrow (SBB), add "1" (INC), subtract "1" (DEC), negate (NEG), unsigned/signed multiply (MUL/IMUL) with double-length result, unsigned/signed divide (DIV/IDIV) double-length dividend by single-length divisor.
- **Boolean.** AND, OR, XOR, NOT, bit test, and set (BTS) which copies a bit operand to flag and sets the original bit to "1", bit scan forward (BSF) which scans an operand for a "1" bit and stores the number of the first "1" bit into a register.
- **Shift.** Logic shift left/right (SHL/SHR), arithmetic shift left/right (SAL/SAR), rotate left/right (ROL/ROR), rotate left/right through carry (RCL/RCR).
- **Test/Compare.** Test (TST), which AND two operands and sets flags; compare (CMP), which sets flags based on SRC1–SRC2; SETcc, which sets a byte to "0" or "1" depending on any of 16 conditions, cc, defined by status flags.

[Note: The Pentium® status bits: C (carry), P (parity), Z (zero), S (sign), and O (overflow).]

cc = A (above) or NBE (not below or equal): $\overline{C} \cdot \overline{Z}$	(unsigned >)	
cc = AE (above or equal) or NB (not below) or NC (not carry): $\overline{Z}$	(unsigned ≥)	
cc = B (below) or NAE (not above or equal) or C (carry): C	(unsigned <)	
cc = BE (below or equal) or NA (not above): $C+Z$	(unsigned ≤)	
cc = E (equal) or Z (zero): Z	(unsigned or signed =)	
cc = G (greater than) or NLE (not less than or equal): $(S \cdot O + \overline{S} \cdot \overline{O})\overline{Z}$	(signed >)	
cc = GE (greater than or equal) or NL (not less than): $S \cdot O + \overline{S} \cdot \overline{O}$	(signed ≥)	
cc = L (less than) or NGE (not greater than or equal): $S \cdot \overline{O} + \overline{S} \cdot O$	(signed <)	

CC = LE (less than or equal) or NG (not greater than): $(S \cdot \overline{O} + \overline{S} \cdot O) + Z$ (signed $\leq$)

CC = NE (not equal) or NZ (not zero): $\overline{Z}$ (unsigned or signed $\neq$)

CC = NO (no overflow): $\overline{O}$ (no overflow)

CC = NS (not sign): $\overline{S}$ (not negative)

CC = NP (not parity) or PO (parity odd): $\overline{P}$ (parity odd)

CC = O (overflow): O (overflow)

CC = P (parity): P (parity even)

CC = S (sign): S (negative)

- **Transfer of control.** Jump (JMP), conditional jump (Jxx) based on flags, CALL, return from procedure (RET), return from interrupt (iRET), initiate a software interrupt (INT), interrupt if overflow (INTO), loop until condition met (LOOPxx).
- **Binary-coded decimal.** Decimal adjust (DAA), decimal adjust for subtraction (DAS), ASCII adjust for addition (AAA), ASCII adjust for subtraction (AAS), ASCII adjust for multiplication (AAM), ASCII adjust for division (AAD).
- **Strings.** Load string (LODS), store string (STOS), move string (MOVS), compare two strings (CMPS), scan strings (SCAS).
- **Condition codes in the EFLAGS register.** Set/clear/complement carry bit (STC/CLC/CMC), set/clear direction bit (STD/CLD), set/clear interrupt bit (STI/CLI), push/pop EFLAGS register (PUSHFD/POPFD), load/store AH register from/in EFLAGS register (LAHF/SAHF). ∎

or two 32-bit double words (D). To support these data types by hardware, the CPU is equipped with eight extended data registers, MM0–MM7, each 64 bits wide. All the MMX instructions are preceded by the prefix "P" to indicate their 64-bit parallel operations. For example, the PADDB (parallel add byte) instruction performs parallel additions of two packed byte operands, with each byte position processed independently, to produce a packed byte result. In this way, the MMX instructions can yield a speedup of two to eight times over regular instructions. There are two methods of treating the overflow. The traditional method is to use the so-called *wraparound arithmetic* by truncating the carry-out of the MSB as usual. However, this method will produce a result smaller than the two input operands, which is not the expected result from processing two image intensities. To correct this result, a new method has been introduced using *saturation arithmetic*, which sets the result of the overflow to the largest value or the result of underflow to the smallest value. The PADD instruction corresponding to this new method, which generates results closer to reality, is denoted as PADDS (parallel add with saturation).

7.4 REDUCED INSTRUCTION SET COMPUTERS (RISC)

Traditionally, large computer systems such as the IBM mainframes and the DEC VAX super minicomputers developed in the 1970s were classified in the category of complex instruction set computers (CISC), whose design goal was to close the "semantic gap" between machine instructions and high-level programming languages. The original attempt of designing a complex instruction set for a computer was to provide effective support for increasingly powerful high-level languages and, thus, simplify the task of writing compilers. In the extreme case, researchers even tried to develop high-level language processors that could directly execute the high-level language programs. This resulted in a general-purpose computer, which had a complex instruction set with the following features:

- a long variable instruction length,
- a large repertoire of machine instructions,
- a complete set of addressing modes to support various data structures in memory, and
- a relatively small size general-purpose register set.

The implementation of such a complex instruction set relies heavily on the microprogrammed control. A typical example of a CISC machine was the DEC VAX11/780 developed in 1978, which had a variable instruction size of 2–57 bytes, an instruction set of 303 operations, a maximum of six memory operands per instruction (e.g., adding two decimal strings to obtain a result string required six operands, each having a length and a starting address), 22 addressing modes, and only 16 general-purpose registers. Toward the end of the 1970s, a new trend of designing reduced instruction set computers (RISC) appeared. Researchers began to view CISC designs differently. Although the complex instruction set could generate an assembly-language program with fewer instructions, the actual program size in bytes was larger. Some instructions specially designed for compiler writers were used so infrequently that their long execution time was not justified. Based on this research, the new design philosophy of RISC was proposed as follows:

- *A single fixed instruction size, normally of 4 bytes, with a regular instruction format for all types of instructions.* This requirement is critical for a short instruction decoding time, which improves the start-up rate of the instruction stream entering the pipeline. It is the instruction issuing rate, rather than the instruction execution time, that determines the actual execution time of a program in a pipelined organization.

- *A limited number of addressing modes for accessing operands (which are mostly from registers and seldom from memory)*. This requirement maximally utilizes the general-purpose register set for all the operands of all the arithmetic-logic instructions. Therefore, arithmetic-logic instructions use only the register direct and immediate addressing modes, branch instructions use only the PC-relative addressing mode, and only load/store instructions use the few available memory addressing modes. No memory indirect addressing mode is allowed since it requires an unlimited number of memory references in a single instruction.

- *Load/store architecture*. Only load-store instructions access memory for the data operands. There exist the following requirements on memory addressing: (1) no more than one memory operand per instruction, (2) memory access must be aligned, (3) the maximum number of uses of the memory management unit (MMU) for a data address in an instruction equals "1", and (4) although a load/store instruction needs an arithmetic operation to calculate the effective address, no instruction should combine load/store with an arithmetic-logic operation for data, that is, no memory operand is allowed in an arithmetic-logic instruction.

- A large number of general-purpose registers (at least 32) or floating-point registers (at least 16) can be explicitly addressed in an instruction.

- *Pipelined implementation by hardwired control*. All the above-stated requirements serve the purpose of facilitating the exploitation of instruction-level parallelism in terms of an efficient pipeline organization. At the same time, all the instructions are controlled by hardwired logic. Microprogrammed control is no longer desired.

- *An intelligent compiler*. The pipeline scheduling needs the support of an intelligent compiler for detection of data and control dependencies in the program. The final goal is to exploit the parallelism implied at different levels (the instruction level, the loop level, and the processor level) of the program to optimize its execution on a multi-issue superscalar processor.

The RISC design philosophy summarized above has been widely accepted and applied by computer architects in designing new processor chips. The two design philosophies, CISC and RISC, are now being merged so that each can take advantage of the other in order to achieve maximum performance. New CISC designs are now focused on issues traditionally associated with the RISC, for example, the increased use of a large general-purpose register set and emphasis on the instruction pipeline design. New RISC machines are now becoming more complex to better utilize increased chip density, faster clocks, and faster hardware. However, quite a few "pure" RISC machines still exist that satisfy all the above-stated conditions of RISC design philosophy. Two representative systems are the SPARC® (Scalable Processor Architecture) machines and the MIPS R-series.

The SPARC® architecture was originally inspired by the Berkeley RISC I machine and implemented by Sun Microsystems in 1987 as a SPARC® machine. As with the Berkeley RISC, the common feature of the SPARC® machines is the unusually large size of the general-purpose register set and its windowing organization. It consists of 136 physical general-purpose registers, eight of which are shared by all procedures to store global variables, and the remaining 128 registers are organized into eight overlapping windows. The window layout is shown in Figure 7.14. Each window consists of 24 logical registers, divided into three portions, each eight registers wide. The middle portion, denoted as "Locals," is dedicated to a procedure to store its local variables. Another portion denoted as "Outs" is used by the same procedure to store temporary variables shared with any child procedure it may call. The third portion denoted as "Ins" is shared with the parent procedure which called the current procedure. Through these two shared portions, the parameters can be passed between the parent and child procedures simply by switching the current window pointer (CWP) to a new active procedure without the actual movement of data. This saves the time which would otherwise be required to perform context switching through a stack.

At any given time, only the active window, with 32 registers indicated as r0–r31 in Figure 7.14, is visible and addressable, as if it was the only set of registers in the processor. Therefore, each address field for a register operand in the SPARC® instruction format uses only 5 bits. The entire register set of 136 registers is organized as a circular buffer of overlapping windows. However, to handle any possible pattern of program nesting, the number of register windows would have to be unbounded. Instead, the number of nested procedures that can use the eight windows of the buffer at the same time is limited to seven. In case this limit is exceeded, older activations must be saved in memory and restored later when the nesting depth decreases. Because of this situation, the SAVE and RESTORE instructions must be included in the instruction set.

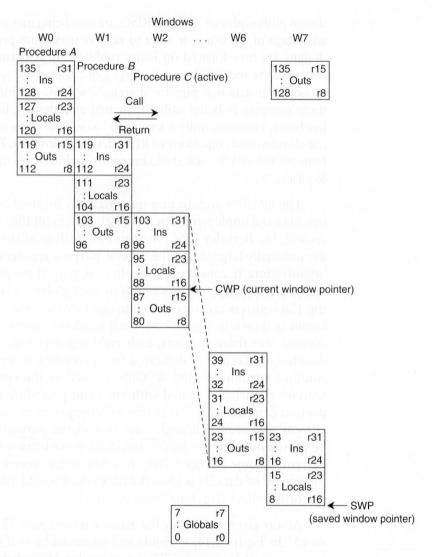

Figure 7.14 The SPARC® register window layout

Example 7.5   Case Study: The SPARC® Instruction Set

- **Load/Store.** Load signed/unsigned byte (LDSB/LDUB), load signed/ unsigned half word (LDSH/LDUH), load word/double word(LD/LDD), store byte/half word/word/double word (STB/STH/STD/STDD).
- **Shift.** Shift left/right logic (SLL/SRL), shift right arithmetic (SRA).
- **Boolean.** AND, nand (ANDN), OR, nor (ORN), XOR, XNOR; same operations, set *icc* (ANDCC/ANDNCC/ORCC/ORNCC/XORCC/XNORCC).

- **Arithmetic.** ADD/SUB, set *icc* (ADDCC/SUBCC), with carry (ADDX/SUBX), with carry, set *icc* (ADDXCC), multiply step, set *icc* (MULSCC).
- **Jump/Branch.** Branch on condition/floating point condition/coprocessor condition (BCC/FBCC/CBCC), trap on condition (TCC), return from trap (RETT), CALL, jump and link (JMPL), advance register window (SAVE), move windows backward (RESTORE).
  ■

The MIPS R-series was originally inspired by an experimental system, also called MIPS, developed at Stanford University, and implemented as R-2000, R-3000, R-4000 (1991), and R-10000 (1996). Starting from R-4000, the processor had internal and external datapaths and addresses of 64 bits. As a result, the processor supports a 32×64-bit general-purpose register set and 2×64-Kbyte split caches for instructions and data. This enables the processor to avoid the windowing organization of a large register set. The RISC design allows the processor chip to accommodate a separate coprocessor for memory management.

Example 7.6   Case Study: The MIPS R-Series Instruction Set

- **Load/Store.** Load signed/unsigned byte (LB/LBU), load signed/unsigned half word (LH/LUH), load word/word left/word right (LW/LWL/LWR), store byte/half word/word/word left/word right (SB/SH/SW/SWL/SWR).
- **ALU immediate.** ADDI, unsigned (ADDIU), set on less than immediate/unsigned (SLTI/SLTIU, ANDI), ORI, XORI, load upper immediate (LUI).
- **ALU functions.** ADD, unsigned (ADDU), SUB, unsigned (SUBU), set on less than/unsigned (SLT/SLTU), AND, OR, XOR, NOR.
- **Shift.** Shift left/right logical (SLL/SRL), shift right arithmetic (SRA), same operations, variable (SLLV/SRLV/SRAV).
- **Multiply/Divide.** MULT, unsigned (MULTU), DIV, unsigned (DIVU), move from/to HI (MFHI/MTHI), move from/to LO (MFLO/MTLO).
- **Jump/Branch.** Jump (J), jump and link (JAL), jump to register (JR), Jump and link register (JALR), branch on equal/not equal (BEQ/BNE), branch on $\leq, >, <, \geq$ (BLEZ/BGTZ/BLTZ/BGEZ), branch on $<, \geq$ and link (BLTZAL/BGEZAL).
- **Coprocessor instructions.**
- **Special.** System call (SYSCALL), break (BREAK).
  ■

SUMMARY

In Chapter 1, the computer design process was viewed as a multilayered structure (see Figure 1.2), the first level of which is the instruction set architecture. In this chapter, the instruction format is the first topic of the instruction set architecture that is studied in Section 7.1. Different instruction formats allow different number of addresses to be explicitly specified for their operands. According to this category, we can distinguish among four machine organizations: three- or two-address R-R machine, three- or two-address R-M machine, one-address accumulator-based machine, and zero-address stack machine. The next topic of the instruction set architecture is the addressing modes that deserve detailed discussion with a practical example in Section 7.2. Instruction set design is the third topic discussed in Section 7.3, also accompanied with two examples. Finally, RISC computers versus the CISC computers is discussed in Section 7.4. The current tendency of development is that the two design philosophies are now being merged together so that each can take advantage of the other in order to achieve maximum performance.

EXERCISES

7.1 Assume that R1, R2, and R3 contain the following values:

$(R1) = \$00000100$; $ denotes hexadecimal representation

$(R2) = \$00008124$

$(R3) = \$1234FF78,$

The memory locations contain the following values:

mem[$00008520] = $00678210

mem[$00008224] = $00082386

and that label *ALPHA* has the following value:

ALPHA   00001000

For each of the following instructions (executed separately), specify the addressing mode used, write the expression for effective address *EA* in register transfer language, calculate it, and give the result of operation. (If the address is pointing to a register, give the 32-bit contents of the register; if it is pointing to a memory location, plot the corresponding memory map.)

(a) ADDI R4, R3, #$80FE   ; add immediate: add (Rs1) and *imm* to Rd

(b) BNEZ R3, ALPHA-36   ; branch not equal to zero: if (Rs) ≠ 0, branch

(c) ADD R4, R0, R3   ; add (Rs1) and (Rs2) to Rd

(d) NOT $100(R2)   ; NOT the content of a register or a memory location

(e) CLEAR -4(R1) ; clear a register or a memory location to zero

(f) LOAD R4, -4(R2)(R1) ; load the content of a memory location to Rd;

(g) SUB R4, (R2+R1), R3 ; subtract: subtract (Rs2) from (Rs1) to Rd

(h) STORE (R1)+, R3 ; store (Rs) into a memory location

(i) LOAD R3, -(R3) ; load the content of a memory location to Rd

7.2 Given the following data before execution of instruction, for each of the indicated instructions (executed separately), write the expressions for the effective addresses of the source and destination operands (if applicable) in register transfer language, calculate them, and give the resulting 32-bit contents of registers R2 and R3 (if changed) and the contents of affected memory locations after execution.

Address	Contents
001018	$00000007
00101A	$00000006
00101C	$FFFFFFFD
00101E	$000001A3
001020	$0000000E
(R2) = $00000001
(R3) = $0000101A
LOOP = 001018

(a) ADD   R4, -2(R3,R2), R2

(b) MOVE   R4, (R3)+

(c) MOVE   -(R3), 6(R3)

(d) SUB   R4, (R3), #$101A

(e) MOVE   ($101C), R3

(f) BNEZ   R2, LOOP

[Note: The order of specifying operands in the instructions is from left to right, destination, source 1, and source 2 (if any).]

7.3 Write an instruction or a shortest sequence of instructions with proper addressing modes on a 32-bit stack machine to perform each of the following independent operations:

(a) Push the data $00008764 onto the stack.

(b) Duplicate the 32-bit contents of the locations at the top of the stack.

(c) Exchange the 32-bit contents of the two top-of-stack locations.

(d) Push the element $A[15]$ of a 32-bit data array $A[0..127]$ onto the stack, assuming that the starting address of the array A in memory is given by the label *Astart*.

(e) Based on the same assumption as in Part (a), move through the 32-bit CPU stack the given data array $A[0..127]$ to a distinct memory area with the starting address specified as *Bstart*.

7.4 Given two binary signed numbers in two's complement representation:

$A = 01001001 \quad B = 10111010$

and two labels with addresses

$ALPHA = \$00010000 \quad$ and $\quad BETA = \$0000F068$

for locating A and B in memory, respectively. Write an instruction or a shortest sequence of instructions with proper addressing modes for performing each of the following independent activities. Also describe the operation of each instruction in register transfer language.

(a) Move number A to register R1.

(b) Move address *ALPHA* to register R1.

(c) Move number B to memory location whose address is in register R1.

(d) Make a copy of number B from memory location pointed to by (R1) to memory location whose address is *BETA*.

(e) Redo Part (d) by addressing destination through register R1 based on the displacement between addresses *ALPHA* and *BETA*.

(f) Add number A in register R1 to number B in memory with address in register R2.

(g) Subtract number A in register R1 from number B in memory with address *BETA*.

(h) Push number A in register R1 onto the stack (using stack pointer register SP).

[Note: Make your own assumption about the type of instructions, e.g., M-M or M-R.]

7.5 Among the four logic operations AND, OR, XOR, and NOT, it is necessary to include only two in the instruction set because we can choose two out of four to generate the rest.

(a) If we choose only "A AND B" and "A XOR B" as the Opcodes, we may use the following sequence of three-address instructions (in register transfer language) to generate (R5) = A OR B, where A = (R1), B = (R2):

```
R3 ← (R1) XOR (R2)
R4 ← (R1) AND (R2)
R5 ← (R3) XOR (R4)
```

Prove that this instruction sequence actually performs an OR operation.

(b) Write similar instruction(s) to perform a NOT operation using only AND and/or XOR Opcodes.

(c) Try to implement AND and NOT operations using only OR and XOR operation codes.

7.6 Rewrite the following three-address program in one-address format:

```
ADD  U, X, Y   ;  U ← (X) + (Y)
SUB  V, X, Y   ;  V ← (X) - (Y)
DIV  Z, U, V   ;  Z ← (U)/(V)
```

[Note: U, V, and Z are memory addresses. Limit seven one-address instructions.]

7.7 Given a function

$$G = \frac{A + B \times C}{D - E \times F}$$

where A, B, C, D, E, and F are operands initially stored in memory, and G is the result to be calculated and stored in memory after calculation.

Compare 3-, 2-, 1-, and 0-address instruction formats by writing programs to compute X for each of the four machines. The instructions available for use are given in Table 7.3.

Table 7.3 Instructions available for use in Problem 7.7

Three-Address	Two-Address	One-Address	Zero-Address
MOV X,Y (X←Y)	MOV X,Y(X←Y)	LDA M	LOAD M
LOAD Rx,Mx (Rx←Mx)	LOAD Rx, Mx	STA M	STORE M
STORE Mx,Rx (Mx←Rx)	STORE Mx, Rx	CLR M	POP
ADD X,Y,Z(X←Y+Z)	ADD X,Y(X←X+Y)	ADD M	ADD
SUB X,Y,Z(X←Y-Z)	SUB X,Y(X←X-Y)	SUB M	SUB
MUL X,Y,Z(X←Y*Z)	MUL X,Y(X←X*Y)	MUL M	MUL
DIV X,Y,Z(X←Y/Z)	DIV X,Y (X←X/Y)	DIV M	DIV
			DUP
			SWAP

where M and Mx are 16-bit memory address, Rx is a 4-bit register number, and X, Y, and Z are either 16-bit addresses or 4-bit register numbers. However, when they are used in the register transfer language, they denote the contents of the memory locations or registers. The 0-address machine uses a stack, the one-address machine uses an accumulator, and the other two have 16 registers and instructions operating on all combinations of memory locations and registers. Assuming 8-bit Opcodes and instruction lengths that are multiples of 4-bits, how many bits does each machine need to compute G?

7.8 Given the high-level-language assignment statement as follows, where the variables A, B, C, and D are initially in memory:

$$D = \frac{(A^2 + B - C) \times (A^2 - B + C)}{B^2 - C^2}$$

(a) Write the best equivalent assembly-language code for this expression on four different instruction set architectures as given below:

   (i) *Accumulator.* All operations occur between the accumulator and a memory location.

   (ii) *Memory-memory.* All three operands of each instruction are in memory.

   (iii) *Stack.* All operations occur on top of the stack. Only PUSH and POP access memory and all other instructions remove their operands from stack and replace them with the result. The implementation uses a stack for the top two entries; accesses that use other stack positions are memory references.

   (iv) *Load-store.* All operations occur in registers, and register-to-register instructions have three operands per instruction. There are 16 general-purpose registers, and register specifiers are 4-bits long.

(b) For the purpose of comparing the memory efficiency, calculate the instruction bytes fetched and the memory-data bytes transferred for each architecture under the following assumptions:

   ■ The Opcode is always 1 byte.

   ■ All memory addresses are 2 bytes.

   ■ All data operands are 4 bytes.

   ■ All instructions are an integral number of bytes.

   ■ There are no other optimizations to reduce memory traffic.

(c) Which architecture is most efficient as measured by code size? Which architecture is most efficient as measured by total memory bandwidth required (code + data)?

7.9 Suppose a memory system uses aligned big-endian addressing (see Section 7.3.1) to access 32-bit words, 16-bit half words, or 8-bit bytes. The following word contents are found in consecutive locations of memory:

Address	Contents
00101A	F0CE
00101C	3BAB
?	07FC
?	B760
?	2FB3

(a) Fill in the missing addresses.

(b) What is the value of the 32-bit word at address 00101C?

(c) What are the byte contents at address 001021?

(d) At which byte addresses can the hexadecimal digit "B" be found?

(e) What are the contents of the MSB of the 32-bit word at address 001020?

(f) List all 32-bit words that contain the hexadecimal digit "0".

8

The Central Processing Unit

8.1 THE FUNCTIONS AND FUNCTIONAL PARTS OF A CPU

Simply speaking, a CPU is the processing center of a computer. As seen in Figure 5.1, the CPU is one of the three major functional blocks of the von Neumann computer model. The other two functional blocks are main memory and I/O. When a program is running on a computer, its executable image and data are stored in the main memory. The computer uses an I/O subsystem to communicate with the outside world, for example, input of data and printing results. All processing functions in the execution of a program at the instruction level are placed in the ALU. In addition to the concept of a stored-program computer, another important concept derived from the von Neumann computer architecture is a *sequential single-sequence computer*. At any given time, a sequential single-sequence computer runs a single sequential program, including the running of multiple programs on a uniprocessor in the same time period, but in a time-sharing or time-interleaved fashion. From the viewpoint of control, running a program in the CPU involves a single instruction stream sequentially executing a single sequence of basic instruction cycles. Each *basic instruction cycle* or so-called *fetch-execute cycle* executes an instruction through a number of steps, such as instruction fetch, instruction decode, data fetch, operation execute, result storage, and next instruction identification. The ALU repeats such basic instruction cycles while executing a program, one instruction after another, until the final result is obtained.

As shown in Figure 5.1, the four functional parts of a CPU are the ALU, the registers, the internal bus, and the control unit. The first three parts can be combined into a single part called the *datapath*. When a program is executed in the CPU, data is transferred along the datapath and processed by various components, such as registers, the ALU, and other functional units, as specified by the program. This is a description of computer organization at the register transfer level. At this level, globally speaking, the CPU consists of two parts: the datapath and the control unit. We view the control unit as part of the CPU because of the following considerations. As a computer system grows larger, its configuration can change, and a large variety of configurations are possible. Consequently, a global centralized control unit is not suitable for controlling a complicated computer system. Instead, distributed control can better meet the different control needs of various functional blocks of a computer. Since the major function of instruction-level control is concentrated in the CPU, a control unit is explicitly shown in its block diagram, while the control units of memory and the I/O subsystem are not shown explicitly, with the understanding that their control is implied. Therefore, the block diagram of the stored-program computer in Figure 5.1 is redrawn in Figure 8.1.

In this chapter, we will study various organizational schemes of a CPU. Each scheme will correspond to a different instruction set architecture. Then, we will study the functional parts of the CPU, including the internal bus and the general-purpose register set. Based on these components, we will be able to construct block diagrams for several organizational schemes of the CPU. Finally, examples of practical CPUs will be given. The other functional part of the CPU, that is, the control unit, will be studied in the next chapter.

8.2 BASIC ORGANIZATION OF THE CPU

From the discussion in the last chapter, we see that different instruction formats require different organizations for the CPU; the organization of the CPU, in turn, serves as a basis for classifying the computer into different classes. Globally speaking, the three-address and the two-address instruction formats create general-purpose register machines, the one-address instruction format creates accumulator-based machines, and the zero-address instruction format creates stack machines. We will discuss the basic organization of the CPU using this classification scheme.

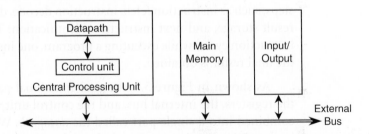

Figure 8.1 Block diagram of a stored-program computer

8.2.1 CPU Organization Based on General-Purpose Registers

A general-purpose register machine makes extensive use of general-purpose register sets for arithmetic (integer and floating-point) operations, logic operations, addressing as well as control (e.g., in program branching and stack-related operations). The general-purpose register machines can be further divided into two types: complex instruction set computers (CISC) and reduced instruction set computers (RISC). The former provides a large variety of addressing modes for accessing operands so that memory-memory or memory-register operations are allowed for most of the instructions. The latter allows only load/store instructions with a limited variety of memory addressing modes, and all the remaining instructions must be of the register-register type. While the CISC machine may have increased capability and flexibility in assembly language programming, its complex control logic makes CPU performance inferior to that of the RISC machine. Furthermore, since the RISC instruction set has a shorter instruction cycle, it makes the implementation of an instruction pipeline easier and more efficient. The effective use of multiple instruction pipelines in superscalar processors of the RISC style is an innovative technique widely applied in CPU organization.

The functionality of a basic instruction cycle for a generic instruction depends on the architecture of the CPU. For the traditional *memory-memory* and *memory-register* architectures, the source and the destination operands for a binary arithmetic-logic operation of an instruction can be specified in addressing modes that need to access memory. The basic instruction cycle for the memory-memory architecture can be stated as follows:

- fetching the instruction,
- decoding the instruction,
- generating the effective memory addresses of the operands corresponding to their addressing modes,
- fetching the source operands from memory or registers,
- executing the operation,
- storing the result into memory or a register according to the addressing mode, and
- identifying the next instruction to be fetched.

For the contemporary *register-register* architecture, only load/store instructions can access memory for data. The arithmetic-logic instructions can access data only from/to the general-purpose register set for both the source operands and the destination result. This is the operating principle of a *load/store architecture*, which is normally used to characterize the architecture of RISC machines.

Therefore, a general basic instruction cycle for the register-register architecture can be stated to include the following steps:

- fetching the instruction,
- decoding the instruction,
- generating the effective address of the memory operand (only for load/store instructions),
- fetching the source operands from registers (from memory only for a load instruction),
- executing the operation,
- storing the result into a register (into memory only for a store instruction),
- identifying the next instruction to be fetched.

To run a program means to repeat the basic instruction cycles (depending on the architecture) some number of times (depending on the running program), thus enabling the computer to execute programs of any length and complexity. It is this essential simplicity that makes a computer so flexible, general-purpose, and powerful.

8.2.2 CPU Organization Based on an Accumulator

In a *one-address instruction format*, the number of explicit addresses is further reduced to one source operand. The other source address and destination address are implicit. It is sufficient to specify just one source address in the instruction format, with another source operand and destination operand both referring to a special-purpose register called an accumulator. Because there is no general-purpose register set in the CPU, the instruction usually specifies an absolute memory address in its address field, corresponding to the memory direct addressing mode. Due to the limited length of an instruction, an explicit address should not be very large. To perform a binary operation, the instruction always takes one operand from the accumulator, performs the operation with the operand from memory, and stores the result back in the accumulator. Consequently, the one-address instruction format requires that the CPU organization be based on an accumulator. A computer with this CPU organization is called an *accumulator-based machine*. Besides the accumulator, the CPU of an accumulator-based machine usually needs a small number of other special-purpose registers, each being dedicated to a special task in the instruction execution. For example, an index register may be used to implement an indexed addressing mode, a stack-pointer register to manage the processor stack, and so on. To manage these special-purpose registers, the instruction set must have corresponding instructions to load/store values from/to memory, to increment/decrement the index values or stack pointers, and so on. The use of special-purpose registers minimizes the instruction length, but diminishes flexibility. A pure accumulator-based CPU organization is simple, but it lacks generality and relies too much on memory operands, which seriously degrades the CPU performance. Therefore, it is used only in low-end microprocessors. The performance of an accumulator-based machine can be improved by adding a small set of general-purpose registers or making use of some special-purpose registers as general-purpose ones in some instructions. This is a mixed CPU organization that allows operands to be fetched either from memory or directly from explicitly specified registers, thus reducing memory references. Some upgraded models of microprocessors take this approach.

The basic instruction cycle for a binary operation in the accumulator-based architecture can be stated to include the following steps:

- fetching the instruction,
- decoding the instruction,
- generating the effective memory addresses of the specified operand corresponding to its addressing mode,
- fetching the specified source operand from memory,
- executing the operation on the operand in the accumulator and the operand from memory,
- keeping the result in the accumulator, and
- identifying the next instruction to be fetched.

8.2.3 CPU Organization Based on a Processor Stack

In the *zero-address instruction format*, the two source addresses and one destination address required by a binary operation all point to a processor stack, so no address must be explicitly specified in the instruction. All addresses are fixed and implicit, except in a few instructions, which need to exchange data between memory and the processor stack. The implementation requires that the CPU organization has the processor stack managed with a set of special-purpose registers. A computer using this CPU organization is called a *stack machine*. Of the special-purpose registers, the most important one is the *stack-pointer register* that always points to the current *top-of-stack location* of the processor stack. According to the contents of the stack-pointer register, any binary operation pops out two operands from the two successive top-of-stack locations, operates on them, and pushes the result into the new top-of-stack location. Only two instructions—PUSH and POP—need to explicitly specify a memory address, and it normally uses a *relative* addressing mode (relative to the stack-frame pointer). However, since the large-capacity processor stack is implemented in memory, with only a few top-of-stack locations implemented in the CPU registers, the management of the stack creates just as much memory traffic as an accumulator-based machine.

The stack machine was originally designed to support the structure of high-level languages such as Algol-60 and provide a multiprogramming and multitasking environment. As a result, management of the processor stack for program nesting, recursion, context switching, and so on, can be very complicated. This has led, in turn, to a large number of special-purpose registers and a complicated CPU organization for a stack machine. The newest example of the stack machine is the Java Virtual Machine (JVM) [for details, please see Tanenbaum (1999)].

From the above discussion, it can be seen that using implicit addresses in the instruction format reduces the number of addresses that must be explicitly specified in an instruction and therefore, provides efficient utilization of instruction bits. However, it lacks the flexibility of assigning registers to different types of operations. On the other hand, using more explicit addresses in the instruction format requires more instruction bits for the operands, but provides more flexibility in usage. The compromise between code compactness and generality of programming is a general problem. Therefore, many design schemes are possible. For the CISC design, the CPU organization can support variable instruction formats. They use variable-length instruction formats that can accommodate a variable number of address fields to satisfy the requirements of different types of operations. For the RISC design, all instructions have the same length and a standard format, so that all binary ALU operations use three register-address fields, and only load/store instructions can access data in memory.

8.3 STRUCTURE OF A CPU BASED ON AN ACCUMULATOR

As we have stated above, the accumulator-based CPU matches the one-address instruction format. For brevity of analysis, we assume that the one-address instruction format contains an operation code field and a memory address field. A binary arithmetic or logic operation operates on two operands—one already residing in the accumulator and the other fetched from memory. After the operation, the result remains in the accumulator, available for the next instruction. Therefore, the CPU has the simplest possible structure, consisting of an ALU (usually with a shifter attached to its output), a special-purpose register called an *accumulator*, and several other special-purpose registers. Variety in CPU organization derives mainly from the large variety of available registers. In an accumulator-based CPU organization, the following special-purpose registers other than the accumulator may be found useful:

- **Status register**. Used by the ALU to store the status bits as a result of execution of an instruction. Among the most useful status bits are sign, zero, carry/borrow, overflow, and so on. A status register may contain other information used by the operating system, for example, mode bits and priority bits; therefore, it can usually be managed only by privileged instructions.

- **Intermediate register**. Used implicitly for complex arithmetic operations such as multiplication, division, and floating-point operations. This register may be accessed in different ways, either by machine instructions or by microinstructions. The intermediate result or operand stored in this register, like the results in other programmable registers, may need to be loaded, stored, or operated on. There could be other intermediate registers used for other purposes, such as for temporary data and count.

- **Stack-pointer register**. Used by the processor stack for subroutine calling/returning and interrupt handling. The register contains a running stack pointer that is updated each time a push or pop operation is performed on the stack. This updating could be done automatically by hardware during interrupt or by special instructions such as subroutine call, return from subroutine, push, and pop.

- **Index register**. Used by the indexed addressing mode. Since the index value should be updated each time it is used, we need special instructions that can explicitly specify the index register as an operand. Load, store, increment, and decrement index register are examples of possible instructions.

- **Base register**. Used for memory management purpose. It contains the base address of a memory segment such that the effective address can be calculated once a relative address is given by the instruction. If different segments are used for the program code, data, stack, and so on, there could be several base registers. Usually, base registers are managed by the operating system for implementation of position-independent code and memory protection.

In addition to these user-visible or instruction-accessible registers (except the base register), there are some registers that are used by the control unit for the purpose of controlling the basic instruction cycles. For example:

- **Program counter (PC)**. Used to store the address of the next instruction to be fetched.

- **Instruction register (IR)**. Used to store the current instruction being executed.

- **Memory address register (MAR)**. Used to store the address of a memory location to be referenced.

- **Memory buffer register (MBR)**. Used to store the information read from or written to memory.

The accumulator and registers should be provided with a datapath, which establishes interconnections among the registers, ALU, control unit, and memory, so that the contents of the registers can be loaded, stored, transferred, and processed. We can build the datapath for different interconnection schemes based on an internal bus, an ALU, or a multiplexer, resulting in different structures of implementation, as illustrated in the following sections.

8.3.1 Design of an Accumulator-based CPU Built on a Single Bus

A general block diagram of an accumulator-based CPU consisting of the ALU, registers, and a bus is shown in Figure 8.2. In general, different bus structures can be used to build the datapath for an accumulator-based CPU. The bus can be composed of a data bus, an address bus, and a control bus, or it can be a unified bus combining different types of information. One-bus, two-bus, and three-bus systems are possible. In Figure 8.2, we have a one-bus datapath that contains registers, including the registers associated with the control and main memory, as follows:

A	n-bit accumulator, providing one of the source operands and holding the result,
SR	status register, storing various statuses,
Q	n-bit intermediate register, used for complex arithmetic operations,
X	m-bit index register, storing the index value for the indexed addressing mode,
SP	m-bit stack-pointer register, pointing to the top-of-stack location of the stack in memory,
PC	m-bit program counter, pointing to the next instruction to be fetched,
IR	n-bit instruction register, storing the current instruction being executed,
MAR	m-bit memory address register, storing the memory address during read/write operations,
MBR	n-bit memory buffer register, storing the information read from or written to memory,

where n is the word length and m is the address length.

All these registers are interconnected via an internal bus. The basic property of the bus originates from its alternative names: *shared bus* or *common bus*. All the registers must have exclusive access to the bus, that is, only one register can complete the connection of its data output onto the bus at any given time. Therefore, all the connections of the data outputs to the bus are implemented through *tri-state devices*. The graphical symbols of tri-state devices are shown in Figure 8.3. A tri-state device is similar to an ordinary driver. However, a distinctive property of a tri-state device is added by its extra control input. The control input can be active high or active low. In the case of active-high control input,

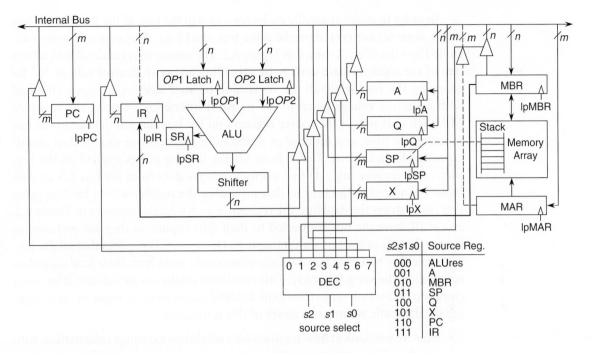

Figure 8.2 Block diagram of a one-bus accumulator-based CPU

Notes: (1) A bold line indicates a dedicated path isolated from the shared datapath.
(2) A dashed line indicates an unused connection removable from the datapath.

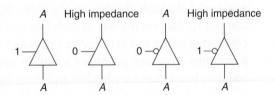

Figure 8.3 Tri-state devices and their functions

when the control voltage equals "1", the tri-state device acts just like an ordinary driver, which passes any binary input, A, to its output. When the control voltage equals "0", the device is *open-circuited*, presenting a *high impedance* at its output. Hence, the output appears to be disconnected from the bus, independent of the value of the input A. For the case of an active-low control input, its action is just the opposite. Control value "0" lets the input signal, A, pass the tri-state device. Control value "1" blocks the tri-state device and generates high impedance on its output. We use a bubble attached to the control input to distinguish the active-low tri-state device from its active-high counterpart.

In order to assure mutually exclusive access to the bus, all the tri-state devices in the same set connected on the same bus must have their control inputs controlled by a decoder, as shown in Figure 8.2. The source select code, $s2s1s0$, selects one of the eight tri-state devices by providing an active control voltage "1" for accessing the bus, while all the remaining tri-state devices are open-circuited with a control voltage equal to "0" to avoid interference among the registers. Although only one of the source registers on the bus can put data onto the bus at any given time, any number of destination registers can receive data simultaneously from the bus. This is done via the loading pulses applied on the registers. Any register (e.g., A) that wants to receive data from the bus has its data input connected to the bus, so that providing the register with a loading pulse (e.g., lpA) stores the data into the register (e.g., A). All the registers in Figure 8.2, except IR, have the bus connected to their data inputs, so they are prepared to receive data from the bus simultaneously. However, this requires that all the registers needing to access bus data simultaneously must have their loading pulses active all in the same bus cycle. This condition might not be fulfilled if we use a common demultiplexer to distribute loading pulses to these registers. In designing the datapath, we must be aware of this restriction.

Now we will look at how registers on a single bus exchange information with one another. For a binary operation to be executed by the ALU, two registers that provide the source operands, $OP1$ and $OP2$, must send their data through the bus to the $OP1$ latch and $OP2$ latch, respectively, in two separate bus cycles. In each bus cycle, only one operand can be put on the bus. After the operation, the result (through a shifter on the output of the ALU) can be sent back to any register(s) through the bus in the third bus cycle. Although only one register can put its data on the bus in each bus cycle, multiple registers with their inputs connected to the bus can receive this data from the bus at the same time. Hence, a one-bus structure performs a binary operation very inefficiently because it requires two temporary latches and three bus transactions.

Furthermore, to fetch an instruction from main memory and update the program counter immediately, the following three bus transactions may be necessary:

- In the first bus cycle, the program counter (PC) puts the address of the instruction to be fetched onto the bus, and the memory address register (MAR) receives this address from the bus by its loading pulse, lpMAR. At the same time, the $OP1$ latch receives the same address from the bus by its loading pulse, lp$OP1$, in order to use it for updating the program counter in the next bus cycle.

- The address from the MAR is automatically sent to the memory array through a dedicated path. When a READ command is applied to memory, the instruction in that addressed location will be read from memory to the memory buffer register, MBR. This memory operation can be done without using the bus. Therefore, a bus cycle can be initiated concurrently to update the program counter using the ALU, and the ALU will put the updated PC value back onto the bus so that it can be received by the program counter using its loading pulse, lpPC.

- After the newly fetched instruction enters the memory buffer register (MBR) it is sent from there to the instruction register (IR) through the bus during the third bus cycle. If there is a dedicated path between the output of MBR and the input of IR, this bus cycle can be omitted.

It should be noted that the bus configuration of the datapath depends on the instruction set to be implemented. To design a specific bus specification fitting a given instruction set, we should analyze all the cases of information transfer among registers when different instructions in the instruction set are executing their basic instruction cycles on the bus. The entire instruction set may exercise many different cases of bus usage in the execution of basic instruction cycles. This would require that the datapath designer have complete knowledge of the execution procedures of all the instructions under the control of the control unit. We will learn about this in the next chapter on the design of the control unit. In this chapter, we give a few examples of analyzing the information flow in the datapath shown in Figure 8.2. For example, the MAR needs to receive the address from the IR (address part of an instruction), the ALU, and the MBR, during the following addressing modes:

- **Memory direct addressing mode**. The address field of the instruction in the IR may contain a direct memory address, and it should be sent to the MAR for fetching an operand from memory.

- **Indexed addressing mode**. The ALU may need to calculate the effective memory address by adding the contents of the indexed register, X, to the formal address specified in the instruction. This effective address should be sent from the ALU to the MAR to fetch/store the data from/to memory during the execution of, for example, a CPU/load instruction.[1]

- **PC-relative addressing mode**. For writing position-independent assembly-language programs, this addressing mode requires that the effective address be generated by adding an offset to the updated PC value to be used as the destination address for a taken branch instruction. This effective address needs to be also calculated by the ALU, as is done in the indexed addressing mode.

- **Memory indirect addressing mode**. The address specified in the instruction may not be the memory address of the data, but the memory address

---

[1] This definition of indexed addressing mode for the accumulator-based machine is different from that defined in Section 7.2.3

of a location that contains a pointer pointing to another memory location. After accessing this pointer from memory, the address is in the MBR and should be sent back to the MAR for accessing the memory again. This process may repeat if the addressing mode has multiple levels of indirection.

However, does any other register require that the address information be sent out from the MAR? Probably not; the address in the MAR may be used only by the memory array, so we need to keep only the direct path from the MAR to the memory array and remove the tri-state devices that connect the MAR to the shared bus. Another example of the analysis of the datapath is related to the IR. It contains the instruction code being executed by the CPU, so its address information in the address field may be needed by the MAR (in memory indirect addressing mode) and the ALU (in indexed addressing mode), and its immediate data in the address field may be needed by many registers, such as the accumulator, A, the index register, X, the stack-pointer register, SP, and others. However, when we examine the input path to the IR, the only source seems to be the instruction from the MBR after it has been fetched from memory. Therefore, we could establish a dedicated path from the MBR to the IR, so that we can save one bus cycle in the instruction fetch procedure.

A general strategy concerning dedicated paths versus shared paths can be formulated as follows. A shared bus can most efficiently replace $k(k-1)$ dedicated paths originating from k registers, but with the loss of speed of information exchange due to the serialization of bus transactions. It excludes the possibility of any parallel point-to-point message transmissions. If one of these $k(k-1)$ paths has a very high frequency of usage, it could be replaced by a dedicated path working in parallel with the bus to reduce traffic. If most of the paths originating from a register have very low (or even zero) frequency of usage, then that register could be removed from the group that uses the bus to share information, and the paths used by it can be replaced by dedicated ones. Since the accumulator and the latches of the ALU are the most frequently used registers in an accumulator-based CPU, the bus configuration should be designed around them. Most of the paths between other registers could be arranged to go via the ALU, thus transforming dedicated paths into shared ones and thus saving hardware. There is inherently a compromise between cost and speed.

Examples corresponding to the above-stated strategy can be found in Figure 8.2. Since every instruction must be fetched from memory and sent to the IR through the MBR, the route from MBR to IR is the most frequently used path. It may be more advantageous to replace it with a dedicated path than to use a bus cycle to fetch every instruction. Hence, we designed it as a dedicated path. Analysis of the message patterns shows that the memory array is the only destination of addresses sent from the MAR, so the shared path from the MAR to the bus may not be useful and can thus be removed.

8.3.2   Design of a Two-Bus or Three-Bus Accumulator-based CPU

Connecting all of the registers to a single bus is an extreme case that makes the bus very busy and excludes any possibility of parallel operations. All transfer and processing operations must be done sequentially. In designing a control unit, it is desirable to allow some operations to be performed in parallel if they are given distinct paths for transferring information. This method has been stated earlier, when we established a dedicated path between the MBR and IR in the one-bus datapath in Figure 8.2. Another method to allow parallel operations on the bus requires building parallel buses that will allow bus transactions to be executed in parallel. This is the basis for two-bus and three-bus systems.

The one-bus datapath of the accumulator-based CPU in Figure 8.2 can be modified into a two-bus datapath as shown in Figure 8.4 (with the loading pulses and the decoder controlling the tri-state devices omitted). From the previous description of the procedure for performing a binary operation on a single bus, we know that three bus cycles are necessary and must be implemented sequentially. To alleviate this limitation, we may divide the single bus into Bus1 and Bus2 and let the two operands be directly fed from the two buses. This makes the two input operands available at the same time and allows the ALU operation to be performed immediately without storing them in the two input latches. These two input latches can thus be omitted. However, since both buses are busy, no bus cycle is available for storing the ALU result into a destination register. The ALU result must be stored in a temporary output latch through a dedicated path. In the next bus cycle, the ALU result can be moved from the output latch into the desired destination register. This modification of the datapath changes the procedure of a binary operation from using three bus cycles to using two bus cycles, and, at the same time, reduces the number of latches from two to one.

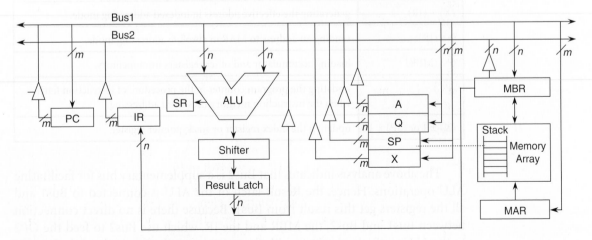

Figure 8.4   Block diagram of a two-bus accumulator-based CPU

Another problem we face while designing a two-bus accumulator-based CPU is how to reasonably distribute the registers onto the two buses. Theoretically speaking, all the registers can have their outputs connected to both buses so that any two registers can be paired to perform any operation on the ALU. Although this is the most flexible bus configuration, it wastes hardware, because the number of tri-state devices and the size of the decoders needed to control them will be doubled. The control of these decoders will also be unnecessarily complicated. Therefore, reasonable allocation of registers on the two buses becomes a necessary step of CPU design. This requires an analysis of the instruction set to find all the cases of bus usage and ALU operations, and then reasonably distribute their operands onto the two buses. Preliminary analysis of the required operations between registers results in the following distribution scheme, which is implemented in Figure 8.4.

On Bus1:	A, PC, Q, Result latch, X, SP
On Bus2:	MBR, IR

All registers, except the *OP2* input of the ALU, receive information from Bus1.

Operations:	
(A) op (MBR)	where op is the arithmetic-logic operation specified by a register-register ALU instruction.
(A) op (IR)	where op is the arithmetic-logic operation specified by a register-immediate ALU instruction ("immediate" means the immediate data specified in the address field of the instruction code).
(X) + (IR)	generating the effective address in indexed addressing mode.
0 + (IR)	sending an address to MAR in absolute addressing mode.
0 + (MBR)	loading accumulator and other registers from memory.
(PC) + 1	updating the program counter in the procedure of instruction fetch when the instruction memory uses word addressing.
(X) $\pm$ 1 or (SP) $\pm$ 1	updating the index register or stack-pointer register.

The above analysis indicates that Bus2 is a supplementary bus for facilitating ALU operations. Hence, the Result latch of the ALU is connected to Bus1 and all the registers get this result from Bus1. Because there is no direct connection between Bus1 and Bus2, the MBR and the IR, which use Bus2 to feed the *OP2* to the ALU, can communicate with the registers on Bus1 only through the ALU

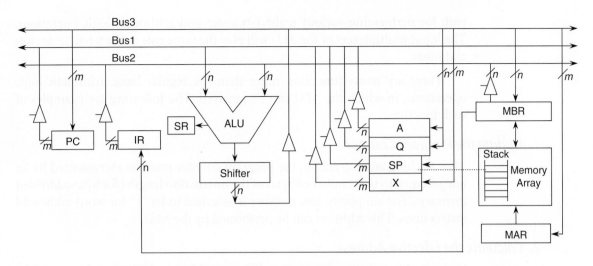

Figure 8.5 Block diagram of a three-bus accumulator-based CPU

operations (MBR) + 0 and (IR) + 0, respectively. This appears to be a waste of time, because each transfer operation requires two bus cycles. A further improvement of the speed of ALU operations including the transfer across two buses is possible by introducing a third bus in the datapath, thus obtaining the three-bus accumulator-based CPU as shown in Figure 8.5.

The four differences between the two-bus system in Figure 8.4 and the three-bus system in Figure 8.5 are as follows:

- the additional bus, Bus3,
- the removal of the Result latch from the ALU,
- the connection of the ALU output to Bus3 through the shifter, and
- the change of all registers' input connections to Bus3.

All the remaining connections remain unchanged. Although all the supported transfer and ALU operations appear to be the same as in a two-bus configuration, each has an execution time of one bus cycle.

8.3.3 Design of an Accumulator-based CPU Built on an ALU

This section presents a design for an accumulator-based CPU built on an ALU. In the datapath of the three-bus accumulator-based CPU derived above, because all the three buses have no direct connections among themselves, all the transfer and ALU operations must be performed through the ALU. Hence, the ALU becomes the center of the CPU datapath. This motivates an alternative approach to structuring the CPU that involves transferring all or part of the datapath from internal buses into the ALU and then using the ALU as the common connecting path for performing various register-transfer and arithmetic-logic operations. The input multiplexers of the ALU will play the same role as the tri-state devices and buses.

There are many functions, other than the regular basic arithmetic-logic operations, in which the ALU can be involved. The following are examples of such functions:

1. Update the Program Counter

After fetching an instruction, the program counter must be incremented by an integer equal to the number of bytes of the instruction length (for byte-addressed memory). For simplicity, this number is assumed to be "1" for word-addressed instructions. This addition can be performed by the ALU.

2. Calculate the Effective Address

Various addressing modes require different address calculations. For example, the index value in the index register needs to be added to the formal address in the address field of the instruction. The contents of the index register should be incremented or decremented in each iteration of the program. As in the above example, we assume that the index is updated by "1" each time. The ALU can be used for this purpose.

3. Perform Special Control Functions

The stack pointer register must be updated during the push and pop operations (This register is also incremented/decremented by one each time under the same assumption as above). Other registers can be used for handling the intermediate results or loop control in performing multiplication or division at the hardware or microprogram level. The ALU can be used for these functions.

4. Provide a Common Datapath for Communication between Registers

Providing a common, shared datapath between different registers is more economical than establishing a dedicated path between every pair of registers. Many registers can be connected to the input and output of the ALU for data transfer operations.

These considerations provide the background for using an ALU to build the datapaths in a CPU. As an example, Table 8.1 shows how the operands on the inputs of $OP1$ and $OP2$ of the ALU can be chosen. It results in the design in which (1) the value zero and the registers A, Q, X, SP, and PC are multiplexed to the input $OP1$ of the ALU and (2) the value zero, the registers MBR, IR, and constant 00...01 are multiplexed to the input $OP2$ of the ALU. The result from the ALU, after passing through the shifter, can be loaded into any register(s) or not loaded at all. The implementation of this design, which replaces an internal bus by multiplexers, is shown in Figure 8.6. A decoder working as a demultiplexer is used to select the register, which should be loaded with the output of the shifter. Many select codes are specified in the figure, namely $f_2 f_1 f_0$ for ALU function select, $h_2 h_1$ for shifter select, $u1_2 u1_1 u1_0$ for operand1 select, $u2_2 u2_1 u2_0$ for operand2 select, and $d_2 d_1 d_0$ for destination select. Together they form the fields of a control word or a microinstruction, in accordance with the design of the control unit. The details of the microinstruction format and microprogrammed control will be discussed in Chapter 9.

It should be noted that the design of a CPU depends on many factors, particularly the ALU and the control unit. For example, if the ALU includes increment and decrement operations in its function set, the constant operand $00\ldots01$ to the $OP2$-multiplexer in Figure 8.6 may be removed. Also, the incremented or decremented constant value could be "4" if the instruction size or data size equals 4 bytes and the memory is designed as byte-addressing. The operand of value "0" can be sent to the ALU by simply disabling its input multiplexer, thus optimizing the size of the multiplexer. In case multiple registers should receive the ALU/shifter result at the same time, their loading pulses should not be distributed by a demultiplexer. All the control select codes in the CPU should be organized as a control word in order to be managed by the control unit.

Table 8.1 Truth table for designing the datapaths of a simple CPU

Operations	OP1	OP2	Destination	Explanation
Arithmetic-logic	A	MBR	A	operand1 in A, operand2 from memory
Instruction fetch	PC	0	MAR	send the address in PC to MAR
	PC	00..1	PC	update PC by "1"
	0	MBR	IR	send the instruction in MBR to IR
Address generation	X	IR	MAR	add index in X to formal address in IR
Update index	X	00..1	X	increment or decrement index by "1"
Data load	0	MBR	A, X, ...	load registers A, X, SP, Q, ... from memory
Data store	A, X, Q	0	MBR	store registers A, X, Q, ... into memory
Stack push or pop	SP	00..1	SP	increment or decrement stack-pointer by "1"
Other operations	Q	?	?	reserved for operations on the Q register

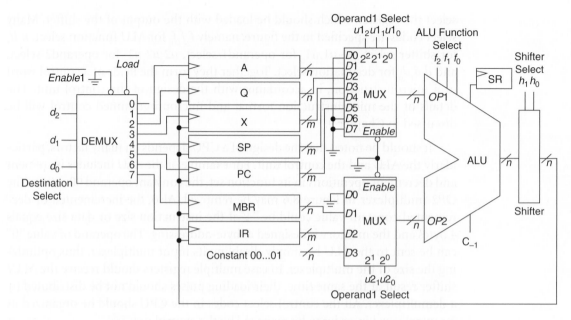

Figure 8.6 Block diagram of an accumulator-based CPU built on an ALU

8.4 STRUCTURE OF A CPU BASED ON GENERAL-PURPOSE REGISTERS

The organization of an accumulator-based CPU can be easily transformed into a CPU structure based on general-purpose registers. The registers A, Q, X, and SP, are implemented as general-purpose registers, and they are collectively called the *general-purpose register set*. Historically, in the early design of minicomputers, the general-purpose registers included the PC for facilitating *PC-relative* addressing mode. If the SP or PC is implemented as a general-purpose register, it is usually assigned a fixed register number in the register set. In this section, we will look at the structure of the general-purpose register set. Then, we will design the datapath of the CPU according to the requirement of the register-register architecture for implementation of its basic instruction cycles.

8.4.1 Structure of a General-Purpose Register Set

Two interconnection schemes can be used to construct a general-purpose register set. One scheme is based on internal buses. The other scheme is based on multiplexers. These design choices are similar to those for the two possible structures for the accumulator-based CPU, based either on a three-bus configuration (*see* Figure 8.5) or on two sets of input multiplexers to the CPU (*see* Figure 8.6), respectively.

The general-purpose register set has several parameters in its specification: the word length, the number of registers in the set, the number of read ports, the number of write ports, and other special features of the set. A typical register set for a general-purpose computer may have the following parameters:

- 32-bit word length.
- 32 integer registers in the set.
- All registers, except register 0, share two read ports and one write port.
- Register 0 contains an implied constant value "0", so it is read-only.

Block diagrams of the small general-purpose register sets based either on internal buses or on multiplexers are shown in Figure 8.7 and Figure 8.8, respectively. Without loss of generality, assume that each register set has eight registers, numbered from 0 to 7, where $R0$ is read-only, always containing a constant zero. When used in a three-address register-register computer, the register set should have two read ports and one write port. In the three-address instruction format, two source addresses are specified as $s1_2 s1_1 s1_0$ for the source operand 1 and $s2_2 s2_1 s2_0$ for the source operand 2, while the destination address is specified as $d_2 d_1 d_0$. These addresses are the actual register numbers. In Figure 8.7, the two source registers numbered $s1_2 s1_1 s1_0$ and $s2_2 s2_1 s2_0$ are selected by the decoders that control two sets of tri-state devices, and the contents are output on the two output buses, Bus 1 and Bus 2, respectively. In Figure 8.8, the multiplexers are controlled by the source register numbers $s1_2 s1_1 s1_0$ and $s2_2 s2_1 s2_0$ and output the contents of the two registers, R_{src1} and R_{src2}, respectively. In both figures, the

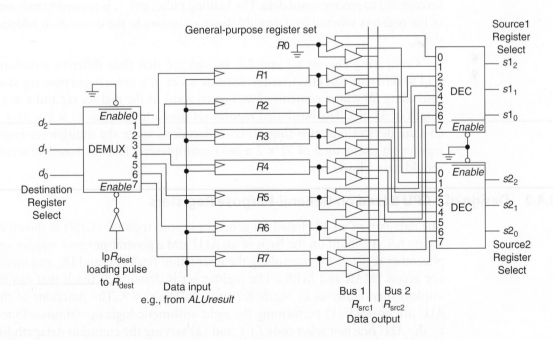

Figure 8.7   Block diagram of a general-purpose register set based on internal buses

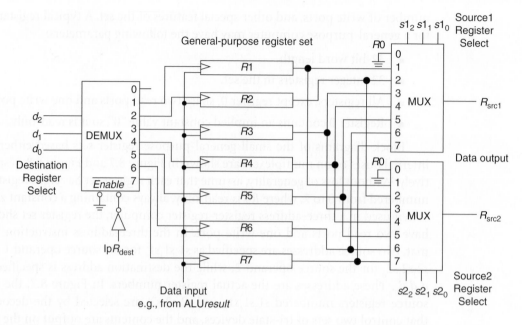

Figure 8.8   Block diagram of a general-purpose register set based on multiplexers

output of ALU result (through a shifter) is connected directly to all the registers (except $R0$) to receive input data. The loading pulse, $\text{lp}R_{\text{dest}}$, is applied to only one of the registers selected by a demultiplexer according to the destination address, $d_2 d_1 d_0$.

Comparing Figures 8.7 and 8.8, we can see that their different structures lead to different cost effectiveness. Assume a size of n general-purpose registers (including $R0$ whose contents always equal zero) in the register set and a word length of 32 bits. The bus-based register set uses a total of $(n-1) \times 2 \times 32 + 2$ tri-state devices plus two $(\log_2 n)$-by-n decoders, while the multiplexer-based register set uses a total of 32×2 n-by-1 multiplexers. The bus-based structure should have a lower cost.

8.4.2   Design of a CPU Based on General-Purpose Registers

The datapath of a CPU based on general-purpose registers (GPR) is shown in Figure 8.9. It is built on the basis of an ALU and a general-purpose register set, plus other registers for controlling the instruction fetch (PC and IR) and memory access (MAR and MBR). The register set is drawn as a block that can be implemented either as in Figure 8.7 or as in Figure 8.8. The functions of the ALU are twofold: (1) performing the eight arithmetic-logic operations selected by the *ALU function select* code $f_2 f_1 f_0$ and (2) serving the common datapath for most of the register transfer operations required by the basic instruction cycles.

The *operand1* and *operand2 select* codes, $u1_1 u1_0$ and $u2_1 u2_0$, select the input operands for *OP1* and *OP2*, respectively, through two multiplexers at the inputs of the ALU. The multiplexer on the *OP1* input selects from among R_{src1}, PC, IR (address field, e.g., memory address or immediate data), and zero. The multiplexer on the *OP2*, input selects from among R_{src2}, MBR, constant 00...01, and zero. These input arguments can be adjusted for different instruction set requirements and ALU functions.

The ALU result through a shifter can be loaded into different registers in the datapath by the two-level demultiplexers. The first demultiplexer selects from among PC, IR, MAR, MBR, and the register set as a group. The second demultiplexer selects from this group of registers a specific register, from $R1$ to $R7$, using the destination address $d_2 d_1 d_0$ (i.e., the destination register number). If the selection of source and destination registers is made at the assembly language level by the instruction codes, then the following control codes can make selections at the hardware or microprogram level:

- $u1_1 u1_0$ selects input *OP1* to the ALU from value 0, any one of $R0$ to $R7$, PC, and IR;

- $u2_1 u2_0$ selects input *OP2* to the ALU from value 0, any one of $R0$ to $R7$, MBR, and constant 00...01;

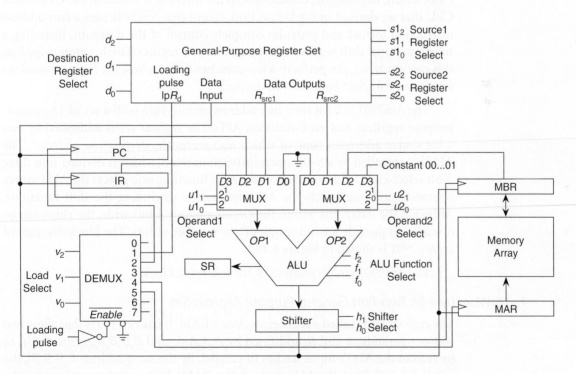

Figure 8.9   Block diagram of a CPU based on general-purpose registers

- $v_2v_1v_0$ selects from among any one of $R0$ to $R7$, PC, IR, MBR, and MAR for receiving the output of the ALU through a shifter, while $v_2v_1v_0 = 000$ means no loading;

- $f_2f_1f_0$ selects among eight ALU operations; and

- h_1h_0 selects among four shift operations, including no shift.

In Chapter 9, we will learn about the control unit. We will see that these control signals constitute the microinstruction format with various fields of control, thus obtaining the complete control of the datapath for execution of basic instruction cycles.

8.5 CPU BIT-SLICE DEVICE—A CASE STUDY

In this section, we will conduct a case study of the circuit of an Am2901 4-bit CPU bit-slice device, which is an LSI product made by Advanced Micro Devices, Inc. Although the bit-slice architecture is becoming less important nowadays, due to the rapid development of VLSI high-performance microprocessor chips, it is still a good example of CPU organization from the instructional point of view because of both its simplicity and the typicality of its CPU organization. The purpose of our case study of Am2901 is to learn the organization of a practical CPU, which, in principle, coincides with the theoretical model of the GPR-based CPU that we derived in the last section, except that Am2901 uses a two-address instruction format and provides complete control of the datapath, including a fully functional shift register with an auxiliary Q register. Furthermore, based on this case study, we can perform a few exercises to learn how the logic expressions for its control select codes can be derived.

The Am2901 is built on a two-address architecture with a set of 16 general-purpose registers and an 8-function ALU. The register set is addressed by two 4-bit source addresses (one of which also serves the destination address). The ALU is controlled by a 9-bit microinstruction word, which is divided into three 3-bit select-code fields: one selects the ALU function, one selects the ALU source operands, and one selects the ALU destination (including the shift function). Although the datapaths within the circuit are only 4 bits wide, the chips can be cascaded to provide a word length of any number of bits. The block diagram of an Am2901 is shown in Figure 8.10.

The Am2901 circuit consists of the following blocks:

1. 16-Word by 4-Bit Two-Port General-Purpose Register Set

The register set is called a register stack or a RAM. It has two ports that allow two source operands, A and B, addressed by $A_3A_2A_1A_0$ and $B_3B_2B_1B_0$, respectively, to be read to the ALU's input latches in parallel. By the same address $B_3B_2B_1B_0$, the result $F_3F_2F_1F_0$ from the ALU through the RAM-shifter can be written into the RAM when the write-enable voltage, EN, is enabled and the write-enable pulse,

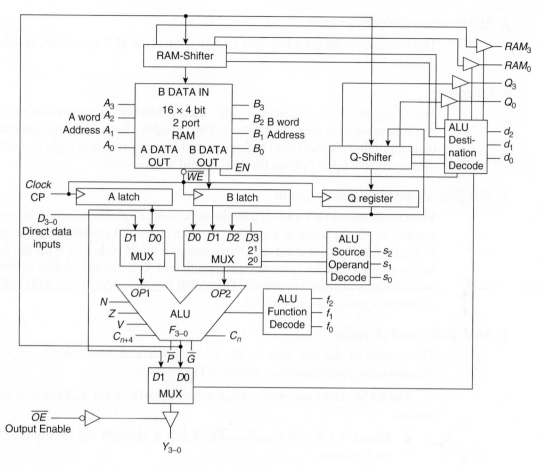

Figure 8.10   Block diagram of an Am2901 CPU bit-slice device

$\overline{WE}$, is low. During this period, the latches A and B are closed by a low clock input, thus eliminating any possible race conditions between the read and write operations of the RAM.

2. Carry Look-Ahead ALU

The ALU performs three (binary) arithmetic and five logic operations on the two 4-bit input operands $OP1$ and $OP2$. The operations are controlled by the function select code $f_2 f_1 f_0$, according to the function table shown in Table 5.19 in Problem 5.5. The output $F_3 F_2 F_1 F_0$ of the ALU can be stored in the RAM (through the RAM-shifter) or the Q register, or can be routed to the output pins Y_3–Y_0 through a multiplexer.

The ALU contains a carry look-ahead adder that works in combination with a block look-ahead carry generator, Am2902, to construct a CPU of a large size, similar to the use of the SN74182 chip described in Section 5.2.4.

3. ALU Function Decode Circuit

This circuit decodes the select code $f_2f_1f_0$ to control the ALU operations as shown in Table 5.19.

4. Q Register

The Q register is an auxiliary register used primarily for multiplication and division, as we have seen in Chapter 6. The Q register has a Q-shifter connected to its input that enables the Q register to shift its contents left or right by 1 bit or directly receive $F_3F_2F_1F_0$ from the ALU output without shift.

5. ALU Source Operand Decode Circuit

This circuit selects $OP1$ and $OP2$ by the select code $s_2s_1s_0$. The selection is implemented by multiplexers in the same manner as we did in designing the ALU in Figure 8.9. By combining the source operand select code $s_2s_1s_0$ with the ALU function select code $f_2f_1f_0$, we can specify different ALU operations with different combinations of source operands. The global function table of the ALU will be obtained as an exercise in Problem 8.7.

6. RAM-Shifter and Q-Shifter

The circuits of the two shifters, the RAM-shifter and the Q-shifter, are constructed using multiplexers, as shown in Figure 8.11.

The RAM-shifter can receive the result of the ALU, $F_3F_2F_1F_0$, by way of three modes:

- **Direct**: $F_3F_2F_1F_0$ is transferred to $B_3B_2B_1B_0$ through the $D1$ input of the multiplexers.
- **Right shift**: $RAM_3F_3F_2F_1F_0$ is transferred to $B_3B_2B_1B_0RAM_0$ through the $D2$ input of the multiplexers, connecting the shift path with the outside.
- **Left shift**: $F_3F_2F_1F_0RAM_0$ is transferred to $RAM_3B_3B_2B_1B_0$ through the $D0$ input of the multiplexers, connecting the shift path with the outside.

The Q-shifter works in a similar way, except that during direct transfer $F_3F_2F_1F_0$ is transferred to $Q_3Q_2Q_1Q_0$, and during shift operations the Q register shifts its own contents through the multiplexers.

7. ALU Destination Decode Circuit

This circuit controls the shift operations of the two shifters as well as the loading and output of the ALU result. The control code is $d_2d_1d_0$. The function table for the ALU destination selection is shown in Table 8.2. The ALU destination decode circuit acts on the multiplexers and tri-state devices in the manner shown in Figures 8.10 and 8.11.

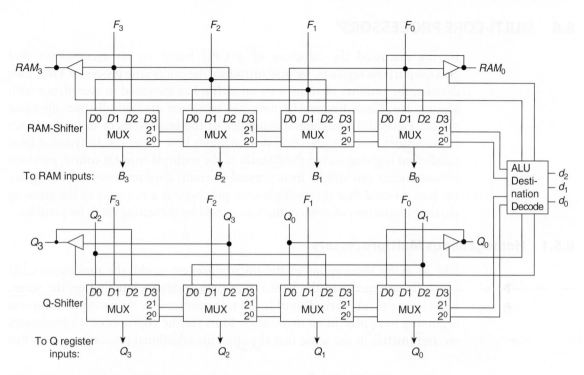

Figure 8.11 Circuits of the shifters of the Am2901 CPU bit-slice device

Table 8.2 Function table for the ALU destination selection of the Am2901

d_2	d_1	d_0	Mnemonic	RAM-Shifter	Q-Shifter	Y Output	Explanation
0	0	0	QREG	—	$Q \leftarrow F$	$Y \leftarrow F$	Load Q from ALU, output F
0	0	1	NOP	—	—	$Y \leftarrow F$	No operation, output F
0	1	0	RAMA	$B \leftarrow F$	—	$Y \leftarrow A$	Load RAM from ALU, output A
0	1	1	RAMF	$B \leftarrow F$	—	$Y \leftarrow F$	Load RAM from ALU, output F
1	0	0	RAMQD	$B \leftarrow F/2$	$Q \leftarrow Q/2$	$Y \leftarrow F$	Right shift F into RAM, right shift Q
1	0	1	RAMD	$B \leftarrow F/2$	—	$Y \leftarrow F$	Right shift F into RAM
1	1	0	RAMQU	$B \leftarrow 2F$	$Q \leftarrow 2Q$	$Y \leftarrow F$	Left shift F into RAM, left shift Q
1	1	1	RAMU	$B \leftarrow 2F$	—	$Y \leftarrow F$	Left shift F into RAM

8.6 MULTI-CORE PROCESSORS[2]

Having discussed the structure of a CPU based on an accumulator and general-purpose registers, we now introduce the multi-core processor. Over four decades, the number of transistors on a chip has increased in accordance with Moore's law. Clock frequencies have also increased dramatically over the same period. Figure 8.12 provides a reminder of the improvement in performance of processors over the years and demonstrates how the era of instruction level parallelism is giving way to the domain of the multiple core. Of course, previous enhancements can still be incorporated in multi-core processors. Once again, we, have to state that the multiple-core processor is a response to the growing physical limitations of semiconductors caused by increasing clock frequencies.

8.6.1 Homogeneous Multiprocessors

Like so many innovations in the microprocessor world, the multi-core CPU gradually emerged into the light rather than suddenly bursting on the scene. Right from the very early days of 16-bit microprocessors, the multiprocessor was beginning to appear in an *asymmetric* form via the coprocessor. Coprocessors are asymmetric in the sense that they provide additional processing power but

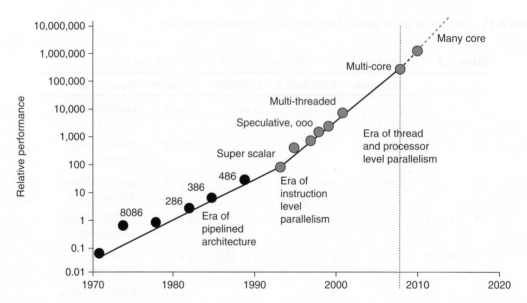

Figure 8.12 Processor performance

Source: Intel Education, 2008 Asia Academic Forum, October 20–22, 2008. Taipei, Taiwan. Reprinted with permisson of Intel Corporation.

---

[2] Reprinted with permission from Section 13–7 (pp. 851–865) of Alan Clements, *Computer Organization and Architecture: Themes and Variations* (Boston, MA: Cengage Learning, 2014).

WHAT IS A CORE?

The term *core* in multi-core computing is rather misleading, because its meaning is not precisely defined. At one extreme, a core could be the same as a microprocessor and a multi-core chip could have two or more identical processors on the same chip. Such an arrangement would imply that the CPU, cache memory, memory management system, and even the bus interface were duplicated for each chip. At the other extreme, a core could have just a processing unit, while a multi-core chip could have a CPU plus several processing units (without associated program control and sequencing). Finally, a multi-core chip could have several CPUs that share certain common facilities, such as memory and the external interface.

Homogenous and Heterogeneous Processors

Multi-core processors can be divided into two categories: homogeneous or heterogeneous. The distinction is rather like that between uniform and non-uniform memory access. A homogeneous processor employs a set of cores where every core is an identical copy of all the other cores. A heterogeneous multi-core processor includes cores that differ in ISA, chip area, performance, or power dissipation. Early multi-core processors were generally homogeneous with one core being duplicated. With the passage of time, the benevolent Moore's law has enabled sufficient numbers of active devices to be fabricated on a chip to develop systems where different types of cores can be optimized for different functions. This is particularly true of the advanced processors found in commodity applications such as games consoles.

in a different form (floating-point, graphics, or physics engines). The Pentium® was designed to support symmetric multiprocessing and incorporated hardware mechanisms to allow dual-processor motherboards. Moreover, the number of transistors on a chip increased from about three million in 1993 to two billion in 2011. The next step was obvious: put two processors in the same physical housing. IBM introduced a high-end, dual-core processor that put two 64-bit POWER processors on its POWER4 chip in 2001. Intel introduced its mass-marketed dual-core processor in 2005 (a Pentium® 840 Extreme Edition). At almost exactly the same time, AMD brought out its Opteron™ 800 Series.[3] Intel's first dual-core processor was really two processors in the same package that were not

---

[3] The near simultaneous introduction of Intel and AMD multi-core processors demonstrates two points. The first is the inevitability of multi-core processing and the second is, given that Intel and AMD were operating in the same markets with similar levels of technology and in similar cultural environments, it is not surprising that both organizations made similar innovations at roughly the same time.

well integrated. Intel rapidly brought out the Core 2 Duo to replace the Dual Core Pentium®. The Core 2 Duo was specifically designed for dual-processor systems.

Figure 8.13 summarizes the growth of the multiprocessor chip and its relationship with cache that we will study in Chapter 10. Figure 8.13a describes the three blocks of a conventional processor. The CPU state incorporates the registers (including the PC and status register) that define the current state of the processor and the thread (line of code) it is executing. In Figure 8.13b, we have added a second set of CPU state registers to allow two threads to be executed concurrently by switching between state registers whenever one thread is stalled by a data load.

Figure 8.13c describes a multiprocessor system whose two processors share the same environment (motherboard). The dashed line indicates that they are in the same system but not on the same chip. Figure 8.13d describes a multi-core processor which is the same as (c) but the processors are now on the same chip. Figure 8.13e is an extension of (d) in which the cache is shared between processors. This indicates an increasing degree of coupling between individual processors on the same chip. In Figure 8.13f, we have added hyperthreading to

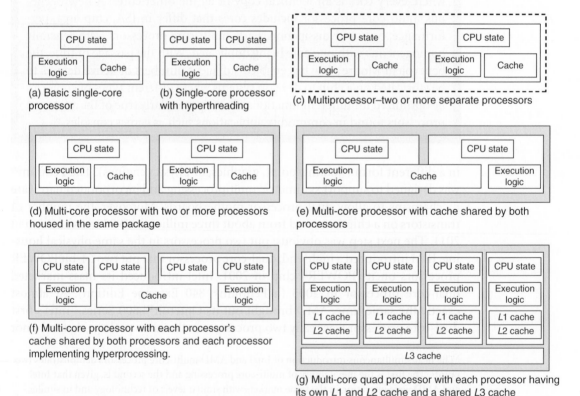

(a) Basic single-core processor

(b) Single-core processor with hyperthreading

(c) Multiprocessor–two or more separate processors

(d) Multi-core processor with two or more processors housed in the same package

(e) Multi-core processor with cache shared by both processors

(f) Multi-core processor with each processor's cache shared by both processors and each processor implementing hyperprocessing.

(g) Multi-core quad processor with each processor having its own L1 and L2 cache and a shared L3 cache

Figure 8.13   Progressive development of the multi-core processor

allow each of the individual processors to execute multiple threads. Figure 8.13g increases the number of cores to four and shows that we can choose how to distribute the individual cache levels. In this case, each processor has a private level 1 and 2 cache but shares the much larger *L3* cache.

SMP BACKGROUND

In 2001, Intel introduced the Pentium® III Xeon intended for use in servers. This processor was intended to be used in two-processor or four-processor *glueless* multiprocessors. The term *glueless* refers to the logic and auxiliary systems necessary to link processors with each other or with memory and implies that the interface logic is on-chip and that the designer does not have to spend a lot of time creating a special multiprocessor system. In 2002, Intel introduced the Pentium® 4 family and the corresponding Xeon family targeted at desktop PCs and high-end workstations and servers, respectively.

The Pentium® III Xeon was intended for use in symmetric multiprocessing (SMP) systems that have a simple structure based on a common bus shared between processors. The term *symmetric* implies that all processors are equal and logically interchangeable. The following figure illustrates the concept of SMP. Some multiprocessor systems have a topology that reflects the application; that is, the system is optimized for an application such as signal processing. An SMP architecture treats all processors equally, and it is the operating system that has the task of partitioning the computation between the individual processors.

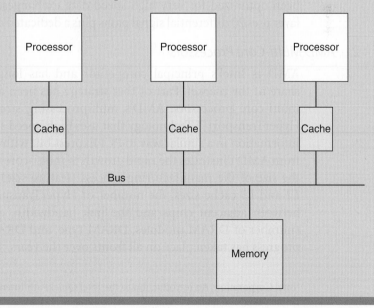

The weakness of SMP is that the bus becomes a bottleneck between the processors and between the processors and memory. SMP is successful when the individual processors make good use of their internal data/instruction caches and limit the number of accesses to main memory. Programs can be written to take advantage of SMP structures. However, a consequence of this is that such a program will have a degraded performance when run on a uniprocessor system. This is a problem in the personal computing arena where someone playing a game, optimized for an SMP architecture, on a uniprocessor, is having to pay a performance penalty.

1. Intel Nehalem® Multi-Core Processor

Intel's Nehalem® architecture was introduced in November 2008 with the Core i7 processor and was to become Intel's flagship PC processor for several years. Figure 8.14 describes a multiprocessor system using two Nehalem® chips. Each chip has four cores where a core has a CPU, $L1$, and $L2$ cache, and all four cores share a common $L3$ cache. A *quick path interconnect* (QPI) provides an external interface allowing clusters of chips to be connected together.[4] The QPI interface can transfer data on both the rising and the falling edge of the clock (at 3.2 GHz) to achieve a bandwidth of 25.6 GB/sec.

Technically, QuickPath is not a bus (remember that *bus* is a contraction of the Latin *omnibus* which means *for all*), because it supports only point-to-point communication. However, QuickPath has a multilayered architecture that has been optimized for very high speed data exchanges. For example, the physical layer uses 20 differential signal paths plus a dedicated clock path in each direction.

2. AMD Multi-Core Processors

AMD is Intel's principal competitor and has long worked to maximize its share of the market. Part of that strategy has been a move from single-core to multi-core processors. AMD's multiprocessing strategy depends strongly on HyperTransport™ Technology that uses high-speed serial data links to exchange information in a similar way to PCI Express but with a lower overhead. Table 8.3 from AMD illustrates the rapid growth in multi-core technology. This table gives the size of the manufacturing process (feature size), the number of cores, the $L2$ and $L3$ cache sizes, the number of HyperTransport™ Technology channels between adjacent chips and the link bandwidth, and the memory interface (number of DRAM modules, DRAM type, and DRAM speed). As you can see, progress has taken place on all fronts over the years.

---

[4]Intel Corporation, An introduction to the Intel QuickPath Interconnect, Intel Whitepaper, January 2009.

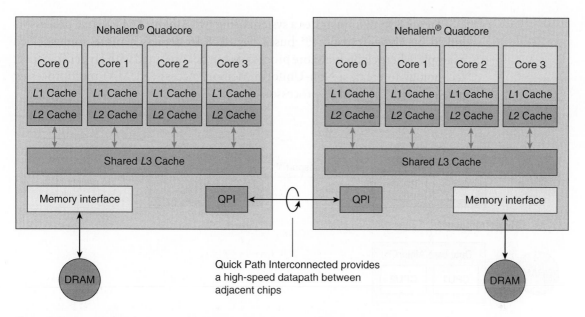

Figure 8.14 Intel eight-core multiprocessor using two Nehalem® chips

Table 8.3 Development of AMD's multi-core processors

Year	2003	2005	2007	2008	2009	2010	2011
Name	Opteron	Opteron	Barcelona	Shanghai	Istanbul	Magny-Cours	Interlagos
Feature size	90 nm	90 nm	65 nm	45 nm	45 nm	45 nm	32 nm
Cores	1	2	4	4	6	12	16
L2 Cache	1 MB	1 MB	512 KB	512 KB	512 KB	512 KB	2 MB
L3 Cache	–	–	2 MB	6 MB	6 MB	12 MB	16 MB
HTT	3 × 1.6 GT/sec	3 × 1.6 GT/sec	3 × 2.0 GT/sec	3 × 4.0 GT/sec	3 × 4.8 GT/sec	4 × 6.4 GT/sec	4 × 6.4 GT/sec
Memory	2 × DDR 300	2 × DDR 400	2 × DDR2 677	2 × DDR2 800	2 × DDR2 1066	4 × DDR3 1333	4 × DDR3 1866

HTT, HyperTransport™ Technology.

Figure 8.15 demonstrates a system using two Athlon™ 64 FX dual processors linked by HyperTransport™ buses. Figure 8.16 depicts a more sophisticated example, where eight dual-core processors can be combined with HyperTransport technology to create a Non-Uniform Memory Access (NUMA) multiprocessor network with crosslinked processors.

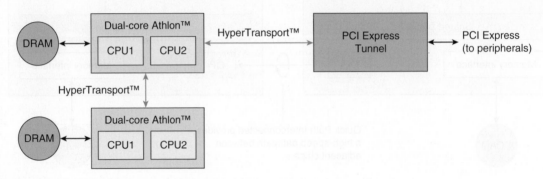

Figure 8.15   AMD's use of HyperTransport™ Technology in multiprocessors

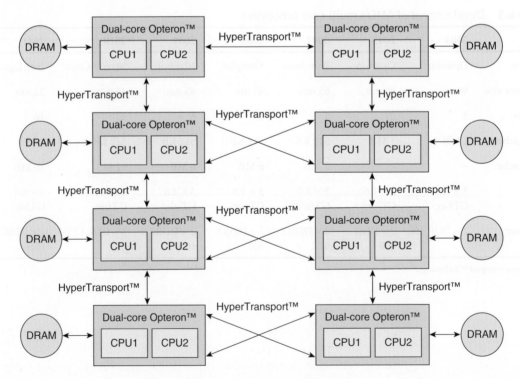

Figure 8.16   AMD's use of HyperTransport™ to create complex NUMA structures

CPU Throttling

For a long time, computers ran at the highest speed possible. That was axiomatic—no sane person would buy a processor and then deliberately run it at a slower speed than necessary. However, in an age where power is limited by batteries or the equipment is in danger of becoming too hot, reducing the clock rate from the maximum becomes essential.

CPU throttling or dynamic frequency scaling is a technique used to lower power consumption by reducing the frequency of the clock. Throttling can be used to reduce the clock rate of processors that are idle or to reduce CPU clock rates when long-latency memory accesses are taking place. Another power-saving technique is to power down areas of the processor not currently in use.

Intel calls its power reduction system SpeedStep® technology and AMD uses the term Cool'n'Quiet™ in desktop environments and PowerNow!™ in mobile environments. As its name suggests, Cool'n'Quiet™ technology also works in conjunction with fan control in desktop processors to reduce fan speed and noise when the chip's temperature falls.

3. ARM Cortex™ A9 Multi Core

ARM produce a range of processors based on the ARM's core architecture but with various power/performance/cost tradeoffs. The Cortex™ A9 is a general-purpose processor intended for mobile applications and is available with one, two, three, or four cores. Cortex™ A9 processors can be configured for specific applications. Some of the attributes of the A9 are given here:

- Superscalar pipelined processor core.
- NEON™ media processing engine—ARM's own SIMD instruction set with thirty-two 64-bit-wide registers that can be used as sixteen 128-bit registers.
- Floating-point unit.
- Thumb-2® technology—ARM's compressed code mechanism.
- Jazelle® technology—this is ARM's on-chip support for Java and enables the direct execution of Java's native bytecode. This allows ARM processors to have three states—each executing a different native instruction set architecture.

Figure 8.17 describes the structure of the Cortex™ A9. Note that ARM is an intellectual property company, and this processor can be configured in several different ways depending on the wishes of the user. Other special-purpose coprocessors, such as cryptographic accelerators, can be incorporated. Bus snooping control is incorporated on chip, but there is no *L2* cache.

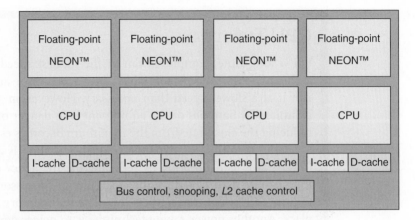

Figure 8.17 Structure of ARM's Cortex™ A9 multi-core processor

4. IBM POWER7

IBM championed RISC architecture from the very beginning. Credit for RISC architectures is given to John Cock at IBM for his pioneering work on the 801 project (a RISC architecture that was never implemented) in 1974. IBM's first commercially successful RISC processor was the POWER architecture that later formed the basis for the PowerPC used by Apple. IBM's first computers using this architecture appeared in 1990 (the RS/6000 series). The POWER architecture itself continued to be developed for IBM's high-performance workstations, with POWER7 being introduced in 2010.

Figure 8.18 describes the organization of POWER7 which has eight cores using 1.2 billion transistors. The individual cores can be turned off to save energy. Similarly, the clock frequencies of the cores can also be modified to *reallocate* energy. The *L2* caches are each 256 kilobytes, and the shared *L3* cache is 32 megabytes. The cores themselves support out-of-order execution and provide two fixed-point ALUs, two floating-point units, and a *decimal floating-point* (DFP) unit. A decimal FPU is rather unusual today and first appeared in the POWER6 in 2007. In this context, the word *decimal* refers to both the representation of numbers and the operations available to be performed. The advantage of DFP is that it can improve the performance of systems that carry out very large numbers of financial operations. It is estimated that over half of the numeric data in commercial databases is decimal and that operations in decimal arithmetic are normally carried out in software 100 to 1,000 times slower than in hardware. POWER7 conforms to the IEEE-754R standard and defines 32-, 64-, and 128-bit formats. The 128-bit format has a 34-bit precision and a 16-bit exponent.

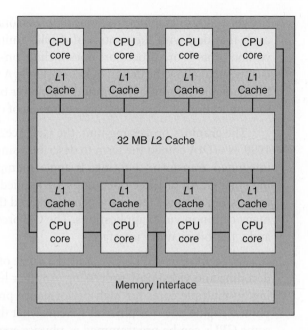

Figure 8.18 Organization of the IBM POWER7

THE WAR IS ON ALL FRONTS

Where is the battle to improve computer performance taking place? The answer is that it is on all fronts and the POWER7 demonstrates the truth of this. POWER7 is a development of previous versions of this architecture, and like its contemporaries, it takes an aggressive approach to multiprocessing.

However, the inclusion of a dedicated decimal floating-point unit to accelerate large numbers of financial transactions in commercial databases demonstrates how progress takes place in a number of directions simultaneously. Each new generation of processors incorporates lessons learned from previous generations, lessons from the state-of-the-art globally, and innovations peculiar to the current generation.

This multifaceted progress is one of the driving forces behind the modified versions of Moore's law stating that computer performance is increasing year by year.

5.   *Graphics Processing Unit (GPU)*

What do you get if you really take multi-core processing to heart and put very large numbers of processors on a single chip—not two or four or eight, but hundreds?

You get a GPU or *graphics processing unit*.[5] Personal computers typically have video cards that deal with the control of display units, although Intel's Sandy Bridge version of its iCore processors does include on-chip hardware video-processing facilities that allow the design of low-cost PCs. A video processor card can include a remarkable amount of computational power because video processing requires the application of immensely large numbers of operations for video data.

The graphics processing unit, the GeForce256, was invented by NVIDIA in 1999. NVIDIA coined the term to describe a single-chip processor that included integrated transform, lighting, triangle manipulation, clipping, and rendering engines. All of these operations are applied to the digital representation of images, but within a few years, people realized that GPU chips could be used for many common video applications. The GeForce256 has a 256-bit graphics core and a 128-bit memory interface.

In recent years, GPUs have added a range of new functions, including video decoding and video post-processing. Another highly-specialized processor relying on multiple cores for high-performance processing is the *physics engine*. A physics engine does for physical systems what the GPU does for images; indeed, some GPUs can be programmed as physics engines. For a long time, physicists have been concerned with dynamics such as the motion of the atmosphere (weather forecasting) or fluid flow (turbine blade design). Today, games players demand high-speed real-time dynamics. If an object explodes, its pieces should all obey the laws of Newtonian dynamics. Other physics operations are collision detection (for example, when a ball hits a wall) and deformation physics, which deals with the way in which an object behaves under crushing forces (for example, when Tom hits Jerry's head with a brick).

The goal of GPU technology is *Extreme High Definition Gaming* (XHD). In the 1980s, crude, chunky games were the state of the art. Today, the effort of both software and hardware designers is focused on high resolution (not least because of the tremendous drop in the cost of high resolution displays). "Extreme" high-resolution gaming refers to widescreen displays with resolutions of over 2,560 × 1,600 pixels, which is seven times greater than the 1,080 HD used by Blu-ray.

Initially, GPUs were not easy to apply to general computing problems, because they had been constructed specifically for graphics processing and you accessed them via *application programming interfaces* (APIs). An API is essentially a system call from software to some resource which may be a library function or the gateway to hardware acceleration, like a GPU. By 2006, NVIDIA's extended APIs were available to GPUs that allowed programming in C. Now, users could access the power of the GPU directly.

---

[5] It is rather interesting that people make a lot of fuss over Intel or AMD's multi-core processors with four or eight cores when GPU manufacturers like NVIDIA are churning out chips with 512 cores largely unnoticed.

PIPELINING—TIME AND SPACE

The GPU pipeline differs from the type of pipelining we have associated with CPUs when discussing instruction level parallelism. When a CPU performs software pipelining, it sequentially executes the code for each stage of the pipeline. The pipeline stages are distributed in time.

The GPU pipeline is distributed in space; that is, the individual processors are divided between the different functions to be carried out by the graphics pipeline.

Early GPUs implemented different stages of the graphics pipeline with different processors in order to achieve the best performance. As time passed, the complexity of operations in all pipeline stages has increased, and there has been a movement toward a so-called unified shader architecture in which all stages share the same programmable core.

In 2008, NVIDIA introduced the GT2000 series that increased the number of *streaming processor cores* to 240. Figure 8.19 describes the organization of the cores in a later 512-core version of the GPU. Each core can execute a new integer or floating-point instruction at each clock. The cores are organized as 16 groups, called *streaming multiprocessors* (SMs), of 32 cores. A part of the GPU called the *Giga Thread global scheduler* is responsible for allocating blocks of threads.

The heart of a GPU card is its *graphics pipeline*, which is responsible for taking a description of an image from the computer and presenting a raster-scan (i.e., line-by-line or bitmap) image to the video display. A photograph is just a bitmapped image that cannot be separated into parts, it is simply stored and displayed pixel by pixel after suitable scaling. A graphics image of the type that you see in computer games and animations is a complex set of objects and lighting effects; that is, a graphics image exists as a description of a scene that the GPU has to draw. Consider an image with a person standing in front of a house. The person is a collection of drawing objects overlaid on another collection of drawing objects. If the person moves, even though a million pixels may have been shifted on the final images, the computer needs to tell the graphics card only that an object has moved. It is the job of the graphics pipeline to create the new image dynamically.

The source image from the computer is presented to the graphics card as triangles, which are the fundamental component of a video image. All complex shapes are composed of triangles. The higher the resolution, the greater the number of triangles. The triangles themselves are transmitted as vertices. The GPU has to process the vertices and then operate as a pipeline with each stage performing successive transformations on the image. Figure 8.20 illustrates the concept of a graphics pipeline—the details vary from system to system. Another operation taking place in the pipeline is the generation of lighting effects. It is necessary to work out how each point behaves under the influence of a complex

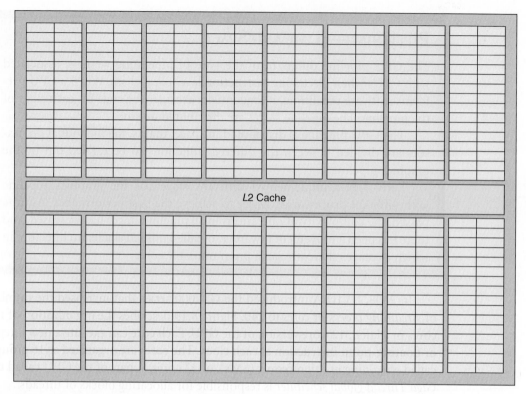

Figure 8.19 NVIDIA GT2000 series architecture

Note: This is not an empty figure—it consists of 512 CPUs.

lighting system with light from many sources. The rasterization stage takes the images as described by the triangles and converts them into images that can be stored in memory and displayed.

The GPU is highly optimized for its role as a video processing machine, which can lead to remarkable performance enhancements over a CPU. For example, a GPU may achieve a throughput of over 100 times that of a CPU. GPUs achieve their high throughput by dedicating chip area to processing and by not incorporating the massive cache and control logic overhead associated with CPUs.

Not everyone is quite as enthusiastic about GPUs. A paper by G.C. Caragea, *et al.* appeared on Usenix.org that presented the results of an investigation into the performance of general-purpose multi-core processors versus CPUs when executing *irregular workloads*.[6] Although this paper refers to a specific multi-core processor, XMT, its general conclusion is that GPUs show high performance

---

[6] G. Caragea, F. Keceli, A. Tzannes, and U. Vishkin, "General-purpose vs. GPU: Comparison of many-cores on irregular workloads," in: *USENIX, Hotpar '10: Proceedings of the 2nd workshop on hot topics in parallelsim*. Berkeley, CA, June 14-15, 2010.

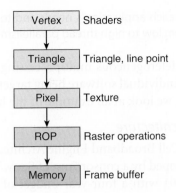

Figure 8.20   The GPU pipeline

GAMES CONSOLES CONSIDERED HARMFUL

Low-cost games consoles, like the Sony PlayStation 3 that use the Cell processor or Microsoft's Xbox 360 which also has a multi-core processor supporting SIMD extensions, are creating headaches in some quarters. *The Economist* reports that sophisticated computer simulation games and high-performance software are being run on low-cost consumer consoles. With such technology being widely available, wealthy countries that have long enjoyed a technological monopoly on high-performance computing are realizing that it is now available to all.

Source: The military-consumer complex. *The Economist*, December 12, 2009.

---

increases on regular workloads but much poorer performance on irregular workloads (i.e., those demonstrating highly irregular patterns of memory access).

8.6.2   Heterogeneous Multiprocessors

In 2007, Kumar, Tullsen, and Jouppi in an article in *Computer*[7] stated that

> Heterogeneous chip multiprocessors present unique opportunities for improving system throughput, reducing processor power, and mitigating Amdahl's law. On-chip heterogeneity allows the processor to better match execution resources

---

[7] R. Kumar, D.M. Tullsen, and N.P. Jouppi, Heterogeneous chip multiprocessors, *Computers*, 38(11), pp. 32–38.

to each application's needs and to address a wider spectrum of system loads—from low to high thread parallelism—with high efficiency.

Heterogeneous multiprocessing permits the use of multi-ISA architectures with individual software being targeted on the most appropriate ISA on the chip. Here, we look at an example of the heterogeneous multiprocessor.

1. The Cell Architecture

The Cell Broadband Engine Architecture (Cell) is a microprocessor architecture developed by a consortium of Sony, Toshiba, and IBM (STI). The project started in 2001 with a four-year budget of $400 million. The consortium's first commercial product was used in Sony's PlayStation 3 game console released in 2006.

Cell was developed to overcome the three walls of computer architecture: the power wall (limitations due to increasing power dissipation), the frequency wall (the problems of deep pipelines at high frequencies), and the memory wall (the problem of DRAM memory latency at high speeds). The Cell processor used in the PlayStation 3 has 234 million transistors, which is comparable with the Itanium™ 2 developed at approximately the same time.

Cell takes an unusual approach to multiprocessing by employing different architectures on the same chip,[8] that is, the Cell is said to be a *heterogeneous processor*. The organization of the Cell is given in Figure 8.21. The *main* processor is called a *Power Processing Element* that is compatible with IBM's POWER 970 architecture. This has a split $L1$ cache with 32-KB data, 32-KB instruction, and a 512-KB $L2$ cache. This processor also incorporates the AltiVec (now called VMX) instruction set extensions to provide SIMD multimedia support. The SIMD processor has thirty-two 128-bit vector registers.

As well as the central power processing element, the Cell has eight *synergistic processor elements* (SPEs) arranged as a network with a high-bandwidth internal element interconnect bus (EIB). This bus is also connected to an interface to external memory and an I/O controller. The data bus itself consists of four 16-byte wide data rings that support multiple simultaneous transfers per ring. The peak bandwidth is 96 bytes per clock cycle. The EIB can sustain a data rate of 200 GB/sec.

The eight SPEs are special purpose RISC-based SIMD processors optimized for *data-rich operations*. The SPEs each have 128 registers in a 128-bit register file and 256 kilobytes of local store. SPEs are designed to process application-level data and do not run the operating system; that is the function of the power processor element (PPE) core. Most instructions operate on 128-bit operands divided into four 32-bit words. This fits in well with the Cell's role as a high-performance multimedia processor and its role in PlayStation 3. Anyone interested in the

---

[8] M. Gschwind, P. Hofstee, B. Flachs, M. Hopkins, Y. Watanabe, and T. Yamazaki, A novel SIMD architecture for the Cell heterogeneous chip-multiprocessor, in: *Proceedings of Hot Chips 17: A symposium on high-performance chips,* August 14–16, 2005, Stanford, CA.

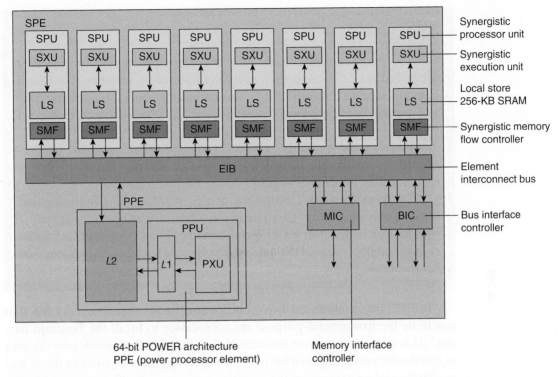

Figure 8.21 The Cell architecture

history of computer technology will find it quite remarkable that a low-cost commodity item like the PlayStation contains a state-of-the art network on a chip processor with a computational throughput unimaginable a few years ago.

The PPE core provides the 64-bit Power architecture together with the *L*1 and *L*2 caches, an instruction control unit, a load and store unit, a fixed-point integer unit, a floating-point unit, a branch unit, and a memory management unit.

8.6.3 Network on a Chip

In 2011, the Wikipedia entry for *Network on a Chip* (NoC) called it an *emerging paradigm* that links multiple processor cores on a chip with multiple point-to-point routes. In other words, the NoC represents the next stage in multi-core processors with more processing units than the first generation of multi-core processors and with more complicated inter-processor communication methods. There is an overlap between NoC and SoC; the latter refers to a *system on a chip* and implies a single chip solution to an engineering problem that may include multiple CPUs, memory, I/O, and special-purpose circuits that might be necessary in cell phones or GPS receivers. A SoC is normally intended for a specific purpose, whereas a NoC is a general-purpose processing device.

TILES

Cores in multi-core processors are often referred to as *tiles*. In general, a tile includes a CPU, memory, and a communications interface that allows communications between tiles. The communications technology usually uses packet switches or wormhole routing rather than a conventional switched bus.

The term tile is used because cores in a multi-core processor are frequently set out like the tiles on a roof (that is, a rectangular array of tiles often forming a mesh network).

The term tiling has a second use in high-performance computing that refers to software, rather than hardware. Tiling also refers to the transformation of a loop construct to include smaller blocks of data that can be cached and hence reduce the miss rate. Such a tile is a block of memory that fits within the cache.

In 2007, Intel announced its NoC processor, the *Teraflops Research Chip*, that was to be the first general-purpose microprocessor to break the Teraflops barrier.[9] This *terascale* processor was intended to lead Intel's research into the area of multi-core processing well beyond the modest number of cores in the i7 and to achieve a lower power/core than existing processors. Teraflops uses an 80-core *tiled architecture* with a two-dimensional mesh of cores—each implemented with 100 million transistors using a 65-nm process technology. Teraflops is a research vehicle and a platform for processor evaluation rather than a commercial processor. The cores or tiles are arranged as an 8×10 array.

Each Teraflops tile has two floating-point units, 3 kilobytes of instruction memory arranged as 256 96-bit instructions, and 2 kilobytes of data memory sufficient to hold 512 single-precision numbers. The register file has 32 entries with six read ports and four write ports. The floating-point units, FPMAC0 and FPMAC1 are two independent, fully pipelined, single-precision, floating-point, multiply accumulate devices that can provide a peak performance of 20 GFLOPS. Clearly, Teraflops is not intended for conventional programming. It is optimized for scientific computing and graphics. The underlying ISA is VLIW with 96-bit instructions. Each long instruction word contains eight operations (i.e., an instruction bundle has eight instructions). The instruction set is tiny. Table 8.4 describes the Teraflops instruction set. A Teraflops tile also includes a router to enable messages to be passed to and from other tiles. Figure 8.22 gives a diagram of the structure of a Teraflops tile. The communications unit is a five-port packet-switched router

[9] T. Mattson, R.Van der Wijngaart, and M.Frumkin, Programming Intel's 80-core Terascale processor, in : *SC'08 Proceedings of the 2008 ACM/IEEE conference on supercomputing*, November 15-21, 2008, Austin, TX. Piscataway, NJ: IEEE Press, 2008.

Table 8.4 Teraflops instruction set

Mnemonic	Instruction
LOAD, STORE	Move a pair of 32-bit floats between the register file and data memory.
LOADO, STOREO, OFFSET	Move a pair of 32-bit floats between the register file and data memory at address plus OFFSET.
BRNE, INDEX	The native loop capability. INDEX sets a register for loop count and BRNE branches while the index register is greater than zero.
JUMP	Jump to the specified program counter address.
SENDI[H|A|D|T]	Send instruction header, address, data, and tail to a core.
SENDD[H|A|D|T]	Send data header, address, data, and tail to a core.
WFD	Stall while waiting for data to arrive from any tile.
MULT	Multiply operands.
ACCUM	Accumulate with previous result.
STAL	Stall program counter (PC) while waiting for a new PC.
NAP	Put FPUs to sleep.
WAKE	Wake FPUs from sleep.

that links a tile to its four neighbors and to the clock. The data timing is called *mesosynchronous*, which means that the data is insensitive to phase errors because the timing is derived locally from the data signal. Local clocks are synchronized to a master clock, and buffering is used to ensure that the data and the locally generated clock are in synchronism. If the data stream were treated as a synchronous signal (as might happen in systems with much lower clock rates), it would be difficult to ensure that the clock phase relationship would be the same at all 80 tiles.

An advantage of Terascale architectures, like Teraflops, is their ability for partitioning[10] and, as a consequence, reliability and fault-tolerance. The tiled topology combined with the ability to route messages through the mesh network means that tasks can be partitioned and the tiles allocated particular subfunctions. However, tiling provides fault tolerance and the potential for graceful degradation. If one or more tiles fail, they can be switched out and tasks assigned to good tiles.

---

[10] M. Azimi, *et al.*, Integration challenges and tradeoffs for Terascale architectures, *Intel Technology Journal*, 11(3), 173–184.

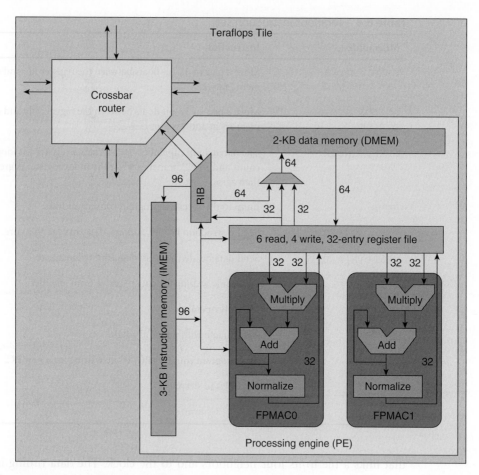

Figure 8.22   Structure of the Teraflops tile

Figure 8.23 provides an example of fault-tolerant routing. At reset and initialization time, all of the tiles in the array can be individually tested. Errors may be present in individual tiles or in the links between tiles. Figure 8.23, illustrates the situation in which an array has four dead tiles and a faulty link. Note that in Figure 8.23, several nodes have been marked as unsafe. These are removed from the array. In the center, they are removed to make the region containing the dead tiles a rectangle in order to simplify routing algorithms. The two unsafe tiles at the top right-hand corner have been removed because of the faulty link.

An interesting feature is the ability to issue instructions that send floating-point units to sleep or wake them up. This facility can be used to save power and reduce heat dissipation. It can be used dynamically to move active floating-point units round the chip to ensure that heat dissipation is averaged across the die. Power management is remarkably aggressive with the ability to put floating-point

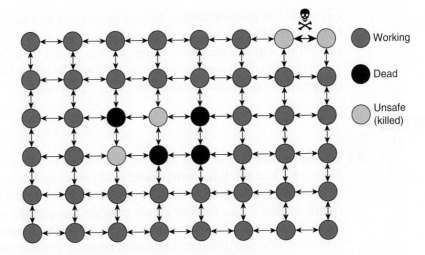

Figure 8.23 Example of fault tolerant routing

Source: M. Azimi *et al.*, Integration challenges and tradeoffs for Terascale architectures, *Intel Technology Journal*, 11(3), 173–184. Reprinted with permission of Intel Corporation.

units into 90% power down mode and to reduce the power consumption of most of the other elements of a tile by factors ranging from 10 to 72%.

A limitation of the instruction set is the provision of a single-level loop construct that uses the `INDEX`, `OFFSET`, and `BRNE` instructions. However, Teraflops was designed as a research machine.

SUMMARY

The (CPU) consists of four functional parts: the ALU, the register set, the internal bus, and the control unit. The first three parts can be combined into a single module called the datapath of the CPU. Based on the analysis of the instruction set architecture in Chapter 7, we present a similar analysis of the CPU organization in Section 8.2 and thus, distinguish among three types of CPU organizations: the CPU based on general-purpose registers (Section 8.2.1), the CPU based on an accumulator (Section 8.2.2), and the CPU based on a processor stack (Section 8.2.3). By the internal interconnection scheme, the structure of the CPU based on an accumulator is further distinguished between two types: connection on one, two, or three buses (Sections 8.3.1 and 8.3.2) and connection on an ALU (Section 8.3.3). The structure of the CPU based on general-purpose registers is emphasized and analyzed in Section 8.4. A practical CPU bit-slice device is chosen as a practical example of the CPU based on general-purpose registers. Its datapath and functional characteristics are described in Section 8.5. The increasing number of transistors per chip has made the construction of several processors in a single package a possibility. In the last section, we discussed the use of multiprocessing in graphics processing where thousands of cores are integrated on a chip. We also looked at the way in which some semiconductor manufacturers have approached the design and organization of their multi-core processors.

EXERCISES

8.1 The block diagrams of an 8×32-bit general-purpose register set are given in Figures 8.7 and 8.8. It has two parallel read ports and one write port controlled by two source addresses and one destination address. Modify the design of either circuit so that it can simultaneously provide two parallel read ports and two parallel write ports. The two write ports can receive two different data items and load them into two different destination registers without conflict. In case there are two different data items trying to go to the same register, the load command should be changed to a No-Operation (NOP) plus the generation of an error signal. This modification could be useful for exchanging the contents of two registers directly by hardware.

8.2 Consider the datapath of a single-bus accumulator-based CPU as shown in Figure 8.2. Both the word length and instruction length are 32 bits, and memory is byte-addressing.

Shown below is a short assembly-language code that calculates the absolute value of the difference of two numbers, $|M[1000] - M[1004]|$ without checking overflow and stores it in memory location 1008.

Address

400	LDA 1000	;	Load accumulator A with $M[1000]$
404	SUBA 1004	;	Subtract accumulator by $M[1004]$, keep status N
408	BGE $L1$	;	Branch if $A \geq 0$, that is, if $N = 0$, branch to $L1$, else continue
412	NEGA	;	Negate accumulator, that is, $A \leftarrow -(A)$
$L1$ = 416:	STA 1008	;	Store accumulator in memory location 1008

Design a timing sequence of microoperations that controls the execution of the above five instructions on the given datapath. Each instruction is controlled in several steps to implement a basic instruction cycle. For each step of control, you should design a control word of the format as given in Figure 8.24. The control word specifies all the required control signals acting on the above datapath. For simplicity, assume that the branch instruction is always taken, that is, the branch condition is always true.

Source onto bus				Load to register				ALU operation			External data to shifter			Shifter operation		Memory operation	
s3	s2	s1	s0	L3	L2	L1	L0	f2	f1	f0	D2	D1	D0	h1	h0	m1	m0

$s=0$ ALUres	$L=0$ MAR	$f=0$ OP1	$h=0$ no shift
$s=1$ A	$L=1$ A	$f=1$ OP2	$h=1$ external
$s=2$ MBR	$L=2$ MBR	$f=2$ OP1–OP2	$h=2$ ROT left
$s=3$ SP	$L=3$ SP	$f=3$ OP2–OP1	with C
$s=4$ Q	$L=4$ Q	$f=4$ OP1+OP2	$h=3$ ROT right
$s=5$ X	$L=5$ X	$f=5$ OP1 xor OP2	with C
$s=6$ PC	$L=6$ PC	$f=6$ OP1 and OP2	
$s=7$ IR*	$L=7$ IR	$f=7$ OP1 or OP2	
	$L=8$ SR		
	$L=9$ Latch1		
	$L=10$ Latch2		

Memory operation: $m=0$ none, $m=1$ read, $m=2$ write

IR* means the second field of IR, i.e., the memory address, immediate data, or offset for branch instructions. $s>7$ or $L>10$ means none.

Figure 8.24 Format of the control word for Problem 8.2

Your designed timing sequence should be written in a table giving the time and microoperations involved for each instruction and the active bits of the corresponding control word. [Note: You must modify and complete the datapath in Figure 8.2.]

8.3 Repeat Problem 8.2 with the same short assembly-language code running on the datapath given in Figure 8.4 with an accumulator-based CPU built on a two-bus structure. [Note: You must modify and complete the datapath in Figure 8.4.]

8.4 Repeat Problem 8.2 with the same short assembly-language code running on the datapath given in Figure 8.5 with an accumulator-based CPU built on a three-bus structure. [Note: You must modify and complete the datapath in Figure 8.5.]

8.5 Repeat Problem 8.2 with the same short assembly-language code running on the datapath given in Figures 8.6 with an accumulator-based CPU built on an ALU. [Note: You must redesign the format of the control word in order to completely match the datapath in Figure 8.6.]

8.6 This problem is similar to Problem 8.2, but on a datapath of the CPU based on a general-purpose register set as shown in Figure 8.9 (with a constant "4" instead of "1" on the input OP2 of the ALU).

The assembly-language code for the same problem of calculating the absolute value of the difference of two numbers, M[1000] and M[1004], is given as follows:

Address
```
400  LW R1, 1000(R₀)      ; Load word: R1 ← M[0 + 1000]
404  LW R2, 1004(R₀)      ; Load word: R2 ← M[0 + 1004]
408  SUB R3, R1, R2       ; Subtract: R3 ← (R1) − (R2)
```

```
412  BGE R3, L1              ; Branch if (R3) ≥ 0, i.e., branch to L1,
                               else continue
416  SUB R3, R2, R1          ; Subtract: R3 ← (R2) – (R1)
L1 = 420:  SW 1008(R0), R3   ; Store word: M[0 + 1008] ← (R3)
```

Note: LW Rd, disp(Rs) executes the steps: MAR ¬ (Rs) + disp; ReadM;
Rd ¬ (MBR).

BGE $R3$, $L1$(converted into offset):
if branch condition = true, PC ¬ (PC)updated + offset
SW disp(Rs), Rd executes the steps: MAR ¬ (Rs) + disp;
MBR ¬ (Rd); WriteM

The control word for the above datapath can be designed using the format as shown in Figure 8.25.

The other conditions and requirements are the same as in Problem 8.2. Assume that the branch instruction is taken. Your designed timing sequence should be written in a table of similar format as in Problem 8.2.

Operand1					Operand2								Destination			ALU operation			Memory operation	
$u1_1$	$u1_0$	$s1_2$	$s1_1$	$s1_0$	$u2_1$	$u2_0$	$s2_2$	$s2_1$	$s2_0$	v_2	v_1	v_0	$d2$	$d1$	$d0$	$f2$	$f1$	$f0$	$m1$	$m0$

$h=0$ as default value.

Branch condition is not considered at this moment.

$f=0$ OP1
$f=1$ OP2
$f=2$ OP1 – OP2
$f=3$ OP2 – OP1
$f=4$ OP1 + OP2
$f=5$ OP1 xor OP2
$f=6$ OP1 and OP2
$f=7$ OP1 or OP2

$m=0$ none
$m=1$ read
$m=2$ write

Figure 8.25 Format of the control word for Problem 8.6

8.7 Referring to the block diagram of an Am2901 CPU bit-slice device in Figure 8.10 and the function table of its ALU in Table 5.19, derive the following function tables for describing the complete arithmetic-logic functionality of the device:

(a) The function table for the source operand selection by the input multiplexers for the ALU, that is, the table for OP1 and OP2 in terms of the operand select code $s2s1s0$.

(b) A complete function table for the arithmetic operations performed by the ALU of the Am2901 device in terms of the combination of the function select code $f2f1f0$ and the operand select code $s2s1s0$. Note that the input carry of the device, Cn, should be considered as an input variable to be included in the table such that the ALU actually performs OP1 + OP2 + Cn or OP1 – OP2 – Cn .

(c) A complete function table for the logic operations performed by the ALU of the Am2901 device similar to the table in Part (b).

8.8 Referring to the material of Am2901 bit-slice device described in Section 8.5, design a 16-bit CPU using four Am2901 chips (using ripple-carry connections between chips) to implement the datapath and control for a small instruction set given in Table 8.5. All the eight instructions are of two-address format as shown in Figure 8.26.

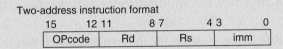

Two-address instruction format

15	12	11	8	7	4	3	0
OPcode		Rd		Rs		imm	

Figure 8.26 Instruction format for Problem 8.8

Table 8.5 Instruction set for Problem 8.8

OPcode $x_2x_1x_0$	Mnemonic	Name	Operation	Remarks
0 0 0	ADD	add	$Rd \leftarrow (Rd) + (Rs)$	*imm* field is don't care
0 0 1	ADDI	add *imm*	$Rd \leftarrow (Rs) + imm$	$0 \le imm \le 15$
0 1 0	SUB	subtract	$Rd \leftarrow (Rd) - (Rs)$	*imm* field is don't care
0 1 1	SUBI	sub *imm*	$Rd \leftarrow (Rs) - imm$	$0 \le imm \le 15$
1 0 0	AND	and	$Rd \leftarrow (Rd) \wedge (Rs)$	*imm* field is don't care
1 0 1	OR	or	$Rd \leftarrow (Rd) \vee (Rs)$	*imm* field is don't care
1 1 0	XOR	xor	$Rd \leftarrow (Rd) \oplus (Rs)$	*imm* field is don't care
1 1 1	LSH	logic shift	$Rd \leftarrow (Rs) << 1$ $Rd \leftarrow (Rs) >> 1$ $Rd \leftarrow (Rs)$ no shift	if *imm* = 1 if *imm* = + 1 Signed *imm* is in *Rs* field if *imm* = 0

Your task is to choose the corresponding control signals of the Am2901 chip for implementation of the eight required functions for the operands stored in the register set. Since the operations of instruction fetch and operand fetch from memory are not considered, the execution of each of the above-listed ALU operations requires only one clock cycle. Give the following results of design:

(a) The datapath inside the chip used by each instruction with possible specially designed additional datapath connected from outside the chip if necessary.

(b) The truth table with the control signals as output variables and the instruction fields as input variables.

(c) The simplified expressions for the control signals in terms of the instruction fields.

(d) The circuit diagram with the Am2901 devices and external circuits if necessary.

8.9 What is a multi-core processor?

8.10 Is an n-core multiprocessor n times as fast as the equivalent single-core processor? Give your reasoning.

8.11 What, if any, is the difference between a multi-core processor and a coprocessor?

8.12 What is the difference between a multi-core processor and a GPU?

9

The Control Unit

9.1 FUNCTIONS AND GENERAL ORGANIZATION OF A CONTROL UNIT

The control unit of a computer may perform many functions involving the control of the CPU, memory, and I/O. This is the most common understanding of a control unit. However, in the design of the control unit of contemporary computers, there exist the following tendencies:

- I/O and memory often use asynchronous control, which can be better suited to the particular operating modes and speed characteristics of I/O and memory, as compared to those of the CPU. Therefore, the control of I/O and memory may not rely on synchronous control by means of a central clock.

- In order to relieve the CPU of the burden of control functions, the control part of a computer is usually not designed as a centralized, system-wide unit. Distributed, decentralized control is more advantageous than centralized control, in the sense that the control functions can be distributed over all the functional units of a computer. I/O and memory thus become autonomous functional units with their own control units.

- The control unit is the most nonstandard part of a computer. Decentralization of control functions allows the control unit to be standardized in the form of small blocks that perform local specialized functions. Because different instruction sets require different control, the most flexible and common way to achieve standardization of CPU control is microprogramming.

These considerations make it reasonable to discuss a control unit that acts primarily on the CPU for execution of instructions, as shown in Figure 5.1.

However, in order to control CPU instructions, the control unit must also handle memory access and interrupt. Interrupt is the primary means by which the CPU gets involved in I/O operations. Specifically, a control unit performs the following functions:

- The generation of a central clock signal.

- The generation of timing signals, that is, a sequence of control voltages and pulses that serves as the time base for the synchronous control of various machine instructions.

- The generation of the control signals required by the execution of a basic instruction cycle (as stated in Sections 8.2.1 and 8.2.2). This instruction cycle is divided into phases that perform functions such as instruction fetch, instruction decode, address generation, operand fetch, instruction execution, and result store. The control unit generates all the control signals for these operations, including memory access operations, at prespecified time points.

- The providing of responses to interrupt requests issued to the CPU from various interrupt sources, including I/O devices. The term *interrupt* may include general cases known as *exceptions*, which are caused by various hardware and software events. Exception or interrupt handling requires the CPU to cease execution of the current program, save the program context, identify the interrupt source, and transfer control to the corresponding interrupt service routine. Upon servicing the interrupt, if no new interrupt request is pending, the CPU must resume the execution of the interrupted program. This process is controlled by the control unit.

We will describe the principles and design methodology for a control unit using the specific example of a simple computer. Either a RISC or a CISC computer could be chosen as an example. Since RISC machines have become more popular in recent years, we will use an example of a simple RISC computer based on a CPU organization of general-purpose registers. The main difference between a RISC machine and a CISC machine is in the instruction set. Given a particular instruction set, the same methodology can be applied to the design of a CISC machine.

9.2   PRELIMINARY STEPS FOR DESIGNING CONTROL CIRCUITS

Before designing the complete control unit of a simple computer, we will introduce some basic concepts and methodologies for designing simple control circuits for individual operations, such as signal generators, serial binary adders, and sequential multipliers.

9.2.1 Control Voltage Signals vs. Control Pulse Signals

For instruction execution control at the register-transfer level, we need to use two types of control signals—voltage signals and pulse signals. Both types of signals are useful for control, but they perform different control actions. Generally speaking, combinational circuits generate and transfer information using voltage signals because the output voltage of the combinational circuit can maintain a stable level, High or Low, as long as the input voltages do not change. Sequential circuits are different. They have memory elements (e.g., flip-flops) that require voltage signals and pulse signals to match in order to store information. Let us look at a typical case common to the design of a control unit at the register-transfer level, as shown in Figure 9.1. Usually a *central signal generator* generates a sequence of central voltage signals and central pulse signals from a central clock. In the control unit, these central control signals are used to create various specific control signals acting on the combinational circuits and registers in the datapath of the CPU. Suppose the output voltage of a source register carrying some information is transferred to the input of a destination register. During data transfer, source information is processed by the combinational circuits in the datapath to produce new information. When this information, represented by a voltage signal, reaches the data input (e.g., D or J,K) of a destination flip-flop, a control pulse signal is needed on the flip-flop's clock input to receive and store it. Therefore, the voltage signal carries useful information and the pulse signal determines the time at which the information is stored in a register. Although both the voltage signal and the pulse signal may be delayed during transfer, the correct design of the control should minimize the delay of the pulse signal rather than the delay of the voltage signal. Thus, for a given register, there should be a larger delay associated with the voltage signal than with the pulse signal. The correct timing relationship between the control voltage and the control pulse involves having the voltage signal at the data input of a flip-flop stabilized before the pulse signal on the clock input of the flip-flop reaches its rising edge. In other

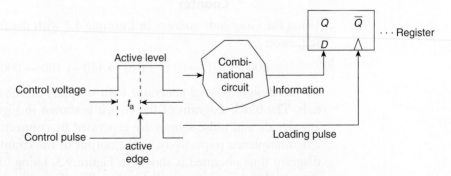

Figure 9.1 Cooperation between a control voltage and a control pulse

words, the rising edge of the pulse signal must fall within the range of the active level of the voltage signal. This rule is depicted in Figure 9.1, where t_a denotes the time between the rising edge of the active level of the control voltage and the rising edge of the control pulse. This time is the maximum time allowable for the voltage signal to propagate with delay and become stabilized before the pulse signal reaches its rising edge. It is also the maximum allowable time used to compensate the delay introduced by the combinational circuit to process information from its source register to its destination register.

9.2.2 Design of a Signal Generator Based on a Counter

The above analysis shows a typical pattern of control voltage signals and control pulse signals that we expect to create from a central signal generator. In general, we want to repeatedly generate this pattern a specified number of times and use time-multiplexing to distribute the patterns on multiple output channels from the signal generator. Therefore, a counter can be used for controlling the number of repeated patterns. In Chapter 4, we learned how to design a counter that provides a means to count events in a sequential order according to a prespecified counting sequence. However, except for the state variables at the outputs of the flip-flops, a counter does not generate specific control signals that can control these events and perform the required operations. Therefore, we need to extend the counter design to the design of a signal generator based on a counter. Specifically, we will use a Gray code counter to design a signal generator in the next example. Since the Gray code sequence has the advantage of changing only one bit between any two neighboring codes, the Gray code counter is especially suitable for the implementation of a signal generator that decodes the state variables of the counter into output voltage signals with smooth waveforms that are free of glitches.

Example 9.1   Design of a Signal Generator Based on a Gray Code Counter

Using the Gray code counter in Example 4.2 with the following counting sequence:

$$000 \rightarrow 001 \rightarrow 011 \rightarrow 010 \rightarrow 110 \rightarrow 100 \rightarrow 000 \text{ (repeat)}$$

we can design a signal generator with six pairs of voltage and pulse signals. The block diagram of the circuit is shown in Figure 9.2. The voltage signals and pulse signals are generated by connecting a decoder and a demultiplexer, respectively, to the output of the counter. The waveform diagram thus obtained is shown in Figure 9.3. Using $\overline{Clock}$ to enable the demultiplexer (i.e., a controllable decoder) allows the $\overline{Clock}$ to be ANDed with the voltage signals and generates the pulse signals matching the voltage signals in the manner shown in Figure 9.1.

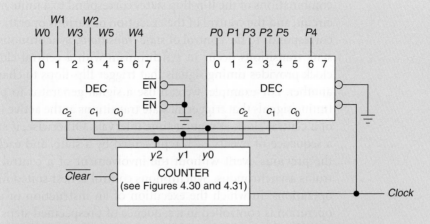

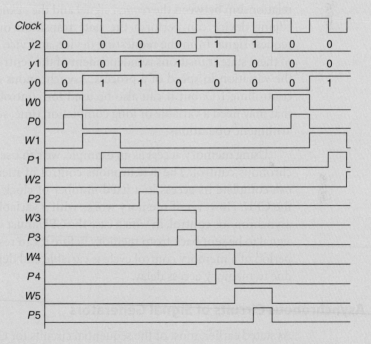

Figure 9.2   Block diagram of the signal generator of Example 9.1

Figure 9.3   Waveform diagram of the signal generator in Figure 9.2

9.2.3 Synchronous Control vs. Asynchronous Control

In designing a control unit, we distinguish between two control methods—*synchronous* control and *asynchronous* control. In Chapter 4, we introduced the concepts of synchronous and asynchronous logic circuits, based on a general model of sequential logic circuits. According to this model, a sequential circuit can be abstracted as a *finite-state machine*. The values represented by different combinations of the flip-flop states correspond to a finite number of *states* of the circuit, and the control of the execution of various operations on these flip-flops corresponds to the control of *state transitions*. Synchronous control requires that state transitions occur in synchronism with a central clock. That is, a central clock provides timing signals that trigger flip-flops to change from one state to another. For example, we can use a signal generator to provide a sequence of timing signals that trigger all state transitions at the active (rising or falling) edge of a central clock at regular time intervals. Otherwise, if state transitions create a sequence of events each represented by a state, and each event is invoked by the previous event without the involvement of a central clock, then the control is asynchronous. Synchronous control is best suited for the control of CPU operations, in which the execution of an instruction or a complex arithmetic operation is controlled in a sequence of prespecified steps in synchronism with a central clock. Asynchronous control is based on a different principle, in which state transitions between events are controlled by *handshaking*, which defines the relationship between the *request* signal and the *acknowledge* signal. The acknowledging device can perform the state transition only after it has received the request signal from the requesting device, and vice versa. Therefore, the control of these state transitions is independent of the central clock and can better match the variation in speed of a process. Asynchronous control is normally used for controlling I/O, but it can also be used for controlling the step(s) of a process that may need a variable or long completion time, such as memory and complex arithmetic operations.

Using memory access as an example, we can use either synchronous or asynchronous control. The synchronous control of memory assumes that memory can complete its access in a fixed number of clock cycles, in synchronism with the CPU. However, if memory works with a variable delay, we should switch to asynchronous control, in which case the CPU must wait for a *memory completion* signal to be sent back from memory before it can resume its operation. Thus, the period of a memory control cycle is variable and depends upon the waiting time due to memory access delay.

9.2.4 Asynchronous Circuits of Signal Generators

As stated earlier, most of the sequential circuits for CPU control are synchronous circuits. However, the *clock generators* used to feed these circuits with clock signals should be asynchronous circuits because they contain a part of the circuit that must be manually operated. The human operator can start or stop these clock signals at any random time, asynchronously, with respect to the main clock signal generated by a crystal oscillator in the computer. A manually controllable clock generator can work in different modes:

- *Start/Stop mode.* This mode is asynchronous with respect to the central clock since the operation is controlled by a human operator.

- *Single step mode.* This mode is synchronous with respect to the central clock since at each step of the operation, the clock may be stopped and restarted by a signal coming from a control signal issued for that operation. For example, during hardware debugging of instructions, we may need to stop and then restart the clock at every instruction or every step of an instruction. Therefore, the stop duration of this mode can vary.

- *Continuous mode.* This mode is used during the normal operation of a computer. It generates a continuous stream of clock signals that can be used by a *signal generator* to organize the control signals into multiple phases and control cycles.

With the aid of an additional control circuit, a clock generator can easily be upgraded into a signal generator that can have additional operational modes:

- *Single-sequence mode.* Generate a single sequence of control cycles of a fixed length, with each control cycle consisting of a voltage signal and a pulse signal, which form a control pattern like the one shown in Figure 9.1. The active edge of each control pulse must lie within the range of the active level of the corresponding control voltage. For example, a signal generator can generate a sequence of eight channels of voltage signals named $W0$, $W1$, …, $W7$ and eight channels of pulse signals named $p0$, $p1$, …, $p7$ to cooperatively or separately control eight sequential steps of an instruction or an operation running in a single iteration.

- *Multi-sequence mode.* Repeat the above sequence of control cycles of fixed length for a specified number of times. This mode may be used to control either a set of instructions or a set of operations running successively.

- *Continuous mode.* Similar to the multi-sequence mode, but it continues the sequences of control cycles until the sequence is stopped by a stop command or by a control signal feedback from the control unit.

Now, we will provide some examples of designing signal generators for general-purpose use, especially for use in the design of relatively simple functional units and control units for mini-projects and laboratory exercises.

Example 9.2 Design of a Signal Generator Operating in Single-Sequence Mode

The circuit diagram of a signal generator that generates a single sequence of eight channels of voltage signals, $W0$, $W1$, …, $W7$, and eight channels of pulse signals, $P0$, $P1$, …, $P7$ is given in Figure 9.4. Each pair of Wi and Pi, for $i = 0, 1, …, 7$, forms a control pattern as shown in Figure 9.1. The circuit diagram consists of three major parts: (1) a manually operated clock generator, (2) a control counter, and (3) two decoders.

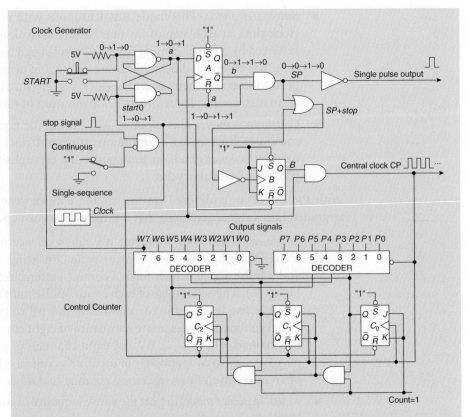

Figure 9.4 Circuit diagram of the signal generator in Example 9.2

The clock generator uses a push-button switch to start operation. Since the manual operation can push the *START* button at any random time independent of the clock, it must be synchronized with the clock so that all the clock signals output from the circuit have regular waveforms and the number of output signals is under the control of the circuit. The basic principle of designing an asynchronous circuit for the purpose of synchronization is as follows:

1. Use the manually created pulse to trigger a *synchronizing flip-flop* (denoted by *A* in Figure 9.4) to generate a single pulse that has a deterministic timing relationship with respect to the clock.
2. Use this single pulse to trigger another *output flip-flop* (denoted by *B* in Figure 9.4) that enables the clock pulses to be output from the circuit.

3. When a stop pulse needs to stop the output sequence of clock signals, it triggers flip-flop B back to its original state to prevent clock pulses from getting pass the output gate.

The second and third steps of the design stated above can easily be seen in Figure 9.4. Flip-flop B is connected as a T flip-flop so that it can be triggered successively between two states, which enable and disable the clock by way of a pulse named "$SP + stop$," which results from ORing along with the single pulse SP, and the *stop* pulse.

Now, we will study the first step of the above design. The process of generating the single pulse, SP, from the manually created pulse can be seen from the waveform diagram in Figure 9.5 and the result of circuit tracing in Figure 9.4. The waveforms at the points "*start0*" and "*a*" are due to the manual operation $1 \to 0 \to 1$. This causes flip-flop A to change initially from state "1" to state "0", but later flip-flop A changes back to state "1" according to the rising edge of the clock, as seen from the waveform at point "*b*". By ANDing together the signals at points a and b, we get the required single pulse SP. It can be clearly seen that the falling edge of this single pulse has been synchronized with the clock. However, if we want

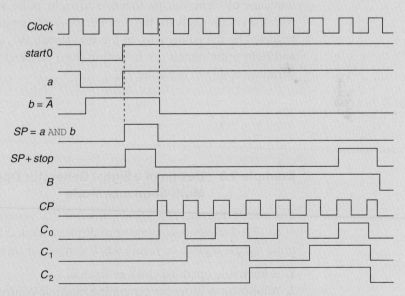

Figure 9.5 Waveform diagram of the signal generator in Figure 9.4

to use its rising edge for the purpose of synchronization, we should use its inverted pulse. Therefore, we use SP to trigger flip-flop B and output through an inverter, and output the inverted single pulse, $\overline{SP}$, for external use.

Now, we will look at the other two parts of the signal generator—the control counter and its associated decoders. Flip-flop B was initialized to state "0" by the signal "$start0$". After it is triggered by the signal "$SP + stop$" to state "1", it can output a continuous stream of controllable clock pulses, CP, from its output gate for outside use, as shown in Figure 9.4. This stream of clock pulses can also feed the control counter, which changes its state every clock cycle at the rising edge of the clock signal. The output of the counter is decoded by two 3×8 decoders into eight channels of voltage signals, $W0$, $W1$, …, $W7$, and eight channels of pulse signals, $P0$, $P1$, …, $P7$. The second decoder for generation of pulse signals works as a demultiplexer by connecting the clock signal on its *enable* input. Hence, the *clock* signal is ANDed with the voltage signals to create the corresponding pulse signals, with a timing relationship clearly seen in Figure 9.5. If we feedback the signal $W7$ (or $P7$) to stop the counter and the signal generator is set to the "single sequence" mode of operation, the signal generator issues a single sequence of eight voltage signals and eight pulse signals and then stops, with the circuit ready for the next iteration of operation. Since flip-flop B is triggered by the falling edge of the stop signal, $W7$, all eight voltage signals and eight pulse signals can be output from the clock generator during each iteration, as shown in Figure 9.5.

∎

Example 9.3   Design of a Signal Generator Operating in Multi-Sequence Mode

The circuit diagram of a signal generator that generates a variable number (1 to 15) of sequences (single or multiple sequences) of voltage signals and pulse signals is given in Figure 9.6. It consists of three major parts:

1. A manually operated clock generator,
2. A Johnson counter for generating multiple control signals, and
3. A control counter for controlling the number of sequences.

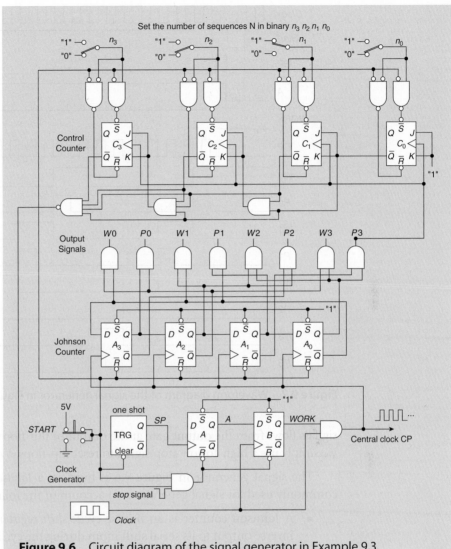

Figure 9.6 Circuit diagram of the signal generator in Example 9.3. ∎

The clock generator in Figure 9.6 is designed on the same principles as the circuit in Figure 9.4, but with a small difference. We use a special electronic device called a *one shot* to automatically create a single pulse, *SP*, which is then synchronized with the clock using two flip-flops, *A* and *B*, in the same way as in Figure 9.4. The single pulse triggers flip-flop *A* so as to convert itself into a voltage, and this voltage is applied to the input of flip-flop *B*. When flip-flop *B* is triggered by the clock, it can create an output voltage, *WORK*, synchronized to the clock. The relationship between the rising edge of *WORK* and the rising edge of the clock is shown in the waveform diagram in Figure 9.7. A stream of controllable clock

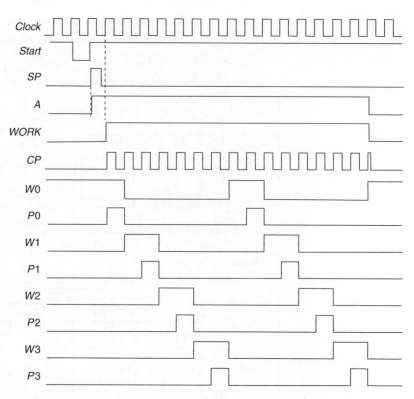

Figure 9.7 Waveform diagram of the signal generator in Figure 9.6.

signals flows from the output gate at the output of flip-flop *B*. To stop the clock, we simply use a high-to-low stop signal to reset flip-flops *A* and *B* to state "0".

The signal generator in Figure 9.6 is built on a *Johnson counter*, which is commonly used for signal generation on account of the following advantages:

- A Johnson counter is an *inverse cyclic shift register* that feeds back its inverse output to its serial shift input during the cyclic shift (either left or right) operation. Hence, the circuit of a Johnson counter is simpler than that of an ordinary binary counter.

- During any shift operation, there is only one bit changing between two successive codes of a Johnson counter. Therefore, when the output of the Johnson counter is decoded to generate control signals, the waveforms of the output signals are smoother than those from a binary counter. The waveforms are free of glitches.

- An *n*-bit Johnson counter generates only 2*n* distinct codes as compared to the 2^n codes of an *n*-bit binary counter. Decoding 2*n* codes is much simpler than decoding a full set of binary codes if we take advantage of don't care conditions. As an example, the decoding table for a 4-bit

Johnson counter is given in Table 9.1. It contains three different decoding schemes with different numbers and combinations of voltage signals and pulse signals. None of these schemes uses AND gates with more than two inputs. If we use a 3-bit binary counter to generate eight signals, we would need three-input AND gates, and the combination of neighboring codes would not be as simple as that shown in Table 9.1.

The circuit in Figure 9.6 uses Decoding Scheme 2 for designing and implementing the signal generator. The waveform diagram shown in Figure 9.7 is based on the logic expressions of Table 9.1. It depicts the four voltage signals—$W0$, $W1$, $W2$, and $W3$—and the four enclosed pulse signals—$P0$, $P1$, $P2$, and $P3$. Each of the Wi signals for $i = 0, 1, ..., 3$ combines two neighboring codes $0000 + 1000, 1100 + 1110, ..., 0011 + 0001$, respectively. The other two decoding schemes are also possible and are simple to implement as follows:

- *Decoding Scheme 1:*

  The eight voltage signals, $W0$, $W1$, ..., $W7$, can be operating individually and also ANDed with the inverted clock pulse $\overline{CP}$ to produce eight pulse signals, $P0$, $P1$, ..., $P7$. Each pair of Wi and Pi, for $i = 0, 1, ..., 7$, can work cooperatively in the control pattern shown in Figure 9.1.

Table 9.1 Decoding of individual codes or combinations of codes in a Johnson counter

Codes in order A3 A2 A1 A0	Decoding Scheme 1 W0 – W7 individually	Decoding Scheme 2 W0, P0 – W3, P3 each W combines two	Decoding Scheme 3 W0, P0 – W1, P1 each W combines four
0 0 0 0	$\overline{A3} \cdot \overline{A0}$	$W0 = \overline{A2} \cdot \overline{A0}$	
1 0 0 0	$A3 \cdot \overline{A2}$	$P0 = A3 \cdot \overline{A2}$	$W0 = \overline{A0}$
1 1 0 0	$A2 \cdot \overline{A1}$	$W1 = A2 \cdot \overline{A0}$	$P0 = A1 \cdot \overline{A0}$
1 1 1 0	$A1 \cdot \overline{A0}$	$P1 = A1 \cdot \overline{A0}$	
1 1 1 1	$A3 \cdot A0$	$W2 = A2 \cdot A0$	
0 1 1 1	$\overline{A3} \cdot A2$	$P2 = \overline{A3} \cdot A2$	$W1 = A0$
0 0 1 1	$\overline{A2} \cdot A1$	$W3 = \overline{A2} \cdot A0$	$P1 = \overline{A1} \cdot A0$
0 0 0 1	$\overline{A1} \cdot A0$	$P3 = \overline{A1} \cdot A0$	

- *Decoding Scheme 3:*

   This is a two-phase control signal scheme—$W0$, $P0$ and $W1$, $P1$. The two pulse signals are taken from the original voltage signals $W3$ and $W7$ as in Scheme 1, but the voltage signals are four times wider than the original voltage signals by combining four successive codes such that

$$W0 = 0000 + 1000 + 1100 + 1110 \text{ and}$$
$$W1 = 1111 + 0111 + 0011 + 0001.$$

   This decoding scheme may allow the voltage signals to propagate through slower combinational circuits with longer delay times than in Decoding Schemes 1 and 2.

   Now, we will look at the control counter C as the third part of the circuit diagram in Figure 9.6. With the aid of this counter, the sequence $W0$, $P0 - W3$, $P3$ can be generated repeatedly for a specified number of iterations. Since the number of iterations can vary in the range of 1 to 15, the counter is designed as a 4-bit binary down counter. The binary code of the specified number of iterations is previously set on four binary switches. When the signal generator starts its operation, the *START* bush-button switch initializes the counter to this number. Then, at the end of every sequence, the counter will be decremented by "1" using the ending pulse signal $P3$. When the count in the control counter C reaches zero, a signal carrying the condition $\overline{C_3} \cdot \overline{C_2} \cdot \overline{C_1} \cdot \overline{C_0} = 1$ will be used to trigger the flip-flop B and stop the clock generator. The waveform diagram for the case of setting the number of iterations to "2" is shown in Figure 9.7.

9.3 DESIGN OF THE SEQUENTIAL CONTROL OF ARITHMETIC OPERATIONS

In this section, we will look at the control of some arithmetic operations that need to use the sequential control signals we have generated in the last section. The complex arithmetic operations we studied in Chapter 6 can use different methods of control. The simplest direct hardware method is to execute the operation in a sequential order of microoperations and control this sequence of microoperations by a signal generator to perform the required sequential control. Two examples will be given below.

9.3.1 Design of a Bit-Serial Adder

A bit-serial adder uses the minimum hardware—a single 1-bit full adder—to perform n-bit addition/subtraction in a serial fashion, where n is the word length. Each time, it performs 1-bit addition and saves the carry, but repeats the operation n times. Bit-serial adders were used in the early days of first-generation computers when hardware was very expensive. They were also used more recently in large-scale *array processors*, which perform a large number of parallel operations on a large number of processing elements interconnected in a two-dimensional array, where each processing element can be simply a 1-bit full adder. This mode of parallel operation can be viewed as a mode of *word-parallel bit-serial* processing. Now, we will make use of the principles of operation of a bit-serial adder to describe the design methodology of a control unit for controlling the sequencing of activities in a sequential operation.

The block diagram of the bit-serial adder together with two n-bit shift registers and an incomplete control unit is shown in Figure 9.8.

The bit-serial adder consists of a 1-bit combinational full adder connected to a flip-flop, C, which serves as the memory element for storing the carry signal. In each clock period, the full adder adds three pieces of 1-bit data:

the 1-bit operand A_i,
the 1-bit operand B_i, and
the current carry, C_{i-1}, supplied from the flip-flop C.

Each time, the adder produces two 1-bit results:

the 1-bit sum S_i, and
the next carry, C_i, which is saved back to the flip-flop C.

Before operation, the two shift registers, RA and RB, are loaded with the two's complement codes of the two operands, A and B, respectively, and then set to the modes of "right shift" and "right rotate," respectively. Hence, during operation, two n-bit serial binary codes are supplied to the inputs A_i and B_i of the full adder from RA and RB, respectively, with the LSBs going first. After operation, the shift register RB keeps the operand B unchanged, while the shift register

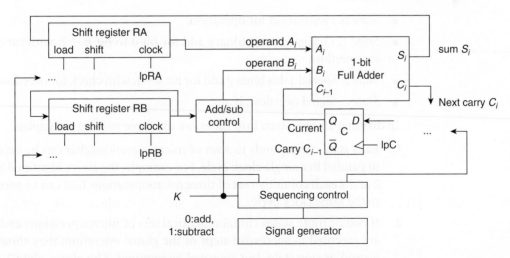

Figure 9.8 Block diagram of a bit-serial adder with registers and control

RA replaces its original operand A with the result of the operation (the original operand A was overwritten). The control of the serial adder must satisfy the following requirements:

- The serial adder can perform two's complement addition $A + B$ and subtraction $A - B$, selected by a control signal, K, such that when $K = 0$, the adder performs addition, when $K = 1$, the adder performs subtraction. This means that every bit of the operand B, including its sign bit, input to the full adder, should be inverted if $K = 1$.

- The control unit should initially load the shift registers, RA and RB, with the operand data, A and B, respectively, from outside and then set to their working modes, "right shift" for RA and "right rotate" for RB.

- In the first cycle of operation, the input C_{i-1} of the full adder should automatically receive the initial carry "0" for addition and "1" for subtraction, while in all subsequent cycles it receives the current carry from the output of the flip-flop C.

- In the last cycle of operation, the serial adder should check the status of overflow by comparing the carry into the sign bit, C_{n-2}, and the carry out of the sign bit, C_{n-1}, and then signal an error condition if overflow occurs.

- The 1-bit operation of the full adder should repeat n times for the given word length n.

To design the control unit in the model of a finite-state machine, we draw the state diagram for the n-bit serial adder as shown in Figure 9.9. By the functions of the control unit specified above, we can distinguish among four functionally distinct states:

- *State 0.* Preparation for operation,
- *State 1.* Ordinary 1-bit binary add for bit 0 to bit $n - 2$, without check for overflow,
- *State 2.* Special 1-bit binary add for bit $n - 1$, with check for overflow, and
- *State 3.* Signal overflow, if any.

In dividing an operation into states, we use three guiding principles:

1. Each state corresponds to a set of microoperations that can be executed in parallel in a single clock cycle. For example, the above identified States 0 and 2 each contains a set of three microoperations that can be executed in the same clock cycle.

2. If two or more states contain identical sets of microoperations and they are executed in successive steps of the global operation, they should be viewed as one state, but repeated as required. The above State 1 is an example of such a state, which should be repeated $n - 1$ times.

3.   The division of states must follow the execution steps of the global operation.

The state diagram derived in Figure 9.9 can be mapped to a timing chart called an *operation chart*, as shown in Figure 9.10. Like a state graph, the operation chart is also a graphical form that shows the execution steps of an operation, but it depicts the physical implementation of the state diagram on the control hardware. In the operation chart, the entire operation is also decomposed into a sequence of microoperations, which are then scheduled into the successive time slots of the chart. Each state in the state diagram is mapped to a control cycle in the operation chart. Hence, the operation chart gives more specific information about the schedule of microoperations than the state diagram. For example,

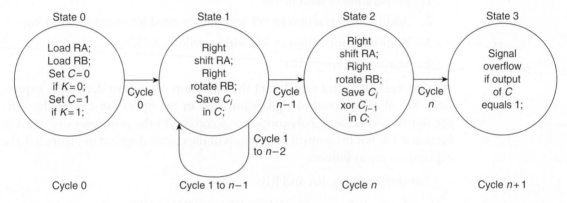

Figure 9.9   State diagram for the *n*-bit serial adder in Figure 9.8.

W0	W1	W2	W3
P0	P1	P2	P3
RA ← OPA	RightShift RA	RightShift RA	Signal
lpRA	lpRA	lpRA	overflow
RB ← OPB	RightRotate RB	RightRotate RB	if $C_{i-1}=1$
lpRB	lpRB	lpRB	
$C \leftarrow 0$ if $K=0$	$C \leftarrow C_i$	$C \leftarrow C_i \oplus C_{i-1}$	
$C \leftarrow 1$ if $K=1$	lpC	lpC	
lpC			
CR ← 0	CR ← CR + 1	CR ← CR + 1	
lpCR	lpCR	lpCR	
goto W1	goto W2	goto W3	goto W0
if *run* = 1	if CR = *n* − 1	if C = 1	set *run* = 0
		goto W0	
		if C = 0	

Figure 9.10   Operation chart of the control unit for the serial adder in Figure 9.8

the operation chart gives the names of all the control voltage signals and control pulse signals that implement the corresponding microoperations. It also gives the timing and logic conditions for each control command to be activated. Therefore, an operation chart is actually a space-time diagram for the activities of a control unit, since horizontally it represents the "time" axis in terms of the control voltage signals and control pulse signals, and vertically it represents the "space" axis in terms of the control commands and their logic conditions. Therefore, it is easy to derive the logic expressions for the control signals directly from the operation chart, as we can see later in the design of a control unit.

As we see from the operation chart in Figure 9.10, the entire operation of serial addition/subtraction is composed of four control cycles:

1. Preparation of data in $W0$
2. Addition/subtraction in $W1$ without the need for overflow checking
3. Addition/subtraction in $W2$ with overflow checking
4. Signal overflow in $W3$

The next step after scheduling the operation chart is to derive the expressions for all of the control signals involved in the operation chart. The voltage signals and pulse signals cooperate according to the principles discussed in Section 9.2.1. For the control commands in the circuit diagram in Figure 9.8, the expressions are as follows:

For shift registers, RA and RB:

$$load = W0 \qquad \text{for RA} \leftarrow OPA \text{ and } RB \leftarrow OPB$$
$$shift = W1 + W2 \quad \text{for Right Shift RA and Right Rotate RB}$$
$$lpRA = lpRB = P0 + P1 + P2 \tag{9.1}$$

For flip-flop, C:

$$\text{input on } D = W0 \cdot K + W1 \cdot C_i + W2 \cdot (C_i \oplus C_{i-1})$$
$$lpC = P0 + P1 + P2 \tag{9.2}$$

For the overflow signal:

$$overflow = W3 \cdot C_{i-1} \tag{9.3}$$

The circuit for implementation of these expressions is omitted.

Now, we will do the last step of design—the design of the signal generator for implementation of the "time" axis of the operation chart in Figure 9.10. Since we have four states, $W0 - W3$, we need to use two JK flip-flops, C_1 and C_0, with the following state assignments in a Gray code sequence:

$$C_1C_0 = 00 = W0, \quad C_1C_0 = 01 = W1, \quad C_1C_0 = 11 = W2, \quad C_1C_0 = 10 = W3.$$

This assignment simplifies the circuit of the signal generator due to the property of Gray code. From the operation chart, we derive the state-transition diagram as shown in Figure 9.11.

The operation starts from state $W0$, in which the registers, RA and RB, and the flip-flop, C, are initialized as required. Only when the command "*run*" is asserted to "1", the state $W0$ is allowed to make a transition to state $W1$. Then, the state $W1$ should be repeated $n - 1$ times to allow the bit-serial operation to be performed successively on the operands of bit 0 to bit $n - 2$. Therefore, we need a counter, CR, to count the number of iterations by pulse signal $p1$. When the counter reaches $n - 1$, state $W1$ should make a transition to state $W2$, in which the adder performs its bit-serial operation on the operands of the last bit and, at the same time, checks for overflow by comparing carry signals C_{n-1} and C_{n-2}. So, the operation stays in state $W2$ only once, and then goes to either state $W0$ if overflow did not occur or state $W3$ if overflow occurred. In state $W3$, the control unit signals overflow and then goes to state $W0$ and, at the same time, stops the operation by de-asserting the "*run*" command.

To synthesize a circuit of the signal generator composed of two JK flip-flops, C_1 and C_0, a decoder, and a control counter, CR, to implement the state-transition diagram in Figure 9.11, we can derive the expressions for the excitation signals of C_1 and C_0 as follows:

$$\text{Flip-flop } C_1 : J = W1 \cdot (count = n-1)$$

$$K = W2 \cdot \overline{C}$$

$$\text{Flip-flop } C_0 : J = W0 \cdot run$$

$$K = W2 \tag{9.4}$$

The circuit diagram of the signal generator thus synthesized is shown in Figure 9.12.

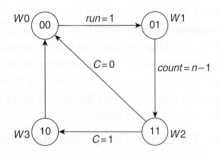

Figure 9.11   State transition diagram for the control cycles

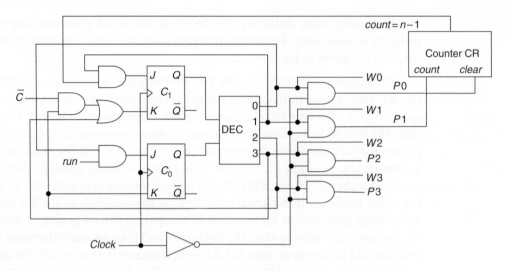

Figure 9.12 Circuit diagram for generation of the timing signals

9.3.2 Design of a Sequential Two's Complement Multiplier

In this section, we will study the design of a control unit for the sequential operation of two's complement multiplication. We will follow the regular add/shift algorithm of two's complement multiplication studied in Section 6.1.1. Since this algorithm for an n-bit by n-bit multiplication requires the add (or no add) and shift operations to be repeated n times, the simplest way of designing its control unit is to use the same method based on the operation chart as we have used in the last section. For example, we can use the initial control cycle, $W0$, to prepare for data, then repeat control cycle $W1$ for the $n - 1$ iterations of regular add/shift operations, and, finally, handle the subtract/shift operations in control cycle $W2$ for the sign bit of the multiplier. The entire control process is very similar to that of the serial adder as shown in Figure 9.10. However, directly using the method of operation chart in this manner does not satisfy our requirement of optimizing the design to perform the controlled operation as fast as possible. A better design of the control for multiplication should save addition time by skipping the "no add" control steps, which are not necessary for the multiplier bits of "0". This optimization is especially necessary if we design a control unit for the implementation of Booth algorithm (see Section 6.1.2.1), which is a fast algorithm just because it saves time that would otherwise be wasted on the "0" bits of the multiplier.

The circuit of a sequential two's complement multiplier with its control unit that satisfies the above-stated requirement of fast control by skipping the multiplier bits of "0" is shown in Figure 9.13. It consists of the following parts:

1. Three n-bit registers required by the sequential algorithm of multiplication stated in Section 6.1.1. They are:

   - *Accumulator A*. A shift register for storing the most significant half of the partial product and the final product.

   - *Register Q*. A shift register for storing the multiplier and the least significant half of the partial product and final product.

   - *Register M*. A register for storing the multiplicand without changing its contents in the entire process of multiplication.

2. An n-bit adder with the following associated circuits:

   - A set of n XOR gates used for subtraction in the last control cycle for handling the sign bit of the multiplier.

   - A circuit for creating and storing the overflow status of the adder, which consists of an XOR gate for comparing carry signals, an inhibit gate for enabling the overflow signal, and a flip-flop for storing it.

   - A set of n 2×1 multiplexers that either passes the sum/difference of the adder to the accumulator A (when $s = 1$) or initializes A with data zero (when $s = 0$).

3. A modulo-$2n$ binary up-counter, used to control the number of iterations of the multiplication algorithm to repeat n times. It should have an AND gate to create an output voltage $C[n − 1]$, which becomes "1" when the count equals $n − 1$, corresponding to the binary code $(0)111..1$.

4. A JK flop-flop T, used to control the "*loadA*" signal, which loads the partial product from the adder into the accumulator A only when the least significant bit of the multiplier in the register Q equals "1". Otherwise, if this bit of the multiplier is "0", "*loadA*" signal and the corresponding control cycle will not be created, thus saving the time of control.

5. A clock generator for generating a single pulse, *SP*, ORed with a stream of clock signals controlled by the counter stated in point 3. The single pulse (with other associated signals such as "*b*") is used for initializing the above-stated three registers with initial data, the counter with "0", and flip-flop T with state "1".

Now, having introduced the circuit diagram in Figure 9.13, we can see how the multiplication process is controlled by the control unit. To be specific, we will use a numerical example to analyze the detailed steps of calculation and control of a multiplication operation on 8-bit data ($n = 8$), as demonstrated in Table 9.2. Each row of the table is a step of control. Normally, for controlling an 8-bit by 8-bit multiplication, we need 16 control steps including 8 "add/no add" steps and 8 "shift" steps. However, our control scheme can skip the "no add" control steps. For the specific data given in Table 9.2, the multiplier has only 5 bits equal to "1", so we need

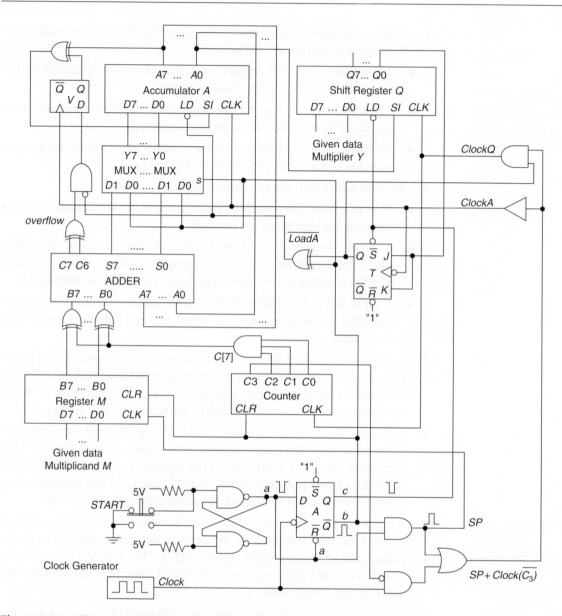

Figure 9.13 The circuit diagram of a sequential multiplier with a control unit

only $8 + 5 = 13$ steps in total. This can be seen in the second column of Table 9.2, where the 13 steps are numbered from 0 to 12. Since the adder always works without control, it generates the result $A \pm M$ in every step as indicated in a special column of the table. However, we cannot load the result of $A \pm M$ into A in every step. Only when a $Q0$ bit of "1" was obtained in the previous step after a shift operation, a "*loadA*" signal can be produced in the current step in order to load the new partial product of the adder into the accumulator. In this way of control, we will have only as many control steps for loading A as the multiplier requires according to its number of bits "1". To control the number of iterations, we designed a counter that counts the number of "shift" steps. Since the counter is triggered by the shift control signals, every control cycle starts from a shift operation. When $Q0 = 1$, we have a long control cycle with two steps of control (*shift* and *loadA*), and when $Q0 = 0$, we have a short control cycle with only one step of control (*shift*). The control cycles counted by the counter is shown in the first column of Table 9.2. It can be seen that in Cycle 7, the adder performs the operation A-M as required by the algorithm, and the first Cycle 0 and last Cycle 8 are incomplete, each being a half cycle.

The analysis made in Table 9.2 allows us to derive the logic expressions for the control signals in Figure 9.13 in terms of the independent variable $Q0$, where $Q0$ is the value of the multiplier bit when it is shifted into the least significant position of the register Q. In Table 9.2, we introduce a variable T in the last column to control the shift operations in the third column so that when $T = 1$ and

Table 9.2   Control process of an 8-bit multiplication

$M = 01011011, Q = 11011001$

Cycles	Control	Pulses	A	Q7–Q1	Q0	A ± M	Overflow	T
–	–	–	00000000	1101100	1	01011011	0	1
0	0	loadA	01011011		1	10110110	1	0
1	1	shift	00101101	1110110	0	10001000	1	1
2	2	shift	00010110	1111011	0	01110001	0	1
3	3	shift	00001011	0111101	1	01100110	0	1
3	4	loadA	01100110		1	11000001	1	0
4	5	shift	00110011	0011110	1	10001110	1	1
4	6	loadA	10001110		1	11101001	0	0
5	7	shift	01000111	0001111	0	10100010	1	1
6	8	shift	00100011	1000111	1	01111110	0	1
6	9	loadA	01111110		1	11011001	1	0
7	10	shift	00111111	0100011	1	11100100(sub)	0	1
7	11	loadA	11100100		1	10001001(sub)	0	0
8	12	shift	11110010	0010001	1	01001101	0	1
								0

counter is not zero, a shift operation is required. We store this variable T in a flip-flop with the same name as T in Figure 9.13. Furthermore, from Table 9.2, we can see that the flip-flop T should be flipped from state "1" to "0" or from "0" to "1" whenever $Q0 = 1$ by the main clock stream, $SP + Clock(\overline{C_3})$. As for the signals for controlling the registers A and Q, we can see that, in Figure 9.13, each register has a voltage control input, $\overline{LD}$, and a pulse control input, CLK. Both the load and shift operations share a common loading pulse, $ClockA$ or $ClockQ$, but can be distinguished by the level of a control voltage signal. When $\overline{LD} = 0$, the register performs a load operation, receiving a parallel input from data inputs $D7...D0$. When $\overline{LD} = 1$, the register performs a shift operation, receiving a one-bit data from the serial input, SI. Therefore, $ClockA$ should include all the pulse signals, $loadA$ and $shift$, listed in the third column in Table 9.2, while $ClockQ$ should include only the shift pulse signals in the same column of the table. These shift signals are selected from the main clock stream, $SP + Clock(\overline{C_3})$, by the voltage signal T. Summarizing the above analysis, we obtain the following expressions:

$$ClockA = SP + Clock(\overline{C_3}) = SP + Clock \cdot \overline{C_3}$$

$$ClockQ = [SP + Clock(\overline{C_3})] \cdot T$$

The J, K inputs of flip-flop $T = Q0$

The clock input of flip-flop $T = ClockA$

The clock input of the counter $= ClockQ$

The $\overline{LD}$ input of register $Q = c$

The $\overline{LD}$ input of register A $= \overline{loadA} = T \oplus b$ (9.5)

where $c = \overline{b}$ is a 1 0 1 voltage signal created by the clock generator during the $START$ phase of the operation (see Figure 9.5).

The waveform diagram for the complete multiplication process as illustrated above is shown in Figure 9.14. We can see that $ClockA$ is created by ORing the single pulse SP and the clock pulse selected by $\overline{C_3}$, and $ClockQ$ is the $ClockA$ signal further selected by the voltage signal T. The waveform of $ClockA$ contains all 13 pulses for $loadA$ and shift operations, plus a single phase, SP, used for initialization purpose. The waveform of $ClockQ$ contains nine pulses, eight of which perform shift operations when the input control voltage $\overline{loadA} = 1$, and the first pulse of $ClockQ$ coming from the single pulse, SP, performs the load operation when $\overline{loadA} = 0$. The waveform of $\overline{loadA}$ is that of the voltage signal T except the initial value which must be "0" instead of "1" to initialize the accumulator to zero. Then, look at the waveforms of T and the counter. The flip-flop T is flipped by the falling edge of $ClockA$ whenever $Q0 = 1$. The counter is controlled to count from 0 to 8 by the rising edge of $ClockQ$ except in the initializing phase. The counter does not count by the first pulse of $ClockQ$ because at that time the signal b is still acting on its $Clear$ input.

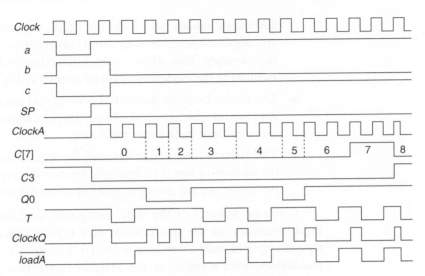

Figure 9.14 Waveform diagram for the multiplication process in Table 9.2

9.4 DESIGN OF HARDWIRED CONTROL OF A SIMPLE COMPUTER

In this section, we discuss the specification of a simple RISC processor and the basic instruction cycle. After which, we will learn to design the operation chart for the basic instruction cycle, and also learn to design and implement the control signals, datapath, and timing signals.

9.4.1 Specification of a Simple RISC Processor

Many high-performance processors have been developed based on the RISC design philosophy. The key concepts of the instruction-set architecture of a RISC machine have been studied in Section 7.4. They are as follows:

- The major criterion of designing a reduced instruction set is the frequency of usage of different instructions. Only frequently used operations and addressing modes are included in the instruction set for direct implementation by hardware. The addition of a new, less frequently used operation to the instruction set must not slow down the execution speed of other instructions.

- Basic arithmetic-logic operations use a three-address (or two-address) register-register instruction format, which best fits the CPU organization based on general-purpose registers.

- The instruction format has fixed length and regular fields to make instruction decoding easier and faster.

- For data fetch, only load/store instructions access memory using a limited number of addressing modes. Besides the *register direct* and *immediate* addressing modes (which do not access memory), the *register deferred* and *displacement* addressing modes are most commonly used for accessing memory. This allows short instruction cycles for all instructions, facilitating the implementation of an instruction pipeline.

- The choice between hardwired control and microprogrammed control depends on which control scheme provides shorter instruction cycles for more efficient instruction pipelining.

- The reduced instruction set and the exploitation of instruction-level parallelism in terms of multiple instruction pipelines in a superscalar processor require strong support of an intelligent compiler.

Common features of the RISC computers described above have enabled the formulation of the specification of a typical educational RISC machine. One example of such a machine is the DLX computer derived from the *MIPS architecture*, with a subset of the MIPS64 instruction set and a 32-bit word length. Without loss of generality, for the following example, we propose the specification of a simple computer, which is like the MIPS, but has a smaller and much simpler instruction set than the MIPS. Simplification is necessary for easier implementation using any available simulation software. However, the simplification is mostly quantitative, that is, to decrease the word length, the instruction length, the size of the instruction set, and the memory capacity, while still maintaining the above-mentioned RISC design features. The specification of our simple RISC computer is as follows:

There are 15 general-purpose registers, $R1 - R15$, and $R0$ stands for the constant zero.

All registers have 16-bit word length. All arithmetic data are in two's complement representation.

All instructions have 16-bit instruction length. The instruction format is given below.

Load/store instructions:

OPcode	Rs	Rd	imm
4 bits	4 bits	4 bits	4 bits

All other instructions:

OPcode	Rs1	Rs2	Rd
4 bits	4 bits	4 bits	4 bits

Since the address length is 16 bits, the directly accessible memory capacity is 64K words if we use the word addressing scheme for our example.

Besides the 15 general-purpose registers mentioned above, we may need the following registers with 16-bit word length and 16-bit address length:

- *PC*. 16-bit program counter pointing to the next instruction to be fetched
- *IR*. 16-bit instruction register storing the current instruction being executed
- *MAR*. 16-bit memory address register storing the memory address during read/write operations
- *MBR*. 16-bit memory buffer register storing the information read from or written into memory

Additional registers may be useful for the implementation of certain complex operations.

Since there is only one 16-bit size for both data and instructions, it would be simpler to design memory as *word-addressable*. Byte operations are possible with the proper use of shift and logical instructions.

The simplified subset of the instruction set of the MIPS processor is given in Table 9.3 as the main portion of the specification of our design goal.

The following are some considerations of the instruction set.

- The instruction set given above is typical for RISC machines. All instructions have a regular format, including a 4-bit operation code (OPcode) field, which allows a maximum of 16 different operations to be specified directly. All *arithmetic-logic* instructions are of register-register type with a three-address format (except *shift*, which performs an unary operation and uses an address field to specify the shift amount). Besides the operation code in bits 15–12, bits 11–0 specify three register numbers, two of which point to two source operands participating in a binary operation, and the third one points to the destination. For a *multiply* instruction that needs two registers to store a double-length product, two consecutive registers should be used as the destination. Therefore, the instruction should specify an even-numbered register, *Rd*, so that the accompanying register, *Rd*+1, can be obtained by simply XORing the LSB of *Rd* with a control signal of value "1".
- For *load/store* instructions, a general *displacement addressing mode* is used for specifying a memory address. The 16-bit effective address is generated as (*Rs*) + *imm*, that is, the sum of a 16-bit address in register *Rs* and the value of *imm*. When *imm* = 0, the addressing mode becomes *register deferred* with the effective address equal to (*Rs*). The field *Rd* specifies the destination or source register for the load or store

Table 9.3 Instruction set of a simple MIPS-like RISC computer

OPcode $x_3 x_2 x_1 x_0$	Mnemonic	Name	Operation	Remarks
0000	ADD	add	$Rd \leftarrow (Rs1) + (Rs2)$	
0001	ADDI	add *imm*	$Rd \leftarrow (Rs1) + \#imm$	Signed *imm* is in *Rs2* field.
0010	SUB	subtract	$Rd \leftarrow (Rs1) - (Rs2)$	
0011	MUL	multiply	$Rd, Rd + 1 \leftarrow (Rs1) * (Rs2)$	Two's complement multiply. *Rd* is an even-numbered reg.
0100	AND	and	$Rd \leftarrow (Rs1) \wedge (Rs2)$	
0101	OR	or	$Rd \leftarrow (Rs1) \vee (Rs2)$	
0110	XOR	xor	$Rd \leftarrow (Rs1) \oplus (Rs2)$	
0111	LSH	logical shift	$Rd \leftarrow (Rs1) << imm$ if $imm < 0$ $Rd \leftarrow (Rs1) >> imm$ if $imm > 0$	Signed *imm* is in *Rs2* field. Shift amount *imm* is -8 to $+7$.
1000	LW	load word	$Rd \leftarrow (\text{Mem}[(Rs) + imm])$	
1001	SW	store word	$\text{Mem}[(Rs) + imm] \leftarrow (Rd)$	
1010	SLT	set on less than	if $(Rs1) < (Rs2), Rd \leftarrow 1,$ else $Rd \leftarrow 0$	
1011	SGT	set on greater than	if $(Rs1) > (Rs2), Rd \leftarrow 1,$ else $Rd \leftarrow 0$	
1100	BEQ	branch equal	if $(Rs1) = 0, PC \leftarrow (PC) + imm$	*imm* is in *Rs2*, *Rd* field. *imm* should be sign-extended.
1101	BNE	branch not equal	if $(Rs1) \neq 0, PC \leftarrow (PC) + imm$	*imm* is in *Rs2*, *Rd* field. *imm* should be sign-extended
1110	JR	jump register	$PC \leftarrow (Rs1)$	*Rs2, Rd* field is not used.
1111	JAL	jump and link	$Rd \leftarrow (PC) + 1; PC \leftarrow (Rs1)$	*Rs2* field is not used.

instruction, respectively. It should be noted that *imm* could be a label pointing to the starting address or base address of a data array in memory. In this case, *imm* is usually unsigned.

■ There are two compare and four control instructions. The *set-on-comparison* instructions include only *set on less than* and *set on greater than*, because comparison for zero can be done by an ordinary subtract instruction. The jump instructions use the register deferred addressing mode in order to allow a 16-bit destination address in memory. The branch instructions use the *PC-relative* addressing mode in order to facilitate writing relocatable code.

9.4.2 The Basic Instruction Cycle

As we have shown in Section 8.2.1, a basic instruction cycle consists of seven steps, namely

1. instruction fetch
2. instruction decode
3. address generation
4. operand fetch
5. operation execution
6. result storage
7. next instruction-address identification

The division of a basic instruction cycle into the seven steps listed earlier is more suitable for a CISC machine than for a RISC machine, because most, if not all, CISC instructions with complex addressing modes may access memory for reading and writing data. For the load/store architecture of a RISC machine, only load and store instructions need to access memory for data. Therefore, not all seven steps are common to RISC instructions. If we group the steps into two, then the first part common to all instructions contains only steps 1, 2, and 7, while the second part is specific to each instruction and contains only selected steps from the remaining four. Step 7 is a default for all instructions, except jump and branch. Without program transfer, the program counter is always incremented to fetch the next successive instruction in the program. For the second part, *arithmetic-logic* and *set-on-comparison* instructions need only Step 4 to read the source registers, Step 5 to perform the operation, and Step 6 to store the result into the destination register. The *load* instruction needs Steps 3 and 4 for accessing memory and Step 6 for storing the memory data into the destination register. The *store* instruction needs Step 3 for generating the memory address, Step 4 for reading the source register, and Step 6 for storing the data into memory.

The *jump* and *branch* instructions need Step 4 to read a register in order to prepare a destination address for Step 7 (The JAL instruction also needs Step 6 for storing the return address).

For our simple RISC machine with the instruction set given in Table 9.3, it is reasonable to define the steps according to the operations of functional units required by different instructions. For example, since all instructions need to read registers, then we can define the operation "register read" as a step. Thus, we obtain the following steps for selection by different instructions:

- instruction fetch—common to all instructions,
- instruction decoding—common to all instructions,
- register read—necessary for all instructions,
- operation execution—performing different operations depending on the instruction type, mostly on the ALU, for example, result calculation for ALU instructions, address generation for load/store instructions, branch-condition checking for compare and branch instructions, PC setting for jump instructions, and so on,
- memory read/write—useful for load/store instructions only, and
- result storage—useful for almost all instructions except store, jump, and branch instructions.

Although in the above analysis we divided the instruction cycle into steps, it does not mean that each step is equivalent to a control cycle. The difference between a control cycle and a step is that a control cycle involves a state transition that takes one clock cycle time in synchronous control, while a step has no fixed relation with a state transition. Several steps may be combined into a single control cycle, if they form a sequence that causes a state transition. Several independent steps can be executed in parallel, with each step causing a state transition. If they altogether require only one clock cycle, they form a single control cycle. An example of the first case is the three successive steps of reading the source registers, performing an arithmetic-logic operation on the ALU, and loading the result into a destination register, which are combined into a single control cycle that takes only one clock cycle. If there are no working registers to store the intermediate result, the three steps result in only one state transition. An example of the second case is an instruction fetch. After we prepare the address, we need to read memory, load the instruction register, and update the program counter. If these steps use disjoint datapaths, they can be performed simultaneously in only one clock cycle. So, even if they cause more than one state transition, they form a single control cycle. Finally, memory references by instructions may cause additional problems in designing the control of an instruction set. Because of the large speed gap between the CPU and memory, the design of the control unit may suffer from additional difficulties of matching the speed requirements of different types of instructions. One of the most effective solutions to this problem is the extensive use of cache memories, which we will study in Chapter 10. Right now, we can just imagine cache as a fast memory that can work as an instruction buffer and/or a data buffer that is accessible with the CPU speed. Therefore, we assume that after the memory address register, MAR, is loaded with a memory address, each memory read takes one clock cycle to read the memory contents into a register, or each memory write takes one clock cycle to write the contents of the memory buffer register, MBR, into memory.

9.4.3 Design of the Operation Chart for the Instruction Set

In this section, we will use the method of operation chart to start the first step of designing the control unit for the instruction set given in Table 9.3. The first step is to design the timing sequences of the microoperations for implementation of various instructions in the instruction set. The basic idea and use of the operation chart in designing the control unit have been introduced in Section 9.3.1, but the example handled there was very simple—to control the sequential operation of a simple n-bit serial adder. In this section, however, we will extend the use of the method for designing the control of an entire instruction set, and continue the design work up to its complete implementation.

In the hierarchical structure of computer design, the design of the control unit is located at the *register-transfer level*. That is, the CPU is modeled as a datapath that consists of many *registers* and many *data processing/transferring paths* interconnecting registers. If the data processing/ transferring paths are combinational circuits, then the registers are memory elements. This model is consistent with the general model of a sequential logic circuit introduced in Chapter 4 (see Figure 4.1). Therefore, we can treat the control unit as a *finite-state machine* and use the method of designing sequential logic circuits to design the control unit. Since each register-transfer operation processes data and changes the state of the related register(s), we need two control signals—a control voltage and a control pulse. The control voltage acts on the input gates of a register to enable the arriving information to be loaded in. The control pulse acts on the clock input of a register to complete the information loading (triggering of its flip-flops). The two control signals must match each other in time, just as the J, K, or D input of a flip-flop must match the clock transition in time. The active edge of the control pulse should take place and trigger the flip-flops of a register only after the input voltage supplied by the combinational circuit has stabilized. This explains how the clock frequency is determined by the maximum delay of the *critical path* of the combinational circuit used for processing and transferring data. This control scheme requires the control unit to provide a sequence of central timing signals, with each pair of central control voltage and central clock pulse, for example, $W0, P0$; $W1, P1$; … forming a control cycle. Based on these central timing signals, the control unit generates specific control signals for various register-transfer operations.

The design of a control unit thus leads to the scheduling of events for each instruction as a sequence of control cycles in time. We will use the term *micro-operation*, taken from the jargon of microprogrammed control, to refer to these events. In microprogrammed control, microoperations are specified in multiple fields of a microinstruction and executed at the microprogram level. In hardwired control, the microoperations are designed as individual register-transfer micro-operations performed by logic circuits as control commands. For a description of the scheduling of these microoperations in the hardwired control, we will use a timing chart called an *operation chart* (see Section 9.3.1). The operation chart lists a sequence of microoperations for each instruction in a sequential order relative to time. For example, the chart for our simple computer will have four columns corresponding to four control cycles from $W0/P0$ to $W3/P3$, where Wi and Pi for $i = 0$ to 3, denote the central control voltage and central clock pulse, respectively, generated for control cycle i. Each sequence of microoperations for an instruction will form a row of the chart, and each group of microoperations that can be executed in parallel will be written as a group under the header of the same control cycle.

It should be emphasized that the design of the operation chart and the design of the CPU datapath are two interrelated processes affecting each other, and should be done in an interleaved manner to achieve the best result. Whenever two or more independent microoperations can be performed in parallel, we should give them distinct datapaths. Otherwise, when two microoperations must be performed sequentially, we can design them using a common datapath. Common datapaths usually save hardware and dedicated datapaths usually save time. This is a tradeoff between time and space. A good compromise should minimize the number of distinct datapaths and the number of control cycles per instruction at the same time. The resulting block diagram of the datapath of the CPU for a simple RISC computer with hardwired control is shown in Figure 9.15, and the operation chart for the instruction set (except the MUL and LSH instructions, which are controlled asynchronously) of Table 9.3 is shown in Figure 9.16. In the operation chart of Figure 9.16, we use "*" to mark the micro-operations performed on dedicated datapaths. All the other microoperations use the common datapath through the ALU.

From Figure 9.15, we can see the basic organization of the CPU and its connections to memory. The general-purpose register set should have two output ports for reading $Rs1$ and $Rs2$ selected by the *source*1 and *source*2 *register select* codes, $s1_3$–$s1_0$ and $s2_3$–$s2_0$, respectively. The circuit for these output ports can be implemented with multiplexers or tri-state devices controlled by decoders (see Figures 9.18 and 9.19 for details). The input port for the register

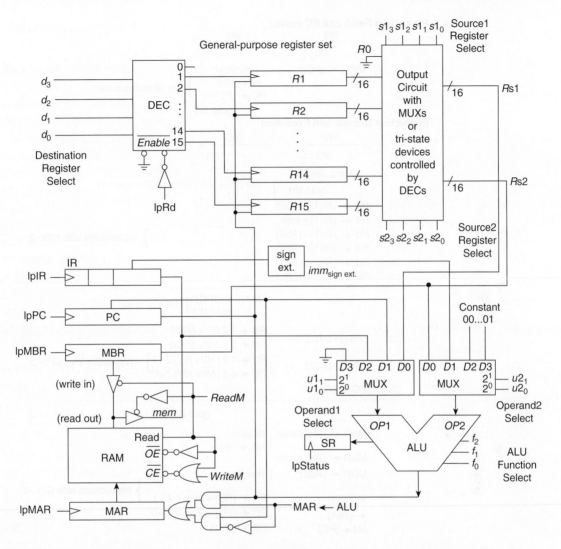

Figure 9.15 The block diagram of the CPU of a simple RISC machine with hardwired control

set is implemented with a decoder used as a demultiplexer and controlled by the *destination register select* code d_3–d_0 as well as the loading pulse lpRd. The functions of the ALU are twofold:

1. Performing the eight arithmetic-logic operations selected by the *ALU function select* code f_2–f_0.

2. Serving as the common datapath for most of the microoperations in the operation chart shown in Figure 9.16.

The *operand1* and *operand2 select* codes, $u1_1 u1_0$ and $u2_1 u2_0$, select the input operands for *OP1* and *OP2*, respectively, through two multiplexers at the inputs

Instruction Fetch and PC update

$W0$	$W1$
$P0$ ⌐⌐	$P1$ ⌐⌐

MAR ← (PC)*

ReadM
IR ← imm*
PC ← (PC)+1 $\Big\}$ (for all instructions)
goto $W2$

Instruction Decode and Execution

$W2$	$W3$
$P2$ ⌐⌐	$P3$ ⌐⌐

MAR ← (PC)*
goto $W1$ $\Big\}$ (for ADD+ADDI+SUB+AND+OR+XOR)

ADD	$Rd \leftarrow (Rs1)+(Rs2)$	
ADDI	$Rd \leftarrow (Rs1)+imm$	
SUB	$Rd \leftarrow (Rs1)-(Rs2)$	$\Big\}$ Instructions with $CPI=2$
AND	$Rd \leftarrow (Rs1)\wedge(Rs2)$	
OR	$Rd \leftarrow (Rs1)\vee(Rs2)$	
XOR	$Rd \leftarrow (Rs1)\oplus(Rs2)$	

- -

MAR ← (PC)* $\Big\}$ (for SLT + SGT + JR)
goto $W1$

SLT	$(Rs1)-(Rs2)$	$\begin{cases} Rd \leftarrow 1 \text{ if } N\overline{V}+\overline{N}V=1 \\ Rd \leftarrow 0 \text{ if } N\overline{V}+\overline{N}V=0 \end{cases}$
SGT	$(Rs1)-(Rs2)$	$\begin{cases} Rd \leftarrow 1 \text{ if } (\overline{N}\overline{V}+NV)\overline{Z}=1 \\ Rd \leftarrow 0 \text{ if } (\overline{N}\overline{V}+NV)\overline{Z}=0 \end{cases}$ $\Big\}$ Instructions with $CPI=3$
JR	$PC \leftarrow (Rs1)$	

- -

goto $W0$ (for LW + SW + BEQ + BNE + JAL)

LW	MAR ← (Rs) + imm	$\begin{cases} ReadM \\ Rd \leftarrow mem \end{cases}$
	MAR ← (Rs) + imm	
SW	MBR ← (Rs2)*	$\Big\}$ WriteM $\Big\}$ Instructions with $CPI=4$
BEQ	← (Rs1)	$PC \leftarrow (PC) + imm$ if $Z=1$
BNE	← (Rs1)	$PC \leftarrow (PC) + imm$ if $Z=0$
JAL	$Rd \leftarrow (PC)$	$PC \leftarrow (Rs1)$

Figure 9.16 Operation chart for the instruction set given in Table 9.3

Note: All microoperations except those marked " * " are performed by the ALU. MUL and LSH are not implemented by hardwired control.

of the ALU. The memory chip has its internal register for reading and writing information under the control of two sets of tri-state devices. The action of the memory chip will be described when we explain the operation chart.

The various sequences of microoperations contained in the operation chart are explained below:

1. **Instruction fetch and PC update in cycles $W0$ and $W1$**

   In cycle $W0$, the memory address register, MAR, is loaded with the contents of PC as the address of the next instruction. Then, in cycle $W1$, we have a memory read operation controlled by the command *ReadM* that activates the voltage signals *Read* = 1, $\overline{OE(\textit{output-enable})} = 0$, and $\overline{CE(\textit{chip-enable})} = 0$ of the memory chip (see Figure 9.15). The memory contents read out from the memory location are assumed to appear in the internal register of the memory chip by the end of cycle *W1*. The voltage signal *ReadM* also enables the "read-out" tri-state devices to transfer the memory output, *mem*, to the instruction register, IR, so that the control pulse *P1* can complete the loading of the newly-read instruction into IR. The program counter, PC, is also updated in cycle *W1* by the microoperation PC ← (PC) + 1, in parallel with the above memory operation.

2. **Instruction decode and execution in cycle *W2* for the class of instructions with *CPI* = 2**

We assume that the instruction decode takes enough time that, after the instruction decode, cycle *W2* can still be used for the execution of instructions. This allows all the basic arithmetic-logic instructions (except MUL and LSH) to complete execution in cycle *W2*. To optimize the utilization of the CPU time, we should prepare the memory address for the next instruction by loading MAR with the contents of PC in this cycle, then upon completion of the current instruction we can directly go back to cycle *W1* to fetch the next instruction. Therefore, in cycle *W2*, we add two microoperations "MAR ← (PC)" and "goto *W1*" with the condition "ADD + ADDI + SUB + AND + OR + XOR = 1". However, for implementation of the microoperation MAR ← (PC), we must add a dedicated datapath from PC to MAR so that this transfer operation can be done in parallel with the regular ALU operation of the instruction. In Figure 9.15, we can see this dedicated datapath on the MAR as the AND gates connected with the PC and enabled by the control signal $\overline{MAR \leftarrow ALU}$. This design allows for the execution of a basic arithmetic-logic instruction in only two cycles. If we use Cycles Per Instruction (*CPI*) as a measure of the instruction speed, then the above six basic arithmetic-logic instructions form a class of instructions with *CPI* = 2.

3. **Control for the class of instructions with *CPI* = 3**

The instructions SLT, SGT, and JR belong to the class of instructions with *CPI* = 3. The "set-on-comparison" instructions SLT and SGT need two cycles for execution—a compare followed by a register load, and the "jump-register" instruction JR can prepare the PC only in *W2*. These three instructions would require the microoperations "MAR ← (PC)" and "goto *W2*" to be delayed to *W3*. The conditions for setting/resetting *Rd* for the instructions SLT and SGT need some explanation. We check the result of the comparison (*Rs1*) − (*Rs2*) by the statuses *N* (sign), *V* (overflow), and *Z* (zero). The "less than" condition $N\overline{V} + \overline{N}V = 1$ indicates negative (*N* = 1) if no overflow (*V* = 0) or positive (*N* = 0) if overflow (*V* = 1). This is based on the fact that the occurrence of overflow changes the true sign bit of the result. The "greater than" condition $(\overline{NV} + NV)\overline{Z} = 1$ is the inverse of the "less than" condition ($\overline{N}V + N\overline{V} = 1$ which means "greater than or equal to") ANDed with the "not zero" condition ($\overline{Z} = 1$).

4. **Control for the class of instructions with *CPI* = 4**

The remaining five instructions, LW, SW, BEQ, BNE, and JAL, belong to the class of instructions with *CPI* = 4. For LW and SW, two cycles, *W*2 and *W*3, are needed to prepare the effective address and access memory. For BEQ and BNE, *R*s1 is tested in *W*2, followed by a conditional PC loading in *W*3. For JAL, PC can be loaded only in *W*3 after its original contents were saved in *R*d as the return address in *W*2. All these cases would require the state transition to be made from *W*3 to *W*0, thus causing the *CPI* to become 4.

From the operation chart designed above, we can see more examples of trading off speed with complexity. At one extreme, we may design the operation chart such that all instructions take the same number of cycles, slowing down the execution speed of fast instructions. At the other extreme, the number of cycles for each instruction can be minimized independently by scheduling the microoperations in as few cycles as possible. However, there are two problems to be considered here. First, more parallel microoperations in a cycle would lead to more parallel datapaths or more complicated control in the CPU. For example, we can reduce the *CPI* of JR by one cycle if we add a microoperation MAR ← (*R*s1) in parallel with the PC ← (*R*s1) in cycle *W*2 for JR. However, the circuits for the control signals MAR ← ALU and lpMAR would be more complicated, even though the dedicated datapath from the ALU to MAR already exists. Similarly, we can reduce the *CPI* of the instructions BEQ, BNE, and JAL by 1 cycle, as well. Second, a longer sequence of microoperations scheduled in a control cycle would require a longer clock cycle time. For example, the arithmetic-logic operation contains a long sequence of microoperations from reading the registers to writing the result. This could easily become a critical path that places a limitation on the clock frequency.

9.4.4 Design and Implementation of the Control Signals

As we have stated before, the design of the datapath and the design of the operation chart are two interrelated processes affecting each other. After designing the block diagram of the datapath and the associated operation chart, we can now write the comprehensive logic expressions for all the register-transfer, register-load, and memory-access control signals specified in the operation chart. Each expression is written in terms of three kinds of parameters:

- Central timing signals *Wi* / *Pi* for *i* = 0 to 3. In what control cycle does the control signal act?

- Operation codes ADD, ADDI, ... What instructions need this control signal?
- Conditions such as $Z, N\overline{V} + \overline{N}V, \ldots$ Under what condition is the control signal activated?

Memory Access Control:

$$ReadM: \quad W1 + W3 \cdot LW \tag{9.6}$$

(Memory read needs $\overline{CE} = 0$, $\overline{OE} = 0$, $Read = 1$, and read-out tri-state devices enabled.)

$$WriteM: \quad W3 \cdot SW \tag{9.7}$$

(Memory write needs $\overline{CE} = 0$, $\overline{OE} = 1$, $Read = 0$, and write-in tri-state devices enabled.)

Load MAR:

$$MAR \leftarrow (Rs) + imm: \quad \text{(through ALU, so denoted MAR} \leftarrow \text{ALU in Figure 9.15)}$$

$$W2 \cdot (LW + SW) \tag{9.8}$$

$MAR \leftarrow (PC)$: (a dedicated path)

$$W0 + W2 \cdot (ADD + ADDI + SUB + AND + OR + XOR) + W3 \cdot (SLT + SGT + JR)$$

$$= W0 + W2 \cdot \overline{IR_{15}} + W3 \cdot (SLT + SGT + JR) \tag{9.9}$$

(For simplicity, this signal is implemented as $\overline{MAR \leftarrow ALU}$ in Figure 9.15)

$$lpMAR = P0 + P2 \cdot (\overline{IR_{15}} + LW + SW) + P3 \cdot (SLT + SGT + JR) \tag{9.10}$$

(While accurate control of the voltage signals is unnecessary, control of the loading pulse must be accurate. The expression of lpMAR involves all the cases of load MAR.)

Load MBR:

$MBR \leftarrow (Rs2)$: (a dedicated path)

$$W2 \cdot SW \tag{9.11}$$

$$lpMBR = P2 \cdot SW \tag{9.12}$$

(Since lpMBR is controlled accurately, the control voltage $MBR \leftarrow (Rs2)$ is unnecessary. The $Rs2$ can be connected directly to the input of MBR as shown in Figure 9.15.)

Load PC:

$$PC \leftarrow ALU:$$
$$PC \leftarrow (Rs1): W2 \cdot JR + W3 \cdot JAL$$
$$PC \leftarrow (PC) + imm: W3 \cdot (BEQ \cdot Z + BNE \cdot \overline{Z})$$
$$PC \leftarrow (PC) + 1: W1$$

$$\text{(9.13)}$$

$$lpPC = P1 + P2 \cdot JR + P3 \cdot (JAL + BEQ \cdot Z + BNE \cdot \overline{Z}) \tag{9.14}$$

(lpPC involves all the cases of load PC. Since lpPC is controlled accurately, all the control voltages PC ← ALU are unnecessary. The ALU output can be connected directly to the input of PC as shown in Figure 9.15.)

Load IR:

$$IR \leftarrow mem: \text{(a dedicated path)}$$

$$W1 \tag{9.15}$$

$$lpIR = P1 \tag{9.16}$$

(Since lpIR is controlled accurately, the control voltage IR ← mem is unnecessary. The memory output *mem* can be connected directly to the input of IR as shown in Figure 9.15.)

Load *Rd* and load statuses:

$$Rd \leftarrow ALU: \text{(also load the statuses except in } W3 \text{ and for JAL)}$$

$Rd \leftarrow (Rs1) + (Rs2)$	$W2 \cdot ADD$
$Rd \leftarrow (Rs1) + imm$	$W2 \cdot ADDI$
$Rd \leftarrow (Rs1) - (Rs2)$	$W2 \cdot SUB$
$Rd \leftarrow (Rs1) \wedge (Rs2)$	$W2 \cdot AND$
$Rd \leftarrow (Rs1) \vee (Rs2)$	$W2 \cdot OR$
$Rd \leftarrow (Rs1) \oplus (Rs2)$	$W2 \cdot XOR$
$Rd \leftarrow (PC)$	$W2 \cdot JAL$
$Rd \leftarrow 1$	$W3 \cdot [SLT \cdot (N\overline{V} + \overline{N}V) + SGT \cdot (\overline{NV} + NV)\overline{Z}]$
$Rd \leftarrow 0$	$W3 \cdot [\overline{SLT \cdot N\overline{V} + \overline{N}V} + SGT \cdot \overline{(\overline{NV} + NV)\overline{Z}}]$
$Rd \leftarrow mem$	$W3 \cdot LW$

$$\text{(9.17)}$$

$$lpRd = P2 \cdot (ADD + ADDI + SUB + AND + OR + XOR + JAL) +$$
$$P3 \cdot (LW + SLT + SGT)$$
$$= P2 \cdot (\overline{IR_{15}} + JAL) + P3 \cdot (LW + SLT + SGT) \tag{9.18}$$

(lpRd involves all the cases of load Rd. Since lpRd is controlled accurately, all the control voltages PC ← ALU are unnecessary. The ALU output can be connected directly to the input of $R1 - R15$ as shown in Figure 9.15. However, the expressions of the control voltages will still be useful in deriving the expressions for the $OP1$ and $OP2$ select codes.)

Other ALU operations, loading the statuses only:

$$(Rs1) - (Rs2) \qquad W2 \cdot (\text{SLT} + \text{SGT})$$

$$\leftarrow (Rs1) \qquad W2 \cdot (\text{BEQ} + \text{BNE}) \tag{9.19}$$

$$\text{lpStatus} = P2 \cdot (\text{ADD} + \text{ADDI} + \text{SUB} + \text{AND} + \text{OR} + \text{XOR} + \text{SLT}$$

$$+ \text{SGT} + \text{BEQ} + \text{BNE})$$

$$= P2 \cdot (\overline{IR_{15}} + \text{SLT} + \text{SGT} + \text{BEQ} + \text{BNE}) \tag{9.20}$$

(lpStatus involves all the cases of load statuses. Since lpStatus is controlled accurately, the control voltages are unnecessary. The ALU status output can be connected directly to the input of the status register.)

Synthesis of the input multiplexer for $OP1$ to the ALU (see Figure 9.15):

$u1_1 u1_0 = 00 \quad OP1 \leftarrow (Rs1)$:
  $W2 \cdot ((\text{ADD} + \text{ADDI} + \text{SUB} + \text{AND} + \text{OR} + \text{XOR} + \text{LW} + \text{SW} + \text{SLT} + \text{SGT} + \text{BEQ} + \text{BNE} + \text{JR})$
  $+ W3 \cdot \text{JAL})$

$u1_1 u1_0 = 01 \quad OP1 \leftarrow (PC)$:
  $W1 + W2 \cdot \text{JAL} + W3 \cdot (\text{BEQ} + \text{BNE})$

$u1_1 u1_0 = 10 \quad OP1 \quad mem$:
  $W3 \cdot \text{LW}$

$u1_1 u1_0 = 11 \quad OP1 \leftarrow 0$:

$$W3 \cdot [\text{SLT} \cdot \overline{NV} + \overline{NV} + \text{SGT} \cdot \overline{(NV + NV)}\overline{Z}]$$

These expressions are obtained by searching the operation chart and finding the microoperations that need to use $Rs1$, PC, mem, and zero as $OP1$. From these four select-code combinations, we can derive the expressions for the variables $u1_1$ and $u1_0$ as follows:

$$u1_1 = W3 \cdot [\text{LW} + \text{SLT} \cdot \overline{NV} + \overline{NV} + \text{SGT} \cdot \overline{(NV + NV)}\overline{Z}]$$

$$u1_0 = W1 + W2 \cdot \text{JAL} + W3 \cdot [\text{BEQ} + \text{BNE} + \text{SLT} \cdot \overline{NV} + \overline{NV}$$

$$+ \text{SGT} \cdot \overline{(NV + NV)}\overline{Z}] \tag{9.21}$$

Synthesis of the input multiplexer for $OP2$ to the ALU (see Figure 9.15):

$u2_1 u2_0 = 00 \quad OP2 \leftarrow (Rs2)$:
  $W2 \cdot (\text{ADD} + \text{SUB} + \text{AND} + \text{OR} + \text{XOR} + \text{SLT} + \text{SGT})$

$$u2_1 \; u2_0 = 01 \quad OP2 \leftarrow imm_{\text{sign-ext.}}:$$
$$W2{\cdot}(\text{ADDI} + \text{LW} + \text{SW}) + W3\,(\text{BEQ} + \text{BNE})$$
$$u2_1 \; u2_0 = 10 \quad OP2 \leftarrow 00...01:$$

$$W1 + W3{\cdot}[\text{SLT}{\cdot}(N\overline{V} + \overline{N}V) + \text{SGT}{\cdot}(\overline{NV} + NV)\overline{Z}]$$

$u2_1 \; u2_0 = 11 \quad$ not used.

These expressions are obtained by searching the operation chart and finding the microoperations that need to use $Rs2$, $imm_{\text{sign-ext.}}$, and $00..01$ as $OP2$. From these four select-code combinations, we can derive the expressions for the variables $u2_1$ and $u2_0$ as follows:

$$u2_1 = W1 + W3{\cdot}[\text{SLT}{\cdot}(N\overline{V} + \overline{N}V) + \text{SGT}{\cdot}(\overline{NV} + NV)\overline{Z}]$$
$$u2_0 = W2{\cdot}(\text{ADDI} + \text{LW} + \text{SW}) + W3{\cdot}(\text{BEQ} + \text{BNE})$$

$$\text{(9.22)}$$

Synthesis of ALU functions:

$f_2 f_1 f_0 = 000$ for $OP1$ transfer:

$$W2 \cdot (\text{BEQ} + \text{BNE} + \text{JR} + \text{JAL}) + W3 \cdot [\text{LW} + \text{JAL} + \text{SLT}\cdot \overline{N\overline{V} + \overline{N}V} + \text{SGT}$$

$$\cdot \overline{(\overline{NV} + NV)\overline{Z}}]$$

$f_2 f_1 f_0 = 001$ for $OP2$ transfer:

$$W3 \cdot [\text{SLT} \cdot (N\overline{V} + \overline{N}V) + \text{SGT} \cdot (\overline{NV} + NV)\overline{Z}]$$

$f_2 f_1 f_0 = 010$ for $OP1 - OP2$:
$$W2{\cdot}(\text{SUB} + \text{SLT} + \text{SGT})$$
$f_2 f_1 f_0 = 011$ for $OP2 - OP1$:
not used
$f_2 f_1 f_0 = 100$ for $OP1 + OP2$:
$$W1 + W2{\cdot}(\text{ADD} + \text{ADDI} + \text{LW} + \text{SW}) + W3{\cdot}(\text{BEQ} + \text{BNE})$$
$f_2 f_1 f_0 = 101$ for $OP1 \oplus OP2$:
$$W2{\cdot}\text{XOR}$$
$f_2 f_1 f_0 = 110$ for $OP1 \bigwedge OP2$:
$$W2{\cdot}\text{AND}$$
$f_2 f_1 f_0 = 111$ for $OP1 \bigvee OP2$:

$$W2{\cdot}\text{OR}$$

These expressions are obtained by searching the operation chart and finding the microoperations that need ALU operations. From these eight select-code combinations, we can derive the expressions for the variables f_2, f_1, and f_0 as follows:

$$f_2 = W1 + W2 \cdot (\text{ADD} + \text{ADDI} + \text{LW} + \text{SW} + \text{AND} + \text{OR} + \text{XOR})$$
$$+ W3 \cdot (\text{BEQ} + \text{BNE})$$
$$f_1 = W2 \cdot (\text{SUB} + \text{SLT} + \text{SGT} + \text{AND} + \text{OR})$$
$$f_0 = W2 \cdot (\text{XOR} + \text{OR}) + W3 \cdot [\text{SLT} \cdot (N\overline{V} + \overline{N}V) + \text{SGT} \cdot (\overline{N}\overline{V} + NV)\overline{Z}] \quad \textbf{(9.23)}$$

Expressions (9.6) to (9.8), (9.10), (9.12), (9.14), (9.16), (9.18), (9.20) to (9.23) give all the control signals in Figure 9.15. The implementation of these expressions with basic logic gates is shown in Figure 9.17.

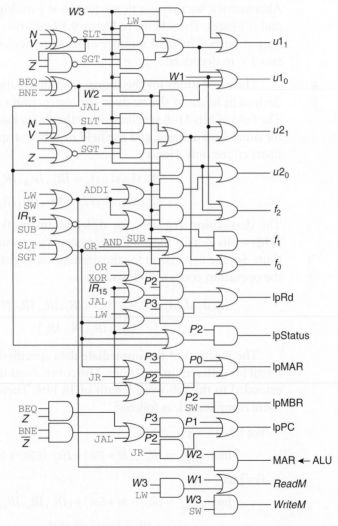

Figure 9.17 Implementation of the control signals in the ALU datapath in Figure

9.4.5 Design and Implementation of the Datapath and Timing Signals

Now, we can complete the design of the hardwired control by looking at how to control the I/O ports of the register set and how to generate the central timing signals.

The two different implementations of the output ports of the register set are shown in Figures 9.18 and 9.19. Both schemes implement the input port in the same way as shown in Figure 9.15. For the two output ports, the scheme in Figure 9.18 uses two sets of multiplexers. The total number of 2×1 multiplexers is equal to $2 \times 8 \times 16 = 256$ plus two 3×8 decoders and thirty-two 8-input OR-gates. Alternatively, we may use thirty-two 16×1 multiplexers without using decoders and OR-gates. The scheme in Figure 9.19 uses two sets of tri-state devices for two output ports. The total number of tri-state devices is equal to $2 \times 16 \times 16$ plus two 4×16 decoders.

The expressions for the source- and destination-register select codes can be derived in terms of the fields of the instruction code in the instruction register. The field of bits 11–8 specifies either the Rs for load/store instructions or the Rs1 for other instructions, and the field of bits 7–4 specifies Rs2 for non-load/store instructions only. Hence,

$$s1_3, s1_2, s1_1, s1_0 = IR_{11}, IR_{10}, IR_9, IR_8$$
$$s2_3, s2_2, s2_1, s2_0 = IR_7, IR_6, IR_5, IR_4 \tag{9.24}$$

The destination registers for different instructions are specified in different fields—bits 7–4 for the load/store instructions and bits 3–0 for the other instructions. So, the expression for the destination-register select code is dependent on the operation codes as follows:

$$d_3, d_2, d_1, d_0 = (\text{LW} + \text{SW}) \cdot (IR_7, IR_6, IR_5, IR_4) + \overline{\text{LW} + \text{SW}}$$
$$\cdot (IR_3, IR_2, IR_1, IR_0) \tag{9.25}$$

The position of the immediate data specified in the instruction is also different for different instructions. Moreover, short immediate data should be sign-extended to the full word length of 16 bits. Therefore, the expressions become more complicated, as follows:

For bits $15 - 8$:

$$imm_{\text{sign-ext.}} = IR_3 \cdot (\text{LW} + \text{SW}) + IR_7 \cdot (\text{BEQ} + \text{BNE} + \text{ADDI} + \text{LSH})$$

For bits $7 - 4$:

$$imm_{\text{sign-ext.}} = IR_3 \cdot (\text{LW} + \text{SW}) + (IR_7, IR_6, IR_5, IR_4) \cdot (\text{BEQ} + \text{BNE})$$
$$+ IR_7 \cdot (\text{ADDI} + \text{LSH})$$

For bits $3-0$:

$$imm_{\text{sign-ext.}} = (IR_3, IR_2, IR_1, IR_0) \cdot (\text{LW} + \text{SW} + \text{BEQ} + \text{BNE})$$
$$+ (IR_7, IR_6, IR_5, IR_4) \cdot (\text{ADDI} + \text{LSH}) \qquad (9.26)$$

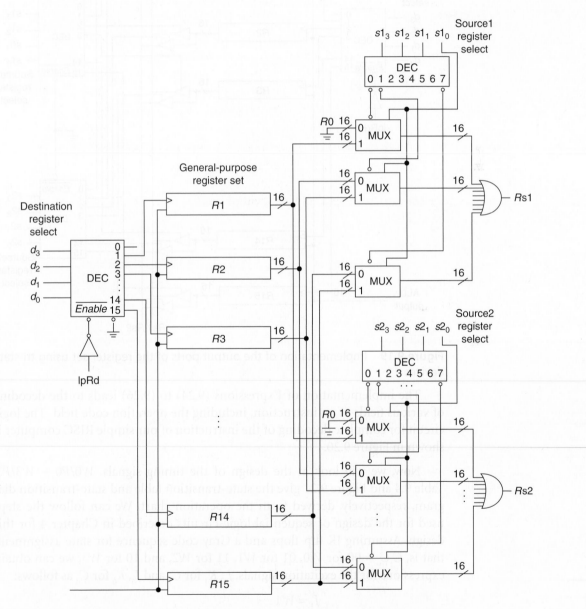

Figure 9.18   Implementation of the output ports of the register set using multiplexers

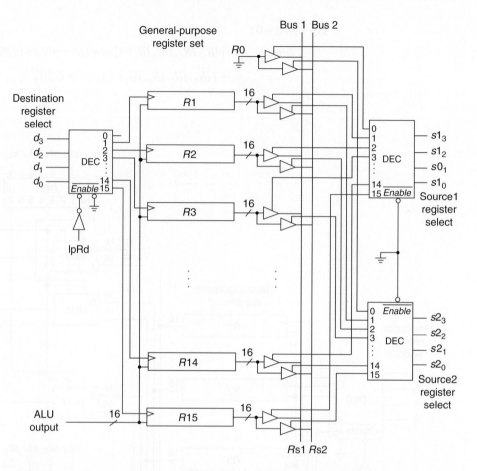

Figure 9.19 Implementation of the output ports of the register set using tri-state devices

The implementation of Expressions (9.24) to (9.26) leads to the decoding of various fields of an instruction, including the operation code field. The logic circuit for complete decoding of the instruction of our simple RISC computer is shown in Figure 9.20.

Now, we will look at the design of the timing signals, $W0/P0 - W3/P3$. Table 9.4 and Figure 9.21 give the state-transition table and state-transition diagram, respectively, derived from the operation chart. We can follow the steps used for the design of sequential logic circuits described in Chapter 4 for this design. Assuming JK flip-flops and a Gray code sequence for state assignment, that is, $C_1 C_0 = 00$ for $W0$, 01 for $W1$, 11 for $W2$, and 10 for $W3$, we can obtain expressions for the excitation signals, J_1, K_1 for C_1 and J_0, K_0 for C_0 as follows:

$$J_1 = W1$$

$$K_1 = W3 + W2 \cdot \overline{IR_{15}}$$

$$J_0 = W0 + W3 \cdot (\text{SLT} + \text{SGT} + \text{JR})$$
$$K_0 = W2 \cdot IR_{15}$$

(9.27)

Thus, we obtain a circuit diagram for the generation of timing signals, as shown in Figure 9.22.

Table 9.4   State transition table for designing the timing signals

Current State	Next State	Condition
W0	W1	unconditional
W2	W2	unconditional
W2	W1	$\text{ADD} + \text{ADDI} + \text{SUB} + \text{AND} + \text{OR} + \text{XOR} = \overline{IR_{15}}$
W2	W3	$\overline{\text{ADD} + \text{ADDI} + \text{SUB} + \text{AND} + \text{OR} + \text{XOR}} = IR_{15}$
W3	W1	$\text{SLT} + \text{SGT} + \text{JR}$
W3	W0	$\text{LW} + \text{SW} + \text{BEQ} + \text{BNE} + \text{JAL or } \overline{\text{SLT} + \text{SGT} + \text{JR}}$

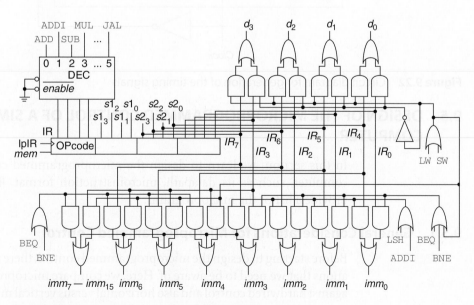

Figure 9.20   Decoding of various fields of instructions

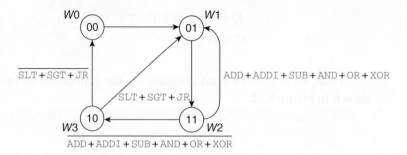

Figure 9.21 State transition diagram for the control cycles

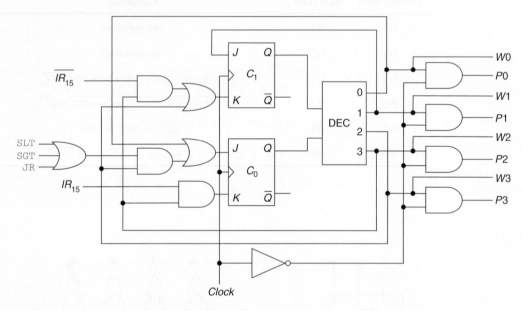

Figure 9.22 Circuit diagram for generation of the timing signals

9.5 DESIGN OF THE MICROPROGRAMMED CONTROL OF A SIMPLE COMPUTER

In this section, we learn to design the microprogrammed control of a simple computer, such as its datapath, microinstruction format, flowchart and also provide a list of the microprograms.

9.5.1 General Considerations for Microprogrammed Control

Before starting to design the microprogrammed control, there are some considerations that we need to be aware of. Here, we compare microprogrammed control against hardwired control and also horizontal versus vertical microprogramming.

1.   *Microprogrammed Control vs. Hardwired Control*

Microprogrammed control refers to the control of the execution of each *machine instruction* by a microcode consisting of a sequence of microinstructions. The design of microprogrammed control follows a different procedure from the design of hardwired control in the following aspects:

1. Although the microcode for each machine instruction needs to perform the same sequence of microoperations, it is unnecessary to create the detailed cycle-by-cycle schedule shown in operation charts for hardwired control. A flowchart that shows just the precedence relations of these microoperations is enough. Each item of the flowchart corresponds to a microinstruction.

2. The design of the flowchart is very closely related to the design of the datapath and the design of the microinstruction format. These three design procedures affect one another and, therefore, must be done in an interleaved manner. Normally, the choice of the microinstruction format is more fundamental than the other two design procedures because it determines the microprogramming strategy and serves as the basis of the entire design.

3. A microinstruction cycle is much simpler than a machine instruction cycle. If a machine instruction, especially a CISC instruction, needs many control cycles for instruction fetch, instruction decode, address generation, operand fetch, instruction execute, and so on, a microinstruction needs only a few control cycles. A microinstruction cycle is executed through the following steps:

    Step 1. Fetch the microinstruction from the microprogram control store and load it into the microinstruction register.

    Step 2. Decode the microinstruction, generating the related control signals, and perform the corresponding microoperations required by the microinstruction.

    Step 3. Create the next microaddress in the microaddress register to prepare for fetching the next microinstruction, and go to Step 1.

4. Microprogramming minimizes the control hardware and creates a logical structure more standardized than hardwired control. A microinstruction requires hardware to perform only simple operations on registers and/or basic memory operations. A large variety of machine instructions are hidden in a microprogram that can easily be changed, thus providing flexibility for the design of the control unit. Microprogramming is especially valuable for controlling both CISC instructions and complex operations using simple control hardware.

In accordance with the special features of microprogramming, a microinstruction should be able to specify part or all of five kinds of control information, as follows:

- The source and destination of the data or address to be involved in the microoperation.
- The function of the arithmetic-logic microoperation to be performed.
- The microoperation of memory Read or Write to be performed.
- The logical condition for controlling a two-way or multi-way branch in the microprogram.
- The next microaddress to be used without modification (if no branching) or with modification for fetching the target microinstruction (if branching).

2. Horizontal Microprogramming vs. Vertical Microprogramming

There are two approaches for the design of a microinstruction format that differ in the way in which the microinstruction specifies the control information. They lead to two different techniques of microprogramming—horizontal and vertical.

Horizontal microprogramming. In *horizontal microprogramming*, in the extreme case, every microoperation specified in the operation chart (for example, see Figure 9.16) uses one control bit of the microinstruction, and a special *next microaddress* field is used for controlling the sequencing of the microprogram. For each control bit of the microinstruction, if the bit is "1", the microoperation specified by that bit is performed. Otherwise, the microoperation is disabled. In this way, all the microoperations are specified independently. Provided that they use disjoint datapaths, their parallel execution is possible. It is this high parallelism that makes horizontal microprogramming advantageous in designing high-speed computers. However, the horizontal microinstruction format requires a very long microinstruction length, up to hundreds of bits. However, not all microinstruction bits need to be used simultaneously. A variant of horizontal microprogramming, with less parallelism and shorter microinstruction length, groups the bits of a microinstruction into fields. Parallelism is allowed only among the fields, but within each field only one microoperation can be specified and performed at a time. In other words, all the microoperations grouped in the same field must be mutually exclusive, and thus cannot be performed in parallel. During execution of the microinstruction, each field is decoded separately to generate only one selected control command corresponding to the specified microoperation. Such *partially horizontal microprogramming* reduces the number of bits in each field of the microinstruction from n bits to $\lceil \log_2 (n+1) \rceil$ bits (the code 00...0 is usually reserved for *none*).

Another problem crucial to horizontal microprogramming is how to control a multi-way branch. For a two-way branch, it is possible to explicitly specify two next microaddresses in a microinstruction and select one of them according to the branch condition. However, this method is uneconomical and cannot be expanded to a multi-way branch. A smarter design for a branching mechanism will be described in Section 9.5.3. It has only one next microaddress field in the microinstruction format and enables the specified branch condition to modify the next microaddress through a control circuit to achieve any multi-way branch.

In the following sections, we will use partially horizontal microprogramming for designing the microprogrammed control of our simple computer.

Vertical microprogramming. The microinstruction format of *vertical micropro-gramming* resembles the format of ordinary machine instructions. It contains a microoperation code field and one or more address fields. Each microinstruction usually selects only one specific microoperation for execution, so no parallelism is allowed. For register-transfer microoperations, each address field of a vertical microinstruction may select one of the hardware registers in the datapath of the CPU. A microprogram counter controls the microinstructions to be executed normally in a sequential order. Each time the microprogram needs to make an unconditional or conditional transfer, it should use a jump or branch microinstruction to specify a destination microaddress in its address field. In contrast to horizontal microprogramming, the advantages of vertical microprogramming are short microinstruction length and ease of writing microprograms. However, the absence of parallelism makes vertical microprograms inefficient and slow. It is interesting to note that vertical microprogramming, in some sense, involves a similar design philosophy as the RISC instruction set. It also emphasizes load/store architecture and simple addressing modes, but solves different problems at a lower microprogram level.

9.5.2   Design of the Datapath for Microprogrammed Control

In the following sections, we will design and implement a simple RISC computer with the same specification as in Section 9.4.1, but use microprogrammed control instead of hardwired control. We will see that the implementation of such complex instructions as multiply (MUL) and shift (LSH) on slightly modified CPU hardware will have almost the same complexity as the implementation for simple instructions. This will be a good example of the implementation of two's complement multiplication at a microprogram level, or at the level of so-called *firmware*. Compared to other methods for implementing complex operations, the firmware method involves less complexity than the hardware method, but achieves faster execution speed than the software method.

For the design of microprogrammed control, there are three interrelated design objects that affect one another—the datapath of the CPU, the micro-instruction format, and the flowchart of the microprogram. To obtain the best result, we should design these three objects in an interleaved manner. Usually, we have a basic organization or datapath for the CPU, and based on this datapath, we have a preliminary microinstruction format to start with. In the process of designing the flowchart of the microprogram, we may need to modify the data-path of the CPU and the microinstruction format by adding more dedicated registers and datapaths for satisfying special functional requirements or improving performance. For our simple RISC computer, the modified datapath of the CPU is shown in Figure 9.23, and the corresponding microinstruction format with microinstruction control circuitry is shown in Figure 9.24.

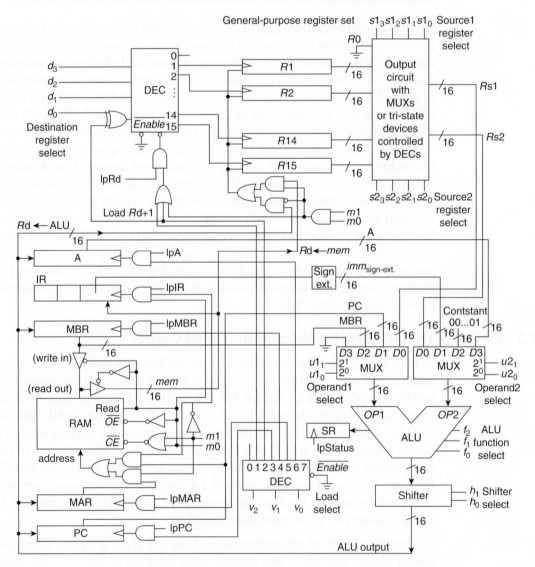

Figure 9.23   Block diagram of the datapath of the CPU for microprogrammed control

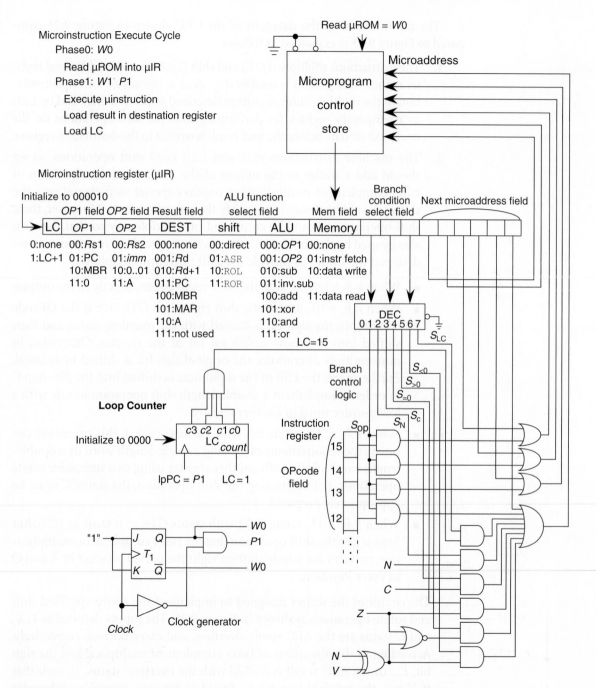

Figure 9.24   Microinstruction format and the microinstruction control circuitry

The modification of the datapath of the CPU shown in Figure 9.23 compared to Figure 9.15 is explained as follows:

1. The instructions multiply (MUL) and shift (LSH) need an additional register named A. Register A is used by MUL as an accumulator for implementation of the multiplication algorithm described in Section 6.1.1 and by LSH as a temporary register for performing multiple shift operations on the intermediate data before the final result is written to the destination register.

2. The machine instructions MUL and LSH need shift operations, so we should add a shifter to the output of the ALU. Since the algorithm of two's complement multiplication requires special shift operations, the shifter should be designed to satisfy these requirements. Moreover, these shift operations should be controlled in a flexible way so that they can also be used by the shift instruction. According to these requirements, we designed the shifter to provide the shift operations as follows:

    ■ When $h_1 h_0 = 00$, no shift: the ALU result passes directly to the output.
    ■ When $h_1 h_0 = 01$, arithmetic shift right with C (ASR): if the OPcode is multiply, the sign bit is XORed with the overflow status and then shifted into the most-significant bit of the register. Otherwise, in non-multiply operations, the original sign bit is shifted in as usual. Furthermore, the LSB of the input data is shifted into the flip-flop C in order to implement a double-length shift operation jointly with a lower-order word in another register.
    ■ When $h_1 h_0 = 10$, rotate left with status C (ROL): this operation can satisfy the requirements of shifting a single-length word or a double-length word jointly with another register using two successive rotate operations. Before starting the shift operation, the status C must be appropriately prepared.
    ■ When $h_1 h_0 = 11$, rotate right with status C (ROR): same as ROL, but ROR is just the shift operation that the two's complement multiplication requires for jointly shifting right the partial product in A and Q in every iteration.

The circuit of the shifter designed to implement the above-specified shift and rotate operations is shown in Figure 9.25. The inputs denoted as F, V, and C status are the ALU result, overflow, and carry/borrow, respectively. According to the algorithm of two's complement multiplication, the sign bit, F_{15}, of the ALU result is XORed with the overflow status, V, such that if $V = 0$, the original sign bit is shifted in for sign extension, otherwise if $V = 1$, the inverted sign bit is shifted in for sign correction. The signal V is ANDed with MUL so that V is involved only in multiply operation, and in all non-MUL operations, an ordinary arithmetic shift right (ASR) operation is performed, and the LSB shifted into the flip-flop C can be ignored. The execution of the rotate operations with C can also be seen in Figure 9.25. When $h_1 h_0 = 10$ for ROL, F_{15} is shifted into C, and C is shifted to $ALUout_0$. When $h_1 h_0 = 11$ for ROR, F_0 is shifted into C, and C is shifted to $ALUout_{15}$. Because F_0 is also shifted into C when $h_1 h_0 = 01$, we can simply use $h_0 = 1$ to control the load of F_0 into C for both operations of ASR and ROR. When $h_1 h_0 = 00$ for all non-shift/rotate cases, the C status created by the ALU is loaded into the flip-flop C as usual.

3. The memory access commands should be encoded in the microinstruction. Therefore, we have a *memory* field in the microinstruction format. To improve the parallelism of memory operations, the 2-bit memory field, $m_1 m_0$, is defined as follows:

   - 01 for instruction fetch—with the memory address directly supplied from the program counter, PC, using the microoperation RAM ← (PC), followed by microoperations *ReadM* and *IR* ← mem to load the instruction from the memory output, *mem*, into the instruction register, IR, when the "read out" tri-state device is enabled by *ReadM*.

   - 10 for data write—with the memory address supplied from the memory address register, MAR, using the microoperation RAM ← (MAR), followed by microoperation *WriteM*, when the "write in" tri-state device is enabled by $\overline{Read}$. The data written into memory has been previously loaded into the memory buffer register, MBR.

   - 11 for data read—with the memory address supplied from the memory address register, MAR, using the microoperation RAM ← (MAR), followed by microopera tions *ReadM* and *Rd* ← mem to load the data from the memory output, *mem*, into the specified destination register, *Rd*, when the "read out" tri-state device is enabled by *ReadM*.

   - 00 for no memory operation—disable the memory chip.

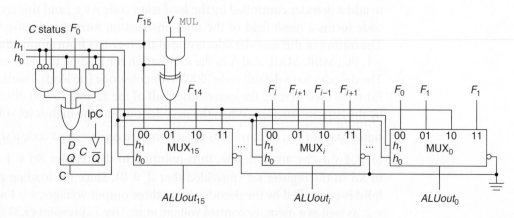

Figure 9.25   Circuit of a shifter for the multiply and shift instructions

By controlling the memory chip in this way (especially by feeding the address directly from PC during instruction fetch), each memory Read or Write operation can be performed by just one microinstruction (not considering the microoperations to load the MAR and the MBR). For implementation, we derive the following expressions for modifying the datapath (see the datapath of the memory device shown in Figure 9.23):

RAM $\leftarrow$ (MAR): m_1 — for replacing the command RAM $\leftarrow$ (MAR)

RAM $\leftarrow$ (PC): $\overline{m_1}$ — for replacing the command RAM $\leftarrow$ (PC)

$$\text{address on RAM} = \overline{m_1} \cdot (\text{PC}) + m_1 \cdot (\text{MAR}) \tag{9.28}$$

$ReadM = m_0$ — for replacing the command $ReadM$

$\overline{OE} = \overline{m_0}$ — "output-enable" pin of the memory chip

$$\overline{CE} = \overline{ReadM + WriteM} = \overline{m_1 + m_0} \text{ — "chip-enable" pin of the memory chip} \tag{9.29}$$

$$loadIR = \text{lpIR} \cdot \overline{m_1} m_0 \quad \text{—for loading } mem \text{ into IR during instruction fetch} \tag{9.30}$$

$$loadRd = m_1 m_0$$
$$\text{data to Rd} = m_1 m_0 \cdot imm + \overline{m_1 m_0} \cdot ALUout \tag{9.31}$$

enabling voltage on "read out" tristate device $= ReadM = m_0$

$$\text{enabling voltage on "write in" tristate device} = \overline{Read} = \overline{m_0} \tag{9.32}$$

4. Since all the microoperations and datapaths used in the microprogram must have their control signals encoded in the microinstruction, we need to add a decoder controlled by the *load select* code $v_2 v_1 v_0$, and this control code forms a *result* field of the microinstruction format in Figure 9.24. The output of this decoder selects one of the registers from among Rd, Rd + 1, PC, MBR, MAR, and A as the destination for loading the ALU result. The decoder has a default code "000" to denote none (no load). Loading to Rd + 1 is used to store the lower-order half of the 32-bit product obtained by the MUL instruction. When the decoder outputs the high-level voltage signal *load Rd + 1*, it transforms the *destination register select* code $d_3 d_2 d_1 d_0$ to $d_3 d_2 d_1 \overline{d_0}$ by an XOR gate, thus pointing to the register Rd + 1 next to Rd in the register set (provided that $d_0 = 0$). Since the loading pulse lpRd is controlled by the decoder using three output voltages, $v = 1$ and $v = 2$, as well as a memory control voltage $m_1 m_0$ [see Expression (9.31)], we should connect a small set of AND–OR gates at the input of the register

set in order to distinguish between two different sources of data, one from memory when $m_1 m_0 = 11$, and the other from the ALU when $m_1 m_0 =$ others.

5. All the loading pulses in Figure 9.23 are the same pulse $P1$ generated by the microinstruction control logic (see Figure 9.24). Because they are controlled by the AND gates, only the register selected by the microinstruction is actually loaded.

9.5.3 Design of the Microinstruction Format for Microprogrammed Control

As we have learned before, a partially horizontal microinstruction consists of many control fields, each of which contains a set of control codes to control a set of mutually exclusive microoperations. We can simply decode these control fields to generate various control signals for controlling the datapath. However, the fields that control the datapath are not the only control fields we need to include in a microinstruction format. A microprogram needs other microinstruction fields to control its program structures of branching, looping, and so on. Hence, the design of a microinstruction format should consist of two parts: one for controlling the datapath and the other for controlling the microprogram sequencing.

For the first part of the design, we group all the control signals in the datapath in Figure 9.23 into the following fields of the microinstruction format as shown in Figure 9.24:

- The *OP1* field for selecting *operand1* among *Rs1*, PC, MBR, and constant zero for an ALU operation.
- The *OP2* field for selecting *operand2* among *Rs2*, *imm*, constant 1, and A for an ALU operation.
- The ALU function select field, part 1, for selecting the shift operations among none (no shift, direct, or straight), ASR, ROL, and ROR.
- The ALU function select field, part 2, for selecting the ALU function among *OP1* transfer, *OP2* transfer, SUB, INV−SUB, ADD, XOR, AND, and OR.
- The Result field for selecting the destination among none (no load), *Rd*, *Rd* + 1, PC, MBR, MAR, and A for loading the ALU-shifter output result.
- The memory function select field for selecting among none, instruction fetch, data write, and data read, as explained above.

Now, as the second part of the design, we will see how the microprogram sequencing can be controlled by simple microinstruction control logic, as shown in Figure 9.24. The basic organization of a microprogrammed control unit is more or less standard. It consists of a control store, a microinstruction register, and a branch control circuit. The *control store* is implemented as a read-only memory

(ROM) in which the microprogram is stored. There can be a *microinstruction register* that holds the microinstruction being currently executed. The *microaddress register* serves as the program counter at the microprogram level. However, the microaddress register was omitted in Figure 9.24 because the microinstruction register in our case contains a *next microaddress* field that can supply the microaddress to the control store through the branch control circuit. Suppose we have preliminarily determined the microinstruction length as 24 bits. Once the microinstruction fields for the datapath control have been determined, the length of the microinstruction is almost known. The major undetermined field is the next microaddress field, whose length in bits depends on the total size of the entire microprogram.

Like the machine instruction that has a basic instruction cycle, the microinstruction also has a basic fetch-execution cycle. In our case, the basic microinstruction cycle of a microinstruction consists of two clock cycles, W0, P0 and W1, P1, as shown in Figure 9.24. Initially, the microinstruction register is set to 000010 (in 6 hexadecimal digits), which means "no operation" with the next microaddress 10 (in hexadecimal). So, its execution will automatically transfer control to a microinstruction at the microaddress 10. This transfer is required by the flowchart in Figure 9.26 in order to start fetching the first microinstruction, which fetches a machine instruction into IR. In phase 0, a microinstruction is fetched from the control store and put into the microinstruction register. Then, in phase 1, the microinstruction is executed with its result loaded into the destination register and the next microaddress modified (if branching) or not modified (if no branching) by the branch control circuit.

The next problem to be described is the branch mechanism for controlling the microprogram sequencing. We have adopted a simple, but general method that can be applied to any *n*-way branch with $n \geq 2$. In designing the flowchart of the microprogram, we found that the control of microprogram sequencing for all 16 machine instructions uses a total of seven different branch conditions. Therefore, we designed a *branch condition select* field of 3 bits in the microinstruction format, where each code from 001 to 111 corresponds to a branch condition and 000 means no branching. In our design, the assignments of codes to branch conditions are as follows:

- 000 corresponds to no branching
- 001 corresponds to branch by the OPcode
- 010 corresponds to branch by the status *N* (negative)
- 011 corresponds to branch by the status *C* (carry/borrow)
- 100 corresponds to branch by the status *Z* (zero)
- 101 corresponds to branch by the condition greater than zero of the result

- 110 corresponds to branch by the condition less than zero of the result
- 111 corresponds to branch by the condition that the 4-bit loop counter counts to 15

This field is decoded by a 3×8 decoder, which generates a high-level voltage signal on one of its outputs 1–7 to enable the corresponding branch condition to modify the original next microaddress specified in the current microinstruction. The principle is simple—for any n-way branch, the enabling action is done by AND gates, and the modifying action is done by OR gates. Take the *OPcode dispatch* as an example. It requires a 16-way branch according to the 4-bit OPcode of the machine instruction. The branch condition select code should be 001, which is decoded as a high-level voltage $S_{op} = 1$ at the output 1 of the decoder. This enabling voltage, S_{op}, is ANDed with the branch condition signal, the OPcode in the IR. After that, the enabled 4-bit OPcode is ORed bitwise with the four LSBs of the next microaddress in the microinstruction register. The result will be a modified microaddress to be used for fetching the next microinstruction. Obviously, the condition for the OR gates to perform a correct modifying action is that the original four LSBs of the next microaddress of the microinstruction must be 0000 before modification. After they are enabled and ORed with the OPcode, the resulting four LSBs of the next microaddress will be 0000–1111, equal to the OPcode of the machine instruction. Therefore, the OPcode dispatch requires that each machine instruction have its microcode starting from the microaddress equal its OPcode. This microaddress assignment can be seen in the flowchart in Figure 9.26.

In general, for any n-way branch, we can use $\lceil \log n \rceil$ AND gates and $\lceil \log n \rceil$ OR gates to modify the $\lceil \log n \rceil$ LSBs of the next microaddress, and the original $\lceil \log n \rceil$ LSBs of the next microaddress field of the microinstruction must be all "0"s. For example, for the two-way branch according to the status C, we must assign the next microaddress of the microinstruction to be even such that the zero LSB of this next microaddress is modified by the status I enabled by a branch condition select code 011.

Besides the branch condition select field stated above, we need to add a single-bit field to control the loop microprogram for the multiply instruction. The field is named as LC, which means that a loop counter, LC, is incremented by "1" if the bit in the LC field of a microinstruction equals "1", otherwise the count of LC remains unchanged. The use of this special field will be seen in the next section.

9.5.4 Design of the Flowchart for Microprogrammed Control

We use flowcharts in writing assembly-language or high-level language programs. However, a microprogram flowchart is different. Instead of showing the major steps of an algorithm, the flowchart of a microprogram shows the precedence relations of the microoperations of various machine instruction cycles.

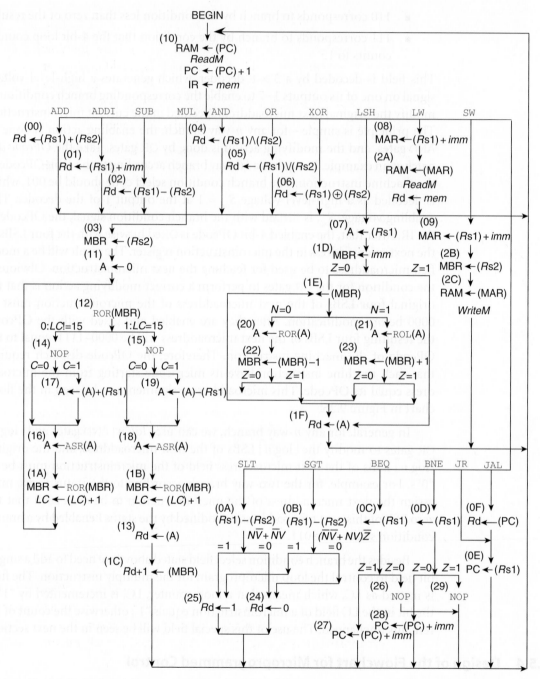

Figure 9.26 Flowchart of microprogram for a simple RISC computer

The flowchart actually depicts the control flow of a microprogram detailed to every step of execution, so that each individually microaddressed item of the flowchart corresponds to a microinstruction. Furthermore, the flowchart of a microprogram contains detailed information of microaddress assignment, such that each microinstruction is assigned a microaddress. The flowchart of the microprogram for our simple RISC computer is designed in Figure 9.26.

The flowchart in Figure 9.26 can be explained as follows:

1. The function of a microprogram is to control the execution of machine instructions. Therefore, the first step of a microprogram should be a machine-instruction fetch. In designing the datapath of the CPU and the microinstruction format, we have taken the measures needed to guarantee that this step will be completed in just one microinstruction. The following microoperations are performed in parallel (see Figure 9.23):

   RAM $\leftarrow$ (PC)—The machine-instruction address in PC is directly connected to the RAM chip through a dedicated path rather than supplied through MAR.
   ReadM—The memory read control signals are activated by the memory field $m_0 = 1$ of the microinstruction.
   PC $\leftarrow$ (PC) + 1—The ALU performs this microoperation.
   IR $\leftarrow$ *mem*—A dedicated path from the memory output, *mem*, to IR is controlled by the memory field $m_1 m_0 = 01$ of the microinstruction.

2. Unlike hardwired control, microprogrammed control does not require an instruction decode step. Instead, the OPcode dispatch is invoked to replace the instruction decode, without using extra microinstruction time. From the example of OPcode dispatch in the last section, we know that the microaddresses, which equal the OPcodes 00 to 0F, should be reserved for this 16-way branch. Therefore, the minimum microaddress that can be assigned to the first microinstruction of the flowchart for machine-instruction fetch is 10.

3. After the OPcode dispatch, each machine instruction begins its execution stage. For all arithmetic-logic instructions, except MUL and LSH, only one microinstruction is adequate for performing a microoperation on the ALU, and after that the control returns to the beginning of the flowchart. The *CPI* of this class of machine instructions equals two microinstruction times, or four clock cycles, if each microinstruction takes two clock cycles.

4. The execution stage of the machine instruction LW consists of two microinstructions—address generation and data read from memory. The step of "data read from memory" is performed by only one microinstruction

with memory field $m_1m_0 = 11$. It consists of the following three microoperations performed in parallel:

RAM ← MAR—by way of a dedicated datapath from MAR to the RAM chip
ReadM—by the control voltage $m_0 = 1$
Rd ← mem—by the datapath through an AND gate controlled by m_1m_0 at the input of the register set

Similarly, the machine instruction SW is executed using three microinstructions—address generation, data preparation in MBR, and data write into memory. The step of "data write into memory" is performed by only one microinstruction with memory field $m_1m_0 = 10$. It consists of the following two microoperations performed in parallel:

RAM ← MAR—by way of a dedicated datapath from MAR to the RAM chip
WriteM—by the control voltage $\overline{m_0} = 1$

5. The machine instructions SLT and SGT each performs a compare followed by a two-way branch to set or reset the register Rd depending on the result of the comparison. The compare microoperation is performed by $(Rs1) - (Rs2)$ without loading. The branch by greater than zero and branch by less than zero are designed for these two instructions. The machine instructions BEQ and BNE also perform the microoperation of testing the branch condition by transferring $(Rs1)$ without loading, but either change or do not change the PC depending on the result of the test. The microinstructions NOP in the microcodes of BEQ and BNE are necessary for the correct implementation of the branch constructs. Their role is to only transfer between two microaddresses.

6. The execution of the machine instruction LSH needs many steps of two-way branches. The microcode for the LSH instruction with the comments to explain its algorithm is shown in Figure 9.27. The shift amount imm should be tested to decide the shift direction, but if imm = 0, a shift is not necessary at all. To keep the original contents of Rs1 unchanged, register A is used to replace Rs1 when performing shift microoperations. The register MBR is used as a counter for incrementing (for left shift) or decrementing (for right shift) the shift amount until it becomes zero. Finally, the shift result in the register A is stored in Rd. As a result, the total number of microinstructions executed by the microcode of the LSH is equal to $3 * |imm| + 4$.

7. The machine instruction MUL is executed according to the algorithm described in Section 6.1.1. The microcode for the MUL instruction with an explanation of its algorithm is shown in Figure 9.28. The multiplicand

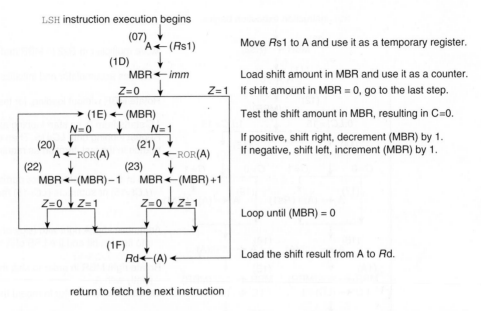

LSH instruction execution begins

(07)   A ← (Rs1)   Move Rs1 to A and use it as a temporary register.

(1D)   MBR ← imm   Load shift amount in MBR and use it as a counter.
Z=0   Z=1   If shift amount in MBR = 0, go to the last step.

(1E) ← (MBR)   Test the shift amount in MBR, resulting in C=0.

N=0   N=1

(20) A ← ROR(A)   (21) A ← ROR(A)   If positive, shift right, decrement (MBR) by 1.
If negative, shift left, increment (MBR) by 1.

(22) MBR ← (MBR) − 1   (23) MBR ← (MBR) + 1

Z=0   Z=1   Z=0   Z=1   Loop until (MBR) = 0

(1F)   Rd ← (A)   Load the shift result from A to Rd.

return to fetch the next instruction

Figure 9.27   Microcode for the execution of the LSH instruction with comments

is in the *Rs1*, and the multiplier is moved from the *Rs2* to the MBR so as to keep both source operands unchanged after the execution of the MUL instruction. Another reason for using MBR instead of *Rs2* as the Q register is that *Rs2* cannot work as a destination register during the shift operations. Register A is used as the accumulator, which is initialized to zero. In each iteration, we rotate the MBR right, without loading, in order to shift the current LSB of the multiplier, $Q0$, into the flip-flop C, and then test C in a two-way branch for a conditional add/subtract microoperation, $A \leftarrow (A) \pm (Rs1)$. After this step, we need a double-length joint shift operation with A and Q. This operation is implemented in two microoperations—an ASR(A) followed by a ROR(MBR). The former shifts $V \oplus A_{sign}$ into A_{15} and A_0 into the flip-flop C, and then the latter shifts A_0 from the flip-flop C into MBR_{15}, thus completing a joint shift right operation to shift the partial product in A and MBR together. The above sequence of microinstructions from testing C to jointly shifting the partial product constitutes the loop body that should be repeated 16 times. For this loop control, we use a 4-bit loop counter LC as shown in Figure 9.24. The LC is previously initialized to 0000. In each microinstruction with the field $LC = 1$, the LC is incremented by 1. When the count of LC reaches 15, the multiplication algorithm requires that the sign bit of the multiplier be treated differently from the numerical bits in the other iterations. After 16 iterations have been executed, the count of LC will return to zero. The execution time of the MUL is data-dependent. The maximum number of

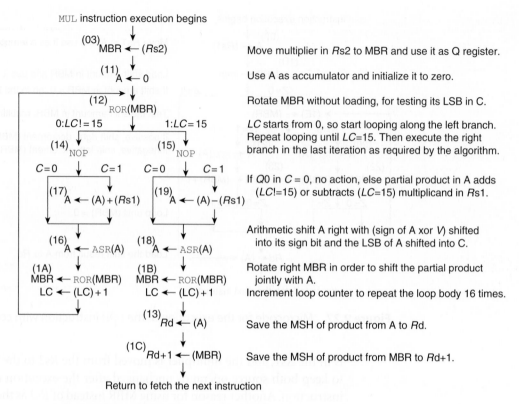

MUL instruction execution begins

(03) MBR ← (Rs2)   Move multiplier in *Rs2* to MBR and use it as Q register.

(11) A ← 0   Use A as accumulator and initialize it to zero.

(12) ROR(MBR)   Rotate MBR without loading, for testing its LSB in C.

0:*LC*! = 15   1:*LC* = 15   *LC* starts from 0, so start looping along the left branch. Repeat looping until *LC*=15. Then execute the right branch in the last iteration as required by the algorithm.

(14) NOP   (15) NOP

C=0   *C*=1   *C*=0   *C*=1   If *Q*0 in *C* = 0, no action, else partial product in A adds (*LC*!=15) or subtracts (*LC*=15) multiplicand in *Rs*1.

(17) A ← (A) + (Rs1)   (19) A ← (A) − (Rs1)

(16) A ← ASR(A)   (18) A ← ASR(A)   Arithmetic shift A right with (sign of A xor *V*) shifted into its sign bit and the LSB of A shifted into C.

(1A) MBR ← ROR(MBR) LC ← (LC) + 1   (1B) MBR ← ROR(MBR) LC ← (LC) + 1   Rotate right MBR in order to shift the partial product jointly with A.
Increment loop counter to repeat the loop body 16 times.

(13) Rd ← (A)   Save the MSH of product from A to *Rd*.

(1C) Rd+1 ← (MBR)   Save the MSH of product from MBR to *Rd*+1.

Return to fetch the next instruction

Figure 9.28 Microcode for the execution of the MUL instruction with comments

executed microinstructions is equal to $5 + 5 * 16 = 85$, including the first microinstruction for fetching the MUL instruction.

8. The final step in the flowchart design is to assign microaddresses to the microinstructions in the flowchart. All the microaddresses in the flowchart in Figure 9.28 are indicated in parentheses. They are assigned according to the requirement of the *branch control logic* in Figure 9.24. Because each microinstruction has a next microaddress to specify its successor, the placement of microinstructions in the control store is more flexible than for regular programming. The only restriction to the microaddress assignment is from the branch mechanism. Although there is no restriction that successive microinstructions must be placed in consecutive locations, we still keep a sequential order of assigning consecutive microaddresses to a non-branching microprogram segment.

9.5.5 Obtaining the Microprogram List

After all the design steps described in Sections 9.5.2 to 9.5.4, the microprogram list can be obtained as shown in Table 9.5.

Table 9.5   Microprogram list for a simple RISC computer

μaddress	LC	OP1	OP2	RES	ALU	Mem	Branch	Next μaddress	Operation
00	0	00	00	001	00100	00	000	10	ADD: $Rd \leftarrow (Rs1) + (Rs2)$
01	0	00	01	001	00100	00	000	10	ADDI: $Rd \leftarrow (Rs1) + imm$
02	0	00	00	001	00010	00	000	10	SUB: $Rd \leftarrow (Rs1) - (Rs2)$
03	0	00	00	100	00001	00	000	11	MUL: MBR $\leftarrow (Rs2)$
04	0	00	00	001	00110	00	000	10	AND: $Rd \leftarrow (Rs1)$ and $(Rs2)$
05	0	00	00	001	00111	00	000	10	OR: $Rd \leftarrow (Rs1)$ or $(Rs2)$
06	0	00	00	001	00101	00	000	10	XOR: $Rd \leftarrow (Rs1)$ xor $(Rs2)$
07	0	00	00	110	00000	00	000	1D	LSH: A $\leftarrow (Rs1)$
08	0	00	01	101	00100	00	000	2A	LW: MAR $\leftarrow (Rs1) + imm$
09	0	00	01	101	00100	00	000	2B	SW: MAR $\leftarrow (Rs1) + imm$
0A	0	00	00	000	00010	00	110	24	SLT: $(Rs1) - (Rs2)$; branch by < 0
0B	0	00	00	000	00010	00	101	24	SGT: $(Rs1) - (Rs2)$; branch by > 0
0C	0	00	00	000	00000	00	100	26	BEQ: $\leftarrow (Rs1)$; branch by Z
0D	0	00	00	000	00000	00	100	28	BNE: $\leftarrow (Rs1)$; branch by Z
0E	0	00	00	011	00000	00	000	10	JR: PC $\leftarrow (Rs1)$
0F	0	01	00	001	00000	00	000	0E	JAL: $Rd \leftarrow (PC)$
10	0	01	10	011	00100	01	001	00	Instr. fetch; PC $\leftarrow (PC) + 1$; OPcode dispatch
11	0	11	00	110	00000	00	000	12	A $\leftarrow 0$
12	0	10	00	000	11000	00	111	14	ROR(MBR); branch by LC
13	0	00	11	001	00001	00	000	1C	$Rd \leftarrow (A)$
14	0	00	00	000	00000	00	011	16	NOP; branch by C
15	0	00	00	000	00000	00	011	18	NOP; branch by C
16	0	00	11	110	01001	00	000	1A	A $\leftarrow$ ASR(A)
17	0	00	11	110	00100	00	000	16	A $\leftarrow (A) + (Rs1)$

(Continues)

Table 9.5 Microprogram list for a simple RISC computer (*continued*)

μaddress	LC	OP1	OP2	RES	ALU	Mem	Branch	Next μaddress	Operation
18	0	00	11	110	01001	00	000	1B	$A \leftarrow \text{ASR}(A)$
19	0	00	11	110	00010	00	000	18	$A \leftarrow (A) - (Rs1)$
1A	1	10	00	100	11000	00	000	12	$\{$ $\begin{array}{l}\text{MBR} \leftarrow \text{ROR(MBR)};\\ \text{LC} \leftarrow (\text{LC}) + 1\end{array}$
1B	1	10	00	100	11000	00	000	13	
1C	0	10	00	010	00000	00	000	10	$Rd + 1 \leftarrow (\text{MBR})$
1D	0	00	01	100	00001	00	100	1E	MBR $\leftarrow$ *imm*; branch by Z
1E	0	10	00	000	00000	00	010	20	$\leftarrow$ MBR; branch by N
1F	0	00	11	001	00001	00	000	10	$Rd \leftarrow (A)$
20	0	00	11	110	11001	00	000	22	$A \leftarrow \text{ROR}(A)$
21	0	00	11	110	10001	00	000	23	$A \leftarrow \text{ROL}(A)$
22	0	10	10	100	00010	00	100	1E	MBR $\leftarrow$ (MBR) $- 1$; branch by Z
23	0	10	10	100	00100	00	100	1E	MBR $\leftarrow$ (MBR) $+ 1$; branch by Z
24	0	11	00	001	00000	00	000	10	$Rd \leftarrow 0$
25	0	00	10	001	00001	00	000	10	$Rd \leftarrow 1$
26	0	00	00	000	00000	00	000	10	NOP
27	0	01	01	011	00100	00	000	10	$PC \leftarrow (PC) + imm$
28	0	01	01	011	00100	00	000	10	$PC \leftarrow (PC) + imm$
29	0	00	00	000	00000	00	000	10	NOP
2A	0	00	00	000	00000	11	000	10	Memory mode: data read
2B	0	00	00	100	00001	00	000	2C	MBR $\leftarrow (Rs2)$
2C	0	00	00	000	00000	10	000	10	Memory mode: data write

The flowchart and program list have the same effectiveness for design documentation. With the microinstruction format already designed, the microprogram list can be written directly from the flowchart. If the flowchart shows the principle of control procedures, then the microprogram list provides the microprogram coding useful for loading the control store.

SUMMARY

Learning the design of the control unit is an important step in learning computer design in general. It uses the knowledge learned in all the previous chapters as the basis and concludes the design of the CPU for realization of the instruction set predetermined as the design target. However, more preliminary knowledge, given in Section 9.2, is still required of a designer in designing the control unit. As a preliminary practice of design, several asynchronous control circuits used in signal generators are designed in Section 9.3. Several control units for the sequential control of some arithmetic operations, for example, bit-serial addition and two's complement multiplication, are designed in Section 9.4.

With this preliminary knowledge, we design the control unit for the instruction set given in Table 9.3. Using the same example, we use two different methods of design. The hardwired control is designed in Section 9.4, and the microprogrammed control is designed in Section 9.5. For the hardwired control, we propose a method based on an operation chart used by all the instructions to schedule their microoperations to be executed in the same timing sequence of control signals. Actually, an operation chart is a special form of the space-time diagram containing the schedules of microoperations executed by all the instructions using the same sequence of central timing signals. From the operation chart, comprehensive logic expressions for all the control signals can be written directly. The example gives the entire process of design from the operation chart up to the implementation of the datapath and all the control signals. For the microprogrammed control, we use a method based on the flowchart of the microprogram. The flowchart in our method is not merely a graph that shows only the algorithms of execution of the machine instructions. We must have a preliminary datapath and microinstruction format in order to design a working microprogram flowchart, in which every entry is an independent microinstruction. Each entry will be assigned a microaddress in the final stage of the design according to the requirement of a branch control mechanism to implement any n-way branch in the flowchart, where n can be as large as the number of instructions in the instruction set for performing the microoperation called the OPcode dispatch. The example gives the entire process of design from the flowchart up to the microprogram list and the hardware support to microprogramming.

EXERCISES

9.1 Given the specification of a two-address RISC computer as follows:

- Word length: 8 bits with arithmetic data in two's complement representation.
- Instruction length: 12 bits.
- Instruction memory: 256×12 bits directly using an 8-bit program counter (PC) as the address register and a 12-bit instruction register (IR) to receive the instruction.

- Data memory: 256×8 bits using an 8-bit memory address register, MAR, and an 8-bit memory buffer register, MBR.
- Register set: 16×8 bits, with $R0$ always denoting constant zero.

The instruction format is shown in Figure 9.29. The instruction set is given in Table 9.6.

(a) Design the operation chart for the above instruction set, including the shift instructions LSH and ASH, which require a variable *CPI*, while for each type of the other instructions, the *CPI* value should be minimum.

(b) Design the ALU with an attached shifter that can serve as the center of the CPU and execute the arithmetic-logic operations for most of the instructions.

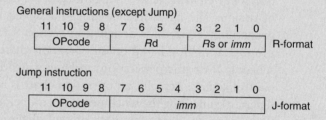

Figure 9.29 Instruction format for Problems 9.1 and 9.2

(c) Design the rest part of the datapath of the CPU, which matches the above operation chart so that all the microoperations specified in the operation chart have the corresponding datapath parts to implement them. Draw the block diagram of the datapath of the CPU.

Table 9.6 The two-address instruction set for Problems 9.1 and 9.2

OPC	Mnemonic	Function	Meaning
0000	ADD Rd, Rs	$Rd \leftarrow (Rd) + (Rs)$	add (Rs) to Rd
0001	SUB Rd, Rs	$Rd \leftarrow (Rd) - (Rs)$	subtract (Rs) from Rd
0010	AND Rd, Rs	$Rd \leftarrow (Rd) \wedge (Rs)$	logic AND (Rs) to Rd
0011	XOR Rd, Rs	$Rd \leftarrow (Rd) \oplus (Rs)$	logic XOR (Rs) to Rd
0100	COPY Rd, Rs	$Rd \leftarrow (Rs)$	copy (Rs) to Rd
0101	COPI Rd, #imm	$Rd \leftarrow imm_{\text{sign-ext.}}$	copy sign-extended imm to Rd
0110	COPL Rd, #imm	$Rd \leftarrow imm_{\text{zero-ext.}}$	copy zero-extended imm to Rd

OPC	Mnemonic	Function	Meaning
0111	COPH Rd, #imm	$Rd_{MSH} \leftarrow imm$	copy *imm* to Rd_{MSH}, Rd_{LSH} unchanged
1000	LW Rd, Rs, *imm*	$Rd \leftarrow Mem[(Rs) + imm]$	load from memory into Rd; $Rs = Rd + 1$
1001	SW Rd, Rs, *imm*	$Mem[(Rs) + imm] \leftarrow (Rd)$	store into memory from Rd; $Rs = Rd + 1$
1010	LSH Rd, *imm*	$Rd \leftarrow (Rd) << \text{ or} >> imm$	logic shift: left if *imm* < 0, else right
1011	ASH Rd, *imm*	$Rd \leftarrow (Rd) <<^a \text{ or} >>^a imm$	arith. shift denoted by $<<^a$ and $>>^a$: left shift if *imm* < 0, else right shift
1100	BEQ Rd, *imm*	if $(Rd) = 0$, $PC \leftarrow (PC_{updated}) + imm$	branch if = 0; $-8 \leq imm \leq 7$
1101	BGT Rd, *imm*	if $(Rd) > 0$, $PC \leftarrow (PC_{updated}) + imm$	branch if > 0; $-8 \leq imm \leq 7$
1110	BLT Rd, *imm*	if $(Rd) < 0$, $PC \leftarrow (PC_{updated}) + imm$	branch if < 0; $-8 \leq imm \leq 7$
1111	JMP *imm*	$PC \leftarrow (PC_{updated}) + imm$	unconditional branch; $-128 \leq imm \leq 127$

Notes: (1) Branch and Jump actually use *Bxx Rd*, label and JMP label, respectively, where label = $(PC)_{updated} + imm$.

(2) LW and SW need three parameters each in a two-address instruction format, so *Rd* and *Rs* are two consecutive registers, with *Rd* even-numbered and $Rs = Rd + 1$.

9.2 Continue with Problem 9.1 but design the microprogrammed control unit for the instruction set given in Table 9.6.

(a) Design the microinstruction format matching the datapath redesigned on the basis of the datapath in Problem 9.1. What modification of the datapath will be necessary so that all control signals in the microinstruction format can be found in the datapath?

(b) Design the flowchart of the microprogram for the given instruction set such that each item of your flowchart must be a specific microinstruction in the above format.

(c) Design the mechanism of sequencing control of the microprogram and assign microaddresses to the microinstructions in your flowchart designed in Part (b).

9.3 Suppose an accumulator-based CPU has the following characteristics:

- Word length: 8 bits for accumulator A, ALU, shifter, as well as latch1 and latch2.
- Data memory: 256 × 8 bits, so MAR and MBR have 8 bits each.
- Instruction length: 12 bits for IR.
- Instruction format: 4-bit OPcode field and 8-bit address or *imm/offset* field as shown in Figure 9.30.
- Instruction memory: 256 × 12 bits, so PC has 8 bits.
- Directly uses PC and IR as address register and buffer register, respectively.
- PC is implemented as a counter, which eases the update operation.

The instruction set is given in Table 9.7.

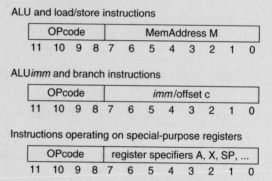

ALU and load/store instructions

OPcode				MemAddress M							
11	10	9	8	7	6	5	4	3	2	1	0

ALU*imm* and branch instructions

OPcode				*imm*/offset c							
11	10	9	8	7	6	5	4	3	2	1	0

Instructions operating on special-purpose registers

OPcode				register specifiers A, X, SP, ...							
11	10	9	8	7	6	5	4	3	2	1	0

Figure 9.30 Instruction format for Problems 9.3 and 9.4

(a) In parallel with the design work in Parts (b) and (c), design the operation chart for the above instruction set. For each type of instruction, the *CPI* value should be minimum.

(b) Design the ALU that can serve as the center of the CPU and execute the arithmetic-logic operations for most of the instructions.

(c) Design the rest part of the datapath of the CPU that matches the above operation chart so that all the microoperations specified in the operation chart have the corresponding datapath parts to implement them. The bus system configuration that was covered in Chapter 8 might be a good reference. Draw the block diagram of the datapath of the CPU.

Table 9.7 The one-address instruction set for Problems 9.3 and 9.4

OPC	Mnemonic	Function	Meaning
0000	ADDA *M*	$A \leftarrow (A) + \text{mem}[M]$	add memory to *A*
0001	SUBA *M*	$A \leftarrow (A) - \text{mem}[M]$	subtract memory from *A*
0010	ANDA *M*	$A \leftarrow (A) \wedge \text{mem}[M]$	bitwise AND memory to *A*
0011	XORA *M*	$A \leftarrow (A) \oplus \text{mem}[M]$	bitwise XOR memory to *A*

OPC	Mnemonic	Function	Meaning
0100	ADDI #c	$A \leftarrow (A) + c_{\text{sign-ext.}}$	add sign-extended c to A, $-128 \leq c \leq 127$
0101	CLR $A, X, \ldots$	$A, X, .. \leftarrow$ zero	clear $A, X, \ldots$ to zero
0110	ANDI #c	$A \leftarrow (A) \bigwedge c_{\text{zero-ext.}}$	bitwise AND zero-extended c to A
0111	XORI #c	$A \leftarrow (A) \oplus c_{\text{zero-ext.}}$	bitwise XOR zero-extended c to A
1000	R2A $X, SP, \ldots$	$A \leftarrow (X), (SP) \ldots$	transfer $(X), \ldots$ to A
1001	A2R $X, SP, \ldots$	$X, SP, \ldots \leftarrow (A)$	transfer (A) to $X, \ldots$
1010	LDA M	$A \leftarrow \text{mem}[M]$	load A from memory
1011	STA M	$\text{mem}[M] \leftarrow (A)$	store A into memory
1100	BEQ #c	if $(A) = 0, PC \leftarrow (PC_{\text{updated}}) + c$	branch equal; $-128 \leq c \leq 127$
1101	BGT #c	if $(A) > 0, PC \leftarrow (PC_{\text{updated}}) + c$	branch greater than; $-128 \leq c \leq 127$
1110	BLT #c	if $(A) < 0, PC \leftarrow (PC_{\text{updated}}) + c$	branch less than; $-128 \leq c \leq 127$
1111	JMP #c	$PC \leftarrow (PC_{\text{updated}}) + c$	unconditional branch; $-128 \leq c \leq 127$

Note: Branch and Jump actually use *Bxx* label and JMP label, respectively. A, X, SP, ... are special-purpose registers, each specified by a corresponding bit of the bit pattern in the address field.

9.4 Continue with Problem 9.3 but design the microprogrammed control unit for the instruction set given in Table 9.7.

(a) Design the microinstruction format matching the datapath redesigned on the basis of the datapath in Problem 9.3. What modification of the datapath will be necessary so that all control signals in the microinstruction format can be found in the datapath?

(b) Design the flowchart of the microprogram for the given instruction set such that each item of your flowchart must be a specific microinstruction in the above format.

(c) Design the mechanism of sequencing control of the microprogram and assign microaddresses to the microinstructions in your flowchart designed in Part (b).

9.5 This problem is related to the design of microprogrammed control of four special instructions in an instruction set. The datapath of the CPU is given in Figure 9.31. The machine instruction format is shown in Figure 9.32. The instruction set is partly given in Table 9.8, and the microinstruction format is given in Figure 9.33.

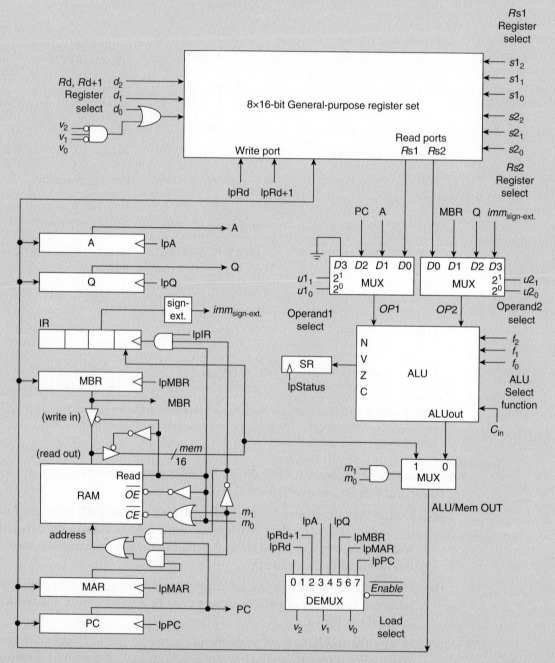

Figure 9.31 Datapath of the CPU for Problems 9.5 and 9.6

	source1	source2	destination
OPcode	Rs1	Rs2	Rd
$x_1 x_0$	$s1_2 \, s1_1 \, s1_0$	$s2_2 \, s2_1 \, s2_0$	$d_2 \, d_1 \, d_0$

Figure 9.32 Machine-instruction format for Problems 9.5 and 9.6

Design the algorithm for the execution of each instruction in the instruction set given in Table 9.8. The algorithms must be so detailed that they can be applied directly to the design of the microprogram flowchart in Problem 9.6.
[Note: It is required that you clearly express the algorithm using a tree-structured graph, which can then be transformed easily and mapped directly into the microprogram flowchart in Problem 9.6. Provide an explanation if necessary.]

(a) For instruction ABS: $Rd \leftarrow |(Rs1) - (Rs2)|$
Find the absolute value of the difference of two signed numbers in two's complement representation in registers $Rs1$ and $Rs2$.

(b) For instruction ASR: $Rd \leftarrow (Rs1) >>^a imm$ if $imm! = 0$,
$Rd \leftarrow (Rs1)$ if $imm = 0$, where imm is an unsigned number and $>>^a$ denotes arithmetic right shift operator.
If $imm \neq 0$, arithmetically right shift $(Rs1)$ imm bits, and load the result in Rd. Otherwise, if $imm = 0$, no shift, but still load $(Rs1)$ in Rd.

(c) For instruction MUL: $Rd, Rd + 1 \leftarrow (Rs1) * (Rs2)$
Multiply two signed single-precision integer numbers, M and Y, in $Rs1$ and $Rs2$ in two's complement representation, and load the double-word product, $M * Y$, in two's complement representation in two successive registers Rd and $Rd + 1$, where Rd is an even-numbered register and $Rd + 1$ is the next consecutive odd-numbered register.
Use the simple algorithm of multiply: repeatedly add (or subtract) the multiplicand to the accumulator $|Rs2|$ times, for example, $M * 3 = 0 + M + M + M$. Your algorithm must consider all possible special cases.

(d) For instruction DIV: $Rd \leftarrow (Rs1) / (Rs2)$
$Rd + 1 \leftarrow (Rs1) \% (Rs2)$
Divide two single-word signed integer numbers, D and Y, in $Rs1$ and $Rs2$ in two's complement representation, and load the single-word quotient, Q, in Rd and the single-word remainder, R, in $Rd + 1$, both in two's complement representation, where Rd is an even-numbered register, and $Rd + 1$ is the next consecutive odd-numbered register.
Use the simple algorithm of divide: repeatedly subtract (or add) the divisor from the dividend until the remainder is just about to change its sign, for example, $7 \div 3$ is done by 7-3-3, getting the quotient 2 and the remainder 1. Your algorithm must consider all possible special cases.

Table 9.8 Instruction set (partly) for Problems 9.5 and 9.6

OPcode	Mnemonic	Function	Meaning
0 0	ABS	absolute difference	$Rd \leftarrow |(Rs1) - (Rs2)|$
0 1	ASR	arithmetic shift right	$Rd \leftarrow (Rs1) >>^a imm$ if $imm! = 0$ $Rd \leftarrow (Rs1)$ no shift if $imm = 0$
1 0	MUL	multiply	$Rd, Rd + 1 \leftarrow (Rs1) * (Rs2)$
1 1	DIV	divide	$Rd \leftarrow (Rs1) / (Rs2);$ $Rd + 1 \leftarrow (Rs1) \% (Rs2)$

OP1 field	OP2 field	Result field	ALU function select field	Memory field	Branch condition select field	Next microaddress field
$u1_1\ u1_0$	$u2_1\ u2_0$	$v_1\ v_0$	$f_2\ \ f_1\ \ f_0\ \ Cin$	$m_1\ m_0$	$b_2\ \ b_1\ \ b_0$				
00: $Rs1$	00: $Rs2$	000: None	000: $OP1+C_{in}$	00: None	000: None				
01: A	01: MBR	001: Rd	001: $OP1+OP2+C_{in}$	01: Instr.	001: S_{op}				
10: PC	10: Q	010: $Rd+1$	010: $OP1-OP2-C_{in}$	fetch	010: S_N				
11: 0	11: imm	011: A	011: $OP2-OP1-C_{in}$	10: Data write	011: S_C				
		100: Q	100: $OP1$ xor $OP2$	11: Data read	100: S_Z				
		101: MBR	101: $OP1$ and $OP2$						
		110: MAR	110: ROL with C						
		111: PC	111: ROR with C						

Figure 9.33 Microinstruction format for Problems 9.5 and 9.6

9.6 Design the microprogram flowchart for implementation of the four machine instructions given in Table 9.8. Your flowchart must be drawn in the same structural form as we have done in the example in Figure 9.26. The flowchart must include all the steps of the basic instruction cycles starting from the instruction fetch to the completion of all four given instructions. You must assign microaddresses to all the microinstructions so that they are consistent with the branch mechanism we have learned in this chapter.

[Note: Consider only four instructions in the given instruction set, so you do not need to reserve microaddresses for the other instructions.]

9.7 This problem is to design the datapath and control of a mini-CPU with the following specification:

(1) General specification:
- Word length: 8 bits with arithmetic data in two's complement representation.
- Instruction length: 16 bits.
- Instruction memory: a 256 × 16-bit PROM directly using an 8-bit program counter (PC) as the address register and a 16-bit instruction register (IR) to store the instruction being executed.

- Data memory: 256×8 bits using an 8-bit memory address register, MAR and an 8-bit memory buffer register, MBR.
- General-purpose register set: 16×8 bits, with $R0$ containing constant zero.
- Addressing modes: immediate, displacement, and PC-relative addressing modes.
- An 8-bit special-purpose register, A, is provided with two functions: either as an address register for implementing displacement addressing mode with load/store instructions, or as a temporary register to be used elsewhere.

(2) Instruction format: As shown in Figure 9.34.

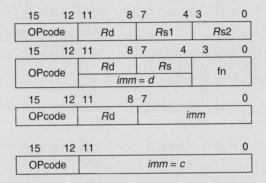

Figure 9.34 Machine-instruction format for Problems 9.7 to 9.9

(3) Mixed three- and two-address instruction set: As shown in Table 9.9.

Table 9.9 Instruction set for Problems 9.7 to 9.9

OPC	Mnemonic	Function	Meaning
0000	ADD Rd, $Rs1$, $Rs2$	$Rd \leftarrow (Rs1) + (Rs2)$	add $(Rs1)$ and $(Rs2)$ to Rd
0001	SUB Rd, $Rs1$, $Rs2$	$Rd \leftarrow (Rs1) - (Rs2)$	subtract $(Rs1)$ and $(Rs2)$ to Rd
0010	AND Rd, $Rs1$, $Rs2$	$Rd \leftarrow (Rs1) \wedge (Rs2)$	bitwise AND $(Rs1)$ and $(Rs2)$ to Rd
0011	XOR Rd, $Rs1$, $Rs2$	$Rd \leftarrow (Rs1) \oplus (Rs2)$	bitwise XOR $(Rs1)$ and $(Rs2)$ to Rd
0100	R2R Rd, Rs	$Rd \leftarrow (Rs)$ if fn = 00	R to R: copy (Rs) to Rd
0100	A2R Rd	$Rd \leftarrow (A)$ if fn = 01 & $Rs = xxx_0$	A to R: copy (A) to Rd
0100	R2A Rd	$A \leftarrow (Rd)$ if fn = 01 & $Rs = xxx_1$	R to A: copy (Rd) to A
0100	SUBA #d	$A \leftarrow (A) - d$ if fn = 10	subA: subtract #d to A
0100	I2A #d	$A \leftarrow d$ if fn = 11	I to A: load #d to A

(Continues)

Table 9.9 Instruction set for Problems 9.7 to 9.9 *(Continued)*

OPC	Mnemonic	Function	Meaning
0101	I2R Rd, #imm	$Rd \leftarrow imm$	*I* to *R*: load *imm* to *Rd*
0110	SUBI Rd, #imm	$Rd \leftarrow (Rd) - imm$	subtract *imm* to *Rd*, $-128 \leq imm \leq +127$
0111	ANDI Rd, #imm	$Rd \leftarrow (Rd) \wedge imm$	AND *imm* to *Rd*, $0 \leq imm \leq 255$
1000	XORI Rd, #imm	$Rd \leftarrow (Rd) \oplus imm$	XOR *imm* to *Rd*, $0 \leq imm \leq 255$
1001	LSH Rd, #imm	$Rd \leftarrow (Rd) << imm$ if $imm < 0$; $Rd \leftarrow (Rd) >> imm$ if $imm > 0$	Logical shift (Rd) *imm* bits
1010	LW Rd, imm	$Rd \leftarrow \text{Mem}[(A) + imm]$	load word from memory into *Rd*
1011	SW imm, Rd	$\text{Mem}[(A) + imm] \leftarrow (Rd)$	store word to memory from *Rd*
1100	BGE Rd, #c	if $(Rd) \geq 0$, $PC \leftarrow (PC_{updated}) + c$	branch if ≥ 0: $-128 \leq$ (offset *c*) $\leq +127$
1101	BLE Rd, #c	if $(Rd) \leq 0$, $PC \leftarrow (PC_{updated}) + c$	branch if ≤ 0: $-128 \leq$ (offset *c*) $\leq +127$
1110	BNE Rd, #c	if $(Rd) \neq 0$, $PC \leftarrow (PC_{updated}) + c$	branch if $\neq 0$: $-128 \leq$ (offset *c*) $\leq +127$
1111	JMP #c	$PC \leftarrow (PC_{updated}) + c$ always	Jump: *c* is a 12-bit signed offset

Note: Branch and Jump are written as "Bxx Rd, label" and "JMP label" so that $(PC_{updated}) + c =$ label.

Study the instruction set provided with its associated instruction format. To show that this instruction set has enough functionality, write the shortest assembly-language code segment to solve the following problem:

Given an array, $A[0..n-1]$, of n signed numbers in two's complement representation. The array is stored in a memory area with the starting address *Astart*. Calculate an array, $B[0..n-1]$, equal to the absolute values of *A*, such that each $B[i] = |A[i]|$ for $i = 0, 1, .., n-1$, and store it in another memory area with the starting address *Bstart*.

To match the given parameters of our mini-CPU, what is the upper limit of the size, *n*, of the array?

9.8 (a) Design the simplest datapath and the operation chart for the hardwired control of the mini-CPU according to the specification and the instruction set given in Problem 9.7.

(b) Give the complete design of the hardwired control of the given instruction set, including the expressions for all related control signals in the datapath and the operation chart as well as the central timing control signals.

9.9 Design the microprogrammed control of the instruction set given above in Problem 9.7. The design includes:

- the microinstruction format with minimized length, but sufficient functionality.
- the datapath of the CPU that best matches the microinstruction format.
- the microprogram flowchart for the entire instruction set given above.
- the control of the microoperations involved in the microinstruction format (especially the microprogram branch) and the timing control of the basic microinstruction cycle.
- the list of the microprogram to be loaded into the microcontrol store.

9.9 Design the microprogrammed control of the instruction set given above in Problem 9.7. The design includes:

- the microinstruction format with minimized length but sufficient functionality
- the datapath of the CPU that best matches the microinstruction format
- the microprogram flowchart for the entire instruction set given above
- the control of the microoperation involved in the micro-operation format, especially the microprogram branch, and the timing control of the basic microinstruction cycle.
- the list of the microprogram to be loaded into the microcontrol store

10

Primary Memory

There are two basic forms of memory in a computer system: primary memory (or main memory) and secondary storage (or auxiliary memory). In this chapter, we will discuss primary memory. Secondary storage will be discussed in Chapter 11.

10.1 THE MEMORY HIERARCHY

In this section, you will learn about the hierarchical organization, functionality, and performance of primary memory in a computer system.

10.1.1 The Hierarchical Organization of a Memory System

Programs in execution and their associated data are stored in *primary memory*. Inactive programs and data are stored in *secondary storage*. Inactive programs can be executed only after they are transferred (or loaded) into primary memory. An instruction, as well as its associated data stored in primary memory, must be loaded into registers in the CPU prior to decoding and execution. These requirements form the basic three-level hierarchical structure for a computer memory system consisting of CPU registers, primary memory, and secondary storage.

We define two performance measures—speed and capacity—for a memory system. First, a CPU and its registers function at an extremely high speed, and this requires primary memory to provide an access speed that matches the processing speed of the CPU. However, primary memory is much slower due to cost considerations. *Memory bottleneck* or *memory latency*, caused by differences in speed between the CPU and memory, profoundly affects the performance of a memory system. Second, every primary memory has an affordable capacity. This limits the size of executable programs that are stored in primary memory. Certain types of secondary storage (e.g., magnetic tape) are considered to have practically unlimited capacity. To remedy these limitations, a more sophisticated memory hierarchical structure, as shown in Figure 10.1, is employed in most computer systems today.

10.1.2 Functionality and Performance of a Memory Hierarchy

The memory hierarchical structure shown in Figure 10.1 is drawn in the shape of a pyramid, with a narrow top layer and a wide bottom layer. At the top of the memory hierarchy, general-purpose *registers* (or scratch-pad memory) are physically close to the ALU and supply operands and store intermediate results with minimum delay. Compared to other memory components, they offer the fastest access speed, matching that of the CPU. This means, for example, a 1-GHz Pentium® processor can be equipped with a set of registers that have an access delay of 1 nanosecond. However, the cost of building these registers and providing space for them on a CPU chip is quite high, and this restricts the registers to a small number, usually a few hundred or less. This is followed by multiple levels of cache memories and the main memory, which provide larger memory spaces to directly support the operating system and running programs.

At the bottom of the memory hierarchy are the secondary storage components, which are relatively inexpensive to construct and operate. They provide large storage space, ranging from several gigabytes to several terabytes. However, the trade-off of the large capacity is a very long access delay time, ranging from a few milliseconds to several seconds. Because of the similar operation mode and interfacing techniques, secondary storage can be classified as I/O devices and will not be studied in this chapter.

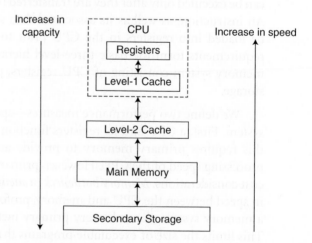

Figure 10.1 Memory hierarchical structure

Between the top and bottom layers of the memory hierarchy, there are several layers of different types of memory components. Their purpose is to bridge the speed gap as well as the capacity gap between the top layer component and the bottom layer component. In general, the closer a memory component is to the CPU in the hierarchy, the faster it functions and the more expensive it is to build, thus, it will have less capacity. The further away a memory component is from the CPU in the hierarchy, the slower it functions and the cheaper it is to build, thus, it may offer more capacity.

Constructed from dynamic random access memory (DRAM) chips, main memory can offer a much shorter access time (e.g., 60 to 80 nanoseconds) than that offered by the secondary storage. However, such a speed still results in the CPU spending most of the time waiting for data to be transferred from the main memory to the registers. The use of cache memory is aimed at reducing this waiting time.

Cache memory, made of static random access memory (SRAM) chips, offers a shorter access time than main memory (e.g., a few nanoseconds). This type of cache memory is built directly into the CPU chip and is called Level-1 cache. It stores instructions and data from the main memory in large quantity before or when the CPU needs them. CPU processing speed can be improved by accessing the fast cache memory for instructions and data, instead of accessing the slow main memory. The most recently used instructions and data are kept in the cache; they are most likely to be used again in the near future. A *cache hit* occurs when an instruction or data is found in the cache and it can be quickly transferred into the CPU registers. In the case of a *cache miss*, an instruction or data does not exist in the cache. Then, a new main memory block (containing the required data) must be brought into cache memory. The most desirable situation is to access a large majority of instructions and data directly from the cache. By properly choosing the cache capacity, the block size, as well as the placement and replacement policies of the cache, we can make the best use of the cache and achieve the ideal case. Due to manufacturing constraints on the size of on-chip cache memory components, a second-level off-chip cache memory component (called Level-2 cache) is often used. This allows larger-sized cache memory (several hundreds of kilobytes) built off-chip, with the trade-off being longer access delay time, due to the signals having to pass through buses on the system board.

The existence of CPU registers and cache in the memory hierarchy helps to reduce main memory traffic and alleviate the memory latency problem. To remedy the limitations of capacity in the primary memory during the execution of a large program, a technique is employed to use secondary storage as an extension of primary memory. Whenever necessary, secondary storage can dynamically supply programs or data to the primary memory in large blocks (called pages or segments). The structure of the memory hierarchy is completely transparent to the user. In other words, the memory hierarchy provides a large amount of *virtual memory* for the user to write programs. The operating system will automatically translate the logical addresses in virtual memory to the physical addresses in main memory. Using the virtual memory technique in a multiprogramming environment, multiple programs and their associated data are swapped between a primary memory and a secondary storage on a time-sharing basis.

The goal of designing and operating a memory hierarchy is the attainment of short effective memory access time close to the access time of the cache and a very large effective memory capacity determined by the secondary storage.

10.2   THE ORGANIZATION OF MAIN MEMORY

Main memory works as *random-access memory* (RAM). All the memory locations of RAM are equally accessible, therefore, the access time to any location is independent of its position (or address) and the sequence of prior accesses. In contrast, the memory locations in a serial-access memory are arranged in lines or blocks and are normally accessed in a serial fashion (e.g., tracks on a magnetic disk or records on a magnetic tape). Therefore, the access time of a particular block of data depends on the position of the data on the magnetic medium relative to the position of the moving magnetic read/write head.

Historically, main memory has been implemented by different techniques. Cathode-ray tubes, delay lines, and magnetic drums (the last two are not really random access) were used in first-generation computers. Ferrite cores were used in second- and third-generation computers. In all contemporary computers, semiconductor integrated circuit (IC) chips are used to construct main memory.

10.2.1 Functions and Characteristics of RAM Chips

Semiconductor RAM can be implemented using different types of memory chips. RAM chips are used for read/write memory. RAM is randomly accessible, with access times independent of physical locations, consistent with the above definition of RAM. RAM chips can be further classified into two types: static and dynamic. They have different construction and properties, however, both types are *volatile*, which means that they lose the stored information after the power is shut off. In *static RAM (SRAM)*, each memory element, storing one bit of information, is a flip-flop circuit composed of at least two cross-coupled transistors. A flip-flop stabilizes in one of the two states, "state-0" or "state-1", and the state lasts for an indefinite time. In *dynamic RAM* (DRAM), each memory element is a simple one-transistor cell, which uses the internal capacitance between electrodes to store a small amount of charge as one bit of information. Since this charge dissipates with time, it must be recharged or refreshed periodically. The refresh frequency must not be lower than the time required to refresh each memory cell, which currently, is typically 2 milliseconds. Comparing static and dynamic RAMs, we can see the following differences in their characteristics:

- A static RAM requires more space for each storage cell, and thus, has lower bit density and smaller capacity than dynamic RAM. Consequently, static RAM chips are more expensive on a per-bit basis.

- A static RAM is usually organized in small quantities and works much faster than dynamic RAM. The cycle time of a dynamic RAM is greater than its access time because some additional recovery time (to restore or recharge the affected memory contents) is needed before initiating the next memory cycle. The cycle time and access time of a static RAM are generally the same.

- A static RAM maintains a continuous current flow from the power supply, so it consumes more average power than a dynamic RAM. On the contrary, a dynamic RAM works most of the time in "standby" mode, which consumes little average power, but requires the consumption of large peak power during a very short period of time from the power supply. As a result, the power supply for a dynamic RAM is more expensive and its voltage must be smoothed by larger numbers of high-frequency bypass capacitors mounted on the printed circuit board.

- A static RAM is free of the overhead, both in hardware and time, resulting from the refresh requirement of a dynamic RAM. It is easier to interface a static RAM to a memory circuit rather than a dynamic RAM. Incorporating refresh logic on more recent dynamic RAM or CPU chips alleviates this problem to some degree.

10.2.2 Internal Organization of a RAM Chip

From the system standpoint, a RAM chip is characterized by capacity, speed, and access requirements. For large-capacity DRAM chips, each chip is usually a $2^n \times 1$-bit memory module. That is, each chip has one data-in pin, one tri-state data-out pin, and n (or $n/2$ for two-way multiplexing) address pins. The number of pins on an IC chip is limited by the chip's physical size. In order to minimize the package size, the row and column addresses are multiplexed into row and column address latches. To address each memory location, a chip uses a sequence of address inputs—first a row address and then, a column address. Therefore, the chip requires additional pins for control. For example, in addition to the pins for power supply and ground connections, it may require one Write/Enable ($\overline{WE}$) pin that specifies an operation to be a Read or a Write, one Chip Select ($\overline{CS}$) pin that is used to activate or deactivate the function of the entire RAM chip, one pin for Row-Address Strobe ($\overline{RAS}$) that is used to control the latching of a row address, and one pin for Column-Address Strobe ($\overline{CAS}$) that is used to control the latching of a column address. The internal organization of a 64K × 1-bit dynamic RAM chip is given in Figure 10.2 as an example.

This DRAM chip consists of the following major parts:

- *An addressing mechanism.* The address lines of this RAM chip are two-way multiplexed (to minimize the package size). There are eight address lines (denoted as A_7 to A_0) for inputting a 16-bit address. First, an 8-bit row address (the low-order byte) is latched in the row-address latch and, subsequently, decoded by a row decoder in order to select one of the 256 rows of the memory array. Then, the 8-bit column address (the high-order byte) is latched in the column-address latch and decoded to select one of the 256 sense/write amplifiers for reading or writing data. The address multiplexing is controlled by two input signals, $\overline{RAS}$ and $\overline{CAS}$, initiating successively the clock generators #1 and #2, respectively.

- *Memory cell array and sense/write amplifiers.* The memory cells are organized in a two-dimensional array. Once a row line is selected by a row address, all of the 256 cells of this row become activated and read out their stored information to a set of 256 sense/write amplifiers. However, only one of these amplifiers is selected by the column address to output or input data.

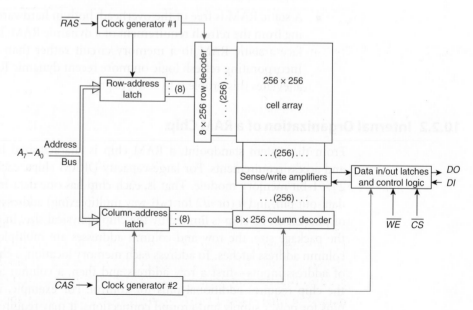

Figure 10.2 Internal organization of a 64K × 1-bit RAM chip

- *Data in/out latches and control logic.* In this example, input data (*DI*) or output data (*DO*), consisting of 1 bit, is latched in the input or output latch. The control logic acts under the control of the $\overline{CS}$ signal. The Read/Write operation is controlled by the $\overline{WE}$ signal.

- *Clock generators.* Clock generator #1 receives the $\overline{RAS}$ signal to generate the timing signals that successively enable the row-address latch and row decoder. Clock generator #2 receives the $\overline{CAS}$ signal and controls the column-address latch, column decoder, and data I/O.

The following shows two examples of chip packaging:

24-pin 16-Mbit ($4M \times 4$) DRAM chip	**32-pin 8-Mbit ($1M \times 8$) EPROM chip**
A_{10}–A_0: Two-way multiplexed for 22-bit addresses	A_{19}–A_0: for 20-bit addresses
D4–D1: for 4-bit data input/output	D7–D0: for 8-bit data output
$\overline{CS}$: Chip Select	$\overline{CE}$: Chip Enable
$\overline{RAS}$: Row-address strobe	Vpp: Program voltage for write during programming operation
$\overline{CAS}$: Column-address strobe	
$\overline{WE}$: Write Enable	
Vcc (power supply) and Vss (ground)	Vcc (power supply) and Vss (ground)

10.2.3 Basic Operations for Accessing RAM

Read and Write are the two common operations for accessing a SRAM or a DRAM. In the case of a DRAM, Refresh is a critical operation for retaining the stored information. The DRAM will lose its contents without a refreshing operation even if it continues to have power supplied to it. In this section, we will take a closer look at these operations.

To illustrate the process of address multiplexing, Figure 10.3 shows the timing diagrams of a Read operation cycle and a Write operation cycle. A memory cycle starts with the latching of the row address when the $\overline{RAS}$ signal becomes active low. Then, the $\overline{CAS}$ signal goes to active low to latch the column address. For a Read operation, the signal $\overline{WE}$ raises to high to enable the output circuit so that the valid data will be available on the data output pin. Because of the tristate output, the output line stays at a high-impedance state before carrying valid data. The time elapsed between the $\overline{RAS}$ signal and the appearance of a valid output data is called the *access time*. An additional recovery time is needed to restore $\overline{RAS}$ and $\overline{CAS}$ signals and the output circuit before the next memory cycle can be initiated again. Recovery time added to the access time is the *cycle time*, which is the minimum time between two successive memory operations. For a Write operation, the $\overline{WE}$ signal drops to low and, at the same time, the input data must be available in the data-in latch so that it can be written into the selected memory cell after the column address is latched. The Data Output line remains at a high-impedance state during the Write cycle.

DRAM refreshing is a time-consuming operation, and it requires special circuitry. A DRAM is refreshed in a row-by-row fashion, that is, each row of memory cells is refreshed at the same time. When no Read or Write operation is being performed on the memory, the refresh circuitry generates an active low $\overline{RAS}$ signal on the row selected to be refreshed. A refresh counter, included in the refresh circuitry, is used to serve as a row selector that cycles through all the rows of a DRAM. The voltages on all the column bit lines of the selected row are amplified and recycled back onto the memory cells.

There exist various designs and implementations of refresh circuitry. Refresh circuitry has been built both on memory cards and as part of the memory interface. Newer DRAM chips are designed for "self-refresh," which means that the DRAM chip has its own refresh circuitry and refreshing does not require intervention from the CPU or external refresh circuitry. Self-refresh dramatically reduces power consumption and is often used in portable computers.

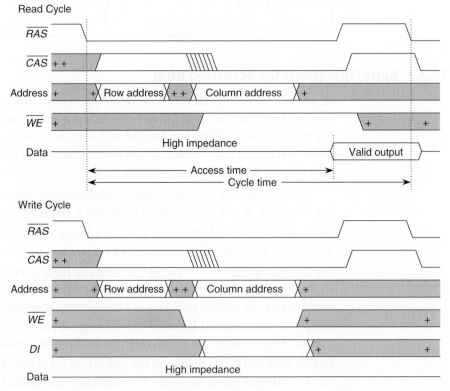

Figure 10.3 Timing diagrams of the Read and Write cycles of a RAM chip

10.2.4 Interconnection of RAM Chips for Larger Capacity

A number of RAM chips can be interconnected to form a main memory module of large size. The number of chips used is determined by the word length and address length of the memory module. The example of a 256K × 16-bit memory module using 64K × 1-bit RAM chips is shown in Figure 10.4. A total of (256/64) × (16/1) = 64 RAM chips are necessary. They are arranged in a two-dimensional configuration with 4 chips per column for 256K capacity and 16 chips per row for 16-bit word length. The address length is 18 bits grouped in three fields: the 8 least significant bits (LSB) form the row address, the next higher 8 bits form the column address, and the remaining 2 most significant bits (MSB) are used to select one of the four rows of RAM chips. Eight 2 × 1 multiplexers are used to multiplex the row address, A_7-A_0, and the column address, $A_{15}-A_8$,

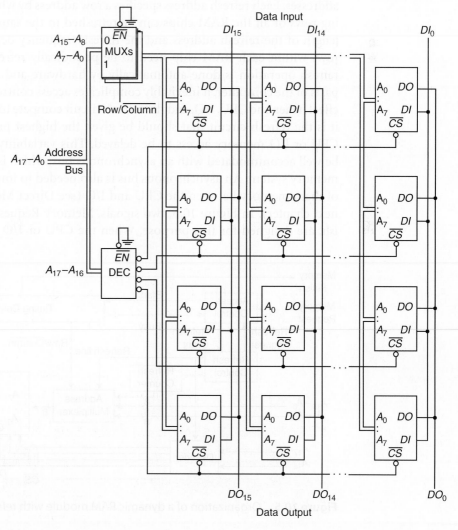

Figure 10.4 Organization of a 256K × 16-bit memory module using 64K × 1-bit chips

under the control of the *Row/Column* signal. This control signal should be synchronized with the signals $\overline{RAS}$ and $\overline{CAS}$ acting on all the RAM chips. A 2×4 decoder is used to decode $A_{17}A_{16}$ to generate the signals $\overline{CS}$, which select a row of RAM chips. The *DI* inputs of all the chips in the same row are connected together to receive one bit of input data, and the *DO* outputs of these chips are wired-ORed through tri-state devices to output 1 bit of output data from the memory module.

If the RAM chips require an external refresh circuit, the circuit in Figure 10.4 can be modified according to the block diagram shown in Figure 10.5. The size of the multiplexers in Figure 10.4 should be expanded to 4×1 in order to multiplex among three addresses: the row address, the column address, and the refresh address. A refresh counter periodically generates successive refresh addresses. Each refresh address specifies a row address by which the corresponding rows of all the RAM chips can be refreshed in the same refresh cycle. The length of the refresh address and the refresh frequency depend on how many rows within each RAM chip need to be periodically refreshed. Although the refresh operation is done automatically by hardware and is invisible to other parts of the computer, it inevitably complicates access control of the memory. In effect, when the CPU, I/O, and the refresh circuit compete to access the memory, it is the refresh circuit that should be given the highest priority, thus causing CPU or I/O memory access to be delayed. This variability in access time can be well accommodated with an asynchronous bus, which is generally used in a memory system. An asynchronous bus is also needed to implement the sharing of main memory between the CPU and I/O (see Direct Memory Access in the next chapter). In Figure 10.5, two signals, Memory Request and Memory Finish, are designed for this purpose. When the CPU or I/O requests a memory

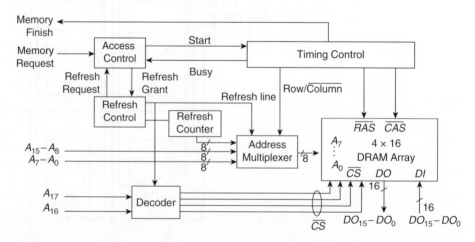

Figure 10.5 Organization of a dynamic RAM module with refresh control

access cycle, it sends a Memory Request signal to memory, and then waits until the memory access cycle finishes and sends back a Memory Finish signal. The refresh control in Figure 10.5 also uses a similar handshaking mechanism, Refresh Request and Refresh Grant, for the asynchronous control of the refresh cycle for memory.

10.3 RAM TECHNIQUES FOR ENHANCED PERFORMANCE

Because of its high density and low cost, DRAM has become the major component used for building main memory in most computer systems. Originally, when CPUs were relatively slow, main memory designs were implemented with single-banked, asynchronous DRAM modules. As CPU and system bus speeds increased, advanced DRAM devices, such as fast page mode (FPM) DRAM modules, emerged that can accommodate processor speeds close to 100 MHz. However, once the newer processors could run at speeds over 100 MHz, outstripping the ability of FPM DRAM to provide data in a timely manner, new memory designs were developed. Most recently, synchronous DRAMs have been produced with advanced features. Even though these high-performance DRAMs have been available for only a few years, it appears that they will soon be replaced by protocol-based designs, such as SyncLink and the DRDRAM design from Rambus and Intel.

The design of a new innovative DRAM is the goal of the Berkeley Intelligent RAM (IRAM) Project, which intends to investigate topics in processor-memory integration. The Berkeley IRAM project seeks to understand the issues involved in designing general-purpose computer systems in which a processor and DRAM have been integrated onto a single chip. This project will investigate circuits, VLSI design, architectures, compilers, and operating systems. IRAM should offer several advantages over today's solutions including (1) considerably reduced latency and dramatically increased bandwidth to main memory, (2) reduced power and energy consumption, and (3) reduced space and weight for embedded, portable, desktop, and parallel computer systems.

10.3.1 Asynchronous DRAM

The structure and functionalities of the DRAM discussed in the previous section are those of a conventional DRAM. This type of DRAM is said to be *asynchronous* and has been widely used in PCs since the development of the original IBM PC. Asynchronous means that the timing of a memory access operation is not coordinated with the system clock. Figure 10.6 depicts the waveforms of two bus cycles for asynchronous DRAM, one for a Read operation and another for a Write operation. A bus cycle is defined as the time period during which a bus activity (e.g., memory Read or memory Write) takes place.

Since asynchronous DRAM does not operate with a common system clock shared with the CPU, the timing of control signals, addresses, and data have to be deliberately taken into account. Illustrated in Figure 10.6, a handshaking mechanism is used in the asynchronous control of Read and Write operations of a DRAM. Each arrow in the diagram shows a cause and effect relationship between different signals. During a memory read cycle, the CPU sets up the address to read data from and then issues the ReadRequest signal to RAM. Upon receiving the ReadRequest, RAM puts the desired data onto the data bus and then issues an Acknowledge signal to the CPU. The CPU then reads the data from the data bus. Upon completion of reading data, the CPU disables the Read-Request signal to inform the RAM that the Read operation has been successfully performed. Finally, the RAM raises the Acknowledge signal to prepare for the next operation cycle.

Similarly, during a memory write cycle, the CPU (1) sets up the data to be written to memory, (2) sets up the address to which data is to be written, and (3) issues the WriteRequest signal to RAM. After receiving this signal, RAM performs the Write operation. Upon completion, RAM sends an Acknowledge signal to the CPU. The CPU withdraws the WriteRequest signal, which causes the RAM to raise the Acknowledge signal to prepare for the next operation cycle.

It is worth noting that internal operations discussed above require a significant amount of time and create a major performance concern. The primary focus of DRAM manufacturers has been to (1) increase the number of bits per access, (2) pipeline various operations to minimize the time required, or (3) eliminate some of the operations for certain types of access.

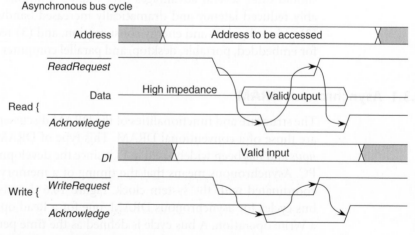

Figure 10.6   An asynchronous bus cycle

10.3.2 FPM and EDO

It is worth mentioning that, in the previous discussion, we simplified the action of address latching in order to emphasize the handshaking mechanism used in an asynchronous DRAM. As discussed in an earlier section, address latching is accomplished through a row address latch (controlled by the *RAS* signal) and a column address latch (controlled by the *CAS* signal). It is through working with these two control signals that designers were able to eliminate some of the internal operations and improve the performance of asynchronous DRAM. One significant implementation is called page mode access.

The goal of page mode access methods is to gain memory access speed by eliminating row address setup and hold times. Specifically, when accessing memory, the *RAS* signal is kept active, while the *CAS* signal changes when accessing a sequence of contiguous memory locations. This reduces access time and lowers the power requirements. Based on the aforementioned design principle, a specific RAM technique used to efficiently transfer large groups of bytes (block transfer) is called *fast page mode*. Block transfers are very effective in caches and high-resolution video displays.

Figure 10.7 shows the timing waveforms in a FPM DRAM. Data output is done in four-word bursts (a word is whatever the default memory chunk size is for the DRAM, usually a byte), where the four words in each burst all come from the same row, or *page*. For the read that fetches the first word of the four-word burst, the process is like a normal read—the row address is put on the address pins, *RAS* goes active, the column address is put on the address pins, *CAS* goes active, and so on. The next three successive reads proceed differently. At the end of the initial read, instead of deactivating *RAS* and then reactivating it to perform the next read, the controller just leaves *RAS* active so that it can get the next three words by simply sending in three column addresses. That is, the row address is applied only once. Since the four words all come from the same row but different columns, it is not necessary to keep sending the same row address. The implementation of FPM requires adding latches for all bits in the selected row and then applying different column addresses to place the corresponding bytes on the output data lines.

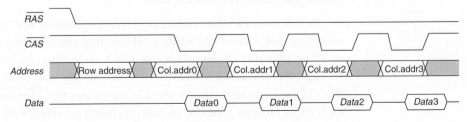

Figure 10.7   Timing diagram of a fast page mode DRAM

FPM became a widely used technique for DRAMs. It is still currently used on many systems. The major benefit of FPM DRAMs is reduced power consumption, mainly because sense and restore current is not necessary during page mode access. However, FPM has some drawbacks. The most significant is that, for the purpose of column precharge, the output buffers require some minimum cycle time to turn off when *CAS* goes high or is deactivated. A column recharge is needed to equalize the bit line voltages before each access. In other words, FPM DRAM cannot latch the column address for the next read until the data from the previous read is complete. A small delay occurs each time because the output for one read must be completely finished before the next read can be started by the placement of the column address on the bus.

The most recent major improvement to asynchronous DRAMs is *extended data output* (EDO). Compared with FPM, EDO does not require that the output buffers be turned off when the *CAS* signal is deactivated by a rising edge; hence, the column precharge time is eliminated. In other words, EDO can hold output data on the pins for a long time even if it means that the data from one read is on the pins when the column address is latched in for the next read. This ability to pipeline reads, that is, having one read start before another read is finished, gives EDO a significant performance improvement over its predecessor FPM DRAM.

10.3.3 Synchronous DRAM (SDRAM)

Asynchronous DRAM works in low-speed memory bus systems, but it is not suitable for use in high-speed (> 66 MHz) memory systems. A newer type of DRAM, called *synchronous* DRAM (SDRAM), is used. "Synchronous" means that the timing of memory access is coordinated with a system clock. The timing of memory access in a SDRAM is better controlled because all signals are tied to the system clock. This type of memory is much faster than asynchronous DRAM and can be used to improve the performance of a system. It is more suitable for the higher-speed memory systems in current PCs.

Figure 10.8 depicts the waveforms for two bus cycles of synchronous DRAM operations, one for a Read operation and one for a Write operation. Synchronous means that the operation of the memory device is directly synchronized with a clock signal. Therefore, the bus cycle for a synchronous operation is defined by an integral number of clock cycles.

In this example, the reading or writing operation will take three bus cycles, assuming that each of the address set-up time and the time required for a Read or Write operation is less than one clock cycle time. In Figure 10.8, part way through the first clock cycle, the CPU sets up the address to be accessed. After the address lines settle down, the CPU activates the $\overline{MemReq}$ signal (i.e., set to logic 0) to indicate that the memory is being accessed. Following that, the $\overline{WE}$ is asserted (i.e., set to logic 1) for a Read operation during the second bus cycle.

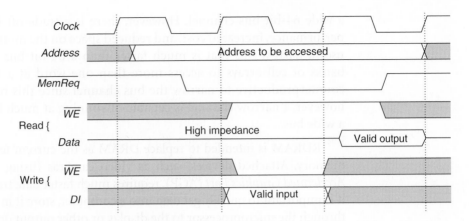

Figure 10.8   A synchronous bus cycle

The memory puts the data onto the data bus during the second clock cycle. After the CPU reads the data during the third cycle, it negates the $\overline{MemReq}$ and $\overline{WE}$ signals for further operation(s). The Write operation cycle works in a similar manner. Address is first set up and then the $\overline{MemReq}$ signal is activated. After the CPU sets up the data to be written into memory, it asserts the $\overline{WE}$ signal (i.e., set to logic 0) for a Write operation. After data is written to memory in the third clock cycle, $\overline{MemReq}$ is resumed (i.e., reset to logic 1) to prepare for the next operation.

Similar to the FPM of asynchronous DRAM, in SDRAM all the bits in a selected row are latched, so block transfer capability is also available. A mode register selects different modes of operation. In the burst mode of operation, the *CAS* signals that select successive columns are generated internally using a column counter and a clock signal. New data can be placed on the data lines during either the rising edge or the falling edge of each clock cycle. For example, *double-data-rate SDRAM* (DDR SDRAM) triggers the column-select and transfer actions on both edges of the clock.

10.3.4 Rambus DRAM (RDRAM)

One of the two main standards competing to replace SDRAM is *Direct Rambus DRAM* (DRDRAM), formerly called *Rambus dynamic random access memory* (RDRAM). Developed and licensed by Rambus Corporation, RDRAM is a memory subsystem that promises a transfer rate of 1.6 billion bytes per second. The subsystem consists of (1) the RAM, (2) the RAM controller, and (3) the bus (a Rambus channel) connecting the RAM to the CPU and other devices that access the RAM. In general, increasing the bus width can increase the bandwidth of memory. Many existing memory systems are accessed over a wide 64-bit bus channel. However, there is a trade-off between improved performance, increased cost, and reduced space on the motherboard. RDRAM uses a narrow bus that is much faster than a 64-bit bus and uses multiple banks of cell arrays to access more than one word at a time. It may seem counterproductive to narrow the bus channel since this reduces bandwidth; however, a narrow channel is capable of running at much higher speeds than a wide bus.

RDRAM is intended to replace DRAM as the current technology for main memory. Attached devices, such as video cameras (using FireWire) and the *Accelerated Graphics Port* (AGP), requires much faster data transfer rates. Hence, it is important to quickly get data into a computer, store it in RAM, and move it through the microprocessor to the display or other output devices.

Direct Rambus DRAM (DRDRAM) is the latest version of RDRAM from Rambus. It is expected to help accelerate the growth of visually intensive interfaces such as 3-D, interactive games, and streaming multimedia. In fact, DRDRAM functions more like an internal bus than a conventional memory subsystem, providing a 2-byte (16-bit) bus rather than a DRAM's 8-bit bus. This two-channel Rambus of 16 data lines is intended to transfer 2 bytes of data at a time. The technology is based on a special design of communication links called the *Direct Rambus Channel,* a high-speed 16-bit bus running at a clock frequency of 400 MHz. The fastest SDRAM used by PCs delivers data at a maximum speed of about 100 MHz, DRSRAM transfers data at a rate of 800 MHz (on both edges of the clock of 400 MHz), providing the peak data transfer rate of 1.6 billion bytes per second. DRSRAM utilizes a fast signaling method known as *differential signaling* that employs very small voltage swings (0.3 volts) around a small reference voltage (2 volts).

RDRAM is already being used in some graphics accelerator boards. Rambus memory is more expensive than conventional DRAM memory, but its use can lower overall system cost, and this makes it attractive for low-cost, high-performance consumer electronics, such as the Nintendo 64 video game console. In 1999, Intel used RDRAM in its Pentium® III Xeon® processors. More recently, Intel used RDRAM in Pentium® 4 processors. Intel and Rambus are also working on a new version of RDRAM, called *nDRAM*, that will support data transfer speed at up to 1,600 MHz. In 1997, Intel announced that it would license the Rambus technology for use on future motherboards. Hence, it is likely that this technology will become a standard for memory architectures. However, a consortium of computer vendors is working on an alternative memory architecture called *SyncLink DRAM* (SLDRAM). SLDRAM is based on the standard SDRAM design. Some view SLDRAM as a solution that is less revolutionary than RDRAM, providing improvements in performance without requiring radical changes in the system architecture.

10.3.5 Flash Memory vs. EEPROM

As previously introduced in Section 3.7.2, an EEPROM is a user-modifiable read-only memory that can be erased and reprogrammed (i.e., written to) repeatedly through the application of an electrical voltage that is higher than those normally found in PCs. A special form of EEPROM is a *flash memory* (sometimes called a *flash EEPROM*) that uses standard PC voltages for erasure and reprogramming. Flash memory is so named because a section of memory cells are erased in a single action or "flash." Erasure is accomplished through Fowler-Nordheim tunneling, in which electrons pierce through a thin dielectric material and remove the electric charge stored in floating gates, each of which is associated with a memory cell.

EEPROM and flash memory share many similarities. Their designs are based on a single transistor controlled by trapped charges. They are both nonvolatile. They retain their memory contents even when the power is turned off. Both EEPROM and flash memory have in-system reprogrammability, which means that they do not need to be removed from the computer to be erased and reprogrammed electronically (unlike EPROM).

While similar in some respects, there are substantial differences between flash memory and EEPROM devices. The principal difference is that EEPROM requires data to be written or erased 1 byte at a time, whereas flash memory allows data to be written or erased in units of memory called *blocks*, and this makes flash memory faster. Furthermore, an EEPROM chip has to be erased and reprogrammed in its entirety, not selectively. An EEPROM also has limited life—the number of times it can be reprogrammed is limited to tens or hundreds of thousands of times. In an EEPROM that is frequently reprogrammed while the computer is in use, the life of the EEPROM can be an important design consideration. On the other hand, flash memory can be reprogrammed at least one million times. Flash memory devices have greater density, which leads to higher capacity and a lower cost per bit. Intel offers a form of flash memory that holds 2 bits (rather than one) in each memory cell, thus doubling the capacity of memory without a corresponding increase in price. Another disadvantage of EEPROMs is that different voltages are needed for erasing, writing, and reading the stored data. Flash memory devices require a single power supply voltage and consume less power for operation.

Flash memory has been the major player in many applications. It is often used to hold control code, such as the basic input/output system (BIOS) in a personal computer. When BIOS needs to be changed (rewritten), the flash memory can be written in block sizes, making it easy to perform the BIOS update. Flash memory is used for easy and fast information storage in devices such as digital cellular phones, digital cameras (e.g., CompactFlash or SmartMedia),

LAN switches, PC cards for notebook computers (e.g., PCMCIA Type I and Type II memory cards), digital set-up boxes, embedded controllers, and home video game consoles.

10.3.6 Split Bus

A split bus is called a *split-transaction bus* or *pipelined bus*. The operation may be either *single-transaction* or *split-transaction*. A single-transaction bus permits only a single operation at a time, keeping the bus unavailable during the period when a read request is being serviced by the memory. A split-transaction bus permits multiple transactions to be outstanding by splitting a read request into two parts. A read request is followed by a release of the bus. Later, when the memory is prepared to return the result, it again arbitrates for the bus, acquiring it just long enough to send the requested data to the processor.

The pipelined bus pushes this idea even further. For example, a Read transaction can be split into three phases: sending address along the address bus, Read operation by the memory controller without using the bus, and returning data to the CPU along the data bus. These three phases can be overlapped or pipelined using different buses for a sequence of transactions. Thus, by taking advantage of parallelism in time, the overall bandwidth of the memory interface to the CPU or cache can be improved. For more detailed discussion on the principle of pipelining, refer to Chapter 12.

10.4 CACHE MEMORY

Computer system performance is limited by the difference between the faster processing speed of the processor and the slower access speed of the main memory. Processors should not spend much of their time waiting to access data and instructions in main memory. Fast cache memory is designed such that the main memory appears faster to the processor than it actually is in reality. The idea is to move data between the cache and the main memory in large quantities called blocks. Copies of portions of main memory are kept in the cache. The processor accesses the cache before accessing the main memory. If the processor reads a cache, a search is made to determine if the target is in the cache. If so, the data is delivered directly to the processor. If not, a block of data will be read from main memory with the required data delivered to the processor. Meanwhile, the block will also be copied into the cache for future reference.

The performance of the cache is critical to that of the processor. Cache size is an important factor. There exist several motivations to minimize cache size. A larger cache tends to work slightly slower than a smaller cache due to the large number of gates involved in the search process even when they are built with the same technology. In addition, the available on-chip silicon area and the cost may limit the cache size. Typically, cache size ranges between 16 KB and 64 KB.

If a cache is used to store both instructions and data, it is called a *unified cache*. Several effective design techniques are based on the idea of using multiple caches. One of them, a *split cache*, has one cache for storing instructions (i.e., *instruction cache*) and another cache for storing data (i.e., *data cache*). By providing two separate memory ports, an instruction cache and a data cache can work independently in parallel, thus doubling the bandwidth of the memory system. Another technique uses multiple caches between the processor and the main memory to reduce the latency in finer steps. We start from the processor itself and name the on-chip cache *Level-1 cache* (L1 cache). An additional cache, called *Level-2 cache* (L2 cache), can be built between the L1 cache and main memory. L2 cache is built off-chip with a high-speed connection to the processor chip. L1 cache can be a split cache. L2 cache is usually a unified cache storing both instructions and data. Typically, the size for L2 cache is between 512 KB and 1 MB. If a third-level cache is desired, it is usually a few megabytes in size and built on the system board. For example, a Pentium® 4 processor has an L1 instruction cache of 8 KB, an L1 data cache of 8 KB, an L2 cache of 256 KB, and no L3 cache. Another example is the PowerPC G4, which has an L1 instruction cache and an L1 data cache, each of 32 KB. The L2 cache may range from 256 KB to 1 MB. An L3 cache of 2 MB is also employed in the PowerPC G4. The newer Intel processor Itanium® uses a 16-KB L1 instruction cache, a 16-KB L1 data cache, a 96-KB L2 cache, and a 4-MB L3 cache.

10.4.1 Locality of Memory References

A cache memory is a high-speed RAM that stores the most commonly accessed data and instructions, so that the processor will most frequently access the faster cache memory rather than go to the slower main memory. This scheme is based on program locality of memory references. Analysis shows that computers have a tendency to repeatedly access the same *locality of memory*. That is, when a program executes on a computer, most of the memory references in a given period of time refer to only a few locations. This locality principle can be further classified as *temporal locality* and *spatial locality*. Temporal locality occurs when a program references a memory location and it is likely that the program will reference that same memory location again soon after. This condition exists because programs, often constructed with loops (simple as well as nested loops) and procedures (which are called repeatedly), spend much time in iteration or in recursion. Spatial locality occurs when a program more likely tends to reference memory locations that are near a recently referenced location than memory locations that are farther away. This condition exists because data is often clustered together in contiguous locations by way of arrays or records.

Now, we will look at the interrelationship between temporal locality and spatial locality. The localization of memory access should be exploited when implementing a fast cache scheme. During the execution of a program, the segments of the program and data that were recently active have been gradually moved into high-speed cache. As the program execution proceeds, the temporal locality of the program will change from time to time, each time updating the spatial locality reflected in the cache by removing the old portion and adding a new portion of its contents. This portion of the most actively accessed memory blocks in the cache forms a window of locality called the *working set window*, which changes as a function of time. Therefore, we have two categories in design. The size of the cache should be designed to accommodate these working sets. The placement and replacement policies of the cache should be designed to make the variations of these working sets smooth and stable in time. These issues will be studied in the following sections.

10.4.2 Mapping Functions

The use of a cache that is considerably smaller than the main memory creates a serious address-mapping problem. The problem is how to map the larger main memory space onto the smaller working space in cache. The choice of a mapping function directly affects the organization of the cache. Here, we will discuss three mapping functions. These mapping functions use either a direct mapping scheme or an associative mapping scheme. Unlike associative mapping, direct mapping does not require the use of an associative memory.

1. Direct-mapped cache

In direct-mapped cache, the main memory space is divided into blocks. The cache space is divided into frames. A main memory block is the same size as a cache frame. The objective of this scheme is to create a direct mapping between a main memory block and a cache frame. It is obvious that there are usually many more main memory blocks than cache frames due to the size difference between main memory and cache. Hence, more than one memory block maps to one cache frame. Using the direct mapping technique, each block of main memory is mapped onto only one possible cache frame.

Figure 10.9 shows an example of a direct-mapped cache. Assume that each memory location stores 1 byte, thus called byte-addressable memory. In this example, the cache has 32 bytes and the main memory has 64 bytes. The cache is organized in eight frames, each of 4 bytes. Therefore, the main memory can be divided into 16 blocks (i.e., 64/4 = 16), and each block contains 4 bytes (the same size as a cache frame). The mapping can be easily implemented with each address. The 6-bit address can be divided into three parts. The least significant 2 bits identify a unique byte within a main memory block and are called *block offset*. The remaining 4 bits can be interpreted as a tag of 1 bit and an index of 3 bits. The 3 index bits are used to identify one of the eight cache frames (i.e., frame number). The tag bit (i.e., the most significant bit) is used to indicate which memory block is to be mapped into a particular cache frame. This can be

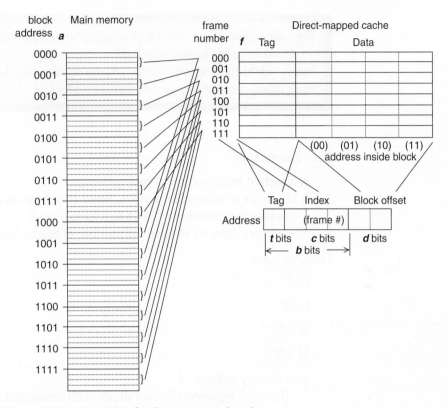

Figure 10.9   Example of a direct-mapped cache

done by associating each cache frame with a unique tag value that matches the tag field of the memory block currently stored in the cache frame. For example, both memory blocks, 0000 and 1000, are mapped to the cache frame 000, but which memory block is currently stored in the cache frame 000 depends on the tag value. If the associated tag has a value of 0, then memory block 0000 is currently stored in the cache.

In general, each block in main memory is mapped to a unique frame in cache according to the mapping function

$$f = a \text{ modulo } m \qquad (10.1)$$

where

f, cache frame number
a, main memory block address (block number)
m, total number of frames in cache (cache capacity)

Each main memory address can be viewed as consisting of three fields—tag, index, and block offset.

Tag—identifies a specific block among all main memory blocks that can fit to the same cache frame.

Index—identifies a specific frame (frame number) in the cache.

Block offset—identifies a specific byte in a block.

If we assume that

b, length of main memory block address;

k, block size in main memory (i.e., number of bytes in a block) or frame size in cache (i.e., number of bytes in a frame); and

M, memory capacity in terms of number of blocks (memory capacity).

Then, we have

$$t = b - c$$

$$k = 2^d$$

$$m = 2^c \qquad (10.2)$$

$$M = 2^b$$

a = memory address / *k*

[here, "/" represents integer divide with remainder neglected]

The advantage of using the direct-mapped cache scheme is that it is straightforward and easy to implement. However, it is not very flexible. Each memory block can only be mapped to one specific frame in cache. More flexible mapping schemes are based on the idea of associative mapping, which allows the mapping of each memory block to more than one cache frame.

Example 10.1 Numerical Calculation for a Direct-Mapped Cache

For the direct-mapped cache depicted in Figure 10.9,

$b = 4, c = 3, d = 2$

Tag has $t = 4 - 3 = 1$ bit.

Each memory block contains $k = 2^2 = 4$ bytes.

The cache has $m = 2^3 = 8$ frames.

Main memory has $M = 2^4 = 16$ blocks.

Block address for memory location 011011 is

$a = 011011 / k = 011011 / 100 = 0110$

■

2. *Fully Associative Cache*

In a fully associative cache, a main memory block can be mapped into any cache frame by way of a fully associative mapping algorithm. In such a scheme, the space in the cache can be used more efficiently. Figure 10.10 shows an example of a fully associative cache. Like the example in the previous section, this cache has 8 frames, and each frame is 4 bytes in size. The main memory contains 16 blocks, and each block is 4 bytes in size. The 6-bit address is divided into two fields— a tag field of 4 bits and a block offset field of 2 bits. Note that there is no need for an index field in an address to identify a cache frame. Each main memory block can be mapped into any cache frame. Therefore, the total number of cache frames is independent of the memory address format. The tag field of a memory address uniquely associates a main memory block with a tagged cache frame. When a memory block is brought into the cache, the tag value of the block is also brought in and stored in the tag field of the cache frame. During a memory reference, the tag value of the address received from the processor is compared with the tag value stored in every cache frame. When a match is found, the desired data is stored in that cache frame. The block offset of the address is used to locate the specified byte within that frame. If no match is found with any tag values in the cache, the memory block that contains the desired data must be brought from main memory into the cache.

By way of a tag value, each block in main memory can be mapped to any cache frame. A memory address can be viewed as consisting of two fields—tag and block offset.

> *Tag*—identifies a specific block among all main memory blocks.
> *Block offset*—identifies a specific byte in a block.

If we assume the same notations as above, then we have

$$t = b$$

$$k = 2^d$$

$$M = 2^b = 2^t \tag{10.3}$$

$$a = \text{memory address} \ / \ k$$

A fully associative cache has great flexibility in mapping a memory block to any cache frame. Despite this advantage, the implementation of fully associative cache is too costly. This is because all tags in the cache must be searched in order to determine whether a given block is in the cache. This type of search is called an associative search and is best if performed in parallel. An associative memory, consisting of complex circuitry, must be used to achieve this purpose.

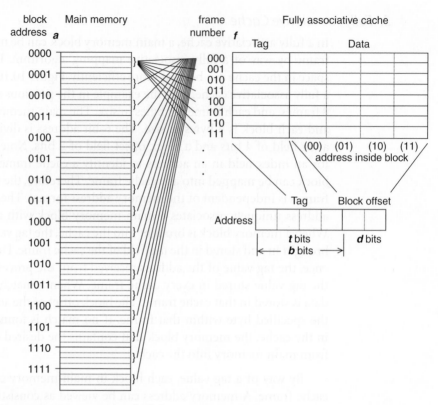

Figure 10.10 Example of a fully associative cache

Example 10.2 Numerical Calculation for a Fully Associative Cache

For the fully associative cache depicted in Figure 10.10,

$b = 4, d = 2$

Tag $t = b = 4$ bits.

Each memory block has $k = 2^2 = 4$ bytes.

Main memory has $M = 2^4 = 16$ blocks.

Block address for memory location 011011 is

$$a = 011011 / k = 011011 / 100 = 0110$$

∎

---

3. Set Associative Cache

Set associative mapping is a mapping function that combines the strengths of both direct and fully associative mappings while reducing their drawbacks. In general, a set associative cache is divided into v sets. Each set consists of n frames. This is called an n-way set associative cache.

When a set associative cache is used, cache frames are grouped into sets. A main memory block can be mapped into any frame in a specific set of the cache. As compared to that in a direct-mapped cache, this scheme provides more choices (more than one) for block placement. On the other hand, compared to that in a fully associative cache, the hardware cost is reduced with the decreased size of the associative search. Only the set numbers are used in the associative search.

An example of a two-way set associative cache is shown in Figure 10.11. Similar to the example in the previous section, this cache has eight frames, and each frame is 4 bytes in size. The main memory contains 16 blocks, each of which is 4 bytes in size. Moreover, the cache frames are organized into four sets, and each set contains two frames. The 6-bit address is divided into three fields. The least significant 2 bits form the block offset. The remaining 4 bits are interpreted as a tag of 2 bits and an index of 2 bits. The 2-bit index is used to identify a specific set of cache frames onto which the required block can be mapped. This index of a main memory block corresponds to the set number of a cache frame. In a two-way set associative

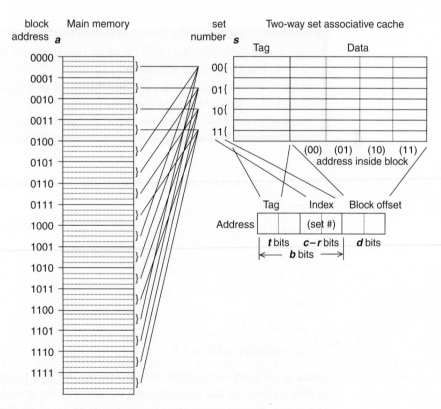

Figure 10.11   Example of a two-way set associative cache

cache, each main memory block can be mapped into one of the two frames in a specified set. The 2-bit tag is used to identify a specific cache frame within the set. For example, if a main memory block has an address of 011011, it can be mapped into any frame in the set numbered 10 (0110 modulo 100) in the cache.

In general, an n-way set associative cache consists of v sets of n frames each. Each main memory block can be mapped into any one of the n frames in a unique set. The mapping relationships are

$$m = v \times n$$
$$s = a \text{ modulo } v$$

where

s, cache set number;
a, main memory block address (block number); and
m, total number of frames in cache (cache capacity).

Each main memory address can be viewed as consisting of three fields—tag, index, and block offset.

> *Tag*—identifies a specific main memory block among all blocks that can fit to the same cache frame set.
> *Index (c-r* bits)—identifies a specific frame set in the cache (set number of $c - r = \log m/n = \log v$ bits).
> *Block offset (d* bits)—identifies a specific byte in a block.

Using the same notations of variables as above, we have

$$v = 2^{(c-r)}$$

$$t = b - (c - r)$$

$$n = 2^r$$

$$k = 2^d \tag{10.4}$$

$$m = 2^c$$

$$M = 2^b$$

$$a = \text{memory address } / k$$

There is an interesting relationship among the mapping techniques discussed in this section. In the extreme case of one-way set associative mapping, $v = m$ and $n = 1$, the set associative technique is reduced to direct mapping (i.e., the mapping function is: a modulo $v = a$ modulo m). In the other extreme case of

Example 10.3 Numerical Calculation for a Two-Way Set Associative Cache

For the two-way set associative cache depicted in Figure 10.11,

$b = 4, c = 3, r = 1, d = 2$

Number of sets in cache is $v = 2^{(3-1)} = 4$.

Tag has $t = 4 - (3 - 1) = 2$ bits.

n-way mapping: $n = 2^1 = 2$ (two-way associative mapping)

Each memory block has $k = 2^2 = 4$ bytes.

The cache has $m = 2^3 = 8$ frames or $m = v \times n = 4 \times 2 = 8$ frames.

Main memory has $M = 2^4 = 16$ blocks.

Block address for memory location 011011 is

$a = 011011 / k = 011011 / 100 = 0110$

The set number for memory location 011011 is

$s = a$ modulo $v = 0110$ modulo $0100 = 10$ ∎

m-way set associative mapping, $v = 1$ and $n = m$, the set associative technique is reduced to fully associative mapping (i.e., the mapping function is: a modulo $v = a$, meaning there is only one set and the entire cache is inside that set).

A two-way set associative mapping (i.e., $v = m/2$ and $k = 2$) is the most common set associative organization. It significantly improves the hit ratio over direct mapping. A four-way set associative mapping (i.e., $v = m/4$ and $k = 4$) achieves a modest additional improvement for a relatively small additional cost. Further increases in the number of frames per set have little effect.

10.4.3 Write Policies

During program execution, a memory reference may be requested by either a Read or a Write operation. New or modified data must be written back to the memory location via a Write operation. If a copy of the content at the referenced memory location currently resides in the cache, then both the cached value and the value in the main memory must be updated. There exist two commonly used write policies that can be implemented in a cache controller—the *write-through* policy or the *write-back* policy.

In a write-through cache, every time the processor updates a value the new/modified value is written into both the cache location and the corresponding location in the main memory. This guarantees that the copy in the main memory is always consistent with the copy in the cache. In a write-back cache, the new/updated value is first written into the cache location. It is written to the location in the main memory only when the value needs to be removed from the cache.

The write-through policy guarantees that both copies, one in the cache and another in the main memory, are always consistent. However, it must spend time to access the main memory with every Write operation. The write-back policy saves the time spent accessing the main memory by postponing the writing to the main memory until the last minute (when the value needs to be replaced in the cache). However, this would create a time period during which the main memory is storing invalid data.

If the referenced memory location is not in the cache at the time of the Write operation, one of the two following policies can be used. A *write-allocate policy* first loads the value from the main memory location into cache and then writes the new/updated value to cache using either the write-back method or the write-through method. A write-no allocate policy writes the new/updated value to the main memory only, without loading the value into cache. Usually, write-through caches use the write-no allocate policy, while write-back caches employ the write-allocate policy.

10.4.4 Replacement Algorithms

Every time the processor performs a memory reference, the system checks the cache. If the desired content is in the cache, the processor receives it from the cache. This is called a *cache hit*. If the desired content is not in the cache, the processor accesses the main memory (and usually writes the content into the cache at the same time). This is called a *cache miss*. In the case of a cache miss, the referred block from main memory needs to be brought into the cache and an existing frame in the cache has to be chosen. If this frame is full, its content needs to be replaced by the new one. Which frame of the cache should be replaced can be determined by using a *replacement algorithm*. Many such algorithms are possible, and the choice of algorithm affects system performance.

In a direct-mapped cache, there is no need for a replacement algorithm because each main memory block must map to one specific frame in cache. In a fully associative cache or a set associative cache, if a cache miss occurs and all possible cache frame positions are full, the cache controller must employ a replacement algorithm to bring the desired block from the main memory, select an existing frame in the cache, and overwrite it with the new block. A general guideline for any replacement algorithm is that the cache frames that are most likely to be referenced should be kept in the cache longer, while those least likely to be referenced should be replaced first. However, it is very difficult to predict which blocks will be referenced.

One algorithm, the *least recently used* (LRU) replacement algorithm, has been utilized extensively. The development of the LRU algorithm is based on the principle of program locality of memory reference. The assumption made is that there is a high probability that cache frames that have been recently referenced will be likely referenced again soon. Therefore, when a cache frame needs to be replaced by a new block, the LRU algorithm selects the one that has gone the longest time without being referenced. It is obvious that there must be some way to keep track of how often each cache frame is referenced during program execution. Counters can be used to serve this purpose. For example, in a set associative cache, a counter can be used for each frame in a set. During the event of a cache hit in the set, all frames whose counter values are smaller than the one associated with the referenced frame will increase their counter values by "1". The counter value of the referenced frame is reset to "0". During the event of a cache miss, if the set is not full, the frame where the new block is brought in will start its counter value at "0". All other frames will increase their counter values by "1". On the other hand, if the set is full during the event of a cache miss, the frame with the highest counter value will be chosen and replaced by the new block, and its counter value will start at "0". The other frames will increase their counter values by "1".

Although LRU is probably the most effective algorithm, other replacement algorithms such as first-in-first-out (FIFO), random, and least frequently used (LFU) exist. The FIFO replacement algorithm uses the cache frames from the top (or first) to the bottom (or last). The cache is full when the last cache frame is filled. At this time, if a new main memory block is needed and brought in, the frame that was loaded into the cache the earliest gets chosen and replaced. The FIFO algorithm is easy to implement and operate. It only requires a pointer that points to the next frame location to be replaced. As its name implies, the random algorithm randomly selects a cache frame to be replaced by the new block. The LFU algorithm selects the frame that has had the fewest hits so far. It is based on the idea that the cache frames that have a smaller number of hits may have a lower chance of being a hit in the future. To implement LFU, a counter can be associated with each cache frame to keep track of the number of hits. It is interesting to note that during simulation studies the random algorithm provided almost as good performance as algorithms based on usage (e.g., LRU or LFU).

10.4.5 Cache Organization and Performance

A typical cache organization is shown in Figure 10.12. In this organization, Level-1 cache is a split cache that is built on the processor chip. L1-I cache is an instruction cache. L1-D cache is a data cache. Level-2 cache is a unified cache that is connected to both the processor and the system bus via a set of address, data, and control lines. An address buffer and a data buffer are used to handle the slower speed of main memory, which is connected to the system bus.

During the event of a memory reference, we consider a number of cases based on (1) a hit or a miss, (2) a Read or a Write operation, and (3) the type of writing policy employed by the cache. A cache read hit will disable the data buffer and the address buffer. Data exchange only occurs between the processor

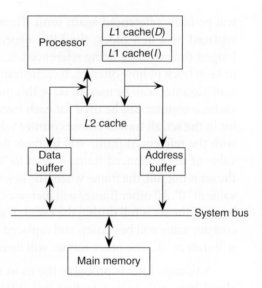

Figure 10.12 Cache organizations

and the *L2* cache. A cache read miss will enable the two buffers to allow the data exchange with the main memory. The data buffer receives the desired data from main memory and sends it to both the *L2* cache and the processor. If it is a write hit and the cache uses the write-back policy, data exchange occurs between the processor and the *L2* cache, not main memory. If it is a write hit and the cache employs the write-through policy, both cache and main memory will be updated. If it is a write miss and the cache uses the write-back with write no-allocate policy, only main memory is updated. If it is a write miss and the cache employs the write-through with write-allocate policy, both main memory and the *L2* cache will be updated.

The performance of a basic cache memory can be defined quantitatively by way of the following two equations:

$$h = \frac{\text{No. of items referenced data are in cache}}{\text{Total no. of memory references}} \tag{10.5}$$

$$T_e = h \times T_{hit} + (1 - h) \times T_{miss} \tag{10.6}$$

where

h, hit ratio;

T_e, effective access time;

T_{hit}, time spent accessing memory during the event of a cache hit, i.e., cache access time; and

T_{miss}, time spent accessing memory during the event of a cache miss, i.e., the time spent for transferring a main memory block to the cache.

> ### Example 10.4 Calculating Hit Ratio and Effective Access Time
>
> Consider computing the hit ratio and effective access time for a cache memory system that employs a 32-KB unified cache with a miss rate of 1.99%. The processor has a clock frequency of 800 MHz. A cache hit takes 1 clock cycle to process and a cache miss costs 50 clock cycles. The hit ratio and effective access time are computed as follows:
>
> $$1 \text{ clock cycle} = 1/800 = 12.5 \text{ ns}$$
> $$T_{hit} = 12.5 \text{ ns}, \ T_{miss} = 50 \times 12.5 \text{ ns} = 625 \text{ ns}$$
> $$h = 1 - \text{miss ratio} = 1 - 0.0199 = 0.9801$$
> $$\begin{aligned} T_e = h \times T_{hit} + (1 - h) \times T_{miss} &= 0.9801 \times 12.5 \text{ ns} + 0.0199 \times 625 \text{ ns} \\ &= 12.25 \text{ ns} + 12.44 \text{ ns} \\ &= 24.69 \text{ ns} \end{aligned}$$
> ∎

In Example 10.4, although the hit ratio is 98%, the effective access time is more than 50% longer than the cache access time. This is because it takes a long time to access a main memory block.

10.5 OVERALL PRIMARY MEMORY ORGANIZATION

As we have studied so far, primary memory includes main memory and cache memory. These constitute the two levels of the memory hierarchy closest to the CPU. Main memory speed is at least one order of magnitude slower than the speed of either the cache or the processor. Thus, the proper design of the overall organization of a primary memory system has a significant influence on the effective speed of a processor's memory references.

The speed performance of a memory system can be characterized by two parameters—*memory latency* and *memory bandwidth*. Memory latency is the time required to complete a memory reference. It is a *temporal* parameter (or a parameter *in time*) that reflects the technological level of memory devices with respect to executing memory references in the shortest period of time. Memory bandwidth is the amount of instructions and data that can be transferred between memory and the processor per unit time. It is a *spatial* parameter (or parameter *in space*) that is significantly affected by the memory organization. Incorporating parallelism into the organization of a memory system can improve the bandwidth. In the following section, we will look at four primary memory organizations and compare their performances.

10.5.1 Serial-Memory Narrow-Bus Organization

The basic, traditional organization of a primary memory system uses a serial main memory to transfer instructions and data to the CPU through a serial cache. The entire connecting path is established by narrow buses with a width equal to the word length of the processor. This scheme is referred to as *serial-memory narrow-bus organization*. Its block diagram can be seen in Figure 10.13. The processor uses a local (usually on-chip) bus to access cache. The width of the local bus always equals the word length, so that the processor can directly exchange data between its register file and the cache.

As we might expect, this simple primary memory organization has the worst speed performance. If we define cache miss penalty as the time required to transfer a block of words between main memory and cache, then we may obtain the following estimation.

Assume

t_c, time spent accessing cache for a word via the narrow bus

t_m, time spent accessing one-word-wide main memory for a word

k, cache frame size in memory words

$$\text{cache miss penalty} = k(t_c + t_m) \tag{10.7}$$

Notice that in the estimation calculated by Expression (10.7), the time required to detect the cache miss and send the address from the processor to main memory

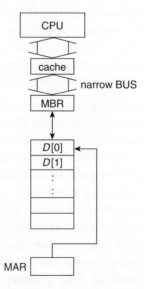

Figure 10.13 Serial-memory narrow-bus organization of a primary memory system

is neglected. The cache hit time is always equal to t_c plus the address sending time. For the purpose of comparing memory systems, the cache miss penalty, estimated by Expression (10.7), will be used as a measure of speed performance of primary memory systems.

10.5.2 Parallel-Memory Wide-Bus Organization

For the best possible speed performance of a primary memory system, both the main memory and the cache can have highly parallel structures that allow all p independent banks of main memory and p independent banks of cache to work at the same time and connect themselves together by a wide bus of p-word width. This scheme is referred to as the *parallel-memory wide-bus organization*. Its block diagram is shown in Figure 10.14, with p equal to 4. It is generally understood that a truly parallel main memory and a truly parallel cache should have all their banks working on independent hardware, besides separate address registers and separate data registers. The addresses of (cache) block elements, for example, $D[0]$, $D[1]$, ..., should be uniformly distributed among the main memory banks as shown in Figure 10.14. The p banks of the cache should be connected to the local bus of the processor through a narrow datapath.

During a Read operation from the cache to the processor, the datapath can be established using either a set of p-by-1 multiplexers as shown in Figure 10.14

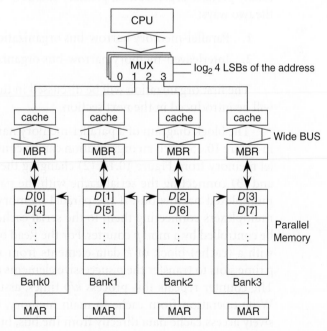

Figure 10.14 Parallel-memory wide-bus organization of a primary memory system

or a set of tri-state devices as described in Chapter 8. The multiplexers are controlled, via their select lines, by the $\log_2 p$ LSBs of the address. The rest of the address bits are sent, in parallel, to the p main memory banks. In this way, a total of p memory elements from p banks are sent forward at the same time to the multiplexers. Only the desired element will be selected and sent to the processor by the multiplexers. For the Write operation from the processor to the cache, a cache bank can access data directly from the local bus. Therefore, no special hardware is needed.

Using the same notations for the variables as in the previous section, we can estimate the speed performance of a parallel-memory wide-bus organization as follows:

$$\text{cache miss penalty} = \frac{k}{p}(t_c + t_m) \qquad (10.8)$$

Here, we assume that k is divisible by p. Therefore, we can conclude that by using a datapath composed of p memory banks, p cache banks, and a p-word-wide bus, the speed performance can be improved by a factor of p times, compared to the serial-memory serial-bus organization.

10.5.3 Parallel-Memory Narrow-Bus Organization

Somewhere between the previously described totally serial organization and totally parallel organization, primary memory can also be organized in one of the two ways:

1. Parallel-memory narrow-bus organization
2. Interleaved-memory narrow-bus organization

The first organization will be discussed in this section, while the second one will be introduced in the next section.

The block diagram of a parallel-memory narrow-bus organization is shown in Figure 10.15. Such an organization can be constructed by (1) taking the parallel memory from Figure 10.14, (2) changing the parallel cache to a serial cache, and (3) connecting the serial cache with the parallel memory through a time-multiplexed narrow bus. If the parallel memory has p independent banks, the multiplexers connecting them to the serial cache should have a size p-by-1 and be controlled by a mod p counter. For the Read operation, which loads the cache with a (cache) block of k data elements from memory, the counter generates p time slots to transfer the p successive elements of the data block into the cache. The counter repeats this process k/p times, assuming that p divides k. For the Write operation from cache to main memory, the memory banks can successively access cache data directly from the bus, but special timing control for the memory banks is needed (not shown in the figure).

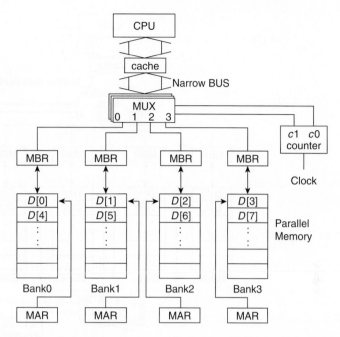

Figure 10.15 Parallel-memory narrow-bus organization of a primary memory system

Using the same notation for variables and the same arguments, we can directly write an expression for the speed performance of a parallel-memory narrow-bus organization as follows:

$$\text{cache miss penalty} = kt_c + \frac{k}{p}t_m \qquad (10.9)$$

10.5.4 Interleaved-Memory Narrow-Bus Organization

If we use an interleaved memory to replace the parallel memory that was used in Figure 10.14, then we have *interleaved-memory narrow-bus organization*, as shown in Figure 10.16.

The interleaved memory consists of p main memory banks, and all banks share the same memory address register, MAR. When these p banks access a cache frame of k data elements, $D[0]$ to $D[k-1]$, the data elements are divided into k/p groups, where k should be divisible by p. Each group is assigned a common group address equal to the address of its first element, but excluding the $\log_2 p$ LSBs. The p memory banks share the same address sequence formed by these group addresses. For example, in Figure 10.16, with $p = 4$, the banks 0 to 3 access the groups $D[0]$ to $D[3]$, $D[4]$ to $D[7]$, ..., $D[k-4]$ to $D[k-1]$, using the same address sequence $A, A + 4, ..., A + k - 4$, where A is the first group address

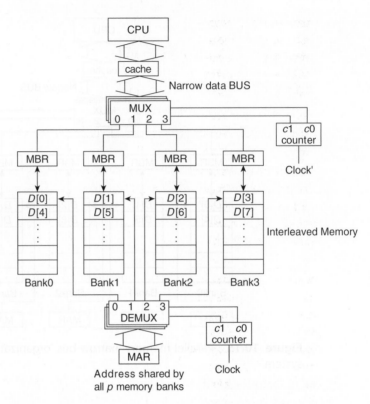

Figure 10.16 Interleaved-memory narrow-bus organization of a primary memory system

equal to the address of the first element, $D[0]$, excluding the two LSBs of the full-length address. At the address A, all four banks read their data elements $D[0]$, $D[1]$, $D[2]$, and $D[3]$, but start the memory read operations at different time instants, t_0, t_1, t_2, and t_3. Similarly, they use addresses $A + 4$, ..., and $A + k - 4$ to access groups $D[4]$ to $D[7]$, ..., and $D[k - 4]$ to $D[k - 1]$, respectively. However, they start the memory read operations to access $D[4]$, $D[5]$, ..., and $D[k - 1]$ at different time instants, t_4, t_5, ..., and $t_k - 1$, respectively. The entire read pattern forms a pipeline as shown in Figure 10.17.

In Figure 10.17, the pipeline is drawn in a time-space diagram. This conceptual pipeline denotes the process of a memory read operation by a memory bank in four stages. The entry stage is the MAR and its contents are denoted by A, $A + 4$, ..., and so on. It takes one time unit to process the address. The second and third stages, denoted by $M1$ and $M2$, perform a memory read operation, which requires two time units. The fourth stage is the memory buffer register, MBR, denoted by the data elements, $D[0]$, $D[1]$, ..., which need to be loaded

Stages

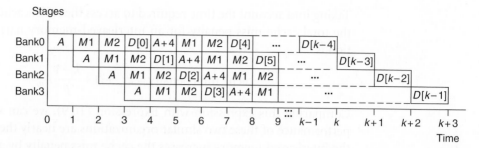

Figure 10.17   Space-time diagram of a four-stage pipeline working on k data elements

into the MBR. The number of stages of the pipeline is chosen to be equal to the number of memory banks, so that the result $D[0], D[1], \ldots, D[k-1]$ can be continuously generated at the output of the pipeline. The latency of the pipeline from the input stage to the output stage is equal to the time of one memory bank read operation. To supply the above-stated address sequence, $A, A + 4, \ldots,$ $A + k - 4,$ (which is, in general, $A, A + p, \ldots, A + p - 4$) to the MAR, we may use a set of 2×4 (in general, $2 \times p$) demultiplexers controlled by a mod4 (in general, mod$p$) counter to count the time sequence $t_0 - t_3, t_4 - t_7, \ldots, t_{k-4} - t_k - 1$ (in general, $t_0 - t_{p-1}, t_p - t_{2p-1}, \ldots, t_{k-p} - t_{k-1}$). The total time required to access the whole cache frame of k elements is $k + 3$ (in general, $k + p - 1$) time units. We can derive a general formula to calculate the latency time of k operations through a p-stage operational pipeline. At the beginning of each time unit, a new operation starts at the entry stage of the pipeline. It takes $p - 1$ time units to fill up the entire pipeline. Since the pipeline can output a word at every time unit, it would take another k time units to finish all the k operations at the pipeline output. Therefore, we have

$$\text{Latency time of } k \text{ operations on a } p\text{-stage}$$
$$\text{pipeline} = k + p - 1 \text{ (time units)} \tag{10.10}$$

Checking the accuracy of the formula, we observe that the time for completing k operations on a four-stage pipeline equals $k + p - 1 = k + 3$.

Now, we can derive the expression for the cache miss penalty of an interleaved-memory narrow-bus organization from the pipeline diagram in Figure 10.17. Since p time units of pipelined operation correspond to the time required to access one word from main memory, t_m, the effective time for accessing a cache frame of k words from an interleaved memory is

$$\text{Memory access time for } k \text{ words} = \frac{k + p - 1}{p} \times t_m = (1 + \frac{k - 1}{p})t_m \tag{10.11}$$

Taking into account the time required to access the serial cache, which equals kt_c, the total cache miss penalty for an interleaved-memory narrow-bus organization is

$$\text{cache miss penalty} = kt_c + (1 + \frac{k-1}{p})t_m \tag{10.12}$$

Comparing this expression with Expression (10.9), we can see that the speed performance of these two similar organizations are nearly the same, except that the interleaved memory increases the cache miss penalty by approximately one additional memory access time, t_m, compared to parallel memory. When $p = 1$, Expression (10.12) becomes Expression (10.7) for the serial-memory narrow-bus organization.

A numerical example is given below to illustrate performance improvements achieved by using different primary memory organizations.

Example 10.5 A Numerical Example of Calculating Speed Performance

Given that the time of accessing a word from cache (t_c) is 2 clock cycles, the time of accessing a word from main memory (t_m) is 8 clock cycles, and cache frame size (k) is 16 words, we can make the following calculations:

1. Serial-memory narrow-bus organization,

   $$\text{cache miss penalty} = k(t_c + t_m) = 16 \times (2 + 8) = 160 \text{ clock cycles}$$

2. Parallel-memory wide-bus organization with $p = 4$,

   $$\text{cache miss penalty} = \frac{k}{p}(t_c + t_m) = 4 \times (2 + 8) = 40 \text{ clock cycles}$$

3. Parallel-memory narrow-bus organization with $p = 4$,

   $$\text{cache miss penalty} = kt_c + \frac{k}{p}t_m = 16 \times 2 + 4 \times 8 = 64 \text{ clock cycles}$$

4. Interleaved-memory narrow-bus organization with $p = 4$,

   $$\text{cache miss penalty} = kt_c + (1 + \frac{k-1}{p})t_m$$

   $$= 16 \times 2 + (1 + \frac{15}{4}) \times 8 = 70 \text{ clock cycles}$$

5. Parallel-memory wide-bus organization with $p = 8$,

   $$\text{cache miss penalty} = \frac{k}{p}(t_c + t_m) = 2 \times (2 + 8) = 20 \text{ clock cycles}$$

6. Parallel-memory narrow-bus organization with $p = 8$,

   $$\text{cache miss penalty} = kt_c + \frac{k}{p}t_m = 16 \times 2 + 2 \times 8 = 48 \text{ clock cycles}$$

7. Interleaved-memory narrow-bus organization with $p = 8$,

$$\text{cache miss penalty} = kt_c + (1 + \frac{k-1}{p})t_m$$

$$= 16 \times 2 + (1 + \frac{15}{8}) \times 8 = 55 \text{ clock cycles}$$

8. Parallel-memory wide-bus organization with $p = 16$,

$$\text{cache miss penalty} = \frac{k}{p}(t_c + t_m) = 1 \times (2 + 8) = 10 \text{ clock cycles}$$

9. Parallel-memory narrow-bus organization with $p = 16$,

$$\text{cache miss penalty} = kt_c + \frac{k}{p}t_m = 16 \times 2 + 1 \times 8 = 40 \text{ clock cycles}$$

10. Interleaved-memory narrow-bus organization with $p = 16$,

$$\text{cache miss penalty} = kt_c + (1 + \frac{k-1}{p})t_m$$

$$= 16 \times 2 + (1 + \frac{15}{16}) \times 8 = 47.5 \text{ clock cycles}$$

■

The speedups of the three parallel organizations, relative to serial organization, are shown in Table 10.1.

Table 10.1 Speedups for three parallel primary memory organizations

Primary Memory Organization	Number of Memory Banks		
	$p = 4$	$p = 8$	$p = 16$
Parallel-memory wide-bus	4	8	16
Parallel-memory narrow-bus	2.5	3.33	4
Interleaved-memory narrow-bus	2.29	2.9	3.37

SUMMARY

The memory hierarchy with its functionality and performance is introduced in Section 10.1. Main memory and cache memory belong to the top layer of the hierarchy closest to the CPU and general-purpose registers. Together, they are called primary memory. The goal of designing and operating a memory hierarchy is to attain an optimal performance that offers a short effective memory access time close to that of a cache and a large effective memory capacity determined by the secondary storage.

The organization of main memory is discussed in Section 10.2. It also contains a hierarchical structure from individual RAM chips (Section 10.2.2) to individual memory banks (Section 10.2.4), and finally to a memory system (Section 10.5) combining the RAM with the cache. The main memory has long been suffering from a latency problem due to the large gap between the speed of RAM and the speed of CPU. Various techniques for enhancement of the speed performance of RAM are described in Section 10.3. Another way of solving the latency problem of memory is the extensive use of cache in the high-performance processors. The principle, organization, and performance of cache memory are discussed in Section 10.4. A comparative study of different global organization of the primary memory system, including the parallel memory and the interleaved memory, is given in Section 10.5.

EXERCISES

10.1 An integrated circuit RAM chip has a capacity of 256K × 4 bits.

(a) How many address and data lines are there in the chip? How many chips are needed to construct a 4M × 32-bit RAM? How many address and data lines are there in the RAM?

(b) Draw the schematic diagram of the 4M × 32-bit RAM constructed from the 256K × 4-bit chips. The schematic diagram should show the interconnection of the chips and the connections with the input address lines and the output data lines.

10.2 The memory of a computer has a capacity of 4M words × 32 bits/word. It consists of two portions: the 64K lower address portion is implemented with 16K × 4 bit SRAM chips, and the remaining upper address portion is implemented with 64K × 8 bit DRAM chips.

Plot the schematic diagram of the memory organization showing the connections of all the address bits and the connections between decoders and memory chips.

10.3 A main memory uses the burst mode of synchronous RAM chips, which allows each new set of 32 data bits to be placed on the output data lines in each clock cycle, after the selected row and column addresses are initially decoded. Assume that this decoding time takes 3 clock cycles, the burst length is 8, each bus cycle can transfer 32 bits of data in parallel, and the clock frequency is 200 MHz. How much time does it take to transfer:

(a) 64 bytes of data?

(b) 128 bytes of data?

What is the latency in each case?

10.4 A computer has a 2-KB cache using two-way set-associative mapping and a block size of eight 32-bit words.

(a) Show how you divide a 32-bit memory address into fields for mapping it on a cache entry, and give the length and name of each field. Draw a figure showing the bit positions of a memory address.

(b) Draw a figure to show how a memory address is mapped into a cache frame and how the search process is accomplished for reading the contents of that memory address.

(c) What is the total number of bits used by the cache?

10.5 A computer has a 2-KB cache, and the block size is eight 32-bit words. Calculate and compare the performances of three different cache organizations as specified in the following parts:

(a) Four-way set associative cache

(b) Fully associative cache

(c) Direct-mapped cache

For each cache,

(i) Draw a figure to show how you divide a 32-bit memory address into fields for mapping it on a cache entry, and give the length and name of each field.

(ii) Show what information is stored in each cache entry and calculate the actual size of the cache that is equal to the product of the length (in bits) of this information and the number of cache entries.

(iii) Calculate the search space that is equal to the product of the number of items to be searched and the length of the information to be matched in searching.

10.6 A machine has two different cache organizations: one cache is direct-mapped and the other is two-way set associative. They have the following common characteristics:

- All instructions normally take 2.0 clock cycles (with a perfect cache causing no memory stalls).

- There is an average of 1.33 memory references per instruction.

- The hit time is 1 clock cycle.

- The cache miss penalty is 40 clock cycles.

They have the following different characteristics:

- The clock cycle time for the CPU with direct-mapped cache is 3 ns, while the clock cycle time for the CPU with set associative cache is 1.10 times longer.

- The miss rate of the direct-mapped cache is 1.5%, while the miss rate for the set associative cache is 1.0%.

(a) Find the average memory access time for each of the two cache organizations.

(b) Compare the CPU performance of the two cache organizations.

10.7 Suppose a computer has main memory with interleaved organization, which consists of:

- 16 memory banks each with an access time of 24 clock cycles to read/write a 32-bit word.

- A narrow address bus that takes 2 clock cycles to send an address to each bank.

- A narrow data bus that takes 2 clock cycles to send/receive a 32-bit word to/from each bank.

The interleaved memory works according to the principle of the split-transaction bus.

(a) What is the minimum effective access time for successively reading sixteen 32-bit words, one from each memory bank?

(b) Draw a space-time diagram of split memory transactions to verify your solution in Part (a).

(c) What is the maximum bandwidth of memory for a continuous flow of such transactions (in bytes/cycle)?

10.8 From Problem 10.7, assume that each cache frame has sixteen 32-bit words. Therefore, you can use the result obtained in Problem 10.7 for the following calculation.

(a) Given the average frequencies of occurrences of instructions in Table 10.2.

Table 10.2 Frequencies of usage of load/store (LW/SW) and other instructions for Problem 10.8

Instruction Types	Frequency of Occurrences (%)
LW	25
SW	15
Others	60

Find the average number of memory accesses per instruction. Find the average number of reads per instruction and the average number of writes per instruction. What percentages of the total memory accesses are reads? What percentages of the total memory accesses are writes?

(b) The cache miss rate is given as 5%, and the whole block is read on any cache miss. For the write-through cache, it writes only the modified word into memory. For the write-back cache, of all the cache misses, 70% replace clean blocks and 30% replace dirty blocks. The whole block should be written back if necessary. Calculate the average number of stall cycles per instruction for each of the write policies: write-through and write-back.

10.9 Consider the following fragment of C code:

```
for (i = 0; i < 100; i++)
{
  B[i] = 0;
  for (j = 0; j <= i; j++)
  B[i] = B[i] - A[j];
  }
```

Assume that A and B are arrays of 100 elements each. The data of A and B are stored in memory with starting addresses Astart and Bstart, respectively, and the variables *i* and *j* are kept in memory at Si and Sj, respectively, except when they are operated on. All the data are 32-bit integers.

Write a short assembly-language code using two-address register-register instruction format (see Section 7.1, Example 7.1, Part (2) for the instruction format). How many instructions are required dynamically? How many memory references (including both instructions and data) will be executed? If each memory operation, on average, takes 2 clock cycles and each ALU operation takes 1 clock cycle, how much time does it take to run the entire program?

11

Input/Output (I/O)

11.1 FUNCTIONS AND CHARACTERISTICS OF THE I/O SUBSYSTEM

In Figure 5.1, we presented the basic organization of a stored-program computer. It is composed of three major functional blocks—the CPU, main memory, and I/O. Thus far, we have studied the CPU and primary memory. We will now study the third important part of a computer—the I/O subsystem. I/O devices are commonly called *peripheral devices* because they provide I/O and communication services for the outside world. Hence, the major responsibility of the I/O subsystem is to control I/O devices in cooperation with the device management software of the operating system. We will focus on the general organization of the I/O subsystem in terms of the following major topics:

- How the I/O subsystem is connected to the CPU and memory.

- How the CPU and memory access the I/O devices.

- How the I/O subsystem provides interfaces with the outside world through various types of I/O devices and device controllers.

I/O has such a wide variety of characteristics that we need to construct a special subsystem to handle it. The factors that make I/O an unusually complex problem are as follows:

- The operating speeds of I/O devices and data transfers exist over a very wide range, although normally lower than the speed of the CPU. Some devices, such as keyboards, are manually operated, so the duration of the operation can be measured in seconds. High-speed devices, such as high-performance disks and interprocessor communication links, work at electronic speeds that are comparable with the speed of the CPU.

- I/O devices need to handle a large variety of signals. The signals vary with respect to physical quantity (voltage, current, temperature, etc.), level (analog or digital), format (serial, parallel, or serial-parallel), frequency spectrum (audio, video, etc.), and so on. Many new types of multimedia signals have been introduced into the computer application field, which makes I/O subsystems even more challenging. In such applications, a computer may become an integral part of an embedded system; hence, the I/O devices may be industrial equipment or home appliances, such as sensors, digital cameras, telephone sets, or robots.

- I/O events occur randomly and asynchronously, but the I/O operations must be somehow synchronized with the CPU clock in order to be properly coordinated between the processor and I/O. I/O operations have various timing and space characteristics that require various control strategies and communication protocols. Handshaking is one example solution. I/O through the interaction of interrupt routines is another example.

- I/O devices are often more prone to failure than the processor, due to the influence of their operational environments. For example, data transmission over a long distance is sometimes exposed to the effects of a power line and errors can occur, due to high voltage spikes. Therefore, error detection may be required for data communication in a given I/O subsystem.

- The I/O subsystem is closely related to I/O software modules, which are referred to as device drivers in the operating system. This situation is particularly important for I/O instructions because many operating systems, such as Windows NT and Unix, expressly deny users the privilege to directly access I/O hardware, due to security reasons. Therefore, the I/O instructions are classified as privileged instructions, which can be executed only when the processor is switched to the system or supervisor mode through an interrupt. The design of the I/O subsystem must take this constraint into consideration.

Since each I/O device presents its own interfacing problem, the key design issue for I/O is to classify I/O devices into several categories and standardize the interface for each category. With respect to usage, I/O devices can be classified into communication devices and storage devices. A communication device, for example, a modem, sends, receives, or transfers messages or signals carrying useful information. A storage device, for example, a disk, stores information to be read and/or be written by any destination or source process. The chief application of communication devices is on a network, and the chief application of storage devices is in a database server on a network. With respect to mode of operation, I/O devices can be classified into block-oriented devices (e.g., disks) and character-oriented devices (e.g., printers). With respect to speed of operation, I/O devices can be classified as low-, medium-, and high-speed devices as follows:

- **Low-speed devices.** This group includes devices such as communication devices that generate individual signals to input a character from a keyboard or activate a control action to interact with an interrupt service routine. The frequency of the signal generation is usually very low, so time-multiplexing can be used at a single I/O port to handle many low-speed devices.

- **Medium-speed devices.** This group includes most character-oriented devices and ordinary communication devices, for example, printers, modems, and low-speed communication lines. Asynchronous communication and interrupt mechanisms are usually suitable for handling the I/O requests from these devices.

- **High-speed devices.** This group includes most block-oriented devices and high-speed communication devices, for example, magnetic disks, tapes, video displays, and high-speed communication lines. Because interrupt handling suffers from a relatively large overhead, which may be intolerable to high-speed devices, synchronous communication and direct memory access (DMA) are usually more suitable. DMA directly reads/writes data from/to main memory without direct involvement of the processor. Hence, the I/O speed can be very high—of the same order of magnitude as the speed of main memory.

Standardization of I/O interfaces can be achieved by dividing an I/O subsystem into three layers:

- **I/O devices.** The standardization of I/O devices of the same type, made by different manufacturers, is impossible and unnecessary because these can have radically different construction and physical parameters. Electrical and logical parameters should be carefully specified so as to provide for the convenient design of the device controller, to facilitate later standardization. In other words, the standardization of the I/O interface does not lead to the standardization of the physical construction of I/O devices.

- **Device controllers.** The device controls the detailed operation of the device and connects the device to the computer's address and data bus through the corresponding interfaces. The device controller should satisfy not only the special requirement of the device it controls, but also the requirement of standardization of the I/O interface. It bridges the gap between these two sides and makes the standardization of the interface possible.

■ **I/O interfaces.** This layer interfaces the I/O device controllers with the processor and main memory, while meeting the corresponding standards. Standardization is achieved by abstracting the operational characteristics of the device controllers into a common high-level definition in the operating system. Many commercial I/O interfaces and DMA chips have been developed and manufactured for different types of processors. Programmers use an abstract I/O paradigm, implemented by the high-level definition of the I/O interface, to write device driver code without knowing the details of the devices.

The interrelationship of the three layers of I/O organization is shown in Figure 11.1. This figure provides a conceptual organization for illustrative purposes. The actual organization may contain many different types of I/O interfaces. The system bus can be expanded to create buses for new types of I/O devices and their interfaces. For a detailed explanation, see Section 11.7.

11.2   SECONDARY STORAGE

The memory devices located in the most distant levels from the CPU in the memory hierarchy are called *auxiliary memory*, *external memory*, or *secondary storage*. These terms are in contrary with the corresponding terms of main memory, internal memory, or primary memory that we studied in Chapter 10. From the viewpoint of the CPU, secondary storage serves as the extension or backup of main memory to support the demand for additional memory capacity of virtual memory. From the viewpoint of users, secondary storage provides a large memory space in which all the software and files can be permanently stored. Therefore, the major requirements to secondary storage are large capacity, versatility of storage media, reliability, and persistency of permanent storage of

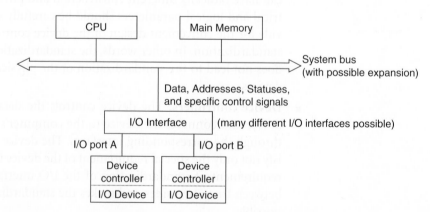

Figure 11.1   Organization and connection of an I/O subsystem

information. Other valuable properties such as high speed, low cost, low power, mobility, and the replaceability of storage media are also desirable.

Based on their accessing mode, storage devices can be divided into two types: *sequentially accessed devices* and *randomly accessed devices*. Both are *block-oriented* storage devices, that is, they can store information only in blocks of bytes so that the minimum addressable unit of information is a data block. A sequentially accessed storage device stores the data blocks on the recording medium in a linear sequence of records. It can access a given data block only by moving a pointer forward or backward along the sequence in order to seek the correct position of the required data block. It is the access mode we are familiarized with in a magnetic tape drive. A randomly accessed storage device can access a data block according to a randomly specified address without a sequential process of moving a pointer. Magnetic disks and optical disks are examples of randomly accessed storage devices. We will look at these storage devices in the following sections.

11.2.1 Magnetic Disk

A magnetic disk uses a rotating medium in the form of one or more disk platters mounted on a spindle as shown in Figure 11.2(a). A platter has two surfaces. One or both of the surfaces can be coated with a very thin layer (2.5 micron) of magnetic material for one-sided or two-sided recording of information. During operation, the platters rotate at a constant speed. A set of read/write heads mounted on the arms moves back and forth in the radial direction. So, we have a two-dimensional movement, one is the movement of the head along the radial coordinate axis, and the other is the rotation of the platters along the angular coordinate axis. These two movements combined together make it possible for the read/write head to reach any spot on the disk surface. To guarantee a high speed of such a two-dimensional movement, in the Winchester disk drive,

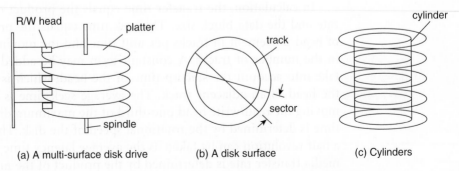

(a) A multi-surface disk drive   (b) A disk surface   (c) Cylinders

Figure 11.2   Construction of a multiple-surface magnetic disk drive

the entire disk package with its heads and arms is sealed into a clean housing to save it from the damaging effect of dust. The read/write head aerodynamically "flies" above the surface at a height of 0.5 micron at a very high linear speed of 100 kilometer/hour. Thus, we can see that the construction of a hard disk is a complicated and delicate process. Among the secondary storage devices, the construction of a floppy disk alone is simple and different. It rotates at 360 rpm, and the read/write head is in direct contact with the magnetic surface of the disk at all times, which does cause some problems with wear or even damage of the surface.

The format of recording on the disk surface is organized as follows: each surface is divided into many concentric circles called *tracks*, and each track is divided into many segments called *sectors* [see Figure 11.2(b)]. The size of each sector determines the size of the data block to be stored in it. To access a specific sector on a specified track, two steps of a two-dimensional movement need to be followed as stated above. First, we should move the read/write head to the position of the required track, and then wait for the instant when the rotating sector passes under the read/write head. The time of moving the read/write head to search for the required track is called the *seek time*, while the wait time until the required sector on that track rotates under the head is called the *latency time*. For the reason of performance, all the tracks having the same diameter on all the surfaces are organized into a cylinder [see Figure 11.2(c)]. All the tracks belonging to the same cylinder are given successive addresses so that they can be accessed without moving the read/write head. The last sector of a cylinder and the first sector of an adjacent cylinder have neighboring addresses, so they can be accessed successively by moving the head one single step. Thus, this address assignment minimizes the seek time. Besides the seek time and latency time, the total access time for a Read/Write operation on a disk has a third component called the transfer time, as shown in the following expression:

$$\text{Disk access time} = \text{seek time} + \text{latency time} + \text{transfer time} \qquad (11.1)$$

In calculation, the transfer time equals the product of the data transfer rate and the data block size. The seek time equals the product of the speed of head movement in tracks per unit time and the moving distance counted in the number of tracks. A constant term may be added to this product to take into account the startup time of the head, which is sufficient to move the head to an adjacent track. The average seek time is usually equated to moving the read/write head one-third of the maximum distance. The latency time is determined by the rotational speed of the disk. The time for rotating a half revolution can be taken as the average latency time in calculation. The media transfer rate is determined by the product of the number of bytes in a complete circular track and the rotational speed of the disk in revolutions per second (rev/sec). To get a more concrete impression about these parameters, the disk performance specifications for Maxtor hard disks are given below (Williams 2001):

Track-to-track seek time	1 ms
Average seek time	< 9 ms
Maximum seek time	20 ms
Rotational speed	5,400 rpm = 90 rev/sec (fast model 15,000 rpm)
Average latency	$1/(2 \times 90) = 5.55$ ms (fast model 2 ms)
Cylinders (tracks per surface)	17,549
Sectors per track	266–462
Bytes per sector	512
Media transfer rate	$< 462 \times 0.5K \times 90 = 20.3$ MB/sec
Drive capacity	$< 17,549 \times 462 \times 0.5K = 3.866$ GB/surface
Data zones per surface	16 (CAV recording, see Section 11.2.3)
Controller overhead	< 0.3 ms
Start time	7.3 sec
Computer interface rate	< 66.7 MB/sec
Integrated buffer size	2 megabytes

It should be noted that these parameters are not intended to show the highest performance of the hard disk drives. An example of the largest capacity disk drive at the present time is the "Big Drive" initiative of Maxtor Corporation, which breaks the barrier of 137 gigabytes in a single disk drive, using 48-bit addressing. This capacity corresponds to 268,435,456 sectors of 512 bytes of data. An example of the fast disk drive is the ATA/133 Maxtor disk drive that clocks data at 133 MB/sec. Thus, ATA/133 is included in the latest ATA standard.

Now, we will look at how to map a logical block address to a physical disk address. As we have learnt, the physical disk address, b, for the so-called CHS (Cylinder, Head, Sector) accessing is a three-dimensional address consisting of three components, c, s, and r, such that

$$b = (c, s, r) \qquad (11.2)$$

where c is the cylinder number, s is the surface number, and r is the sector number, with all the numbers beginning from "0". The arrangement of c, s, and r in the address format of b is shown in Figure 11.3.

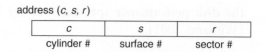

Figure 11.3 Format of a physical disk address

When the physical configuration parameters of the disk are given as follows:

R sectors/track, S tracks/cylinder, and C cylinders/disk drive

The logical block address, b, can be calculated from the physical address (c, s, r) using the following formula:

$$b = r + R(s + cS) \tag{11.3}$$

Since r is the sector number, Expression (11.3) shows that if b is the address of the last block of one cylinder, then $b + 1$ should be the first block of the next higher numbered cylinder. Therefore, successive addresses b and $b + 1$ requires head movement of at most one track. This property can be seen from Figure 11.4, which gives the distribution of block addresses throughout the entire disk space. The total disk capacity

$$V = C \times R \times S \text{ sectors} \tag{11.4}$$

11.2.2 Redundant Array of Independent Disks (RAID)

Just as we use multiple memory banks to construct a parallel memory system or an interleaved memory system with improved bandwidth (see Section 10.5), we can also use multiple independent disk drives working in parallel to increase the speed of a secondary storage system. Such a multiple-disk system is called *Redundant Array of Independent or Inexpensive Disks* (RAID). Besides the improvement of speed, there are two other major purposes of constructing a RAID disk system:

1. To improve the reliability of a disk system based on the principle of hardware redundancy and data redundancy and

2. To increase the total capacity of a disk system using a distributed structure.

The advantages of these features of RAID can potentially find wide applications in different areas of distributed databases, very large databases, and fault-tolerant databases.

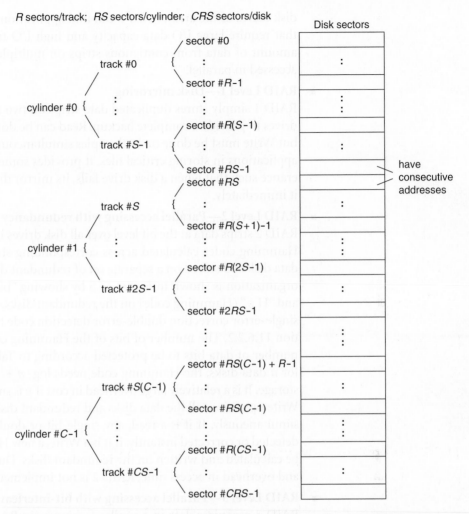

Figure 11.4 Distribution of block addresses throughout the entire disk space

There is a large variety of ways in which the data can be distributed or the redundancy can be added to the RAID system, thus creating seven basic RAID configurations, denoted by their level numbers from 0 to 6. Other configurations such as levels 10 (1+0) and 15 (1+5) can be derived as combinations of these basic levels. The meaning and characteristics of these configurations are summarized as follows and shown in Figure 11.5 (Stallings 2003; Sheldon 2001).

- **RAID Level 0—Data stripping, nonredundant**
  RAID 0 simply strips data over multiple disk drives without data redundancy. The strips may be data blocks in physical sectors of a disk or some other data units. They are mapped round robin on consecutive

disk drives of the array. RAID 0 can find applications in parallel systems that require large I/O data capacity and high I/O transfer rate. A large amount of data from contiguous strips on multiple disk drives can be accessed in parallel.

- **RAID Level 1—Disk mirroring**
  RAID 1 simply stores duplicated data strips on two separate sets of disk drives to provide a complete backup. Read can be done from either copy, but Write must be done on both copies simultaneously. RAID 1 can find applications in storing critical files. It provides some degree of fault tolerance such that when a disk drive fails, its mirror disk drive can replace it immediately.

- **RAID Level 2—Parallel accessing with redundancy via Hamming code**
  RAID 2 strips data at the bit level over all disk drives in the array, with the Hamming codes calculated across corresponding stripped bits on each data disk and stored on a separate set of redundant disk drives. This data organization is shown in Figure 11.5 by showing "bit" on the data disks and "H.c." (Hamming code) on the redundant disks. Hamming code is a single-error correction double-error detection code to be studied in Section 11.6.2.2. The number of bits of the Hamming code depends on the number of data bits to be protected according to Table 11.1. In general, for n data disks, the Hamming code needs $\log_2 n + 2$ separate disks for storage. It is a relatively large overhead in cost if n is small. During a Read/Write operation, all the data disks and redundant disks must be accessed simultaneously. If it is a read, any single-bit or double-bit error can be detected or corrected instantly. If it is a Write, a new Hamming code must be calculated and written on the redundant disks. Due to additional cost and overhead in access time, RAID 2 is not implemented.

- **RAID Level 3—Parallel accessing with bit-interleaved parity**
  RAID 3 organizes data in a similar fashion as in RAID 2, but generates only a single parity bit for each set of individual bits in the same position on all data disks. All the parity bits generated in this manner are written to a single parity disk. Parity check is a simple error detection method to be studied in Section 11.6.2.1. It allows RAID 3 to rebuild the information when any one disk in the array fails. RAID 3 employs parallel access of data distributed in very small strips (byte or word) over multiple disk drives with minimum overhead cost. It is simple and easy to implement.

- **RAID Level 4—Independent access with block-interleaved parity**
  RAID 4 strips data in disk sector units rather than in bits. The strips are relatively large, corresponding to the size of a data block. Each bit-by-bit parity block is calculated across the blocks in the same position on all data disks of the array, then all the parity blocks are written to

the corresponding blocks on a single parity disk. RAID 4 with its independent access mode is more suitable for applications that require high I/O request rates rather than high data transfer rates because multiple I/O requests can perform independent accesses to separate data disks in parallel. However, RAID 4 involves a write penalty when an I/O Write operation requires a small size of data to be updated. It would have to read the old data strip and the old parity strip, modify a small part of the data strip, calculate the new parity, and write back the new data strip and the new parity strip. When multiple writes perform accesses to the parity disk, the parity disk can become a bottleneck.

■ **RAID Level 5—Independent access with block-interleaved distributed parity**
RAID 5 strips data in disk sector units and stores the data blocks over the same number of disk drives (including the parity disk) as in RAID 4, but the parity blocks are written to all the disk drives of the array in an interleaved manner as shown in Figure 11.5(f). Distributing the parity blocks across all disks can avoid the potential I/O bottleneck found in RAID 4.

■ **RAID Level 6—Independent access with block-interleaved dual distributed parity**
RAID 6 strips data in disk sector units and stores the data blocks over all the disk drives of the array in the same way as in RAID 5, but it uses an additional disk so that a second set of parity blocks can be stored together with the data blocks and the first set of parity blocks across all disk drives in an interleaved fashion. This organization of data blocks and parity blocks is shown in Figure 11.5(g) with P1 and P2 denoting two sets of parity blocks. The scheme of RAID 6 with added fault tolerance is equivalent to double mirroring. It provides extremely high data availability.

■ **RAID Level 10 — Striping is applied across multiple RAID 1 pairs.**

■ **RAID Level 15 — Mirroring of two complete RAID 5 systems increases fault tolerance.**

Comparing the above RAID configurations, we can reach the following conclusions. RAID level 0 is not a true member of the RAID family. RAID levels 1, 3, and 5 are most common, while RAID levels 2, 4, and 6 are rarely implemented in commercial products.

Most RAID disk systems allow *hot replacement* of disks, while the system is operating. When a failed disk is replaced, the lost data on it are rebuilt using the information on all the remaining disks in the array. Rebuilding occurs while the operating system continues handling other operations. The only side effect is the graceful degradation of performance during the rebuilding operation.

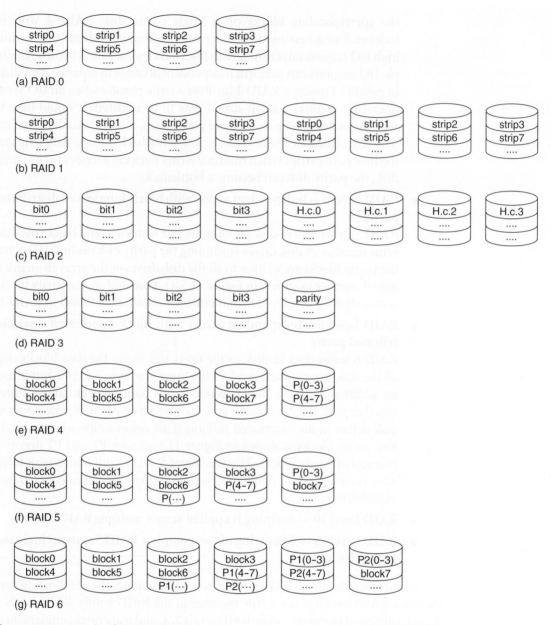

Figure 11.5 Levels of RAID disk systems

11.2.3 Optical Disks

The history of optical disks started from 1983 when *digital audio compact disks* (CD-DA) first appeared in the market. The manufacturing techniques of optical disks were adapted later for manufacturing the *compact disks as read-only memories* (CD-ROMs) for storage of computer data. Both types of CDs have the same recording format. Let us take the CD-DA as an example. The single spiral track on a 12-cm polycarbonate plastic disk is divided into 270,000 blocks, each holding 2 kilobytes. The entire spiral track can hold 74 minutes of stereo music playing at a sampling rate of 150 KB/sec. This sampling rate corresponds to approximately a 9-MB capacity for one minute of playing time. Considering more than 10% of the space used by the error-correcting codes (ECC of 288 bytes appended to every 2-KB data block), we can find a rule of thumb stated as follows: one minute of uncompressed CD music demands 10 megabytes of storage. Therefore, a 12-cm disk in a standard CD system can hold 650 megabytes of useful information (excluding ECC), either music or computer data.

The recording format of CD-DA and CD-ROM has a big difference from that of a magnetic disk. On a magnetic disk, information is recorded in concentric tracks using the *constant angular velocity* (CAV) system, whereas on an optical disk, information is recorded in a single spiral track using the *constant linear velocity* (CLV) system. These two systems are compared below.

On a magnetic disk, the bits are written to the magnetic medium by constant-length pulses. So, all the tracks of a magnetic disk hold the same number of bits, no matter whether the diameter of the track is small (near the center) or large (near the edge). In other words, on a magnetic disk, the number of bits per track is constant, but the density of bits on a track is inversely proportional to its diameter. To keep a more uniform density of recording to allow a higher capacity of storage, the entire surface of a magnetic disk is divided into a number of zones, each of which is assigned a different recording density directly proportional to the distance of the zone from the center.

On an optical disk, the digital signals are imprinted mechanically as a series of microscopic pits on the surface of polycarbonate plastic. Sectors near the outside of the disk have the same length as those near the inside, and all of them have the same number of pits. If the disk rotates at a constant speed, the constant-length sectors would result in a variable data rate directly proportional to the distance of the sector from the center of the disk. To make the data rate more uniform for better reception of information, the disk should be rotating at a variable speed—more slowly for access near the outer edge than those near the center.

Factory-manufactured CD-ROMs are now widely used for distributing computer software and games software. However, they are not suitable for the use of CD as secure backup storage and long-term archiving of documents. For these application purposes, we need a new type of CD that enables the customers to record their own data files at least once and then read the record many times later. This type of CD is called a *recordable CD* (CD-R) or *write once, read many CD* (CD-WORM). Two methods have been developed for writing data to the CD.

One method is to punch little holes in a fine metallic layer by a high-intensity laser. Another alternative method is to include a chemical dye layer in the recording medium and use a lower powered laser to change its reflectivity when writing data to it. Both writing processes are irreversible. When we use the CD-R drives (called a CD burner) on personal computers, the source data stream must be fed continuously without interruption, otherwise the Write operation will fail irrevocably. As high-speed drives of 2×, 4×, 8×, and so on become available, the danger of data underrun increases. To avoid this problem, the drive should be equipped with a RAM buffer of sufficient capacity to smooth the data supply. For example, with a 2× drive, 300 KB/sec data supply is required. If the drive has a buffer of 2 megabytes, a 6-second gap of data supply can be tolerated.

The advent of CD-R has enhanced the functionality of optical storage so significantly that it can successfully compete with the traditional magnetic tapes for archival storage of documents and files. However, to compete with magnetic disks, optical disks that can be erased and rewritten many times must be developed. These disks are called *rewritable CD* (CD-RW). Currently, two methods are most promising—the *magneto-optical disk* (CD-MO) and the *phase-change CD-RW*. The only pure optical approach that has proved its effectiveness is *phase change*. It employs a chemical substance that can be in two stable states, either an ordered crystalline state or a disordered amorphous state. A high-powered laser beam can change the material from one state to another state. The two states of the material exhibit different reflectivities, thus allowing the stored data to be read back. The major disadvantage of phase change is that the material can permanently lose its desirable properties. Current material can be used for between 500,000 and 1,000,000 erase cycles.

The advent of *digital versatile disk* (DVD) has been a big progress of the electronics industry. The DVD will replace not only analog videotapes, but also CD-ROMs in personal computers and servers. It employs a technology for producing digitized, compressed representation of video information as well as other digital data. The DVD-ROM has a larger capacity because it differs from CDs in three aspects:

1. Using a laser with shorter wavelength, the DVD has achieved a sevenfold increase in capacity, reaching 4.7 gigabytes per disk compared to 650 kilobytes per disk for CD. The minimum pit length and track pitch on a DVD are 0.4 µm and 0.75 µm, respectively, half those of a CD.

2. The DVD employs a second layer of signal pits on top of the first layer. It is a semireflective layer on top of the reflective layer. Both layers can be read separately by the laser in the DVD drive by adjusting the focus. This raises the capacity of DVD to about 8.5 gigabytes per disk.

3. The DVD-ROM can be two-sided. This raises the total capacity to 17 gigabytes.

The application of DVD technology for computer storage began with DVD-ROM and DVD-RW, providing 3.9 gigabytes (single-sided) and 5.2 gigabytes (doubled-sided), respectively. The double-layer DVD may begin to emulate the cylinder model of a multi-platter hard disk.

11.2.4 Magnetic Tapes

Magnetic tape drives were among the earliest devices used for secondary storage. They use the same techniques as magnetic disk drives for recording and reading information. The tape widths vary from 0.15" (0.38 cm) to 0.5" (1.27 cm). The tape lengths vary from 600' (183 m) to 2400' (731.5 m). The total capacity can be as large as 110 gigabytes per cartridge, much larger than the capacity of a DVD-ROM stated above. However, the speed of a tape unit is much slower than a DVD driver. The seek time on a tape drive is measured in seconds.

The storage of data on a magnetic tape may take different formats. In principle, three formats are possible:

- **Parallel recording**

  Data on the tape are structured as a sequence of bytes, halfwords or words, with each unit of data plus the error detection bits stored on 9, 18 or 36 parallel tracks, respectively. The sequence of data units runs along the longitudinal direction of the tape.

- **Serial recording or serpentine recording**

  Data are laid out as a sequence of bits along each track of the tape, as if the bit sequence were recorded on each track of a magnetic disk. Data are read and written on a tape in contiguous blocks called *physical records*. Any two consecutive blocks on a track are separated by a gap called *inter-record gap*. As with the disk, the tape is formatted using a special track to assist in locating physical records. The typical serial recording referred to as *serpentine recording* writes the bit sequence to the tape in the following order: write the first set of bits along the whole length of the first data track, then continue to write the second set of bits along the whole length of the second data track, but in a reverse direction as on the first data track, and repeat this process, back and forth, until the tape is full.

- **Serial-parallel recording or blocked recording**

  Data are divided into blocks. Each data block is recorded serially in an individual track on the tape, but successive 2, 4, 8, … data blocks are placed in 2, 4, 8, … parallel tracks, respectively, as a group of records on the tape, so that all the records in this group can be read or written simultaneously. However, successive groups of records organized in this way are still stored serially on the tape. Therefore, *blocked recording* means (1) parallel recording inside each group of 2, 4, 8, … data blocks, depending on the number of tracks in the width of the tape, and (2) serial recording of such groups of data blocks arranged in a sequential order along the length of the tape.

11.2.5 Solid-State Disk Drives[1]

The electromechanical disk drive is a wonder of technology with storage capabilities of 4 terabytes in a small 3½-in. form factor. However, its days may be limited by the introduction of *solid-state drives* (SSD) that mimic the hard drive electrically. The solid-state hard drive uses semiconductor flash technology to store data and an electrical interface that makes it physically compatible with hard disk interfaces; that is, you just plug an SSD into a hard disk SATA socket. The serial advanced technology attachment (SATA) is a low-cost high-speed serial interface that now interfaces mass storage devices from disk drives to host controllers.

The SSD has considerable advantages over the electromechanical disks—the most important of which are higher performance, lower power consumption, lower weight, and greater tolerance to shock. In 2010, SSDs were finding their way into high-end executive laptops (in a 2½-in. form factor) and specialist high-end applications (in 3½-in. form factors). By 2012, SSDs were standard in most premium laptops. The limitations of the SSD are two-fold: their considerable cost premium over hard drives and their limited storage capacity.

Solid-state disks are constructed with flash memory technology; it's only in recent years that the cost of flash memory has declined to the point at which large (over 128 gigabytes) memories are economically feasible.

Because SSDs have no moving parts, they are truly random access devices. There is no rotational latency and no seek time. Consequently, the fragmentation problem associated with hard disks simply goes away. It's not necessary to periodically defragment an SSD when files are scrambled throughout the memory space. As early as 2007, a white paper from IDC[2] indicated the potential savings from an SSD-based notebook:

- IT labor savings for PC deployment—2.4%
- Reliability savings for outsourced repair—1.4%
- Reliability savings for repairs—7.5%
- Reliability savings for user productivity due to hard drive loss—17.2%
- Savings from power enhancements—16.9%
- User productivity savings—54.5%

---

[1] Reprinted with permission from Section 11-5 (pp. 639–698) of Alan Clements, *Computer Organization and Architecture: Themes and Variations* (Boston, MA: Cengage Learning, 2014).

[2] J. Janukowicz and D. Reinsel, "Evaluating the SSD total cost of ownership," *IDC*, November 2007.

Politics of SSD

Commercial organizations tend to be most enthusiastic about "green" issues when doing so is profitable. For example, hotels ask you to reuse towels to save water, which is environmentally good and also saves the hotel energy and water.

Similarly, solid-state disk drives are heavily promoted as green by drive manufacturers. Although such a promotion is self-serving, it is true. Because a SSD has no moving parts (in particular, no rotating platter), its energy consumption is intrinsically lower than a hard disk drive. Moreover, the increased reliability of SSDs means that they will need replacing less frequently, saving the energy incurred in manufacturing replacement drives.

Price of SSD

Like all new technologies, the SSD entered the world with a massive price premium compared to magnetic hard disks. Since the SSD's introduction, its price has rapidly declined.

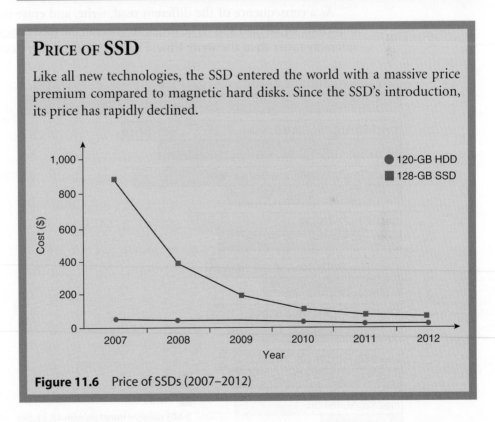

Figure 11.6 Price of SSDs (2007–2012)

Of course, these figures apply to a particular corporate environment at a particular instant and are the basis of a lot of assumptions. However, the principle is valid. The replacement of hard drives by SSDs is going to bring benefits, and the perception of those benefits will lead to the development of new generations of SSDs.

1. Special Features of SSDs

The term *features* in this heading is intended to be ironic, as in the notorious expression "It's not a bug, it's a feature." Magnetic disks have effectively equal read, write, and erase times. Of course, they have to, because the surface moves under the read/write head and the time available to read or write is fixed by the mechanics of the system. Solid-state memory uses different read and write mechanisms. For example, to read a flash memory cell, you just inject a current into a silicon channel and then detect whether the stored charge on a floating gate is letting the current through or not. To write data into the cell, you have to inject a charge onto the floating gate. This can be a multiple step process, because some systems inject a charge in discrete units and test whether the data is stored (several writes may be performed before sufficient charge has been stored). Erasing the cell is even more complicated because the charge has to be stripped off the floating gate.

As a consequence of the different read, write, and erase mechanisms, SSDs don't have equal read and write times. In general, the read time of an SSD is considerably faster than the write time. Figure 11.7 demonstrates the performance

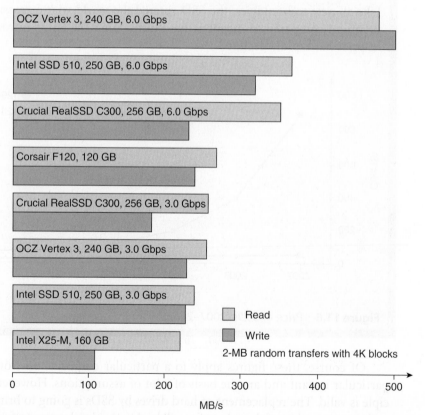

Source: Kevin O'Brien, "SSD 520 Review," *StorageReview.com*, February 6, 2012. Available at: http://www.storagereview.com/intel_ssd_520_review. Reprinted with permission.

Figure 11.7   SSD 2-MB random transfers (4K sector)

of several SSDs for 2-MB random-access data transfers for both read and write accesses. The horizontal length defines the data rate in megabyte/sec. Note the considerable variation between different models of SSD.[3]

Figure 11.8 from storagereview.com demonstrates the sequential data transfer performance of several solid-state disks. These figures are for both Read and

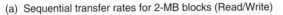

(a) Sequential transfer rates for 2-MB blocks (Read/Write)

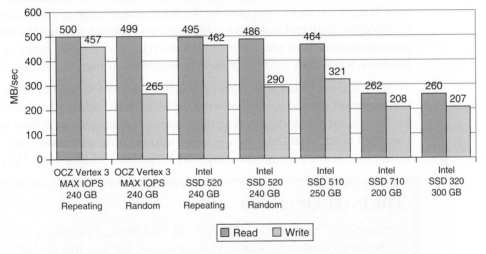

(b) Random transfer rates for 2-MB blocks (Read/Write)

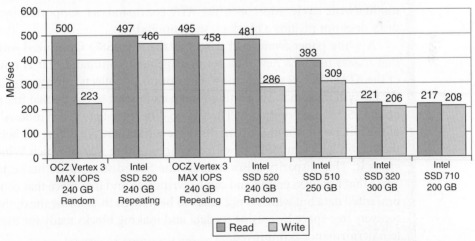

Source: Kevin O'Brien, "SSD 520 Review," *StorageReview.com*, February 6, 2012. Available at: http://www.storagereview.com/intel_ssd_520_review. Reprinted with permission.

Figure 11.8 SSD random reads and writes (the vertical axis is data rate in MB/sec)

---

[3] B. Oliver, "Comparison of 32GB SSD vs 10,000 RPM HDs", http://www.xlr8yourmac.com/IDE/SSD_vs_VelociRaptor_vs_Raptor/SSD_vs_VelociRaptor_Raptor.html

Write operations using 2-MB sequential and random data transfers. Note the variation in performance across several models of SSD. Note also that the write performance can be up to 50% lower than the read performance.

A second feature of SSDs is a limitation on the number of write cycles. When flash memory cells are erased, the dielectric insulator surrounding the gate is damaged, and the cell fails after a certain number of cycles. Moreover, repeated write cycles can lead to *charge trapping,* which leads to cells becoming stuck at zero. When flash memory is used for the BIOS or as storage in digital cameras or MP3 players, flash endurance is not likely to be a problem, because the minimum erase endurance is of the order of 10,000 cycles and 100,000 cycles is typical. However, when flash memory is used as secondary storage, the picture changes.

A technique called *wear leveling*[4] has been devised to help mitigate against the limitation on the number of write cycles in flash memory by spreading the load across the entire device. A form of memory management is used to map a requested block from the drive controller address onto a physical block address within the memory array. The controller keeps track of how often the physical

THE INTEL OPTIMIZER

Conventional hard disks support Read and Write operations. However, SSDs cannot be directly written to (overwriting old data like the hard disk), because an erase operation must first be applied to any 4-KB page that is to be written to. As we have pointed out, an SSD requires a relatively long read/modify/write cycle. Moreover, the ATA command set supported by hard disks does not include a block erase command.

A white paper from Intel describes the Intel SSD Optimized software that makes use of a new data set management command that is not part of the ATA8-ACC-2 specification. The optimizer collects information about the file system from the operating system and uses it to ensure that free space on the SSD is used optimally. There is no difference between Windows' view of the filing system and the hard disk's view, but there is a difference between the way in which an SSD views free space and the way in which Windows views it. This disparity arises because the SSD distinguishes between free space that has been erased and can be written to and free space that contains unwanted data but which is not ready to be written to. Because the optimizer recovers free space by erasing its data and making blocks ready for use, system performance is improved.

Note that the optimizer does not delete files from Windows' recycle bin, as that would prevent you from recovering accidentally deleted files. Files in the recycle bin are retained until the user performs an *empty recycle bin* command—at which time the optimizer recovers the space occupied by files.

---

[4] "Wear-leveling techniques in NAND flash devices," Micron Technical Note TN-29-42.

memory blocks are being used and changes the mapping table to ensure that all physical blocks get a fair share of the load.

Micron's TN-29-42 technical note provides an example of wear leveling. Suppose a system does not use wear leveling, and 50 blocks of data are updated six times an hour. Moreover, suppose that these 50 blocks are allocated a 200-block region of memory. Since each block can use one of four blocks in the device (i.e., 200/50), the endurance is 10,000 cycles × 4 = 40,000 cycles. At an update rate of 6 files/hour, the endurance of the memory is approximately 280 days. However, if wear leveling is used and all 4,096 blocks in the memory are available, the endurance is scaled by 4,096/200 to give approximately 15 years.

There are many ways of implementing wear leveling. For example, the memory space can be partitioned into static and dynamic regions. Static regions are used to store data that is relatively unlikely to change (e.g., programs). Wear leveling is not required to manage static data. Dynamic regions are used to store data that is frequently being changed and are managed by the wear-leveling software.

An information sheet published by Toshiba[5] makes the interesting point that a 128-GB Toshiba ML.C SSD has a five-year estimated storage capacity of 80 terabytes. This class of disk uses both NAND technology and multi-level data storage (i.e., a cell holds more than one bit) and supports fewer write cycles than other technologies. According to Toshiba, this corresponds to over 20 gigabyte/data per day written over the lifetime of the disk, which is an unreasonably large amount for most end-user applications of a mobile computer. If the SSD is larger, the amount that can be written increases correspondingly. Note that a 512-gigabyte SSD based on SLC technology would support the writing of 2 terabytes daily.

THE HYBRID DRIVE

By 2010, SSDs were appearing in high-end applications but were too expensive for large-scale applications. Seagate attempted to bridge the gap between fast but costly silicon and slow but cheap magnetic disks with a hybrid drive. Their 2½-inch Momentus XT combined both technologies to provide a 500-GB disk with 4 gigabytes of flash memory (plus an unusually large conventional 32 megabytes of fast semiconductor cache). The 4 gigabytes of flash memory is relatively small compared to the total capacity, but on-board software monitors disk usage and caches frequently used data. Performance figures indicate that the hybrid drive has a useful performance advantage over conventional hard drives. Other tests have demonstrated that this hybrid drive has a 25% improvement in start-up time (loading Windows) over a conventional hard drive and a 300% increase in performance in shutting down.

[5] "Solid-state drives: Separating myths from facts," Toshiba America Electronic Components, V1.3, June 2009.

11.3 I/O ACCESSING

In this section, we will look at the three basic methods of I/O accessing—programmed I/O, interrupt-driven I/O, and direct memory access (DMA). The key issue that distinguishes these three methods is how deeply the processor is involved in I/O operations. The discussion emphasizes interrupt-driven I/O, because it is based on the concept of *interrupt handling*, which is a general problem that goes beyond I/O operations. The study of interrupt handling also aids in understanding the general concept of *exception processing*, which is an important issue not only for I/O, but also for interfacing a computer with other system control functions.

11.3.1 Addressing I/O Registers

I/O devices communicate with a processor through I/O ports. Through the input ports, a processor receives data from the I/O devices. Through the output ports, a processor sends data to the I/O devices. Each I/O port consists of a small set of registers, such as data buffer registers (the input buffer and/or the output buffer), the status register, and the control register. The processor must have some means to address these registers while communicating with them. There are two common methods of addressing I/O registers—memory-mapped I/O and direct I/O.

1. Memory-Mapped I/O

Memory-mapped I/O maps the I/O registers and main memory into a unified address space in the computer system. I/O registers share the same address space with main memory, but are mapped to a specific section that is reserved just for I/O. Thus, the I/O registers can be addressed in ordinary memory reference instructions as if they are part of the main memory locations. There are no specially designed I/O instructions in the instruction set of the system. Any instruction that references a location in this area is an I/O instruction. Any instruction that can specify a memory address is capable of performing I/O operations. The Motorola MC68000 is an example of a computer system that uses this addressing method.

2. Direct I/O

The method of addressing I/O registers directly without sharing the address space with the main memory is called *direct I/O* or *I/O-mapped I/O*. In other words, I/O registers are not mapped to the same address space with the main memory. Each I/O register has an independent address space. As a result, instructions that reference the main memory space cannot be used for I/O. In the instruction set of the computer system, special I/O instructions must be designed for I/O operations. In these I/O instructions, distinct identification numbers must be used to address different I/O communication channels (i.e., I/O ports). They are called port numbers. The I/O registers of an I/O port are connected to the system I/O bus through which the processor can reference the I/O registers directly to send/receive data to/from an I/O device. An I/O port number is used in the same way as a memory address, except that an I/O port number is not from the same address space as main memory. The Pentium® is an example of a computer system that uses the direct I/O addressing method. It has a 64-GB memory address space (32 address bits) and, at the same time, a 64-KB I/O address space (16 bits I/O address/port number).

We can compare memory-mapped I/O and direct I/O as follows:

- Memory-mapped I/O uses ordinary memory reference instructions to access I/O, so it provides flexibility for I/O programming and simplifies I/O software. Direct I/O does not provide any flexibility in I/O programming, since only a small set of special I/O instructions are allowed to reference I/O registers.

- For memory-mapped I/O, the processor uses the same address lines to access all the addressable I/O registers and the same data lines to send/receive data to/from these registers. This simplifies the connection between I/O ports and the processor, and thus leads to a low-cost hardware design and implementation. For direct I/O, the connection between I/O ports and the processor may be more expensive. This is because either (1) special hardware is needed to implement separate I/O address lines or (2) when memory address lines are used for I/O, a special flag is needed, indicating that the requested address is for an I/O operation.

- In spite of the advantage of using ordinary memory reference instructions to access I/O registers, memory-mapped I/O may complicate the control unit design with regard to the implementation of I/O-related instructions. This is because usually the I/O bus cycles need to be longer than the equivalent memory bus cycles, and this means that the design of different timing control logic is required. This can be used to explain why memory-mapped I/O benefits programmers, but not electronics engineers.

- Direct I/O addressing has another advantage over memory-mapped I/O in that low-level debugging on a differentiated addressing system may be easier because breakpoints or error traps can be imposed more generally.

- With memory-mapped I/O, I/O registers share the same address space with main memory; hence, the memory space available for programs and data is reduced. For direct I/O addressing, I/O does not share memory space with main memory, and a single contiguous memory space can be maintained and used by programmers.

11.3.2 Programmed I/O

Programmed I/O requires that all data transfer operations be placed under the complete control of the processor when executing programs. It is sometimes called *polling* because the program repeatedly polls (checks) the status flag of an I/O device, so that its I/O operation can be synchronized with the processor. A general flowchart of such a program is shown in Figure 11.9. The program continuously polls the status of an I/O device to determine whether (1) data is available in the input buffer or (2) the output device is ready for receiving data from the processor. If the status shows "available," the program will execute a data transfer instruction to complete the I/O operation; otherwise, the busy status of the I/O device will force the program to circulate in a busy waiting loop until the status becomes available. Such a *busy waiting loop* that continuously checks the status of data availability (for input) or device availability (for output) forms the typical program structure of programmed I/O. It is this time-consuming busy waiting loop that wastes processor time and makes programmed I/O very inefficient. The processor must be continuously involved in the entire I/O process. During this time interval, the processor cannot perform any useful computation, but only serve a single I/O device. For certain slow I/O devices, this busy waiting loop interval may be long enough that the processor could execute millions of instructions before the I/O event occurs, for example, a key stroke on a keyboard.

The operational mode of programmed I/O stated above and shown in Figure 11.9 is characterized by the busy waiting loop of the program, during which the processor spends time polling an I/O device. Because of the dedication

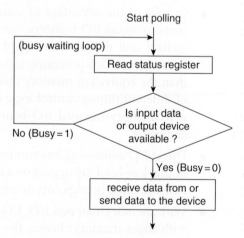

Figure 11.9 Typical structure of programmed I/O

of the processor to a single task, this mode of programmed I/O is called *dedicated polling* or *spin polling*. Although dedicated polling is highly inefficient, sometimes it is necessary and even unavoidable. In a particular case, if an urgent event needs an immediate response without delay, then dedicated polling by a dedicated processor may be the best way to handle it. Once the expected event happens, the processor can react to it immediately. For example, certain real-time systems (e.g., radar echo processing systems) require a reaction to incoming data that is so quick that even an interrupt response is too slow. Under such a circumstance, only a fast dedicated polling loop may suffice.

Another mode of operation of programmed I/O is called *intermittent polling* or *timed polling*. In this mode, the processor may poll the device at a regular timed interval, which can be expected or prescheduled. Such a device can be found in many embedded systems where a special-purpose computer is used for process control, data acquisition, environmental monitoring, traffic counting, and so on. These devices, which measure, collect, or record data, are usually polled periodically in a regular schedule determined by the needs of the application. Such a method of intermittent polling can help save time lost in spin polling and avoid the complexity of interrupt processing. However, it should be noted that intermittent polling may not be applicable in some special cases, in which there is only one device to be polled and the correct polling rate must be achieved with the assistance of an interrupt-driven clock. Using timed polling in this case would result in simply swapping one interrupt requirement for another.

Example 11.1   An Input Operation Followed by an Output Operation to Echo a Line of Characters on a Display

The execution process of a Read operation from an input device followed by a Write operation to echo the input string on a display is shown on the flowchart in Figure 11.10. It uses programmed I/O with two busy waiting loops, one for the input device and the other for the output device. The device controller(s) has an input data register and an output data register to input and echo one character at a time. The combination of the input and output operations should be repeated many times until the end of a line is reached. After echoing each character, the character should be stored in main memory using either a displacement or an indexed addressing mode. The indexed value in a register should be incremented every time a new character is processed.

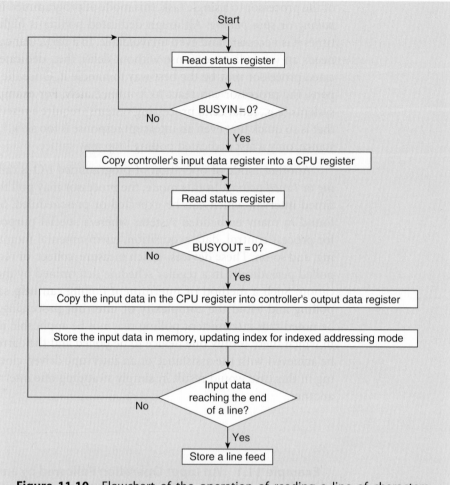

Figure 11.10 Flowchart of the operation of reading a line of characters followed by an output (echoing) operation on a display

11.3.3 Interrupt-Driven I/O

Interrupt-driven I/O is a means to avoid the inefficient busy waiting loops, which characterize programmed I/O. Instead of waiting while the I/O device is busy doing its job of I/O, the processor can run other programs. When the I/O device completes its job and its status becomes "available," it will issue an *interrupt request* to the processor, asking for CPU service. In response, the processor suspends whatever it is currently doing, in order to attend to the needs of that I/O device.

In response to an interrupt request, the processor will first save the contents of both the program counter and the status register for the running program, and then transfer the control to the corresponding interrupt service routine to perform the required data I/O operation. When the interrupt service routine has completed its execution and if no more interrupt requests are pending, the processor will resume the execution of the previously interrupted program and restore the contents of the statuses and program counter. Figure 11.11 shows the simplified process of the interrupt-driven I/O. The processor hardware should check the interrupt request signal upon completion of execution of every instruction. If multiple devices issue their interrupt requests at the same time, the processor must use some method to choose which one to service first, and then service all the other interrupt requests one by one by order of priority. Only after all the

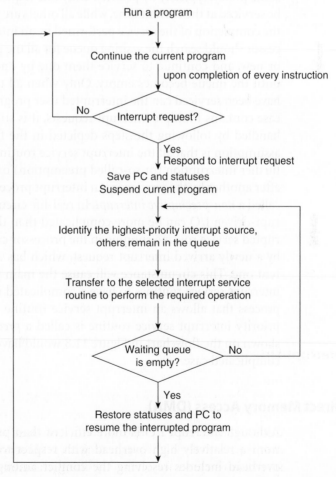

Figure 11.11 A simplified process of interrupt-driven I/O (non-preemptive)

interrupt requests have been serviced will the CPU return to the interrupted user program. In this way, the processor can serve many I/O devices concurrently and spend more time doing useful jobs, rather than running a busy waiting loop to serve a single device. Therefore, interrupt I/O is very effective in handling slow and medium-speed I/O devices. Furthermore, the concept of an interrupt can be generalized to handle any event caused by hardware or software, internally or externally. This general problem is referred to as *exception processing*, and will be discussed in the next section.

The flowchart of an interrupt-driven I/O process shown in Figure 11.11 depicts multiple interrupt requests in more detail. If multiple interrupt requests are issued by different devices at the same time, the processor should have some means to identify the interrupt sources and handle their interrupt requests by some policy, typically by priority. Only one request with the highest priority can be serviced at the current time, while all others are put into a waiting queue. Upon the completion of the service performed by an interrupt service routine, the processor should search the waiting queue for all the pending interrupt requests, old or new, and continue to service them one by one according to their priorities, until the queue becomes empty. Only when all the pending interrupt requests have been serviced can the interrupted user program be resumed. Although this case contains multiple interrupt requests, it is still a simplified case that can be handled by following the steps depicted in the flowchart of Figure 11.11. The assumption is that all the interrupt service routines must be completed without further interruption (or so-called preemption) once they have been started one after another by the processor. An interrupt process satisfying this assumption is called a *non-preemptive interrupt*. In real-life circumstances, the process of interrupt-driven I/O can be more complicated than this simplified case. Each interrupted service routine running in the processor can be preempted (interrupted) by a newly arrived interrupt request, which has a higher priority than the current one. This circumstance will cause the main program and all the requested interrupt service routines to have a complicated interrelationship. An interrupt process that allows an interrupt service routine to be preempted by a higher-priority interrupt service routine is called a *preemptive interrupt*. The process shown on the flowchart in Figure 11.8 would have to be modified to handle this complicated case.

11.3.4 Direct Memory Access (DMA)

Although interrupt I/O is more efficient than programmed I/O, it still suffers from a relatively high overhead with respect to handling the interrupt. This overhead includes resolving the conflict among multiple interrupt requests, saving and restoring the program contexts, pooling for interrupt identification, branching to/from the interrupt service routine, and so on. Using an interrupt is a wasteful activity that can take several microseconds to complete.

Direct memory access (DMA) is a method that can input/output a block of data directly to/from main memory with a speed of one data item per memory cycle, without continuous involvement of the processor. The entire process is implemented by the hardware of a DMA controller, which takes the place of the processor and communicates directly with main memory. As a result, the block diagram of the computer system changes from processor-centered to memory-centered. Hence, from the viewpoint of I/O processing, the processor is no longer the center of a computer, but rather a partner with which the I/O subsystem competes for memory bus cycles to input/output data items to/from main memory. However, a DMA controller is designed to exchange data in blocks, so it works well with the large-volume high-speed block-oriented I/O devices, such as high-speed disks and communication networks.

The DMA controller can work in two different modes. Normally, it works concurrently with the processor, competing for individual memory bus cycles to input/output successive words of a data block. If the I/O speed is not very high, the memory accesses by the processor and the DMA controller can be interwoven. Time is accrued on a cycle-by-cycle basis. Neither the processor nor the DMA controller can continuously use all the memory bus cycles during any time interval. This operational mode of the DMA controller is called *cycle stealing*, so named because the I/O subsystem is essentially "stealing" memory bus cycles from the processor. This mode integrates the DMA memory accesses into CPU activity and avoids serious disruption of the main processing. Alternatively, for even higher I/O transfer speed, DMA operations require bus time, which can be allocated in blocks of cycles known as bursts. During a burst of memory cycles, the processor is totally excluded from accessing memory. The DMA controller is given exclusive access to main memory and continuously inputs/outputs blocks of data at a speed comparable to the memory speed. This operational mode of the DMA controller is called the *block* or *burst* mode. A DMA controller designed for this mode of operation usually incorporates a data storage buffer with a capacity matching the size of at least one data block. When the DMA controller utilizes the memory bus, it can transfer a data block directly between its data storage buffer and main memory.

A simplified block diagram of a DMA controller is shown in Figure 11.12. The following registers are necessary for the DMA to transfer a block of data:

- **Data buffer register (DBR)**—It can be implemented as two registers, one for input and the other for output, or even a set of registers comprising a data storage buffer.
- **DMA address register (DAR)**—Used to store the starting address of the memory buffer area where the block of data is to be read or written.
- **Word counter (WC)**—The contents specify the number of words in the block of data remaining to be transferred and it is automatically decremented after each word is transferred.

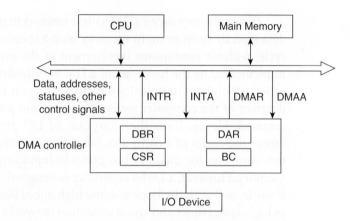

Figure 11.12 Simplified block diagram of a DMA controller

- **Control/status register (CSR)**—Used by the processor to send control information to the DMA controller and to collect the statuses and error information of the DMA controller and the I/O devices attached to it.

Using these registers, the DMA controller knows the addresses of the source and destination data blocks, as well as the quantity of data to be transferred. Once the DMA controller acquires the memory bus, the block transfer operation can be performed autonomously using the information contained in these registers, without the continuous involvement of the processor.

Besides the above registers, the DMA controller should contain the control logic of a *bus request facility*, which performs bus arbitration using the signals of DMA Request (DMAR) and DMA Acknowledge (DMAA). Bus arbitration is the process of resolving the contention among multiple concurrently operating DMA controllers for acquisition of the memory bus. The selection of the bus master is usually based on the priorities of various DMA devices. Among different DMA devices, the priority order is arranged by the degree of urgency of the devices receiving the DMA service, that is, according to their speed requirements. There are two approaches to bus arbitration for DMA devices—centralized and distributed—which are similar to the approaches used to identify interrupt sources using signals for interrupt request (INTR) and interrupt acknowledge (INTA). We will discuss these approaches in Section 11.4.2.

Although the transfer of the data block is performed by the DMA without the involvement of the processor, the overall operation of the DMA controller is still determined by the CPU via interrupts. It serves the following two purposes: (1) Before the DMA controller starts the data transfer, all the registers must be initialized by the processor. (2) When the DMA finishes a block transfer operation, it should inform the processor of completion by issuing an interrupt, which allows the processor to post-process the data in the memory buffer area or handle possible error conditions. Therefore, the DMA controller often issues INTR and receives INTA signals.

DMA relieves the processor from the burden of I/O functions, except for the initialization of the transfer of parameters and the post-processing of data. It is very efficient when serving high-speed I/O devices. However, the role of DMA is not limited to the area of I/O. In contemporary computer systems, DMA has been developed into a general technique of *time-sharing the main memory bandwidth* between I/O subsystem processing and CPU processing. In the I/O subsystem, high-speed I/O devices, such as disks, CD-ROMs, DVDs, graphics, video equipment, and high-speed networks, want to share main memory bandwidth through the DMA. In the area of central processing and the main memory system, (1) running programs, (2) the operating system, and (3) dynamic RAM refreshing share the main memory bandwidth. DMA is the appropriate way to implement this time-sharing. Faster 16-bit Ultra DMA has now replaced the outdated 8-bit facilities. Commercially available DMA controller chips now offer multiple channels, allowing concurrent data transfers. For example, one channel can be reserved for DRAM refreshing, another channel can perform memory-to-memory block moves, and so on. To further free the processor from handling slow tasks, powerful channel processors have been developed with autonomous capabilities including device polling, channel program execution, interrupt activation, and DMA for data and instructions. They have become a growing class of semi-independent coprocessors that communicate with the main processor. They can be assigned dedicated tasks, such as floating-point calculations, graphic processing, network communication, large database management, and so on. The growing bus contention problem, due to time-sharing main memory bandwidth, can be alleviated by more effectively using cache memory. For example, in the Pentium® processor, $L1$ cache allows the CPU pipeline to continue fetching and executing, as long as the demand can be satisfied with instructions held locally in the cache.

11.4 EXCEPTION AND EXCEPTION HANDLING

An *exception* is defined as any event that forces the processor to suspend its currently executing program in order to invoke an interrupt service routine to handle that event. An exception is a general concept. It can originate from various external or internal events. An interrupt-driven I/O event is a special case of an exception. In general, an external exception may be caused by an incoming signal from an I/O device, a real-time clock, a power failure, or malfunctioning hardware. An external exception occurs at an unpredicted point in time and, hence, is not synchronized with the program. An internal exception is caused by a software event, such as a supervisor call, a TRAP instruction, a privileged (including I/O) instruction, a debugging command, a run-time error, or any abnormal operation of a program (e.g., page fault in virtual memory reference, overflow or divide by zero). It occurs at a point in time directly related to the program and is synchronized with the central clock. Exceptions caused by external normal events, such as I/O devices and the real-time clock, are called interrupts, and all other exceptional cases are referred to as exceptions. The unified hardware for handling exceptions and interrupts is usually called the *interrupt handling mechanism*, but the unified software embedded in the operating system for handling exceptions and interrupts is usually called the *exception handler*. Hence, we will use the term *interrupt* for the general case when we describe the interrupt handling mechanism (which is mostly hardware) in the remainder of this section.

11.4.1 Interrupt Request and Interrupt Acknowledge

Interrupt requests may be simultaneously issued from different interrupt sources. They can either be ORed together into a single signal INTR or combined into different groups, with each group issuing a separate INTR signal. Interrupt requests can be further classified into maskable and nonmaskable interrupts. A *maskable interrupt* is one that can be temporarily prohibited by some means, either by a bit vector called a *mask* or by an *interrupt disable* instruction. Each bit of the mask vector is used to represent an interrupt source. A "1" bit means the corresponding interrupt source is prohibited, and "0" bit means otherwise. The mask vector is set according to the priority relationships among the interrupt sources—a higher-priority source has the authority to mask all lower-priority sources. Any particular portion of the program, such as updating the pointer of a queue or saving/restoring the context of a process, can be protected from interruption by starting with an *interrupt disable* instruction and ending with an *interrupt enable* instruction. A *nonmaskable interrupt* is an interrupt that cannot be disabled by software instructions. Nonmaskable interrupts are interrupts caused by extremely urgent events, for example, power failure or memory error, so they must take precedence over all maskable interrupts.

Because an interrupt is generally an unscheduled event, the interrupt request signal can be issued at any random, unpredictable time. The processor must check for possible interrupt requests at the end of execution of every instruction. Only when the interrupt request signal is low (meaning no interrupt request), will the processor fetch the next instruction. Otherwise, if the interrupt request signal is high and enabled, the processor must acknowledge it by sending out an *interrupt acknowledge* signal and saving the current contents of the program counter and the status register (this is done automatically by hardware) and identify the interrupt.

11.4.2 Interrupt Identification

While acknowledging multiple interrupt requests, the processor must have some means to resolve the conflict and determine which requests should be accepted and which should be deferred. This process is called *interrupt identification*. The processor must choose the most urgent interrupt event and locate an interrupt service routine to provide the requested service. There are three methods of interrupt identification.

1. Software Polling

Interrupt identification can be done by software, using an interrupt polling program, whose flowchart is depicted in Figure 11.13. The *interrupt polling program* is global to all interrupt sources and has a fixed starting address known to hardware. Whenever there is an interrupt request, the interrupt mechanism will automatically (by way of hardware) load this address into the program counter to enable transfer of control to the interrupt polling program. Like an ordinary subroutine call, this transfer of control has to be done after saving the original

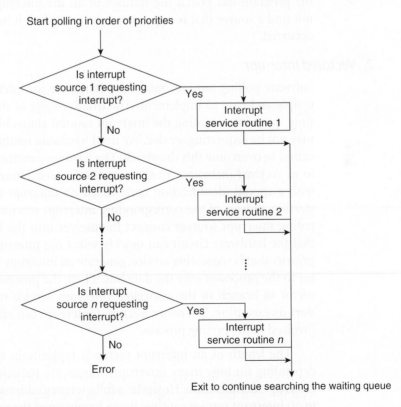

Figure 11.13   Flowchart of an interrupt polling program

context of the processor. The minimum contents to be saved include the existing contents of the program counter and the status register before the program was interrupted. The CPU registers to be used by the interrupt service routine are also considered part of the context, so their contents should be saved and later restored by the interrupt service routine itself.

The interrupt polling program performs the task of interrupt identification. It successively polls the statuses of all the participating interrupt sources in the order of priority, from the highest to the lowest, until it finds the first interrupt source requesting an interrupt. Then the program should branch to the starting address of the interrupt service routine corresponding to the identified interrupt source. The order of polling the interrupt sources is predetermined by the polling program in accordance with the order of their priorities. If the starting addresses of all the interrupt service routines form a jump table using the source number as an index, then using a jump instruction in memory indirect addressing mode can easily branch to the required interrupt service routine. In this way, the polling program can exit through an interrupt service routine. If the program has polled the statuses of all the interrupt sources, but still cannot find a source that is requesting interrupt, then it indicates that an error has occurred.

2. Vectored Interrupt

Software polling requires minimum hardware for interrupt identification. It is simple and easy to implement. The disadvantage of the polling method is the time spent interrogating the interrupt request status bits of all the devices that may not be requesting service. We need hardware methods of interrupt identification to overcome this drawback. The hardware methods are generally referred to as *vectored interrupts*. In these methods, each interrupt source is associated with a special identification code called an *interrupt vector* that points to the starting address of the corresponding interrupt service routine. All the participating interrupt sources connect themselves into the identifying hardware, so that the hardware circuit can quickly select the interrupt source of the highest priority that is requesting service, generate an interrupt vector, and send this vector to the processor over the data bus. Then, the processor can use the interrupt vector to branch to the associated interrupt service routine and immediately start its execution. Therefore, vectored interrupt can effectively reduce the time involved in the polling process.

The length of an interrupt vector is typically in the range of 4 to 8 bits, depending on how many interrupt sources are participating in the process of interrupt identification. However, a full memory address is needed for branching to an interrupt service routine. It can be obtained through a jump table called a vector table, using the interrupt vector as an index.

In the following sections, we will discuss two implementations of vectored interrupt.

1. Vectored interrupt by daisy-chaining

The circuit of vectored interrupt by *daisy-chaining* is shown in Figure 11.14. It consists of the following three parts:

- **Interrupt requesting circuit**—When an interrupt device i, $1 \leq i \leq n$, wants to request an interrupt, it sets the flip-flop INT_i to "1". This signal is then ANDed with the inverse of the corresponding mask bit of the mask register to further generate the $INTR_i$, representing an interrupt request from device i. This means that the $INTR_i$ signal is conditioned by the mask register bit i. That is, by way of an *inhibit gate*, signal $INTR_i$ can be prohibited by the corresponding bit of the mask register. Only when the corresponding mask bit is "0" can the interrupt requesting signal $INTR_i$ be sent to the collecting line INTR. After the interrupt request of device i has been acknowledged, the flip-flop INT_i will be cleared (this is not shown in the diagram).

- **Daisy chain circuit**—After the processor detects an INTR signal, it outputs an interrupt acknowledge signal, INTA, to the first section of the daisy chain controlled by $INTR_1$. Only when $INTR_1 = 0$ will the signal INTA pass through the first section and maintain the signal $INTA_1$ at "1". $INTA_1$ will continue to propagate along the daisy chain as long as the signal $INTR_i = 0$. When the INTA signal meets a section, say j, whose control

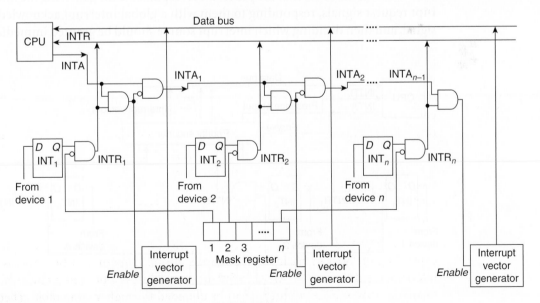

Figure 11.14 Vectored interrupt by daisy-chaining

signal $INTR_j = 1$, it will be blocked, so that the daisy chain outputs a signal $INTA_j = 0$. The interrupt identification is thus completed and the daisy chain has selected the interrupt source j to respond.

- **Interrupt vector generation circuit**—Selected by the daisy chain, interrupt source j has $INTR_j = 1$ and $INTA_{j-1} = 1$ (Note that $INTA_0 = INTA = 1$). These two signals will be ANDed to enable the interrupt vector generator of the interrupt source j. Its interrupt vector will then be put on the data bus and sent to the CPU.

2. **Vectored interrupt by a priority encoder**

A vectored interrupt circuit implemented with a priority encoder is depicted in Figure 11.15. A priority encoder has replaced the daisy chain in the circuit of Figure 11.14. As we can see from Table 3.16, Section 3.6.3, the higher-numbered input of a priority encoder has higher priority than the lower-numbered inputs. Thus, the priority encoder can resolve the conflict among multiple $INTR_i$ signals. The output code of the encoder is used to represent the interrupt source of the highest priority now requesting service. This code is used directly as the interrupt vector, which is sent to the CPU over the data bus. The priority encoder has a presence output (see Table 3.16 for more details) that can be used as the interrupt request signal, INTR, which is sent to the processor.

3. *Distributed Interrupt Identification*

The above-mentioned two hardware methods for interrupt identification are centralized in the sense that the processor is responsible for gathering the interrupt request signals, responding to them with a global interrupt acknowledge signal, and then deciding which interrupt source should be granted immediate

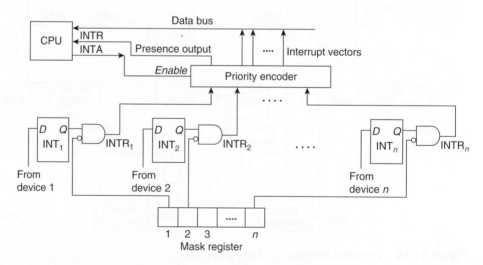

Figure 11.15   Vectored interrupt by a priority encoder

service. An alternative hardware method of interrupt identification can be distributed. All interrupt sources participating in the contention for interrupt service have equal responsibilities in carrying out the identification process without direct involvement by the central processor. Each interrupt source is given a unique interrupt vector such that in a contention for the interrupt service, the interrupt source that has the greatest interrupt vector will be the winner. The basic idea is that all the interrupt sources with a request for service can submit their n-bit interrupt vectors to a set of n open-collector lines. The common signal obtained on these open-collector lines will be the result of the bit-wise OR operation of all the interrupt vectors collected from the requesting interrupt sources. Then, each requesting interrupt source can compare this global result with its own interrupt vector. If the global result is greater than its own interrupt vector, the interrupt source must remove its application from the lines. Each interrupt vector is distinct; therefore, after all the losers of the contention have removed their interrupt vectors, a unique interrupt vector will remain on the lines, and its owner will be the final winner of the contention. This algorithm can be demonstrated by the following example.

Example 11.2   A Distributed Method of Interrupt Identification

Suppose four sources of interrupt are applying for the interrupt service. Their interrupt vectors are assigned as follows:

> Device 1: 01100101
> Device 2: 10001011
> Device 3: 01101101
> Device 4: 10010100

After they put their interrupt vectors on the eight open-collector lines, the global bit-wise OR operation on the lines produces the result 11111111. Suppose the arbitrary order of removing interrupt vectors causes the following changes of the global results:

> Device 1 removes 01100101   global result = 11111111
> Device 4 removes 10010100   global result = 11101111
> Device 3 removes 01101101   global result = 10001011
> Device 4 sees a smaller global result, so it resumes its interrupt vector, global result = 10011011, and Device 4 waits.
> Device 2 removes 10001011   global result = 10010100

Device 4 has waited for a sufficient time and sees the global result steadily equal to its interrupt vector, so it declares its winning status. ∎

From Example 11.2, it can be seen that since the order of removal is arbitrary, an interrupt source has to continue observing the change in global result on the open-collector lines after it has removed its interrupt vector. In case the global result becomes less than its interrupt vector, it must resume its interrupt vector and take the chance of finally winning the contention. Hence, even though the decentralized interrupt identification has the advantage of offering higher reliability due to its avoidance of single-point failure, its operation depends on appropriate responses from all the participating interrupt sources and requires a necessary waiting time for these responses to become stabilized. Generally speaking, it is not easy to design a distributed algorithm that works effectively in a distributed system. The popular distributed election algorithm may work, but it is based on message passing. The above-stated distributed algorithm on hardware may work better if we ask the losers of the contention to remove their interrupt vectors in several steps, from the most significant bits to the least significant bits. Similar distributed algorithms based on this principle work well for bus arbitration in DMA and SCSI bus standards.

11.4.3 Interrupt Servicing and Interrupt Returning

Utilizing an interrupt vector, interrupt servicing begins with branching to a particular program called an *interrupt service routine* that is required by the identified interrupt source. It is usually the responsibility of the interrupt service routine to save additional information about the interrupted program, such as the contents of general-purpose registers. When the interrupt service routine reaches completion, it should restore this information and then execute a *Return From Interrupt* (RTI) instruction to exit, which will restore the contents of the status register and program counter that the interrupted program previously saved by way of hardware.

Since there could be many interrupt requests awaiting service, as we mentioned before in Section 11.3.3, we should distinguish between two schemes, as follows:

- **Non-preemptive interrupt**—While an interrupt is being serviced, it prohibits the occurrence of any new interrupt service until the current interrupt service routine has been completed.

- **Preemptive interrupt**—The interrupt service routine with lower priority can be interrupted by an interrupt service routine that has a higher priority.

Using a non-preemptive interrupt scheme, execution of a given interrupt service routine, once started, always continues to completion before the processor can accept an interrupt request from another device. Using a preemptive interrupt scheme, on the other hand, an interrupt request from a higher-priority device should be accepted while the processor is servicing the current request of a lower-priority device. This higher-priority interrupt service routine can be further interrupted by an interrupt request that has an even higher priority. This type of nesting of interrupt service routines is allowed in the preemptive interrupt scheme. It is necessary for the system stack to manage the context switching between nested routines. To control preemption, the processor is assigned a priority in its status register, which can be changed under program control. This priority is referred to as *the priority of the processor*. It is always equal to the priority of the program currently being executed. When a new interrupt request arrives at the processor, its priority will be compared with the priority of the processor. If its priority is higher than the priority of the processor, the currently running interrupt service routine will be preempted, and the processor will run the new interrupt service routine.

11.5 THE I/O INTERFACES

I/O interfaces, as shown in Figure 11.1, connect various I/O devices to the processor. They implement specific interface protocols to satisfy the requirements of I/O bus standardization. Each implementation is accomplished with a set of I/O registers and signal lines that make up the interface hardware and I/O buses. An I/O interface allows a processor to be connected to a peripheral device in such a way that the processor does not have to learn the details of construction, data formats, and control timing, all of which are taken care of by the interface. In this section, we will study I/O interface protocols of parallel I/O ports and develop an understanding of the general rules for the I/O bus connections.

11.5.1 I/O Bus Protocol

The main activity of an I/O bus is to transfer information between the processor and I/O device controllers. Information to be transferred consists of address, data, and control signals. Thus, an I/O bus is composed of an address bus, a data bus, and a control bus. Synchronization between the processor and an I/O device is necessary, due to the fact that the processor and the I/O subsystem have different clock signals. This makes the data transfer process on the I/O bus quite complex. The rules governing the data transfer process on the I/O bus are collectively called the *I/O bus protocol*.

A bus is classified as either a synchronous bus or an asynchronous bus, depending on the timing mechanism that is used to coordinate the events on the bus. A synchronous bus protocol uses a common clock to coordinate data transfer operations between the processor and an I/O device. An asynchronous bus protocol does not utilize a common clock; rather, it uses a handshake mechanism to coordinate the actions taking place between the processor and an I/O device.

During a handshake procedure, one side is referred to as the master of the bus and the other as the slave of the bus.

1. Synchronous Bus

A synchronous memory bus was discussed in Section 10.3.3, and the timing diagram of a bus cycle was shown in Figure 10.8. The I/O synchronous bus follows the same principle as the one for the memory bus, except that it uses different control signals. A synchronous bus for I/O also requires that a common clock be transferred on the bus. This clock is not necessarily the same as the central processor clock. The clock frequency of a memory bus or an I/O bus is highly technology-dependent, and may range from 50 MHz up to 400 MHz.

An example of the timing diagram for an input operation on a synchronous bus is shown in Figure 11.16. A common clock signal divides the time axis into equally spaced time intervals. The timing information for every device is based on this common clock. As a convention, all signals involved in the operation may change states only at the rising edge of the clock and remain active for some integral number of clock cycles. At time t_0, the processor, acting as a bus master, sends the address of an input port and a Read command to an interface circuit. These signals suffer from both propagation delay and bus skew (i.e., different propagation delays on different lines of the bus). So, only after an expected delay, the interface receives the address and the Read command from the bus. The interface decodes the address received and loads the command into its command register. This triggers the input device to perform the specified input operation. Assume that the input data is available by time t_1. Therefore, at time t_1, the interface can load the input data into its data register and send an active-low signal $\overline{Acknowledge}$ back to the processor. It is expected that the processor will finish reading the data before time t_2. At time t_2, the interface removes the data from its input register and withdraws the $\overline{Acknowledge}$ signal. At this moment, the Read operation has been completed and, if necessary, the processor can start a new I/O operation at the rising edge of the next clock cycle. A similar timing diagram for an output operation can be drawn. The difference is that the output data comes from the processor, and the interface circuit asserts the $\overline{Acknowledge}$ signal after it strobes the data into its output register.

The synchronous bus protocol requires that the successive steps of an I/O operation be completed in limited and prescheduled time durations. For example, in Figure 11.16, the interface requires that the input data arrive within two clock cycles after receiving the Read command from the processor, the interface's data register keeps the valid input data and the $\overline{Acknowledge}$ signal for one clock cycle, and so on. All of these rigid, prescheduled time limits must be carefully determined for a wide range of input devices, or based on these time limits, the

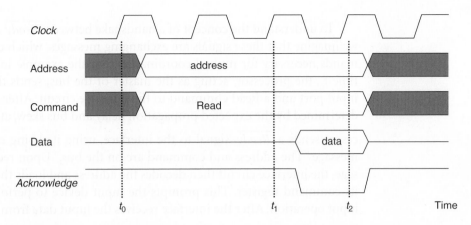

Figure 11.16   Timing diagram of an input operation on a synchronous bus

clock frequency should be carefully determined. Therefore, a synchronous bus is more suitable for high-speed I/O devices than for low-speed I/O devices.

2. Asynchronous Bus

The asynchronous bus is based on a different principle from that of the synchronous bus. It does not require a common clock. It utilizes a handshake mechanism between two special active-low signals to achieve synchronization. One of them is denoted as $\overline{Ready}$, which is always generated by the master of the bus, and the other one is denoted as $\overline{Acknowledge}$, by which the slave of the bus responds to the bus master. Sometimes, $\overline{Ready}$ and $\overline{Acknowledge}$ are referred to as "master-ready" and "slave-ready," respectively. An example of the timing diagram for an input operation on an asynchronous bus is shown in Figure 11.17.

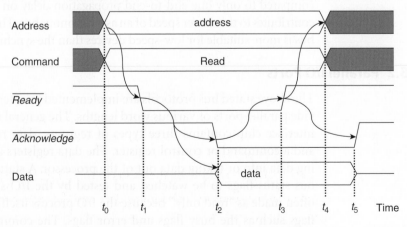

Figure 11.17   Timing diagram of an input operation on an asynchronous bus

To understand the concept of a handshake between $\overline{Ready}$ and $\overline{Acknowledge}$, we imagine that these signals are exchanging messages, which contain the commands necessary for mutual coordination. For the example in Figure 11.14, at time t_0, the processor, acting as the master of the bus, sends the address of an input port and a Read command to the interface circuit. After some time delay determined by the expected propagation delay and bus skew, at time t_1, the processor sends a $\overline{Ready}$ signal to the interface, using its rising edge to carry the message "The address and command are on the bus." Upon receiving this message, the interface circuit then decodes the address and loads the command into its command register. This prompts the input device to perform the specified input operation. After the interface receives the input data from the input device and loads the data into its data register, at time t_2, it sends an $\overline{Acknowledge}$ signal back to the processor, using its rising edge to carry the message "The input operation is done. Data is on the bus." After the processor receives this message and reads the data from the bus into the memory, at time t_3, it withdraws its $\overline{Ready}$ signal. Hence, the falling edge of the $\overline{Ready}$ signal carries the message "I am done with the entire operation." So, the processor withdraws the address and command from the bus at time t_4. After receiving this closing message, the interface withdraws the $\overline{Acknowledge}$ signal at time t_5, and this marks the completion of the full handshake procedure.

The main advantage of the asynchronous bus is that the handshake mechanism eliminates the need for a common clock and thus provides great flexibility for designing the timing schedule of the I/O activities on the bus. The handshake self-adjusts the timing relationship in order to compensate for the delays introduced by the interface circuit, the devices, and the bus lines. However, the data transfer on an asynchronous bus requires two round-trip delays of handshaking signals, as compared to only one end-to-end propagation delay on a synchronous bus. This contributes to the slower speed of an asynchronous bus. Therefore, an asynchronous bus is more suitable for low-speed devices than the synchronous bus.

11.5.2 Parallel I/O Ports

The above stated bus protocols are implemented by interface circuits, which provide parallel ports of various word lengths. The general structure of a peripheral interface chip contains three types of registers: data registers, status registers, and a command or control register. The data registers are responsible for passing data into or taking data out of the processor. A status register contains various status flags to be watched and tested by the I/O software. This register is often made as "read only," because the I/O process itself automatically generates flags such as the busy flags and error flags. The command or control register specifies the type of operation of the I/O chip with the bit pattern to be set up by application or system initialization software. In a sense, the command or control register is made by the hardware as "write only." Peripheral interface chips are usually designed as programmable for general-purpose use. The data ports can be reconfigured as input or output. The command or control register can be used to specify different modes of operation, and so on.

Specifically, let us consider an example of the Intel 82C55A, a Programmable Peripheral Interface (PPI) (Williams 2001; Stallings 2003). The Intel 82C55A is a general-purpose I/O interface chip designed for use with the Intel 80x86 family of processors. Its block diagram is shown in Figure 11.18. The I/O devices can be connected via the ports depicted on the right-hand side of the internal bus, referred to as the external interface. This chip provides three byte-wide bidirectional parallel ports, namely A, B, and C. Each of them can be configured as an input port or an output port by the control logic on the chip. The three ports can operate simultaneously under differing modes of activity.

Mode 0: basic byte-wide input and output ports built on three groups of external lines
Mode 1: bytes passed by strobed (asynchronous) handshake
Mode 2: tri-state bus action

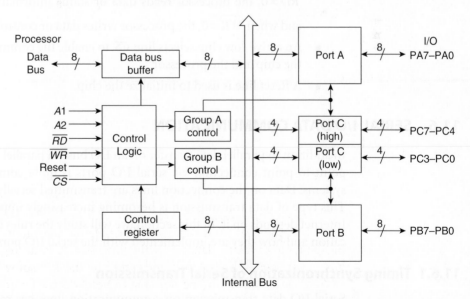

Figure 11.18 Block diagram of Intel 82C55A programmable peripheral interface

The control logic can also configure the 24 lines associated with ports A, B, and C into two groups by splitting the eight lines of port C into two halves so that the higher-order half of port C is combined with port A to form a control group A, and the lower-order half of port C is combined with port B to form a control group B. Then, both control groups will each have eight data lines on port A or B and four control lines on port C. These control lines can be used for handshaking, interrupt request, and other application-related control purposes. The functional configuration of each port is programmed by the system software, which allows the CPU to send a control word to the 82C55A chip. The control word contains information such as "operation mode," "bit set," "bit reset," and so on. Each of the control groups accepts a Read/Write command from the control logic and receives control words from the internal data bus to set up the configuration of the associated port.

The processor is connected via the internal interface, which is on the left-hand side of the internal bus depicted in Figure 11.18. This interface transfers data, address, and control signals as follows:

- An 8-bit data bus buffer is used to connect to the 8-bit bidirectional data bus of the processor.
- Two address lines $A1$ and $A0$ are used for the two least significant bits (LSBs) of the memory-mapped I/O addresses to port A (00), port B (01), port C (10), and control register (11).
- Two active-low command lines $\overline{RD}$ and $\overline{WR}$ acting as follows: when $\overline{RD} = 0$, the processor reads data or status information from the chip, and when $\overline{WR} = 0$, the processor writes data or control words to the chip.
- An active-low chip selects line $\overline{CS}$ to enable the communication between the chip and the processor.
- A Reset line is used to initialize the chip.

11.6   SERIAL I/O DATA COMMUNICATION

In addition to parallel data transfer on an I/O bus via parallel I/O ports, a simple point-to-point connection via serial I/O ports is quite common in computer systems. Data on the connection lines are transmitted serially, that is, bit by bit. This type of data transmission is becoming increasingly important because the Internet depends on it. In this section, we will study the rules of serial communication and how they are implemented with the serial I/O ports.

11.6.1 Timing Synchronization of Serial Transmission

Serial I/O data transmission on communication lines has many characteristics that make it quite different from parallel I/O data transfers on multi-line buses. The following five aspects attribute to the differences:

1. The logical connections between the transmitters and the receivers of serial transmission are usually described as communication paths through simple, point-to-point links. The hardware implementations of these links include twisted wires, coaxial cables, optical fibers, or wireless channels. Serial communication reduces the cost of cables and connectors, compared to parallel bus connections.

2. The multi-line bus suffers from mutual interferences and bus skew, so the distance of transmission that a fast parallel bus can function over is limited to a machine room or within a single building. Although serial transmission is not totally free of interferences, the distance of transmission is practically unlimited on a network of distributed nodes and point-to-point communication links.

3. The data format for serial transmission is more complicated than simple data types. Message passing is the common form of serial transmission, and this requires the use of different schemes for data packaging. Transmission of data packets on a network requires routing and flow control.

4. Serial transmission over a long distance is error prone. Therefore, error handling, which can be implemented by using specific error detection codes or error detection and correction codes, is necessary.

5. Timing synchronization is still the major issue of serial communication. Synchronization based on a common clock on a serial transmission medium is more complicated than the synchronization on a synchronous bus.

With regard to timing synchronization, serial communication can be accomplished in one of two modes: synchronous or asynchronous. We will first look at synchronous communication. Synchronous communication is based on a common clock transmitted along with the data. This clock is used to generate and sample the data at fixed time intervals as accurately as possible. Such a fixed time interval of sampling is determined by the frequency of the clock, called the *transfer rate* measured in bps (bits per second), or referred to as the *baud rate*. An example of synchronous serial transmission is shown in Figure 11.19. The transmitter generates each bit of the data at the rising edge of the *transmitter clock*, and the receiver samples the data in the middle of each bit at the falling edge of the *receiver clock*, that is, half a clock period later. If the receiver clock is in full synchronization with the transmitter clock, the message received will be completely correct. Every falling edge of the clock coincides with the middle line of a data bit. However, if the receiver clock has a frequency slightly different from the frequency of the transmitter clock, the received data will be incorrect. For the example in the figure, since the frequency of the receiver clock is one-thirteenth lower than that of the transmitter clock, the falling edges of a receiver clock will gradually be delayed until they fall out of the correct data bit (see the seventh clock cycle). In general, the maximum allowance of the variation of

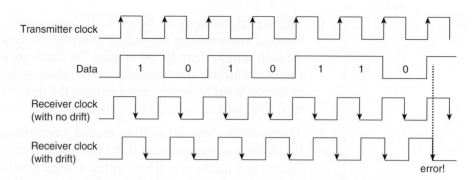

Figure 11.19   An example of synchronous serial communication

the sampling time interval equals one half of the period of the receiver clock. This slight change in the frequency of the system clock is called the *clock drift*. The amount of the clock drift depends on the technology of the crystal oscillator used in a computer. The clock drift of the crystal oscillator typically equals ±0.002%, that is, 20 parts per million (ppm). The clock drift causes the sampling point to hover dangerously over a transition of data bits. To avoid this, the receiver must regularly resynchronize at the bit level. Furthermore, the receiver should have some means to sample the center of the incoming bits and know the width of the bits and their starting points. This requires the receiver to know both the frequency and the phase of the data stream.

Asynchronous communication does not use a common clock. So, it does not send a clock signal along with the data. Instead, it inserts a *Start bit* in front of each transmitted byte and appends a parity bit and a *Stop bit* with each ASCII character so that each character is dealt with as an independent transmission. The Start and Stop bits are the pseudo-clock pulses used for character-by-character synchronization. Asynchronous transmission requires setting the line speed manually before the session begins. The receiver has to detect the onset of the Start bit for getting the phase information. A serial data link standard known as RS-232 has been established. An example of representing the ASCII code for a character "1" for an RS-232 transmission is shown in Figure 11.20, where the entire bit sequence composed of a Start bit, a 7-bit ASCII code "0110001," an odd parity bit "0", and a Stop bit is transmitted using −9V (called Mark) as "1" and +9V (called Space) as "0". More detailed information about RS-232 will be given in Section 11.6.3.

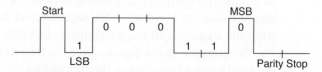

Figure 11.20   Representing ASCII "1" in RS-232

11.6.2 Error Detection and Correction Codes

Serial communication transmits a large amount of data over a long distance in different environments so error detection techniques are commonly used for protecting message transmission from accidental errors. Main memory, secondary storage, and I/O devices which handle large volumes of data are also prone to reading, writing, and transmission errors. The basic idea of protecting data from errors is to use so-called *data redundancy*, that is, to add some redundant (extra) bits to the normal data codes so that when any expected error occurs, the erroneous data would be detected as illegal. In the extreme case, data redundancy can be even made to make multiple (at least, two) redundant copies of the entire data package, transmit them together with the original copy under the same condition, and then compare all the received copies to detect any discrepancy. This method is simple to help understand the meaning of redundancy, but is too costly to be used in ordinary cases. Other methods are based on designing special data codes containing redundant bits for error detection, plus error correction in some cases (Forouzan 2001; Williams 2001).

1. *Parity Check*

The simplest method of inserting redundant bits for error detection is to insert a parity bit to every ASCII character code for protecting serial transmission involving ASCII-coded texts, as we have stated in Section 3.3.3. Also, Figure 11.20 gives an example of inserting an odd-parity bit "0" in the ASCII code of character "1". Adding a single parity bit to a 7-bit ASCII code doubles the size of the code set from 128 to 256, but renders half of the possible binary code patterns illegal. So, when any single-bit error occurs in a character, the resultant code must be in the set of illegal codes and thus can be detected automatically. The parity bit technique is applicable to any length of ASCII-coded text data. It requires parity-bit insertion to every character code prior to transmission, followed by parity checking on reception. This implementation is usually included in all serial transmission devices, normally using the XOR function for comparing parity, as we can see in Section 3.3.3.

To enhance the capability of the parity checking method, we can use it in a two-dimensional data structure, in which the data in both directions, vertical and horizontal, are protected by parity check bits. An example of the use of this method is the magnetic tape unit which stores a data record in a serial-parallel fashion. In other words, it stores each 8-bit character including a parity bit in each row, and records all the successive characters in contiguous rows, thus forming eight columns of bit strings. In each column, we add a parity check bit to the bit string for protecting the individual bits of the characters. Therefore, a redundant row of parity bits for all the columns is added to the entire data record. This data organization generates a two-dimensional parity check: the parity check in the vertical direction (row) is called a *vertical redundancy check* (VRC), and the parity check in the longitudinal direction (column) is called a *longitudinal redundancy check* (LRC). When any single-bit error occurs in a character, it can be detected by both VRC and LRC, the intersection of which can then allocate the exact position of the erroneous bit. More importantly, the LRC increases the likelihood of detecting burst errors. All the burst errors concerning an odd number of bits in the same column can be readily detected by the LRC, as we can see in Example 11.3.

Example 11.3 Parity Check in Two Dimensions

Given a data packet "Hello, World!", demonstrate the VRC and LRC methods.

1. *Transmission*

H	e	l	l	o	,	W	o	r	l	d	!	
48	65	6C	6C	6F	2C	57	6F	72	6C	64	21	— 7-bit ASCII
48	65	6C	6C	6F	AC	D7	6F	72	6C	E4	21	— even-parity ASCII

Two-dimensional data layout:

						LRC						
VRC 0	0	0	0	0	1	1	0	0	0	1	0	1
1	1	1	1	1	0	1	1	1	1	1	0	0
0	1	1	1	1	1	0	1	1	1	1	1	0
0	0	0	0	0	0	1	0	1	0	0	0	0
1	0	1	1	1	1	0	1	0	1	0	0	1
0	1	1	1	1	1	1	1	0	1	1	0	1
0	0	0	0	1	0	1	1	1	0	0	0	0
0	1	0	0	1	0	1	1	0	0	0	1	1

2. *Reception with error*

All erroneous bits are indicated by bold-face letters.

"H" changes from 48 to 59—a double-bit error, undetectable by VRC.

"e" changes from 65 to 61—a single-bit error, detectable by VRC.

"l" changes from 6C to 7C—a single-bit error detectable by VRC.

A double-bit error in the fourth column, undetectable by LRC.

A single-bit error in the sixth column, detectable by LRC.

A single-bit error in the eighth column, detectable by LRC.

Only the single-bit error in "e" can be located by VRC in the second row and LRC in the sixth column.

Although the double-bit error in the first row cannot be detected by VRC, it can be detected by LRC.

Two-dimensional data layout:

						LRC						
VRC 0	0	0	0	0	1	1	0	0	0	1	0	1
1	1	1	1	1	0	1	1	1	1	1	0	0
0	1	1	1	1	1	0	1	1	1	1	1	0
1	0	1	0	0	0	1	0	1	0	0	0	0
1	0	1	1	1	1	0	1	0	1	0	0	1
0	0	1	1	1	1	1	1	0	1	1	0	1
0	0	0	0	1	0	1	1	1	0	0	0	0
1	1	0	0	1	0	1	1	0	0	0	1	1

∎

For the protection of any length of general binary data, we have other methods of insertion of redundant bits. Three methods will be studied in the following section. The Hamming code is mostly used in main memory protection, whereas the other two methods—block checksum and cyclic redundancy code (CRC)— are used in I/O data transfer and serial communication.

2. Hamming Code

Hamming code is more powerful than the simple parity-bit method. A single parity bit added to a bit string can only guard against a single-bit error (strictly speaking, an odd number of errors), but Hamming code can detect a double-bit error and correct a single-bit error in the binary code of a word of any designed length. Hamming code is thus called *single error correction/double error detection (SEC/DED)* code. To explain the principle of Hamming code, we will first give an example of 4 data bits inserted with 3 check bits (also called parity bits) in order to see how many redundant check bits are required and how they can identify the exact position of the single erroneous bit in the word. We add first 3 check bits, p_4, p_2, and p_1, to a 4-bit data word $d_4 d_3 d_2 d_1$. The check bits are created by the following formulae:

$$p_4 = d_4 \oplus d_3 \oplus d_2$$
$$p_2 = d_4 \oplus d_3 \oplus d_1 \qquad\qquad (11.5)$$
$$p_1 = d_4 \oplus d_2 \oplus d_1$$

This relationship can be illustrated by a Venn diagram consisting of three intersecting circles, containing seven compartments as shown in Figure 11.21. Each circle p_i, for $i = 4, 2, 1$, contains three compartments of the data bits d_j that appear on the right-hand side of the corresponding equation in Expression (11.5). For example, the circle p_4 contains the compartments of d_4, d_3, and d_2; the circle p_2 contains the compartments of d_4, d_3, and d_1; the circle p_1 contains the compartments of d_4, d_2, and d_1. Now by checking Expression (11.5) we can see an interesting result: if any single data bit from d_4 to d_1 makes an error, the equations with the erroneous bit on their right-hand sides will no longer hold. The following results will help detect the erroneous bit:

If d_1 is wrong, the equations for p_2 and p_1 will not hold.
If d_2 is wrong, the equations for p_4 and p_1 will not hold.
If d_3 is wrong, the equations for p_4 and p_2 will not hold.
If d_4 is wrong, all the equations for p_4, p_2, and p_1 will not hold.

Therefore, we can use 3 check bits to detect a single-bit error among the 4 data bits.

Next, for implementation of the above-stated principle, we should find an elegant scheme of arranging the order of placement of the data bits and the check bits to form a Hamming code, denoted as $c_7 c_6 c_5 c_4 c_3 c_2 c_1$. The rule of bit positioning for forming a Hamming code is as follows:

- Start numbering the bits of the Hamming code in the order 1, 2, 3, … from the least significant bit c_1.
- Number the check bits in powers of 2 as p_1, p_2, p_4, p_8, p_{16}, … from right to left.
- Allocate all the bit positions of the Hamming code, which are powers of 2, to the check bits, that is, place p_1 to c_1, p_2 to c_2, p_4 to c_4, p_8 to c_8, and so on.
- The remaining bit positions are used for allocating the data bits in the same order as given, that is, place d_1 to c_3, d_2 to c_5, d_3 to c_6, d_4 to c_7, and so on.

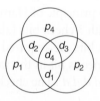

Figure 11.21   Venn diagram showing a 7-bit Hamming code

Therefore, for the example of 4 data bits, the Hamming code will have the following order of arrangement:

$$(c_7 \, c_6 \, c_5 \, c_4 \, c_3 \, c_2 \, c_1) = (d_4 \, d_3 \, d_2 \, p_4 \, d_1 \, p_2 \, p_1)$$

Now, we will find a method of identifying the exact position of the erroneous bit for easy implementation in a computer. We define a *syndrome* by a vector-matrix multiplication, as shown in Figure 11.22 for 4 data bits and 3 check bits, in which an add operation is changed to XOR. It can be seen from the figure that the syndrome just calculates Expression (11.5) in a different, but equivalent form. Therefore, we can use the syndrome for calculating the check bits for a given word before transmission, and check the received Hamming code to identify the location of the erroneous bit, if any. The algorithm of calculation for a 4-bit word is as follows:

- Given a word $D = d_4 d_3 d_2 d_1$. Calculate the syndrome by substituting all the check bits c_4, c_2, and c_1 with zeros. The result will be the values of $[c_4 \, c_2 \, c_1]$. Insert these values into the given data word to form a Hamming code before transmission.

- After reception of the Hamming code, use it to calculate the syndrome. If the result is $[0\,0\,0]$, the transmission is correct, otherwise the result points out the number of the erroneous bit, provided that only a single-bit error has occurred, irrespective of whether it is on a data bit or a check bit.

The above-stated algorithm can be demonstrated on an example of a given number $D = 1001$, as shown in Figure 11.23. Part (a) shows the first step of the algorithm that generates the check bits [100]. Part (b) shows the second step of the algorithm for checking the received Hamming code. The zero result of the syndrome verifies the correct transmission. Each of parts (c) and (d) has a single-bit error, whose location with d_1 and p_1 can be identified by the values of the syndrome [011] and [001], respectively, irrespective of whether the error is at a data bit or a check bit. Part (e) has double erroneous bits with d_3 and d_2, and

Syndrome

$$= [d_4 \; d_3 \; d_2 \; c_4 \; d_1 \; c_2 \; c_1] \times \begin{vmatrix} 1 & 1 & 1 \\ 1 & 1 & 0 \\ 1 & 0 & 1 \\ 1 & 0 & 0 \\ 0 & 1 & 1 \\ 0 & 1 & 0 \\ 0 & 0 & 1 \end{vmatrix}$$

$$= [d_4 \oplus d_3 \oplus d_2 \oplus c_4 \quad d_4 \oplus d_3 \oplus d_1 \oplus c_2 \quad d_4 \oplus d_2 \oplus d_1 \oplus c_1]$$

Figure 11.22 Definition of a syndrome with 4 data bits and 3 parity bits

(a) Syndrome before transmission

$$= [1\,0\,0\,0\,1\,0\,0] \times \begin{vmatrix} 1 & 1 & 1 \\ 1 & 1 & 0 \\ 1 & 0 & 1 \\ 1 & 0 & 0 \\ 0 & 1 & 1 \\ 0 & 1 & 0 \\ 0 & 0 & 1 \end{vmatrix} = [1\,0\,0]$$

So, $c_4 = 1$, $c_2 = 0$, $c_1 = 0$.

(b) Syndrome after correct reception

$$= [1\,0\,0\,1\,1\,0\,0] \times \begin{vmatrix} 1 & 1 & 1 \\ 1 & 1 & 0 \\ 1 & 0 & 1 \\ 1 & 0 & 0 \\ 0 & 1 & 1 \\ 0 & 1 & 0 \\ 0 & 0 & 1 \end{vmatrix} = [0\,0\,0]$$

So, no error has occurred.

(c) Syndrome after reception with d_1 wrong

$$= [1\,0\,0\,1\,0\,0\,0] \times \begin{vmatrix} 1 & 1 & 1 \\ 1 & 1 & 0 \\ 1 & 0 & 1 \\ 1 & 0 & 0 \\ 0 & 1 & 1 \\ 0 & 1 & 0 \\ 0 & 0 & 1 \end{vmatrix} = [0\,1\,1]$$

So, error has occurred at bit 3 with d_1.

(d) Syndrome after reception with p_1 wrong

$$= [1\,0\,0\,1\,1\,0\,1] \times \begin{vmatrix} 1 & 1 & 1 \\ 1 & 1 & 0 \\ 1 & 0 & 1 \\ 1 & 0 & 0 \\ 0 & 1 & 1 \\ 0 & 1 & 0 \\ 0 & 0 & 1 \end{vmatrix} = [0\,0\,1]$$

So, error has occurred at bit 1 with p_1.

(e) Syndrome after reception with d_3 and d_2 wrong

$$= [1\,1\,1\,1\,1\,0\,0] \times \begin{vmatrix} 1 & 1 & 1 \\ 1 & 1 & 0 \\ 1 & 0 & 1 \\ 1 & 0 & 0 \\ 0 & 1 & 1 \\ 0 & 1 & 0 \\ 0 & 0 & 1 \end{vmatrix} = [0\,1\,1]$$

So, double-bit error makes confusion with (c).

Figure 11.23 Examples of Hamming code calculation and correction

the syndrome equals [011], which creates confusion with Part (c). So, it makes the single error correction questionable if we cannot detect a double-bit error to distinguish from it. A method of distinguishing double-bit error from single-bit error is to add an overall parity bit to the Hamming code at the most significant bit (MSB). Therefore, the SEC/DED code corresponding to 4 data bits should have a total length of 8 bits, and the rule of correcting a single-bit error is as follows:

- If the syndrome after reception equals zero and the overall parity checking is correct, no error has occurred.

- If the syndrome after reception is not zero and the overall parity checking is wrong, a single-bit error has occurred. If the syndrome has only one bit equal to "1", the erroneous bit is a check bit, otherwise it is a data bit. The value of the syndrome indicates its bit number.

- If the syndrome after reception is not zero and the overall parity checking is correct, there must be an error which is not a single-bit error. The Hamming code cannot correct it.

Now based on this example as a special case, we can generalize the method to any word length. At first, we derive an expression that determines the minimum number of check bits, n_c, necessary for forming a Hamming code for a given number of data bits, n_d. Since $n_c + n_d$ is the total length of the Hamming code, there must be enough number of check bits, n_c, such that the n_c-bit syndrome defined in Figure 11.23 can point out all single-bit errors in the Hamming code. That means, the following inequality must hold:

$$2^{n_c} - 1 \geq n_c + n_d \tag{11.6}$$

Calculation by this formula for n_c with different values of n_d gives the result of n_c in the second column of Table 11.1. Adding one more parity bit, the total number of redundant bits of an SEC/DED code equals $n_c + 1$, as listed in the third column of the table.

Once the number of check bits has been determined, all the formulae in Expression (11.5) can be generalized by expanding the matrix size in Figure 11.22 to $n_c \times (2^{n_c} - 1)$ and multiplying it to a vector of $n_c + n_d$ bits.

As a conclusion, we can introduce the concept of the *Hamming distance* defined as the "distance" between valid code numbers. For example, the simple even or odd parity code enjoys a Hamming distance of 2 because changing a single bit will result in an illegal value, while changing 2 bits will deliver a neighboring valid code. That explains why simple parity code can detect only a single-bit

Table 11.1 Determining the Hamming code length relative to the length of data bits

Data Bits	Hamming Code without an Overall Parity Bit	SEC/DED Code with an Overall Parity Bit
	No. of Check Bits	No. of Redundant Bits
4	3 (4–1 < 7)	4
8	4 (8–1 < 12)	5
16	5 (16–1 < 21)	6
32	6 (32–1 < 38)	7
64	7 (64–1 < 71)	8
128	8 (128–1 < 136)	9
256	9 (256–1 < 265)	10

error, but cannot detect any error when 2 bits are wrong at the same time. For the above example of 7-bit Hamming code, we can look at all the legal Hamming codes and their corresponding data codes as listed below:

0000000, 0000111, 0011001, 0011110 for 0000, 0001, 0010, 0011, respectively,
0101010, 0101101, 0110011, 0110100 for 0100, 0101, 0110, 0111, respectively,
1001011, 1001100, 1010010, 1010101 for 1000, 1001, 1010, 1011, respectively,
1100001, 1100110, 1111000, 1111111 for 1100, 1101, 1110, 1111, respectively.

We obtain Hamming distance equal to 3 because changing any 2 bits of the Hamming code will result in an illegal value, while changing 3 bits will deliver a neighboring valid code. Moreover, adding an overall parity check bit does not increase the Hamming distance because changing 3 bits does not change the odd/even parity. This analysis explains why Hamming code can detect single bit and double-bit errors, but cannot distinguish between them. It also explains why Hamming code cannot detect any error when three bits are wrong at the same time. Using the concept of Hamming code we can summarize a general principle of error detection—to dig a wide Hamming ditch (distance) around each valid code into which the errors will fall.

3. Block Checksum

The method of *block checksum* is a direct development of the concept of LRC stated in Section 11.6.2.1. It is similar to the LRC by using the concept of redundancy, but processes the data in a global view rather than in viewing individual columns, and changes the XOR operation in the LRC to some kind of add operation. The process is also divided into two parts: checksum generation on the transmitter side and the checksum checking on the receiver side.

The transmitter performs the following steps:

- Divide the data packet into k sections of n bits, where n is determined by the length of the checksum. If the checksum is limited to a single byte value, then $n = 8$.

- Add all the sections of data in the packet. Truncate the resulting sum to less than 256 by neglecting the carry-out signals or truncating the MSBs above 8 bits.

- Invert the checksum and attach it to the data for transmission.

The receiver performs the following steps:

- Add up the data in k sections plus the checksum as they arrive. Truncate the resulting sum to less than 256 in the same way as on the side of the transmitter.

- Invert the value of the above-obtained truncated resulting sum. If zero, the data packet is accepted, else it is rejected.

Example 11.4 Checksum Generation and Checking

Given a data packet "Hello, World!", demonstrate the above-stated algorithms.

1. *Transmission*

   Divide each byte into two nibbles.

   Each byte is split into two nibbles, which are then converted to hex digits (0–F), as shown below:

H	e	l	l	o	,	W	o	r	l	d	!	
48	65	6C	6C	6F	2C	57	6F	72	6C	64	21	— 7-bit ASCII
48	65	6C	6C	6F	AC	D7	6F	72	6C	E4	21	— even-parity ASCII

   Sum up the above 8-bit ASCII character string: 5C9

   Neglect the MSD "5", invert C9, checksum = 36

   Transmit 48   65   6C   6C   6F   AC   D7   6F   72   6C   E4   21   36

2. *Reception without error*

   Sum up the above packet including the checksum: 5C9 + 36 = 5FF

   Neglect the MSD "5", invert FF, result = 00. The data packet is accepted.

3. *Reception with error*

   Suppose a burst error has corrupted "Hel" to "59 61 7C".

   Sum up the corrupted data plus the checksum: 5E6 + 36 = 61C

   Neglect the MSD "6", invert 1C, result = E3. The data packet is rejected. ■

4. Cyclic Redundancy Check (CRC)

The fourth and most powerful redundancy checking method is the *cyclic redundancy check* (CRC). CRC is a sequence of redundant bits generated as the remainder of the binary division of a data block by a predetermined binary divisor. This remainder is appended to the end of the original data block so that the resulting data block with the attached CRC becomes exactly divisible by the same divisor. To attain this purpose, the CRC must have exactly one less bit than the divisor. If the divisor has k bits, then the CRC must have $k - 1$ bits. Before division, $k - 1$ zero bits should be appended to the end of the data block for generation of the CRC. Then, after division, the CRC just replaces these appended zero bits, so that the resulting data block with the attached CRC can be used for transmission. At the destination, the received data packet with the attached CRC will be tested by doing the same binary division by the same divisor. If the remainder is zero, the packet is accepted, otherwise, it is rejected.

Three problems should be discussed for understanding the CRC:

- The principle of binary division for CRC generation and CRC checking.
- The choice of the divisor.
- The hardware implementation of CRC generation and CRC checking.

We will study these problems in the above sequence, and, at first, give an example to explain the principle of binary division for CRC generation and CRC checking.

The binary arithmetic including binary addition, subtraction, multiplication, and division is based on the *modulo-2 arithmetic*, which performs explicit and implicit binary addition/subtraction with no carries. From Section 3.3.3, we know that the basic logic operation in a half adder is the XOR for performing addition with no carries. So, in binary multiplication, the partial products are summed up through XOR operations, and in binary division, the partial remainders are generated through XOR operations, too. An example of binary division for generation of the CRC is given in Figure 11.24. The algorithm for the CRC generation through binary division is as follows:

- The dividend, D, is composed of the given data block, for example, 11110010011001, appended by $n - 1$ zero bits, where n is the length of the divisor, for example, 11011 in Figure 11.24 has $n = 5$.

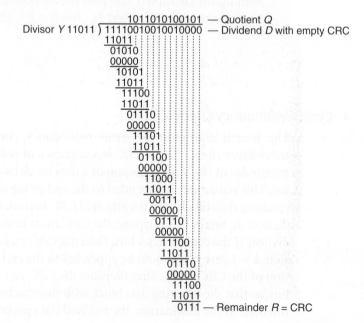

Figure 11.24 An example of binary division $D \div Y$ for CRC generation

- Apply the subtract-shift algorithm similar to ordinary (manual) division in many iterations until all the bits of the dividend have been exhausted. To start the iteration, subtract the divisor from the dividend and get the first partial remainder.

- In each iteration, when the partial remainder has a leading bit "1", the new quotient bit is "1" and the divisor is subtracted from the partial remainder; when the new partial remainder has a leading bit "0", the new quotient bit is "0" and a zero divisor is subtracted from the partial remainder.

- Perform the subtract operation as a bit-wise XOR operation. Just compare each pair of bits, if the two bits are the same, the corresponding bit of the partial remainder is "0", otherwise, if the two bits are different, the corresponding bit of the partial remainder is "1".

The result of binary division can be checked by binary multiplication based on the formula

$$\text{if } \frac{D}{Y} = Q + \frac{R}{Y}, \quad \text{then } D = Q \times Y + R \tag{11.7}$$

where $Q \times Y$ is a binary multiplication with the add operations replaced by XOR operations, as shown in Figure 11.25 for the example in Figure 11.24. The underlined bits are the CRC included in the dividend D.

Next, we will continue the example for CRC checking. If the transmission of the data block with the attached CRC has no error, repeating the binary division by the same divisor should result in a zero remainder, as verified in Figure 11.26. Suppose a double-bit error or a triple-bit error has occurred in transmission, as indicated by the underlined bits in Figure 11.27, then the binary division for CRC checking should give a nonzero remainder. This result has been verified in Figure 11.27.

Now, we will look at the problem of choosing the divisor. Most frequently, the divisor is represented in terms of algebraic polynomials. The polynomial form has a fixed association with the binary form, but is more concise and can best be used for proving the concept of CRC mathematically. We will avoid delving into the details of this problem, but provide some general conclusions.

```
Quotient Q:  1011010100101
   Divisor Y:           11011  (binary multiply
              1011010100101
             1011010100101
            1011010100101
           1011010100101        (XOR
           11110010010010111
           Dividend D with CRC
```

Figure 11.25 Check the result by binary multiplication $Q \times Y$

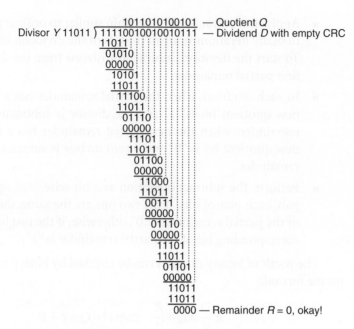

Figure 11.26   An example of binary division $D \div Y$ for CRC checking

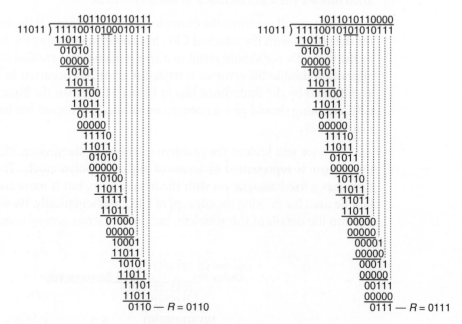

Figure 11.27   Examples of checking a double-bit error and a triple-bit error by CRC

To represent a k-bit binary pattern of the divisor in a polynomial form, we express each "1" bit of the pattern as a term X^i of the polynomial, where X is a dummy variable and i is the bit number lying between $k - 1$ for the MSB and 0 for the LSB. For example, the divisor, "11011", chosen in Figure 11.26 is represented as $X^4 + X^3 + X + 1$. The choice of the divisor for CRC has a great impact on its error detection capability. For example, a polynomial should be selected to have at least the following properties:

- It should not be divisible by X (binary 10). For example, X (binary 10), $X^2 + X$ (binary 110), $X^3 + X^2$ (binary 1100) are not eligible for selection because $110 = 11 \times 10$ and $1100 = 110 \times 10$.

- It should be divisible by $X + 1$ (binary 11). For example, $X + 1$, $X^2 + 1$ (binary 101), and $X^3 + 1$ (binary 1001) are eligible selections, because $101 = 11 \times 11$ and $1001 = 11 \times 111$. The divisor selected for our examples is also divisible by $X + 1$ because $11011 = 11 \times 11 \times 111$.

The first condition is necessary for detecting all burst errors of a length equal to the degree of the polynomial. The second condition is necessary for detecting all burst errors affecting an odd number of bits.

The following standard polynomials are used by popular protocols for CRC generation:

- **CRC-12:**
$X^{12} + X^{11} + X^3 + X^2 + X + 1$

- **CRC-16:**
$X^{16} + X^{15} + X^2 + 1$

- **CRC-CCITT:**
$X^{16} + X^{12} + X^5 + 1$

- **CRC-32:**
$X^{32} + X^{26} + X^{23} + X^{22} + X^{16} + X^{12} + X^{11} + X^{10} + X^8 + X^7 + X^5 + X^4 + X^2 + X + 1$

We are trying to check if these polynomials satisfy the above-stated two necessary conditions. All of them obviously satisfy the first condition, but CRC-32 does not satisfy the second condition.

- For CRC-12, $1100000001111 = 100000000101 \times 11$
- For CRC-16, $11000000000000101 = 1000000000000011 \times 11$
- For CRC-CCITT, $10001000000100001 = 111000000011111 \times 11$
- For CRC-32, $100000100110000010001110110110111$ is not divisible by 11, and gives a remainder, 01. It seems to be an exception.

Each of these CRC systems generates a 12-, 16-, or 32-bit CRC code, using a 13-, 16-, or 33-bit divisor. It can detect all burst errors affecting an odd number of bits, detect all burst errors of length not exceeding the degree of the polynomial, and detect with a very high probability burst errors of length greater than the degree of the polynomial.

Finally, we can now look at the hardware implementation of the CRC generator and the CRC checker. Having chosen a suitable polynomial for the divisor, we can construct a special shift register for implementation of binary division by that divisor. A circuit with our divisor $X^4 + X^3 + X + 1$ (binary 11011) implied in it is shown in Figure 11.28. It has four stages with one flip-flop per stage, since the length of our CRC code equals 4 bits, 1 bit less than our 5-bit divisor. All the terms appearing in the polynomial, except the MSB X^4, have their corresponding flip-flops receive inputs through XOR gates. Since the term X^2 is missing in the polynomial, its corresponding flip-flop, C_2, does not need an XOR gate on its input. In the figure, as the circuit is designed as a general-purpose binary divider, the flip-flop C_2 still has an XOR gate, but one of its inputs is connected to ground so as to eliminate the XOR operation. Each XOR gate participates in the binary division by performing an XOR operation between the data fed back from the last stage of the flip-flop, C_3, and the data shifted in from its right neighbor. The LSB of the shift register has no right neighbor, so it receives data from the serial input of the dividend with its MSB going first. All the flip-flops are connected to a common clock, performing an unordinary left shift operation. The number of shifts equals the number of bits of the dividend. The shift register is initialized to 0; it then shifts the input dividend into the shift register until its LSB has passed the input XOR gate and is stored in flip-flop C_0. The result obtained in the shift register should be the remainder of the binary division.

Then, we can see how the circuit in Figure 11.28 can be used as a CRC generator and a CRC checker. Using the same input data packet as in Figure 11.24 for CRC generation, the step-by-step results of the shift operations are shown in Figure 11.29. The rightmost column is the input data packet with empty CRC. Starting from the MSB, each bit of the input dividend is shifted into flip-flop C_0 through an XOR gate, and every flip-flop performs a left shift operation at the same time. Whenever the flip-flop C_3 gets a bit of value "1", the input XOR

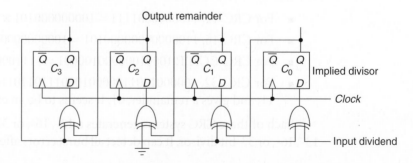

Figure 11.28   Circuit for binary division by an implicit divisor $X^4 + X^3 + X + 1$

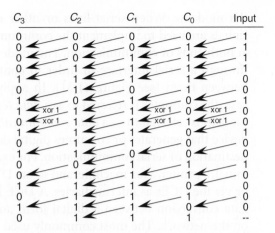

Figure 11.29 Hardware CRC generation using the same dividend as in Figure 11.24

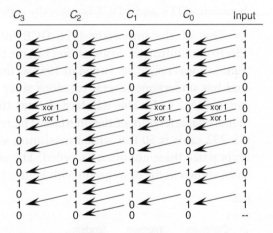

Figure 11.30 Hardware CRC checking using the same dividend as in Figure 11.26

gates on the flip-flops C_3, C_1, and C_0 will take effect and invert the input data, as indicated by the arrows labeled by "xor 1." After 17 shift operations, the code in the shift register becomes 0111, just equal to the CRC code of 0111 as we have found before by manual calculation in Figure 11.24. Similarly, if we input the dividend equal to the same data packet with the appended CRC as in Figure 11.24, then the circuit in Figure 11.28 works as a CRC checker. The work chart shown in Figure 11.30 shows that the output of the shift register equals zero, proving the correctness of the received data packet.

11.6.3 Serial Interfaces and I/O Ports

Serial interfaces are used in two ways—for performing serial communications between computers and for connecting serial peripherals to the computer. Serial communications are usually done across point-to-point links through the modems. When serial lines or other communication media with analog signals are used to implement the communication links, modems are necessary at both ends of communication. The modem is connected to its host computer through a serial interface in order to control the asynchronous data transfer between them (see Figure 11.31). In applying a general terminology for this case, the computer is referred to as a *data terminating equipment* (DTE), and the modem is referred to as a *data communication equipment* (DCE). A DTE is any device that generates or consumes digital data and serves as either a source or a destination of serial communication. For example, DTE can be a computer, a terminal, a printer, a fax machine, and so on. DTEs can communicate either directly or via the DCEs as intermediaries. A DCE is any functional unit that performs data conversion between a digital form and a form suitable for transmission on the network. The most commonly used DCEs are the modems (modulator/demodulators) that modulates digital signals for transmission and demodulates the received signals for digital display or storage. Therefore, the serial interface between a DTE and a DCE is generally called the DTE-DCE interface.

One of the important DTE-DCE interface standards developed by the Electronic Industries Association (EIA) is the EIA-232 (Forouzan 2001; Triebel 1986). It was originally issued in 1962 as the RS-232 standard (Recommended), and has undergone several revisions since then, with the most recent version being EIA-232-D. The standard defines the mechanical, electrical, and functional characteristics of the interface. The recommended maximum length of an RS-232 cable is 50 feet with a maximum signaling rate of 20 KB/sec, although in practice these are often exceeded. The electrical specification of RS-232 has been shown in the description with Figure 11.21. All data must be transmitted as

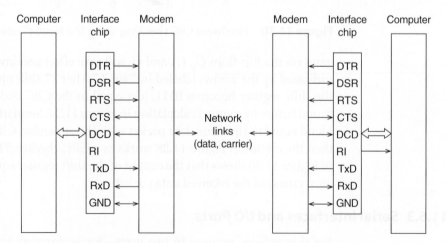

Figure 11.31   Data transfer between two computers via two modems by RS-232-C

logic "1"s and "0"'s (called Mark and Space, respectively) using NRZ-L encoding (that means "nonreturn to zero level"—a type of *polar encoding* that uses two voltage levels: one positive and one negative). To be recognized as data, signal "1" must fall between 3 and 15 volts, and signal "0" must fall between −3 and −15 volts. As long as the valid signals fall within two 12-volt ranges, the precision of the pulses is immaterial.

Two different implementations of EIA-232 are available: DB-25 and DB-9, defining the interface on 25-pin and 9-pin connectors, respectively. Each pin is attached to a single wire on which data is transferred or a specific control signal is sent. However, the original 25-pin connector was often only active on three pins. This is the case in which we connect two computers directly without using modems or connect a peripheral device to a computer (see Figure 11.32). Only a "Transmit Data" line, a "Receive Data" line, and a common "Ground" may be necessary. Many of the other pins in the DB-25 implementation are not necessary on a single asynchronous connection. Therefore, a new implementation known as DB-9 was developed as a simpler 9-pin version of EIA-232. A typical application of RS-232-C (DB-9) standard is to establish the serial ports in IBM-compatible personal computers. Unlike the RS-232-C, Apple's Macintosh computers follow the RS-422 standard for their serial ports.

RS-232-C (DB-9) defines nine lines as follows:

- Three data lines:
  out: Transmit Data (TxD)
  in: Receive Data (RxD)
  … Ground

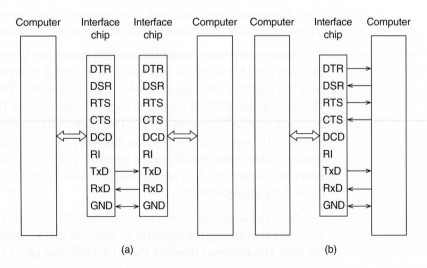

(a)　　　　　　　　　　　(b)

Figure 11.32　Two special cases of using RS-232-C interfaces

- Four control lines:
  out: Request to Send (RTS)
  in: Clear to Send (CTS)
  out: Data Terminal Ready (DTR)
  in: Data Set Ready (DSR)
- Two signal sensing lines:
  out: Ring Indicator
  in: Data Carrier Detect (DCD)

In this standard, some lines defined in the DB-25 implementation are either omitted or replaced by the status bits in the status register of the interface.

Now, we will look at the complete procedure of using RS-232-C (DB-9) for data communication between two computers (DTEs) via two modems (DCEs). The signals used are shown in Figure 11.31 for a case of transmitting data from the left-side computer to the right-side computer. In the beginning, when the computers and modems on both sides are powered on, the computers set the "Data Terminal Ready" (DTR) to "1" and the modems set the "Data Set Ready" (DSR) to "1" to ensure that they are ready for communication. Next, to set up the physical connection between the sending and receiving modems, the sending computer activates the RTS line to send a "Request to Send" message to its modem. Then, the sending modem asserts the "Clear to Send" (CTS) signal and transmits a carrier signal on the Transmit Data (TxD) line. This carrier signal is detected by the receiving modem, which uses the Ring Indicator (RI) line to tell its host computer that a ringing has been detected on its line and a transmission is about to begin. The two modems negotiate about the bit rate, the parity mode, the size of data blocks, the number of stop bits, and other parameters of transmission. Once the connection is set, both modems assert the "Data Carrier Detect" (DCD) signals and maintain them asserted as long as the two modems are connected.

At the same time, while the sending computer is establishing the communication path between the two modems, it begins to transfer data to its modem over the interface. The data transfer is asynchronous. The computer asserts the "Request to Send" (RTS) signal, which tells the modem that it is ready to transmit data on the "Transmit Data" (TxD) line. The modem asserts the "Clear to Send" (CTS) signal, indicating that it is ready to receive data. When the receiving modem receives the data from the network, it should initiate the same process in order to transfer the data on the "Receive Data" (RxD) line to its host computer as the final destination.

After the communication is completed, the computers deassert the RTS and DTR signals, causing the modems to drop the carrier signal and disconnect from the line. The modems deassert the CTS, DSR, and DCD signals.

The signals for two special cases of using RS-232-C (DB-9) are shown in Figure 11.32. Part (a) is to directly connect two compatible computers, for example, in the same building for data transfer without using modems. The transmission never needs to cross analog lines, so it does not need to be modulated and demodulated. Because the two computers must cross the TxD and RxD data lines, this connection is called a *null modem*. Part (b) is to connect a peripheral to a computer. The peripheral may be located anywhere, even in a separate room from the computer. Therefore, using a serial interface is a good solution for taking advantage of high reliability and low cost. Since the peripheral in this case is a terminal consisting of a keyboard and a monitor, the data lines and control lines in both directions are fully utilized.

Special LSI devices have been developed to implement the RS-232 standard. They are commonly called the Universal Asynchronous Receiver/Transmitters (UARTs). Although the UART is an interface chip used to convert the internal parallel data to external RS-232 serial format and vice versa, the CPU treats it just as a parallel I/O device. On its back end, the UART inputs (receives) and outputs (transmits) data serially. In this way, the UART can interact with any device that needs to access serial data, such as the modem, the keyboard, and the serial mouse. The block diagram of a UART based on the Motorola 6850 Universal Asynchronous Communication Interface Adapter (ACIA) is shown in Figure 11.33. It can help illustrate the general principle of operation of a UART. For a transmit operation from the CPU to the outside device, the UART loads

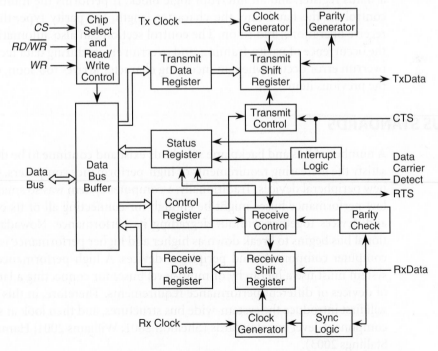

Figure 11.33   Block diagram of the Motorola 6850 ACIA chip as an example of the UART

the CPU data from the data bus into its *Transmit Data Register* and uses a shift register to convert the register contents into a serial bit string for output on its "TxData" line. For a receive operation from the outside device to the CPU, the UART receives a serial bit string from its "RxData" line and uses a shift register to convert the serial data into parallel data. This parallel data is then loaded into the *Receive Data Register* of the UART for the CPU access from the data bus. The two shift registers not only perform the basic functions of data format conversion, but also perform the other important functions of (1) parity generation (before transmission) and parity checking (after reception) and (2) interacting with the outside serial devices for clock synchronization.

Besides the two data sections for the transmitter and the receiver as described above, the UART has two other sections: the input interface section and the control section. The input interface section contains a Data Bus Buffer. It provides a temporary storage space for adjusting the traffic of data transfer with the CPU. For example, the National Semiconductor 16550A UART chip has 16-byte FIFO buffers on both transmit and receive channels. This reduces the timing constraints on the CPU to grab the data from the UART or store the data away in main memory. With a 16-byte input buffer, the interrupt rate is reduced by up to a factor of 16. The input data buffer handles not only the data transfer with the CPU, but also the transfer of the address, control, and status signals useful for the Read and Write operations. The control section contains a control register, a status register, and an interrupt logic block. It performs the multi-functional control on the baud rate, the character length, the parity type, the transmit/receive operations, and so on. The control section can also automatically detect the occurrence of parity, framing, and overrun errors during data reception. The overrun error occurs when an incoming character arrives too soon, overwriting the previous item.

11.7 BUS STANDARDS

A number of bus and backplane standards exist and continue to be developed to satisfy the increasing requirements of high-performance computers, servers, and new peripheral devices. Traditionally, a computer system was so small that a few low-performance buses might be enough for connecting all of its components and devices together without degrading its performance. Nowadays, a traditional bus begins to break down as higher and higher performance is seen in the computer components and peripheral devices. A high-performance computer system must use a hierarchy of multi-level buses for connecting a large number of devices of different performance requirements. Therefore, in this section, we will first introduce the system-wide bus structures, and then look at some of the component-level bus standards (Sheldon 2001; Williams 2001; Hamacher 2002; Stallings 2003).

11.7.1 Peripheral Component Interconnect Bus

The peripheral component interconnect (PCI) bus was first introduced in 1992 by Intel. It was developed as a low-cost, high-performance bus, anticipating a rapidly growing demand for bus bandwidth to support a large variety of high-speed disk, graphic, and video devices. It has become an industry standard widely used not only in all Intel-based computers, but also in workstations and server systems. The PCI bus is a parallel, 32-bit or 64-bit shared-bus architecture. It incorporates 100 signal lines into a single standard, including a 32-bit mandatory data/address multiplexed bus, a 32-bit optional data/address multiplexed bus, and the remaining control bus used for cache, interrupts, error reporting, and so on. The first version of the PCI bus, PCI 2.0, ran at 33 MHz with a 32-bit or 64-bit bus width. This corresponds to a maximum bus bandwidth equal to 33×64/8 = 264 MB/sec on a 64-bit bus. A 64-MHz version, PCI 2.1, was introduced in 1995 that doubled the maximum bus bandwidth on a 64-bit bus to 528 MB/sec. The PCI 2.2 has features for mobile computers, satisfying additional requirement of saving battery power. The PCI-X extended PCI in late 1999 with a faster clock rate of 133 MHz, pushing the bus bandwidth to over 1 GB/sec on the 64-bit bus. It is targeted at high-end servers and workstations.

To understand the motivation of developing the PCI bus, it might be useful to look at the history of its development. The original IBM PC used a 62-pin bus for a 4.77-MHz Intel 8088 processor with an 8-bit data bus and a 20-bit address bus. When IBM introduced the 80286-based PC/AT, the bus was upgraded to the PC/AT bus with an extra 36 pins as its extension, resulting in 16-bit data and 24-bit addressing. The speed was limited to 8.33 MHz to retain compatibility with the slower interface chips. Extra WAIT states were inserted by the CPU so as to match the slower devices. Later, this bus was known as the Industry Standard Architecture (ISA) bus. With the creation of the much faster Pentium® CPU with a 32-bit bus, the difference between the peak bus bandwidth of the main bus (800 MB/sec) and the ISA bus (16.7 MB/sec) became obvious. The old ISA bus was too slow. The Extended ISA (EISA) bus was developed that permitted a 8.33-MHz transfer rate on a 32-bit bus, resulting in a maximum bus bandwidth of 33.3 MB/sec. It was a backward-compatible successor of the ISA bus, with a few new additional features (e.g., multiprocessing). However, few boards had been produced for the EISA bus before the newer PCI bus was introduced and rapidly became the most popular standard for high-performance computers.

The PCI bus is synchronous, running at either 33 MHz or 66 MHz. All transactions on the PCI bus are performed between a master, officially called an *initiator*, and a slave, officially called a *target*. The PCI bus has two modes of operation: the *multiplexed mode* and the *burst mode*. In the multiplexed mode, a single 32-bit bus is shared by address and data in a time-multiplexed fashion. During a Read or Write operation, the address is needed on the bus for only one clock cycle, so the bus can be freed after the first cycle and used for data in subsequent clock cycles. This increases the effective bus width and reduces the cost. In the burst mode, after an address has been sent on the bus, a sequence of successive data words can be sent quickly to/from the consecutive memory locations starting at that address.

The PCI supports three independent address spaces: memory, I/O, and configuration. The I/O address space is intended for use with processors, such as the Pentium®, that have a separate I/O address space. However, the same address and data lines on Intel processor chips are used for both memory-mapped I/O and isolated I/O address spaces. The configuration space is intended to give the PCI bus its plug-and-play functionality. The *plug-and-play* feature means that a new device can be added to the system at any time while the computer is operating. There is no need to restart the computer, as traditionally it should be done by the user. Two commands, Configuration Read and Configuration Write, enable the master to read and update configuration parameters in a device connected to the PCI. More information about plug-and-play will be discussed shortly.

The PCI bus has a high performance. We can use an example to see how it can satisfy the requirement of full-screen full-motion video applications. The bandwidth required for displaying a motion picture with a resolution of 1024×768 pixels and three 1-byte primary colors at a speed of 30 screens/sec can be calculated as $30 \times (1024 \times 768) \times 24 = 30 \times (1K) \times (18K) = 540$ Mbits/sec = 67.5 MB/sec. If the graphics file is read from disk into memory and then transferred to the graphics adapter, this bandwidth may need to be doubled to 135 MB/sec, well within the range of 528 MB/sec for the PCI bus. However, two problems still need to be solved: (1) How to handle the memory traffic on the bus, and (2) How to make the PCI compatible with the old ISA cards. The common solution to these two problems is the *multi-bus hierarchical architecture*. The basic idea is to use multiple buses of different bandwidths to connect devices of different speeds, and then connect these multiple buses through bridges into a hierarchical bus structure, such that the traffic on each section of the bus best matches its design bandwidth. In this way, the first problem can be solved by using a high-speed system bus to connect memory to the CPU and then connect the PCI bus to the same system bus through a PCI bridge. The second problem can be solved by connecting the ISA bus(es) and other buses (to be learned shortly) to the PCI bus through corresponding bridges so that the old ISA cards and other cards can be connected onto the corresponding buses. Therefore, such a multi-bus hierarchical architecture is also called a *bridge-based bus architecture*. The principle of operation of a bus bridge such as the i82443 can be seen from Figure 11.34. Its main function is to decouple the PCI bus from the system bus. The principle of operation is based on *double buffering* commonly used in the I/O transfer. We assume that the PCI bus runs at half the speed of the system bus. For example, while the system bus runs at 132 MHz, the PCI bus should run at 66 MHz with the same data width. The PCI bridge requires two internal buses, each of which uses two data buffers, prefetch buffer and posting buffer, to handle the simultaneous loading and unloading of data. Thus, the data can be passed within the bridge through twin buffers on each side, while both sides are also handling external transfers. In this way, the separation of system-side activity from PCI-side activity can be achieved.

An example of bridge-based bus architecture is shown in Figure 11.35. It consists of three levels of buses: system bus, PCI bus, and ISA bus. The system bus includes the cache bus for connecting multi-level caches and the memory bus for connecting main memory with the CPU and the cache. The CPU communicates with the memory over a dedicated high-speed connection without causing extra traffic on the PCI bus. Through a PCI bridge, the PCI bus can be connected to the memory bus and local bus. All the PCI devices such as the SCSI controller, the graphics adapter, and the network controller are connected to the PCI bus. On the PCI bus, we also connect a Universal Serial Bus (USB)

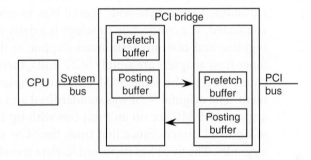

Figure 11.34 Internal structure of the PCI bridge

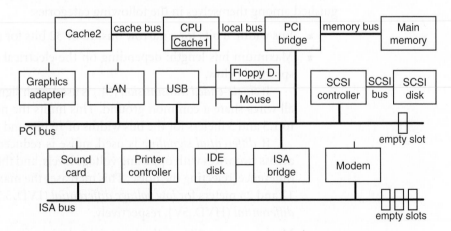

Figure 11.35 An example of the multi-bus hierarchical architecture based on bridges

for interfacing directly with slow devices, such as the floppy disk and the mouse, as it will be described later. Through an ISA bridge, the PCI bus is connected to the ISA bus as the third level of the bus hierarchy. All the ISA devices such as the modem, the printer controller, and the sound card can still be used by connecting them to the ISA bus. The Integrated Drive Electronics (IDE) disk is also connected to the ISA bridge because the IDE interface is actually a simplified version of the ISA bus. It allows the PC users to upgrade their hard disk drive without upgrading to an expensive interface card. The implementation of such a multi-bus hierarchical architecture typically leaves a few empty PCI slots and empty ISA slots for expansion by user choices.

11.7.2 Small Computer System Interface (SCSI) Parallel Interface

SCSI is a family of parallel interface systems that provide access services for I/O devices such as hard disk drives, CD-ROM disks, optical disks, tape drives, and scanners. SCSI is normally implemented in host adapters (or called SCSI controller), which are PCI expansion cards. The host adapter provides a fast asynchronous, 1- or 2-byte-wide shared bus, to which up to 8 or 16 devices can be connected. The connection topology is a daisy chain that connects all controllers in a line and carefully terminates the line at the end for impedance matching. Since host adapters are simply SCSI units, there is the possibility of several PCs connecting to the same SCSI bus, thus implementing a disk-sharing arrangement. The original SCSI was standardized and named SCSI-1 in 1986. It offered a speed of 5 MB/sec on an 8-bit bus with up to eight devices and a bus length of up to 12 meters. Since that time, the SCSI standard has gone through many upgrades. The SCSI has increased its data transfer capability very rapidly, almost doubling every two years. Three generations, Ultra SCSI, Ultra2 SCSI, and Ultra3 SCSI, have been standardized, each with many options. These options are distinguished among themselves in the following categories:

- Bus width: 8 bits for a narrow bus, 16 or 32 bits for a wide bus.
- Maximum bus length: depending on the electrical signaling scheme as specified below.

    If *single-ended transmission* (SE) is used, each signal uses one wire, and all wires share a common ground. This limits the maximum bus length to 1.5 and 3 meters for the bus widths of 16 bits and 8 bits, respectively.

    If *differential signaling* is used, noise is reduced by sending signals across two wires with opposing voltage levels, and the receiver reads their difference, rejecting the noise. This increases the maximum bus length to 12 and 25 meters for *low voltage differential* (LVD, 3.3V) and *high voltage differential* (HVD, 5V), respectively.

- Maximum capacity of the bus: eight devices for a narrow bus and 16 devices for a wide bus.

- Maximum transfer rate:
  - Started from 5 MB/sec (SCSI-1) and 10 MB/sec (Fast SCSI) and then improved to 20 MB/sec (Ultra SCSI) and 40 MB/sec (Ultra2 SCSI), all on 8-bit buses.
  - New Ultra160, Ultra320, and Ultra640 are Ultra3 standards defined in the late 1990s.
  - The transfer rates from 160 MB/sec to 640 MB/sec are included in their names.

The improvement of performances in the SCSI standards has been achieved by many different methods:

1. Doubling the bus width can double the transfer rate without changing the clock rate.
2. Doubling the clock rate on the same bus width can double the transfer rate.
3. Fast transfer rate can be achieved by using synchronous data transfer mode instead of asynchronous transfer mode.
4. Using LVD signaling improves the signal-to-noise ratio and increases the allowable cable length. Also, low voltage levels translate to less power consumption.
5. SCSI cables can be extended up to 75 meters using the special expanders provided by manufacturers.
6. Many new features added to Ultra3 SCSI improve its speed and quality of services, for example, the ability of choosing the highest possible data transfer rate, packetization of multiple commands and messages for transfer at once, and the function of quick arbitrate and select (*QAS*) which reduces connect/ disconnect time on the bus, and so on.

Recent SCSI disk drives that rotate at 15,000 rpm have the potential to deliver a sustained data rate of over 40 MB/sec. A typical server will have four drives, producing a combined data rate over 160 MB/sec. Obviously, the new Ultra3 SCSI standard is needed. However, only when these new devices are installed in a 64-bit, 33-MHz PCI system, the bandwidth of the PCI bus will suffice.

Now, we will look at the operation of the SCSI bus. For simplicity, we assume a narrow 8-bit bus that may connect a SCSI controller and up to seven SCSI peripherals. The SCSI bus is connected to the processor bus through a SCSI controller as shown in Figure 11.35. This controller uses DMA to transfer data packets between the device controllers and main memory. The SCSI controller is allocated "0" as a SCSI address. Each of the SCSI peripherals is allocated a unique bus address, from 1 to 7, which is set by the miniature on-board switches. The addresses of the SCSI devices are not part of the address space of the processor, and they are passed only in decoded form by activating the corresponding bus lines. For example, address 0 corresponds to bus line 0, address 1 to bus line 1, and so on. These addresses carry the priorities of the SCSI devices such that the larger the address is, the higher the priority is assigned to it. A controller connected to the SCSI bus can be an *initiator* that starts a SCSI bus communication, or a *target* that replies to it. The SCSI controller must be able to operate as an initiator and select a particular target to receive a command about the operation to be performed.

The SCSI connector for various options may have 50, 68, or 80 pins, and for 8-bit SCSI it has 50 wires in 25 pairs with each pair having a ground line and a signal line. Among the 25 signal lines, besides the power and reserved lines, there are eight data lines, $\overline{DB_0} - \overline{DB_7}$, one parity line for the 8-bit data, $\overline{DB_p}$, and nine control lines. All the data lines, parity line, and control lines carry active-low signals, that means a signal is asserted if its value is "0", otherwise, the signal is deasserted if its value is "1". The functions of the control lines are described in the following:

- **Specifying the phase of control:**

  $\overline{BSY}\,(\overline{BUSY}) = 0$ if the bus is busy, otherwise if $\overline{BSY} = 1$, the bus is free.

  $\overline{SEL}\,(\overline{SELECT}) = 0$ if it is used by the initiator to select a target or by the target to resume an interrupted session.

- **Specifying the information type:**

  $\overline{C/D}\,(\overline{Control/Data}) = 0$ if control information is being transferred on the data bus, otherwise, $\overline{C/D} = 1$, data is being transferred.

  $\overline{MSG}\,(\overline{Message}) = 0$ if the information being transferred is a message.

- **Specifying the direction of data transfer:**

  $\overline{I/O}\,(\overline{Input/Output}) = 0$ if the target indicates an input operation from target to initiator, otherwise $\overline{I/O} = 1$, if the target indicates an output operation from initiator to target.

- **Handshake signals:**

  $\overline{Request} = 0$ if the target is signaling an initiator that data can be transmitted.

  $\overline{ACK}\,(\overline{Acknowledge}) = 0$ if the initiator is confirming that it has completed a data transfer.

- **Others**

  $\overline{ATN}\,(\overline{Attention}) = 0$ if the initiator wishes to send a message to a target.

  $\overline{RST}\,(\overline{Reset}) = 0$ forces all attached devices to disconnect from the bus and assume their startup state.

It should be noted that data transfers on the SCSI bus are always controlled by the target controller. After an initiator wins the arbitration, it selects a target to communicate with and then hands the bus control over to it. Having got the control of the bus, the target can use the signals $\overline{C/D}$, $\overline{MSG}$, $\overline{I/O}$, to send commands, messages, and data to the initiator, or exchange the handshake signals $\overline{Request}$ and $\overline{ACK}$ with the initiator for asynchronous communication. If the initiator wishes to send a message to the target, it can use the $\overline{ATN}$ signal.

Now, we will describe the phases of control of a SCSI communication session using a disk Read operation as an example. However, let us first use the basic knowledge provided in Section 11.2 to derive the general process of a disk Read operation as follows. At first, the SCSI controller on behalf of the processor should send a Read command over the SCSI bus to the disk controller. Then, the disk should spend a long time called *seek time* to move its read/write head to the required track, and wait an additional time called *latency time* until the required sector on that track rotates under the read/write head and the disk can start reading data from that sector. During this long interval, the disk controller must release the SCSI bus. Only when the disk controller has stored the data block read from the required sector into its data buffer and is ready to begin data transfer to memory, the disk controller will seize the SCSI bus to do so. Since a disk Read operation may need to read data from several nonconsecutive sectors on the same disk, the above seek and data transfer sequence of operations could be repeated several iterations.

Therefore, a SCSI communication session is divided into the following principal phases:

- **Bus Free**—No device is using the bus, so the bus is available for use.
- **Arbitration**—Bus seizure by one device according to a strategy of arbitration so that it can initiate or resume a bus communication.
- **Selection**—The initiator selects a target device to start an I/O operation.
- **Reselection**—The target reselects an initiator to resume an I/O operation previously started by the initiator but suspended by the target.
- **Information transfer**—Transfer of commands, data, statuses, and messages.
- **Command**—The target requests command information from the initiator.
- **Data**—The target requests the transfer of data from the target to the initiator (Data In) or from the initiator to the target (Data Out).
- **Status**—The target requests the transfer of status information from the target to the initiator.

■ **Message**—The target requests the transfer of messages from the target to the initiator (Message In) or from the initiator to the target (Message Out).

The general state diagram of a SCSI communication session describing the repetition of these phases is shown in Figure 11.36. Whenever the bus is free, multiple controllers may apply for using the SCSI bus. The first step is to assert the $\overline{BSY}$ signal and enter the arbitration phase. Only the controller with priority higher than all the other competitors can win the arbitration and enter the select phase, becoming an initiator of the bus. In this phase, it selects a target device it wants to communicate with and hands the control of the bus over to it. The selected target then enters the information transfer phase. It can request that the command be sent to it from the initiator. If the command, for example, disk Read or Write, requires some extra time (e.g., seek time and latency time) to complete without tying up the bus, the target should release the bus and wait until the data is available later. The reselection capability of the SCSI allows the target to reapply for the bus and, after arbitration, enter the reselection phase to resume the connection with the initiator and then enter the information transfer phase again for transfer of the data over the SCSI bus. If the disk operation concerns several nonconsecutive sectors on the disk, this reselection process may repeat several times. The backward paths from any phase to the initial Bus-free phase indicate different cases of failing the arbitration, temporarily releasing the bus, or completion of an I/O operation.

The exact process of a disk Read operation passing through the phases in the above-mentioned state diagram is described below. We will examine each of the phases sequentially.

1. **Arbitration Phase**

   When the bus is free as indicated by $\overline{BSY} = 1$, any controller can assert $\overline{BSY}$ to 0 to initiate the arbitration phase. At the same time, it must assert the data line associated with its address (i.e., its identification number). Two or more controllers may do so at the same time. The SCSI bus uses a simple distributed arbitration scheme (see Section 11.4.2.3). All the active controllers that are requesting the bus examine the data lines. The controller using the

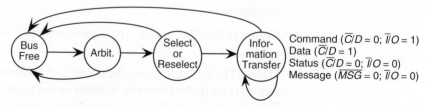

Figure 11.36 General state diagram for a SCSI communication session

highest-numbered line realizes that it has won the arbitration, while all the remaining active controllers disconnect from the bus and leave the arbitration phase, waiting for the next chance. The winning controller proceeds to the selection phase. It becomes the initiator.

2. **Selection Phase**

The winner of arbitration, denoted as controller$_i$, continues to assert $\overline{BSY}$ and $\overline{DB_i}$ (its address line). Suppose it wants to select controller$_k$ as its target. It asserts $\overline{SEL}$ and $\overline{DB_k}$ (the address line of the controller$_k$). After a delay, the initiator deasserts the $\overline{BSY}$ line, signaling the target that the bus control is going to be handed over to it.

When the selected target, controller$_k$, detects the $\overline{SEL}$ and $\overline{DB_k}$ lines being asserted, it responds by asserting $\overline{SEL}$, which informs the initiator that it has taken over the control of the bus. Therefore, the initiator releases both address lines $\overline{DB_i}$ and $\overline{DB_k}$ and deasserts $\overline{SEL}$. The selection phase is now complete and transits to the information transfer phase.

3. **Information Transfer Phase**

The target enters the information transfer phase by, at first, asserting the $\overline{C/D}$ line, which means that it is in the Command stage. Since $\overline{C/D} = 0$, the target is requesting control information be sent from the initiator using the handshake signals $\overline{Request}$ and $\overline{ACK}$ for asynchronous communication. If the received command is a disk Read, the target must temporarily release the bus for later reselection in order to resume the information transfer phase. Otherwise, the target may proceed to the Data stage, in which it should deassert $\overline{C/D}$ to 1 and $\overline{I/O}$ to 0 (Data In) for transferring data from the target to the initiator in a disk Read operation. After the data stage, the target enters the Status stage by asserting the $\overline{C/D}$ line again while keeping $\overline{I/O} = 0$, indicating that the target has successfully completed the data transfer to the initiator. Finally, the target enters the Message stage by asserting the $\overline{MSG}$ line and keeping $\overline{I/O} = 0$. It sends a "Command complete" message to the initiator and then releases all bus signals to return to the bus free phase.

4. **Reselection Phase**

When a target wants to resume its suspended bus after time-out, it must enter the arbitration phase again for regaining control of the bus. Once it wins the arbitration, it enters the reselection phase. Following the same process as in the selection process, the target selects its initiator for data transfer to proceed. The difference of the reselection phase from the selection phase is that the roles of the target and the initiator are reversed.

11.7.3 The USB Serial Bus

The SCSI bus we studied in the last section is a parallel interface that offers the advantages of high performance, fast speed, and large capacity to a class of block-oriented storage devices. There is another even wider class of slower peripheral devices, mostly character-oriented, such as keyboard, display, mouse, joystick, printer, microphone, speaker, audio device, floppy disk, CD-ROM, game interfaces, digital phone, and digital camera, which demand for a simple, convenient, fast, low-cost serial interface. Universal Serial Bus (USB) is just such an interface that provides a single port for connecting all of these devices. It was developed by a consortium of computer manufacturers in the early 1990s.

The USB 1.1 standard supports two speeds of operation: 1.5 Mbits/sec (low speed) and 12 Mbits/sec (full speed). The new USB 2.0 standard has improved the speed to 480 Mbits/sec (high speed). Besides the speed, USB has many new features that make it especially suitable for desktop computers and small systems. The following list characterizes these features from the viewpoint of simplicity and convenience of the USB.

- The USB interface is straightforward and easy to use. No extra PCI card is needed for each device.

- The USB uses a single style of universal connector and cabling that allows easy connection and flexible expansion of the bus. The interconnection paths constitute a tree-shaped tiered star topology. At the root and all the intermediate nodes of the tree, USB hubs are used as repeaters. They provide multiple-port connectors at all levels of the tree. All devices can be connected simply to the hubs. The root hub connects the entire USB tree with all the attached devices to the host computer.

- Up to 127 devices can be connected to a hub-tree topology. The upper limit is set by the address width of the USB. The USB cable can only be up to 5 meters long. So, the USB is intended only for peripherals, and not communication networks.

- No external power supply is required. The hubs can even supply power to some devices so they will not need external power cords or batteries.

- The USB cable is also simple. It uses four shielded wires, two of which are +5V power and ground, and the other two are twisted-pair wires carrying differential data signals using NRZ-I encoding (that means "nonreturn to zero, invert"). NRZ-I is different from the NRZ-L that we studied in Section 11.6.3. NRZ-I represents a "1" bit by a transition between a positive and a negative voltage, not the voltages themselves, and represents a "0" bit by no change of the signal. So, NRZ-I is superior to NRZ-L due to the synchronization provided by the signal change each time a "1" bit is encountered. For the differential data signal, at low speed, "1"s and "0"s are transmitted by sending a high voltage on one or the other of the two signal wires; while at high speed, a differential transmission is used.

- The most important feature provided by the USB for user convenience is its plug-and-play property, which allows the user to connect an I/O device to the USB port at any time while the computer is operating. The user does not need to reboot the computer, as would be required on the traditional I/O ports.

The technical details of the USB standard along with the plug-and-play property are described as follows.

1. Hub Tree Architecture

The USB connectivity is provided by a tree-shaped tiered star topology with hub repeaters at the root and the intermediate nodes. The hub tree consists of three types of units:

- USB host at the root of the tree
- USB hub at the intermediate nodes of the tree
- Peripheral devices attached to the sockets of the hubs

A USB hub may be standalone or incorporated into a device that is also equipped with further sockets, providing the required function of a hub. The typical host PC has two USB sockets so that a pair of peripherals can be directly connected to the PC, or otherwise two additional hubs can be inserted into these sockets to provide four free sockets, and this insertion can be repeated for continuing expansion of the tree to any required number of levels. A typical configuration of the USB hub tree is shown in Figure 11.37. It can be seen that the tiered star may have different levels at different branches of the tree. The number of sockets per hub may also be nonuniform. A hub's sockets may not be fully connected since devices may be connected to or removed from it at any time. The links are marked as either HS (high speed) or F/LS (full/low speed). If a link is connected with a low-speed device, for example, B or D, it should be marked

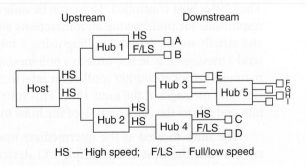

HS — High speed;   F/LS — Full/low speed

Figure 11.37   Tiered star topology of the USB bus

as F/LS, otherwise, all the other links connected to high-speed devices or hubs are marked as HS. As indicated in the figure, the direction toward the root of the tree is called upstream, while the direction toward the leaves of the tree is called downstream. The USB allows the connecting of a large number of devices to the downstream through a few intermediate hubs without the need for many connectors and cables behind the desktop PC. Furthermore, compared to the daisy-chaining topology used in the SCSI standard, the tiered star topology has some more benefits. It does not require careful termination of the bus. Also, it can monitor the power to each device separately and even switch the device off without disrupting other USB devices.

Marking the links as HS or F/LS has the implication in managing *split transactions* by the host computer. Consider the situation in Figure 11.37. Hub 1 and Hub 4 are connected to the root hub directly or indirectly (via other hubs) by all high-speed links labeled "HS". However, each hub (1 to 4) serves two devices with different speeds—one high-speed device by a high-speed link labeled "HS" and one low-speed device by a full/low speed link labeled "F/LS". If a message to a low-speed device is sent from the root hub all the way to the final destination at 1.5 Mbit/sec and during the duration of sending this message no other data transfers can take place, it would introduce unacceptable delays for high-speed devices and unreasonable reduction of the effectiveness of the high-speed links. To solve this problem, the USB protocol requires that a message destined finally to a low-speed device is always transmitted at high speed on high-speed links before it reaches the ultimate link to deliver the message finally to the low-speed device. During the period while the message travels to the low-speed device at low speed over the link marked as F/LS, other high-speed traffic to high-speed devices are allowed to continue. During this period, the bus is said to be split between high-speed and low-speed devices. To manage these split transactions with different speeds, the message to a low-speed device is preceded and followed by special commands to the ultimate hub to start and end the split-transaction mode of operation.

2. Data Flow Model on USB

The USB is host controlled. There can be only one host per bus. The USB host is responsible for undertaking all transactions and scheduling bandwidth. It operates strictly on the basis of polling using a token-based protocol. A device may send a message only in response to a poll message from the host. Hence, upstream messages do not encounter conflicts or interfere with each other, as no two devices can send messages at the same time. This restriction simplifies the function of a hub and allows the construction of the hubs to be simple and low cost.

The hubs located at the intermediate nodes of the tree act as the repeaters between the host and multiple I/O devices. The host establishes its communication path with each I/O device only through the intervening hubs and the related point-to-point serial links. A hub transfers messages in both directions: downstream and upstream. From the viewpoint of the host, the USB bus functions in the same way as a shared common bus on which messages can be transferred between the host and the multiple devices. In the downstream direction, all hubs copy messages from the upstream links to all the downstream sockets. As a result, a message sent by the host is broadcast to all I/O devices, but only the addressed device(s) will receive it. In the upstream direction, any I/O device can send messages to the host through the upstream hubs on the way toward the host. However, from the viewpoint of the devices, the USB bus is not a shared bus that may enable communication between any two devices themselves. The messages sent upstream from an I/O device can only be received by the host and are not visible in any way to the peer devices. Hence, the USB enables the host to communicate with the I/O devices, but it does not enable these devices to communicate with each other.

The messages, especially control messages, sent on the USB bus are used by the software for various functions. In this respect, locations in the device, for example, data, control, and status registers, to or from which data transfer can take place are called *endpoints*. Endpoints are identified by a 4-bit number, each of which identifies a pair of endpoints: one for input and one for output. The links that connect an I/O device to its device driver or, in general, application software, are called *pipes*. A USB pipe is connected to one such pair. The pipe connected to endpoint number 0 exists all the time. This is the control pipe that the USB software uses in the power-on procedure.

USB supports four transfer modes:

- **Control**—Transfer of control information is used by the host's root hub to pass on configuration instructions and data to the devices especially used for automatic configuration.

- **Isochronous**—Transfer of real-time data streams for devices that are allowed to reserve a preassigned amount of bandwidth with guaranteed latency. This is ideal in audio or video applications where congestion may cause data frames to drop.

- **Bulk**—Simple transfer of non-time-sensitive data.

- **Interrupt**—USB is not an interrupt system, so it depends on timed polling from the hub to pick up data from, for example, an input device.

3. Plug-and-Play

The plug-and-play property is an *automatic configuration* property of a computer system. The user simply plugs or unplugs a device into the system at any time while the computer is operating. The system will automatically detect the device and load or unload the related device driver software. By doing this, the system does not need the user to get involved in a manual rebooting procedure. The USB supports this property with dynamically loadable and unloadable drivers, automatic address creation, and system resources assignment. It allows the

USB software to dynamically detect the existence of a newly inserted device. The USB software then interrogates the new device, reads information about it from its ROM, selects the correct configuration parameters for it, and loads the appropriate device driver that has been installed in the system. Once the user deplugs the device, the host will detect its absence and automatically unload the corresponding device driver. The automatic configuration process is done using a PID/VID (Product ID/Vendor ID) combination of the device controller card, supplied by the USB Implementers Forum. Each card outputs its unique 70-bit PID/VID code for competing with other cards in the boot-up query sessions to win the attention of the configuring program. Irrespective of the order in which the devices are configured in these contention procedures, eventually all the devices will have been identified and correctly installed by the USB system. This includes allocating the necessary resources to all devices.

4. USB Protocol

The USB organizes all information to be transferred over the bus in packets. The packets are divided into two categories:

- **Control packet**—Addressing a device to initiate a data transfer, acknowledging the reception of data, or signaling an error.
- **Data packet**—Transferring input or output data inside data packets.

Any packet begins with a packet identifier, pid, which identifies the type of that packet. Actually, the pid field contains two parts: one is the 4-bit original pid, the other is the 4-bit complemented pid ($\overline{pid}$). Both parts concatenated together form an 8-bit pid field to denote 16 different types of packets (see Figure 11.38). Transmitting the same information about packet types in two parts with different formats increases the reliability of transmission.

Some useful control packets include:

- Acknowledge (ACK) packet for acknowledging the reception of a data packet. Its format consists of only the above-stated 8-bit pid field.
- Token packets IN or OUT for addressing a device to initiate an IN or OUT data transfer operation.

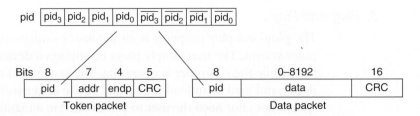

Figure 11.38 Formats of token packet and data packet with detailed pid field

Following the token packet that initiated a data transfer operation, a data packet can be issued to perform the data transfer with the data size up to 8,192 bits (1,024 bytes). If the data size exceeds this limit, subsequent pairs of token packet and data packet can be issued in the same way. The formats of the token and data packets are shown in Figure 11.38. The 7-bit address and 4-bit endpoint fields of a token packet specify the exact register of a device to receive output data or send input data. The CRC fields check the correctness of transmission by calculating the "addr" and "endp" fields for a token packet and the "data" field for a data packet.

Therefore, an output or input transfer operation is performed as follows:

1. A data packet always follows a token packet that was sent by the initiator to specify the device's address and register number to be the destination (for OUT) or source (for IN) of the required data transfer operation.

2. The data packet is normally followed by an ACK packet sent by the receiver of the data packet after it has correctly received that data packet. For an input operation, the token packet of type IN, sent by the initiator, acts just like a poll. The receiver can respond to it by sending either a data packet as input or, if no data is sent, sending an NACK (non-acknowledge) packet instead.

3. The above three packets combined together constitute a sequence for the data transfer of a 1-KB data block. For transferring multiple data blocks successively, this sequence should be repeated as many times as required.

4. Successive full- or low-speed data packets are numbered 0, 1, 0, 1, ... in their pid fields. Successive high-speed data packets are numbered 0, 1, 2, 0, 1, 2, ... in the same way. This simplifies the transmission error recovery process. If any packet is missing, the entire sequence is repeated. By checking the sequence numbers of the data packets, the receiver can detect and discard a duplicate packet.

5. If a data transfer is intended for a full- or low-speed device, then by the requirement of splitted transactions stated above, it should be preceded and followed by special control packets that starts and ends the split-transaction mode.

5. The Isochronous Transfer Mode on USB

The isochronous transfer mode is used in multimedia and data processing applications for transmitting continuous time-sensitive data streams such as sampled voice and video signals. Usually, isochronous signals can only be transmitted over high-speed links, except the audio signals which may use a full/low-speed link to arrive at a final destination of a full-speed device.

The sampled process of isochronous data requires a time reference for generating digitized data. To provide this reference, transmission of data over the USB is divided into frames of equal duration. Each frame starts with a synchronizing packet called *SOF (Start-Of-Frame) packet*, which consists of an 8-bit pid, a 11-bit frame number, and a 5-bit CRC code, as shown in Figure 11.39. The SOF packet can play the role of synchronization because the root hub generates it in regular time intervals. For full- and low-speed data, the SOF packet is generated every 1 ms, so the duration of each frame equals 1 ms, while for high-speed data, it is generated every 1/8 ms, so the duration of each frame equals 125 μs. After the SOF packet, a frame can encapsulate a certain number of data packets. Each data packet should be preceded by an IN or OUT token packet, but an ACK packet that follows each data packet is not necessary. The format of a frame is also shown in Figure 11.39.

From Figure 11.34, we can estimate the maximum transfer rate for isochronous data transmission as follows:

Assume that each frame can transfer n pairs of interleaved token packets and data packets, so we can calculate

$$\text{Total capacity of a frame} = 3 + (3 + 11)n = 3 + 14n \text{ bytes}$$

Since each pair of token packet and data packet contains only 8 bytes of useful data and the remaining bytes are overhead, we have

$$\begin{matrix} \text{Utilization of frame capacity} \\ \text{for transmission of data} \end{matrix} = \frac{8n}{3+14n} \approx \frac{8}{14} = \frac{4}{7} \text{ for large } n.$$

For full-speed (FS) data:

Transfer speed = 12 Mbits/sec = 1.5 MB/sec

$$\begin{matrix} \text{Transfer rate of} \\ \text{isochronous data} \end{matrix} = \frac{4}{7} \times 1.5 \text{ MB}/\text{sec} = 0.85 \text{ MB/sec} = 6.8 \text{ Mbits/sec}$$

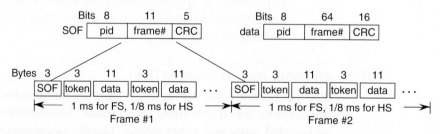

Figure 11.39 Formats of the frame and the SOF packet for isochronous transfer mode

For high-speed (HS) data:

Transfer speed = 480 Mbits/sec = 60 MB/sec

$$\text{Transfer rate of isochronous data} = \frac{4}{7} \times 60 \text{ MB/sec} = 34.2 \text{ MB/sec} = 259 \text{ Mbits/sec}$$

It is known that human speech can be captured at a sampling rate of 8 KHz and high quality music sound needs a sampling rate of 44.1 KHz. Suppose each sample is represented by 4 bytes of data, so the maximum data rate may be about 1.4 Mbits/sec. It is well covered in the range of 6.8 Mbits/sec for the full-speed version of USB. In Section 11.7.1, we have estimated the maximum data rate for a full-screen full-motion TV display. It may be as high as 540 Mbits/sec for only one-way data transfer. Even the USB high-speed standard can hardly satisfy such a high requirement.

11.7.4 FireWire Serial Bus

FireWire is a new serial bus standard developed by Apple Computer and Texas Instruments in 1999 under the name of IEEE P1394. It is often compared with the USB in performing similar functions with about the same performance. Both are serial buses based on similar topologies and support high-speed data transfer rates of up to 400 Mbits/sec (FireWire) or 480 Mbits/sec (USB). The developers are working toward a 1-Gbit/sec data transfer rate. The topology of FireWire is based on the daisy chain, which allows up to 63 devices to be connected to a single controller port. However, FireWire provides its own bus power for peripherals and does not need to connect them strictly in a daisy chain with terminated ends. Moreover, a large number of FireWire buses can be interconnected using bridges in order to accommodate as many peripherals as required. Therefore, a FireWire bus is more flexible than a pure daisy chain and can be configured to a tree structure.

FireWire was designed with special features that effectively support the operations of consumer audio/video equipment. Like the USB, FireWire can equally well handle the transfer of massive amounts of isochronous data between video devices and the computer. It also supports plug-and-play capability that allows the system software to automatically assign addresses to devices, detect the existence or absence of new devices, load or unload corresponding device driver software, and dynamically configure the computer system without involvement by the user. FireWire protocols include commands for controlling (e.g., start/stop) audio/video devices on the bus and stream their data to hard disks with little loss of quality.

FireWire protocol provides arbitration services which guarantee that at any given time, only one device can use the bus to transmit data. When multiple devices apply for the bus at the same time, the arbitration uses a priority-based strategy that determines the priority of each device according to its distance from the root of the tree-structured configuration of the system. The node that is closest to the root is given the highest priority. In case two devices are equidistant from the root, the priority is determined by which one has the lower ID number.

Two methods of arbitration supplement the above-stated basic arbitration strategy:

- **Fair arbitration**—Time is divided into fairness intervals of prespecified duration. In this duration, each node can gain access to the bus at most once. This can be implemented by associating an arbitration_enable flag with each device. At the beginning of each interval, all the devices set the flags to "1". Once a device gains access to the bus, it resets its flag to "0", which will inhibit that device to compete for fair access of the bus during this interval.

- **Urgent arbitration**—The high-speed, real-time data collection nodes can be classified as urgent-priority devices. They may gain control of the bus multiple times during a fairness interval. Up to 75% of the available bus time in a fairness interval can be reserved for urgent-priority devices, while 25% of the bus time remains to serve the nonurgent devices.

The FireWire protocol provides two types of transmission for transferring packets on the bus. The format of the data packet includes a header and a data field. The header contains the source and destination IDs, packet type, parameters, and a CRC for the header. The data field contains the data and a CRC for the data. The two types of transmission are as follows:

- **Asynchronous transmission**—A request/response type of transmission that involves two nodes exchanging a variable amount of data. It can be used by fair arbitration and urgent arbitration. No fixed data rate is required. After gaining the bus through an arbitration process, the requester sends a data packet to the responder, then after some delay an acknowledge packet should be returned from the responder to the requester. These steps form a sequence of events called a subaction for sending a data packet from the requester to the responder. A second sequence of events with the same steps will take place following the first sequence, thus forming a complete transaction of asynchronous data transmission as shown in Figure 11.40(a). It consists of two subactions 1 and 2 plus a subaction gap between them in order to allow the acknowledge packet to be sent out from the responder before a new arbitration can start. This subaction gap could be omitted if the responder can be automatically granted the bus access so that a new arbitration by the responder becomes unnecessary. This is a variant of asynchronous

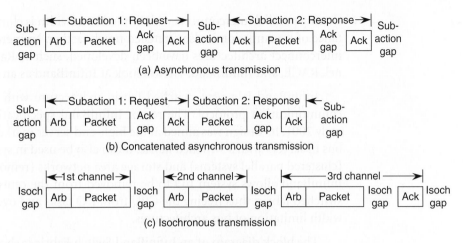

Figure 11.40 Types of transmission of FireWire protocol

transmission called the concatenated asynchronous transmission as shown in Figure 11.40(b).

- **Isochronous transmission**—A time-sensitive continuous transmission of multiple fixed-size data packets. Each sequence of data packets is transmitted at regular intervals using simplified addressing without acknowledgment. This type of transmission is especially useful for audio/video devices to deliver isochronous data within a specified latency and a guaranteed data rate. Since the successive data packets may not necessarily belong to the same pairs of nodes, every data packet needs to be preceded by a separate arbitration process. So, the successive subactions form successive channels as shown in Figure 11.40(c).

11.7.5 Switched-Fabric Architecture and InfiniBand

All the bus standards we have studied so far are classified as shared-bus architecture. The bus architecture, in general, suffers from technical limitations to boosting the bandwidth and the nature of its operating principle—sharing this limited bandwidth among an increasing number of "data-rate crunchers." Even the extended PCI, PCI-X, which was developed in late 1999 to work at 133 MHz with data rates over 1 Gbits/sec can hardly support today's new high-performance Gigahertz processors and Gigabit Ethernet connections. Clearly, the older PCI architecture is potentially becoming a bottleneck. An alternative interconnect scheme called the *switched-fabric architecture* or simply *switched architecture* can be used to scale PCI systems. The basic idea is to take advantage of point-to-point switching architectures that are being employed in clustered parallel processors, distributed systems, and networks. External connections are typically serial links with four-wire cable or fiber-optic cable rather than parallel buses, which are prone to crosstalk interference and bus skew. The problem of contention in sharing parallel interconnects with limited bandwidth is eliminated, and the distance of transmission is also stretched much farther. Numerous switched-fabric interconnect architectures have been developed, such as RapidIO, Fibre Channel, RACE, and InfiniBand. We will look at InfiniBand as an example below.

InfiniBand is a new switched-fabric architecture with a packet-switching communication protocol. The recent InfiniBand specification was released in early 2001. Its design was aimed at the high-end server market to replace the PCI bus in servers with a switched fabric. It can also be used in system-area networks (clustered parallel systems) and storage area networks (remote storage systems). InfiniBand allows system I/O to be removed from the central processor to the switched fabric, thus freeing the CPU from I/O tasks and overcoming the bandwidth limitation of bus architectures.

The block diagram of an InfiniBand Switch Fabric is shown in Figure 11.41. The InfiniBand switch uses *InfiniBand links* (IB links) to establish point-to-point physical connections with *host channel adapters* (HCAs), *target channel adapters* (TCAs), and routers. All InfiniBand links are bidirectional, for both send and receive. The adapters provide interfaces for the host's memory controller and the devices (storage systems or other peripherals) to communicate with external devices through the InfiniBand Switch. Each physical link, in turn, supports up to 16 logical channels called *virtual lanes*. One lane is reserved for fabric management, and the other lanes are allocated dynamically for transport of data in the form of a stream of packets over the InfiniBand fabric. The InfiniBand switch maps traffic from an incoming lane to an outgoing lane in order to route the data between two end nodes connected to the switch. The InfiniBand protocol

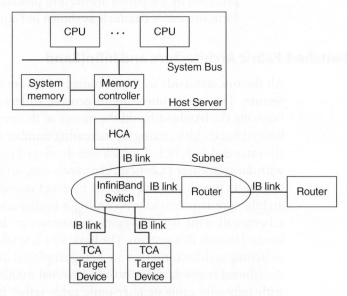

Figure 11.41 Block diagram of an InfiniBand Switch Fabric

defines three link speeds: 1×, 4×, and 12×, which give 2.5 Gbps, 10 Gbps, and 30 Gbps, respectively for unidirectional traffic. The usable capacity for each type of link is only 80% of the defined speeds, that is, 2 Gbps, 8 Gbps, and 24 Gbps, respectively. The effective bidirectional data throughput for each type of link is to double the corresponding usable capacity, that is, 4 Gbps, 16 Gbps, and 48 Gbps, respectively. The InfiniBand switch manages the linkage without interrupting the host server's operation. The devices do not have to share a channel's capacity by arbitration. Therefore, using the virtual lanes significantly increases the bandwidth of the subnet.

SUMMARY

The I/O subsystem is one of the three major functional blocks of a stored-program computer. Its general organization and connection with the CPU and memory are introduced in Section 11.1. By the requirement of standardization of I/O interfaces, the architecture of the I/O subsystem is divided into three layers: I/O devices, device controllers, and I/O interfaces.

This chapter focuses on the I/O interfacing rather than the electromechanical construction of the I/O devices. Although the secondary storage, by its functionality, is part of the memory hierarchy, it has the same mode of communication with the CPU and memory as the regular I/O devices. So, the secondary storage devices are studied in Section 11.2 from the viewpoint of the data storage structure, rather than the electromechanical structure of the devices. We have also introduced solid-state disk technology, which is replacing the rotating disk drive but brings with it its own performance limitations.

Three I/O accessing methods are discussed in Section 11.3: (1) programmed I/O (Section 11.3.2) relies on the full-time involvement of the CPU. It concerns two problems: how to poll the statuses of the I/O devices and how to address I/O registers—memory-mapped I/O or direct I/O (Section 11.3.1). (2) interrupt-driven I/O (Section 11.3.3), and (3) direct memory access (Section 11.3.4). The concept of interrupt is then generalized for studying the exception and exception handling in Section 11.4.

The topic of I/O interfaces is the major topic in this chapter. It is discussed in Section 11.5. The synchronous and asynchronous bus protocols are discussed in Section 11.5.1, followed by an example of implementation in parallel ports in Section 11.5.2. Then, the serial I/O data communication and serial ports are studied in Section 11.6. One of the important topics in serial communication is the error detection and correction codes, which are described in Section 12.6.2. The serial interface standard EIA-232-C is described in Section 11.6.3.

Many system-wide component-level bus standards are available for interconnecting boards and devices of different types and vendors to construct a high-performance computer system. Because of the wide range of performances of different components, a hierarchy of multi-level bus standards is necessary. According to this development trend, Section 11.7 is dedicated to bus standards. Five representative bus standards, such as the PCI bus, the SCSI parallel interface, the USB serial bus, the FireWire serial bus, and the InfiniBand switch fabric are described in Sections 11.7.1 to 11.7.5, respectively.

EXERCISES

11.1 Suppose that we have a multi-programmed batch system that runs four simultaneous jobs of identical characteristics in an interleaved fashion. Each job runs for three phases. The first and third phases each take a computational time, C, spent in processor activity, and the second phase takes a time, T, spent in I/O operation. Assume that neither processor operations nor I/O operations can overlap, but I/O operation can overlap with processor operation. Derive the formulae for the following best-case performance measures:

1. Shortest turnaround time as the average time to complete a job,
2. Highest throughput as the average number of jobs completed per unit time,
3. Best processor utilization as the percentage of time that the processor is active.

Your formulae must take into consideration two cases with different characteristics of processes, compute-bound or I/O-bound, which have different interrelationships between the values of C and T.

11.2 Three processes, p_1, p_2, and p_3, have the following timing characteristics (all parameters are in appropriate time units):

p_1 has $t_{compute1} = 30$, then $t_{I/O} = 10$, and then $t_{compute2} = 10$
p_2 has $t_{compute1} = 5$, then $t_{I/O} = 35$, and then $t_{compute2} = 20$
p_3 has $t_{compute1} = 15$, then $t_{I/O} = 50$, and then $t_{compute2} = 5$

They are attempting to run concurrently on a uniprocessor using direct I/O with interrupt. That means, neither processor operations nor I/O operations themselves can overlap, but the I/O operation should overlap with processor operation in order to minimize the total execution time.

(a) Determine an optimal order of execution of the three given processes such that the total time of execution will be minimum.

(b) What is this minimum value of the total turnaround time? Neglect the overhead for interrupt processing.

(c) What is the throughput?

(d) What is the processor utilization?

11.3 Suppose a movable-head disk has 100 cylinders, 10 tracks per cylinder, and 20 sectors per track. The block addresses on the disk increase through all sectors on a track, then through all tracks in a cylinder, and finally from cylinder 0 to the last cylinder on the disk. Each block is a sector. What will be the logical disk address of a block on cylinder 5, surface 2, and sector 4 (all are numbered from 0)?

11.4 Suppose a disk has a rotating speed of 12,000 rpm and a transfer rate of 250 KB/sec. How much time in milliseconds is needed to locate a sector and transfer a block of 512 bytes from the disk to memory?

11.5 A movable-head disk has 10 surfaces each with 500 tracks. Each track can accommodate 200 sectors. The rotational speed of the disk is 6,000 rpm.

(a) Translate the following two logical addresses into physical addresses:

$b_1 = 309450$

$b_2 = 508150$

(b) It is known that the seek time is directly proportional to the seek distance (in tracks) with the proportional constant equal to 0.1 ms per unit distance and the startup time equal to 10 ms. Calculate the seek time (in ms) for the I/O request to access b_2 starting from the current address b_1.

(c) What is the latency time (in ms) for the above disk access?

(d) What is the transfer time (in ms) of reading 10 successive blocks for the above disk access? Assume that the disk rotates from smaller sector number to larger sector number.

(e) What is the total time (in ms) of the above I/O operation?

11.6 This problem is on writing short assembly-language codes to perform I/O operations with and without memory-mapped I/O. Suppose we have a device controller chip designed for parallel I/O operations. It has two byte-wide I/O ports called A and B. The chip has eight addressable registers, which include two data registers (DR1 and DR2), a command register (CR), and a status register (SR) for each of the I/O ports. Each pair of data registers at both ports A and B can be independently configured as input registers or output registers depending on whether bit 2 of the CR at that port is set to 0 (for input) or 1 (for output). Suppose the address map of the registers is listed in Table 11.2.

Using three-address instructions given in Table 11.3, write an assembly-language program to perform direct I/O with polling for the two cases as follows:

Case (a): without memory-mapped I/O.
Case (b): with memory-mapped I/O.

Each of your programs should configure the chip, output 16 bytes of data from a memory area starting at address 0000A000 to the A port of the chip, and then input 16 bytes of data into a memory area starting at address 0000A010 from the B port of the chip. Each port of the chip should use DR1 and DR2 for double buffering.

Table 11.2 List of I/O address mapping for Problem 11.6

Address	Register
FFFF0120	DR1A
FFFF0121	DR1B
FFFF0122	DR2A
FFFF0123	DR2B
FFFF0124	CRA
FFFF0125	CRB
FFFF0126	SRA
FFFF0127	SRB

Table 11.3 Instructions used in Problem 11.6

ADD	Rd $Rs1$, $Rs2$	; $Rd \leftarrow (Rs1)+(Rs2)$
AND	Rd $Rs1$, $Rs2$	; $Rd \leftarrow (Rs1)$ and $(Rs2)$
ADDI	Rd, Rs, #imm	; $Rd \leftarrow (Rs)+imm$ ($Rd \approx imm$ if $Rs = R0$)
ANDI	Rd, Rs, #imm	; $Rd \leftarrow (Rs)$ and imm
LOAD	Rd, offset(Rm)	; $Rd \leftarrow$ mem[offset + (Rm)]
STORE	offset(Rm), Rs	; mem[offset + (Rm)]$\approx(Rs)$
BEQZ	Rs, label	; if $(Rs) = 0$, goto label
BNEZ	Rs, label	; if $(Rs) \neq 0$, goto label
BLEI	$Rs1$, imm, label	; if $(Rs) \leq imm$, goto label
		; special I/O instructions without memory-mapped I/O
INPUT	Rd, I/O-reg.	; $Rd \leftarrow$ (I/O reg. name with device id)
OUTPUT	I/O-reg., Rs	; I/O reg. name with device id $\approx (Rs)$

11.7 It is necessary to formulate the Hamming code for 8 data bits D_3, D_5, D_6, D_7, D_9, D_{10}, D_{11}, and D_{12}, together with 4 parity bits P_1, P_2, P_4, and P_8.

(a) Evaluate the 12-bit composite code word for the data word 10110011.

(b) Evaluate the 4 check bits C_8, C_4, C_2, and C_1, assuming no error.

(c) Assume an error in bit D_5 during data transmission. Show how the error in the bit is detected and corrected.

(d) Add a parity bit P_{13} to include a double error detection in the code. Assume that errors occurred in bits P_2 and D_5. Show how the double error is detected.

11.8 Compute the CRC for a message to be transmitted 101100110 and a polynomial divisor $X^3 + X^2 + 1$. Check the result by assuming (a) no error in transmission, and (b) a burst error that changed the bit section 100 to 011.

11.9 A machine has memory bus shared by the cache and DMA I/O. When the bus is free during cache hits, it can be used by the DMA I/O. Assume that the operating system can guarantee that there will be no stale-data problem in the cache due to I/O.

(a) Now given the average frequencies of occurrences of instructions in Table 11.4.

Table 11.4 Instruction usage for Problem 11.9

Instruction Types	Frequency of Occurrences (%)
LW (load word)	25
SW (store word)	15
Others	60

Find (i) the average number of memory accesses per instruction, (ii) the average number of memory reads per instruction, and (iii) the average number of memory writes per instruction. What percentages of the total memory accesses are reads and writes respectively?

(b) Assume that each cache block is four words, and the whole block is read on any cache miss. The cache miss rate is given as 5%. For the write-through cache, cache miss takes 23 cycles, and if write-through is needed, it takes 16 cycles to complete. For the write-back cache, cache miss takes 23 cycles for a clean block and 31 cycles for a dirty block. Calculate the average number of stall cycles per instruction for each of the write policies: write-through and write-back.

(c) Assume that the cache is only using the bus when it is involved in a memory stall cycle. Find the traffic ratio of the bus as the percentage of stall cycles relative to the total cycles for each write policy.

If the bus can be loaded up to 80% of capacity without suffering severe performance penalties, how much percentage of bus bandwidth is available for I/O for each write policy?

(d) Assume that a disk sector read takes 1,000 clock cycles to initiate a read, 100,000 clock cycles to find the data on the disk, and 1,000 clock cycles for the DMA to transfer the data to memory. Assume that the DMA I/O can take place simultaneously with CPU cache hits. How many disk reads can occur per million instructions executed for each write policy?

11.10 What are the relative advantages and disadvantages of SSDs and hard disks?

11.11 What is wear leveling? Why is it needed in SSDs?

12

Pipelining

In previous chapters, we studied the principles and design techniques of a computer based on the von Neumann single-sequence machine model. Although we have introduced some examples of exploiting parallel operations in the design of the datapath and the control unit (see, for example, Section 9.4.3 about the tradeoff between time and space), the organization of the entire processor under consideration was still sequential. In this chapter, we will extend this sequential model to introduce more parallel processing techniques into the processor design. *Instruction pipelining* is a technique that is widely used in the organization of contemporary high-performance processors. In the ideal case, a fully-loaded instruction pipeline can execute one instruction per clock cycle and achieve a performance of 1 *cycle per instruction* (CPI). To extend this technique even further, a processor can accommodate multiple instruction pipelines in a processor and run multiple instruction streams in parallel. The speed of scalar operations can be enhanced to a fraction of one clock cycle per instruction. This architecture has created high-performance processors with *CPI*<1 of the new processor type called *superscalar processors*. In this chapter, we will introduce the organization of an instruction pipeline and basic techniques for improving performance by way of exploitation of *instruction-level parallelism*.

12.1 THE BASIC CONCEPT OF PIPELINING

Pipelining is an implementation technique whereby multiple procedures of events of the same kind are controlled so that they progress in an overlapped manner. In modern computers, pipelining is the key technique most commonly used to achieve high performance, especially for fast CPUs and control circuitry. Many procedures and operations in computers can be pipelined. Typically, these operations include: (1) complex arithmetic operations such as multiply, divide, and floating-point add operations that are carried out through various kinds of *operational pipelines* or (2) instruction streams that are executed on various *instructional pipelines* to increase the program execution speed. In this section, we will focus on the study of instruction pipelining and its evolving high-performance processor architecture.

12.1.1 Parallelism in Time vs. Parallelism in Space

We will start with the concept of parallel processing from which pipelining originated. From the architectural point of view, parallelism can be realized in either time or space. In other words, to increase the speed of computer systems, parallel processing relies on the factors of time and space. Parallelism implemented in time is called *temporal parallelism*. Parallelism implemented in space is called *spatial parallelism*. *Overlapping* and *pipelining* multiple arithmetic operations and instructions are examples of *temporal parallelism*. Replicating multiple functional units and memory modules are examples of *spatial parallelism*. All of these parallel techniques have been successfully used in today's high-performance computers. The technique of interleaving different operations in time, for example, interleaving the CPU and I/O was first used in the 1960s and was the first parallel processing technique used in computers. The motivation for using the technique was to overcome the gap between parts of a computer system that have large differences in their speed characteristics. Subsequent developments have created various types of pipelined functional units, pipelined central processors, and pipelined vector computers. The advantage of exploiting parallelism in time is that it does not require significant replication of hardware, but most efficiently utilizes the factor of time to improve the throughput of computer operations, instructions, and programs. However, even if we can attain the theoretical speed of *CPI* equal to 1, the ultimate speed of the pipelined processor is limited by clock frequency. For further performance enhancement, new approaches to parallel processing emphasize the role played by the factor of space. These approaches take full advantage of high-density VLSI chips and inexpensive hardware to replicate a large number of computing resources in a system, which can achieve more parallelism at various levels of program execution, for example, multiprocessing, multi-threading, loop-level parallelism, and instruction-level parallelism. Therefore, a superscalar processor can be viewed as a high-performance computer architecture that utilizes both parallelism in time and parallelism in space. Individual instruction pipelines are the functional blocks that explore parallelism in time, and multiple pipelines working in parallel in a central processor exploit parallelism in space.

12.1.2 Temporal Parallelism in Pipelining

Now we will study, in more depth, pipelining from the viewpoint of temporal parallelism. In a general sense, pipelining results in the overlap of two or more functions in time so that multiple tasks can be done concurrently. The general principles of a pipeline can be formulated in three steps:

1. Divide a task into subtasks.
2. Allocate each subtask to a stage of the pipeline.
3. Overlap the execution of the subtasks belonging to successive tasks in time.

To apply this *time-overlapping* technique to instruction level parallelism, each instruction is decomposed into a sequence of activities, and multiple sequences of activities belonging to different instructions are overlapped in time, resulting in a higher throughput than performing the activities of these instructions sequentially. To support this concurrency in hardware, we need a pipeline structure that consists of a sequence of stages, with each stage performing a specific part of activities. The instruction stream flows through the pipeline, performing the successive instruction steps in successive stages. The pipeline mode of operation requires that, as soon as the current instruction leaves a stage, the subsequent instruction immediately enters this stage. In other words, during each clock cycle, a new instruction can be initiated at the start of the pipeline while other instructions are still in progress through later stages of the pipeline. In this pipelined manner, as many successive instructions can be processed in the pipeline simultaneously as there are stages, with each stage of the pipeline processing a different instruction. As a result, as long as the pipeline is full, it will start one instruction at its input stage and finish another instruction at its output stage every clock cycle, thus yielding a rate of one cycle per instruction. This maximum utilization of the pipelined parallelism in time relies on the following conditions:

- The pipeline has a continuous instruction stream so that the pipeline is always full of activities.
- The instructions in the pipeline do not compete for the same resources and utilize different resources at different stages at a given moment.
- The instructions do not have data or control dependencies on the other instructions in the pipeline. These dependencies would cause the pipeline to stall and wait for the availability of data or control information in order to proceed.

These issues and their effects on the performance of the pipeline will be addressed in later sections. We will now look at some examples to help understand the principles of pipelines.

Example 12.1   A Pipeline in the Real World

A production assembly line is a typical example of a pipeline in the real world. In an automobile assembly line, the assembly process is divided into many steps. Each step contributes something (parts) to the construction of a car. Each step operates in parallel with the other steps, but on a different car. Such parallel operation is a kind of *overlapping*. The simplified conceptual structure of an automobile assembly pipeline is shown in Figure 12.1. Each step of car assembly requires the installation of a few parts, for example, the engine, steering wheel, seats, and wheels. The pipeline assembles these parts on a car in successive steps in a sequential manner. However, at each instant of time, all the stages of the pipeline assemble different parts on different cars in parallel. Therefore, although each single car needs some minimum total time to pass through all the stages until it is output from the end of the pipeline, the entire pipeline, on average, can assemble one car per cycle time. This high performance of the automobile assembly pipeline is achieved by its parallel, overlapped mode of operation. In general, pipelining increases performance by doing multiple things at the same time.

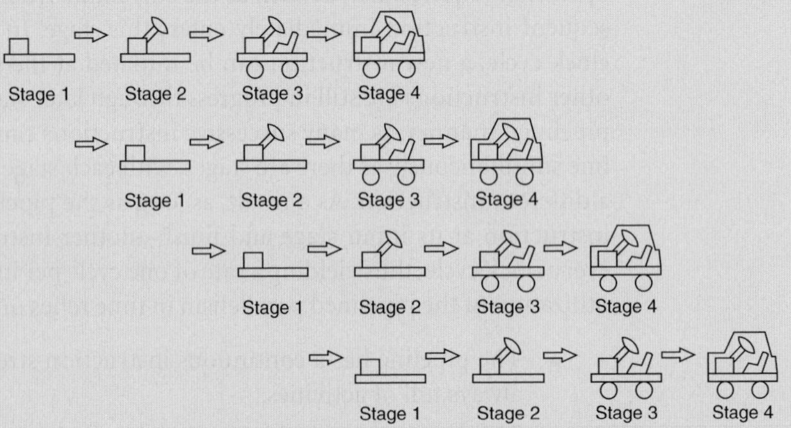

Figure 12.1   Conceptual structure of an automobile assembly pipeline

In summary, an *assembly pipeline* in a manufacturing plant is constructed based on the following principles:

- The assembly process is decomposed into many stages.
- Each stage assembles a few particular parts.
- New input is accepted at stage 1 (stage i) as soon as the previously accepted input leaves stage 1 (stage i) and enters stage 2 (stage $i + 1$).
- Products at various stages can be worked on simultaneously. Each stage takes one cycle time.
- For every cycle, a final product can be output from the last stage, so the productivity is one product per cycle.

■

Example 12.2 The VAX 8600 Instruction Pipeline

Typically, an instruction pipeline is designed to implement a basic instruction cycle in a time-overlapping manner. In this example, we will look at an instruction pipeline for a register-memory or memory-memory machine. Since the instruction pipeline in a CISC machine is usually very complicated, our intention here is only to illustrate principles. As for the design methodology, we will choose a register-register RISC machine for detailed design and study in later sections. According to the basic instruction cycle for a general register-memory machine, an instruction execution can typically be decomposed into six steps:

1. Instruction Fetch
2. Instruction Decode
3. Effective Address Generation
4. Operand Fetch
5. Instruction Execute
6. Result Store

In practical implementations, based on sequences of microoperations, each of these six steps can be decomposed (in a variety of ways) into a small number of independent phases. These phases are interleaved to form an instruction pipeline with a large number of stages. The block diagram of the six-stage instruction pipeline is shown in Figure 12.2.

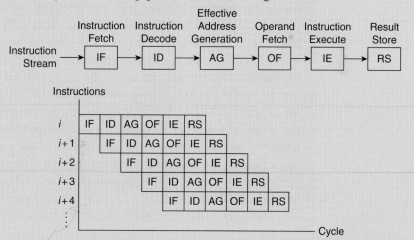

Figure 12.2 The six-stage instruction pipeline of the VAX 8600

Since the pipeline overlaps the execution steps of a large number of instructions, it is suitable to depict the execution pattern of the pipeline on a space-time diagram, as shown in the second part of Figure 12.2. Along the vertical axis representing space, multiple instructions seem to use, in an overlapped manner, multiple virtual copies of the pipeline to perform the same sequence of execution steps.

Along the horizontal axis representing time, continuous streams of instructions enter the pipeline at a speed of one instruction per clock cycle, and the continuous stream of results leaves the pipeline at the speed of one result per clock cycle.

An ideal case is shown in Figure 12.2, in which the above-mentioned six steps for consecutive instructions are assumed to be independent of each other and, therefore, can be pipelined perfectly to yield a six-fold maximum speed increase. However, the actual speed increase will not always be the maximum due to the following reasons:

- For a smooth instruction stream flow through the pipeline, all stages of the pipeline must be timed identically. This imposes a timing constraint—the synchronizing clock period is the execution time of the slowest stage.
- The instruction flow could be interrupted by many factors, such as cache misses, conflict of resource usage, operand unavailability, conditional branches, and the extended execution time of some complex operations. Of course, exception handling will stall the pipeline as well.

The six-stage instruction pipeline shown in Figure 12.2 was used in the VAX 8600, which was introduced in 1985 by Digital Equipment Corporation as a pipelined member of the VAX family. In order to support the pipeline to perform the six steps independently of one another, the CPU consists of several independent subprocessors called the "I box," the "E box," the "F box," and the "M box." The I box fetches instructions, decodes operation codes, fetches source operands, and supplies addresses for storing results. The opcode and operands are presented to the E box (executing the VAX-11 instruction set) or the F box (a floating point accelerator) for execution. The M box controls access to the main memory. Since all the stages of the pipeline must be synchronized by a common clock, the latency (execution time of each operation) of the pipeline is six times the clock period, but the maximum throughput (number of operations per second) corresponds to the upper limit of generating one result per clock when the pipeline is full.

■

Example 12.3 A Floating-Point Add Pipeline

In vector computers that exploit *loop-level parallelism* to process large data arrays, various operational pipelines are used to speed up large volumes of numerical calculations. Memory load/store operations are also treated as pipelines. In an operational pipeline, a complex arithmetic operation is decomposed into several steps, and the steps of the consecutive arithmetic operations are overlapped. Therefore, the construction of the operational pipeline is based on the same principles as the assembly pipeline in Example 12.1. The block diagram of a floating-point add pipeline is shown in Figure 12.3. It decomposes a floating-point add operation into six suboperations:

1. Exponent compare,
2. Mantissa shift/exponent equalization,
3. Mantissa add,
4. Count leading zeros of the result mantissa,
5. Result normalization, and
6. Detection of abnormal conditions such as overflow and machine zero.

Thus, the floating-point add pipeline is composed of six stages, with each stage containing the hardware needed to perform a suboperation of the six-step operation, as stated above. To understand how the pipeline works, the execution process of the following loop program on this six-stage floating-point add pipeline is also shown in Figure 12.3.

$$\text{for } (i = 0; i < 1000; i++)$$
$$C[i] = A[i] + B[i];$$

where A, B, and C are floating-point vectors.

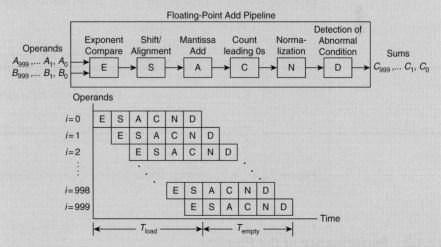

Figure 12.3 A six-stage pipeline calculating 1,000 sums of two vector operands

Example 12.4   A Floating-Point Multiply Pipeline

A simple floating-point multiply pipeline is shown in Figure 12.4. It is composed of three stages matching the pipelined dataflow pattern of a single-precision floating-point multiply operation. The first stage contains combinational circuit modules, which generate a large number of partial products simultaneously. The second stage reduces or sums up all these partial products using combinational circuit modules composed of, for example, carry-save adders or ROMs, by a parallel algorithm of summation. The third stage generates the final product and performs the post-processing of the result, if necessary. This step of processing may include final reduction, normalization, rounding, and overflow checking. Among the three stages, partial product reduction usually represents the most complex hardware and takes the longest time since parallel reduction can only be done with a lesser degree of parallelism [with $O(\log n)$] than the generation of partial products [with $O(n)$]. Therefore, it is usually the second stage that determines the clock frequency of the pipeline. If we want to increase the clock frequency, we can increase the number of stages by decomposing the slowest stage into smaller substages to improve the uniformity of their timing characteristics. In principle, the more we decompose a pipeline into smaller stages, the higher will be its throughput. However, the number of stages is ultimately limited by the additional delay introduced by staging registers. In the extreme case, if we scale the granularity of stages down to a few logic gates, then the delay of interstage registers would dominate the delay of the pipeline and no improvement of the performance could be achieved.

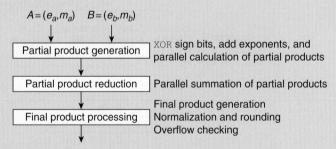

Figure 12.4   A three-stage linear floating-point multiply pipeline

12.1.3   Performance of the Pipeline

The performance of a pipeline can be calculated from the space-time diagrams shown in Figures 12.2 and 12.3. A continuous stream of N instructions or operand pairs flows through d stages of the pipeline. The total execution time is composed of two components. One component is called the *load time*, and is the time used for loading all N instructions or operand pairs into the first stage of the pipeline. The other component is called the *empty time*, and is the time needed by the last instruction or operand pair to complete processing and leave the remaining $(d - 1)$ stages of the pipeline. Therefore, if each stage of the pipeline takes one clock cycle, the total execution time will be

$$T_{\text{pipelined}} = T_{\text{load}} + T_{\text{empty}} = N + (d - 1) \text{ cycles} \qquad (12.1)$$

If the N instructions or operations are executed on an unpipelined machine with the speed of d clock cycles per instruction or operation, then the total execution time would be

$$T_{\text{unpipelined}} = Nd \text{ cycles}$$

Hence, the speedup from d-stage pipelining will be

$$Speedup = \frac{T_{\text{unpipelined}}}{T_{\text{pipelined}}} = \frac{Nd}{N + d - 1} = \frac{d}{1 + \dfrac{d-1}{N}} \qquad (12.2)$$

In the best case, when N is very large relative to d, the maximum speedup approaches d.

From the above derivation, we can see that the performance of a d-stage pipeline is characterized by the following parameters:

- The *throughput*, defined as the rate of tasks completed per unit time, equals one task per clock cycle because a fully-loaded pipeline can start a new task in each clock cycle and complete an old task in each clock cycle.
- The *latency*, defined as the number of clock cycles each task takes for execution from start to completion, equals d because each individual task requires d cycles to travel the full length of the pipeline.
- The *pipeline depth* or *degree of parallelism*, defined as the number of stages of the pipeline, equals d. This parameter determines the maximum attainable value of *speedup*, defined as the ratio of the unpipelined execution time over the pipelined execution time for the same number of tasks and the same speed for the basic unit of hardware.

12.2 GENERAL ORGANIZATION OF A PIPELINE

As we have learned from the previous section, pipelining is a relatively new technique for exploiting parallelism in time. It attempts to gain high performance by executing sequences of instructions or arithmetic operations in a time-overlapped manner. Therefore, the general organization of a pipeline is determined by its timing characteristics, that is, its relationship with the central clock. Just as we used this timing relationship to classify sequential circuits in Chapter 4, we will use the same scheme to classify pipelines into synchronous and asynchronous pipelines.

12.2.1   Synchronous Pipeline

A synchronous pipeline is a pipeline of multiple stages, all of which operate in synchronism with a common central clock. Its construction process consists of the following four steps, resulting in the block diagram shown in Figure 12.5.

1. Divide the task into subtasks.
2. Assign each subtask to a pipeline stage.
3. Insert an *interstage register* (also called a *staging register*) between every pair of successive stages; optionally, put an input register at the beginning of the pipeline and/or an output register at the end of the pipeline.
4. Synchronize the stages of the pipeline with a central clock, which acts on the staging registers.

For the synchronous pipeline, all the subtasks S_1 to S_k, where k is the number of stages, must be finished in one clock cycle each. Therefore, the maximum delay, t_{max}, among the delays, t_i, of all the stages $S_1, S_2, \ldots, S_i, \ldots, S_k$, plus the delay of a staging register, d, must not exceed the clock cycle time, that is,

$$\max(t_1, t_2, \ldots, t_k) + t_d = t_{max} + t_d \leq \text{clock cycle time} \qquad (12.3)$$

Thus, the maximum throughput as the maximum rate of tasks completed per unit time by a synchronous pipeline equals the clock frequency, and the latency as the time to finish each individual task on the pipeline equals the clock cycle time multiplied by the number of stages.

A direct consequence of Expression (12.3) is that the maximum frequency of the clock driving a synchronous pipeline is determined by the slowest stage with the maximum delay $t_{max} + t_d$. This maximum delay, in turn, determines the maximum throughput of the pipeline. Therefore, to design a pipeline with maximized performance, we must divide the pipeline into uniform-latency stages,

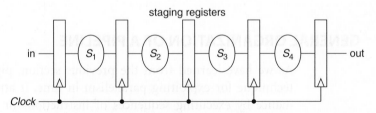

Figure 12.5   Block diagram of a synchronous pipeline

such that each stage will have approximately the same delay. No one stage should have excessive delay and restrict the pipeline from increasing the clock frequency to the maximum value. If such a stage exists and becomes a bottleneck of the pipeline, we may need to decompose it into smaller stages in order to balance all the stages of the pipeline and have a uniform delay in each stage.

While designing uniform pipeline stages, unbalancing of the pipeline can also be caused by an unbalanced datapath. All the parallel datapaths of a balanced pipeline must have the same number of stages so that different parallel streams of signals (instructions or data) can propagate uniformly along the pipeline and reach each staging register in exactly the same clock cycle. An example of an unbalanced datapath is shown in Figure 12.6(a). The datapath is unbalanced because $A + B + C + D$ is obtained by the output stage in three clock cycles, but $E + F$ arrives at the output stage in just two clock cycles. By adding a dummy interstage register in the datapath for $E + F$, the balanced datapath shown in part (b) is obtained.

From the above analysis, using the instruction pipeline as an example, the properties and performance of synchronous pipelines can be summarized as follows:

1. The pipeline designer's goal is to balance all the pipeline stages. Only when all the pipeline stages are perfectly balanced will the speedup from pipelining equal the depth of the pipeline. Usually, however, the stages will not be perfectly balanced. Furthermore, pipelining does involve some overhead. For example, the overhead due to interstage registers is

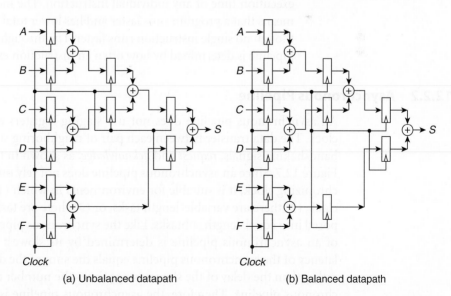

(a) Unbalanced datapath   (b) Balanced datapath

Figure 12.6   Pipeline organization with (a) an unbalanced datapath and (b) a balanced datapath

unavoidable in the pipeline. Thus, the latency of each instruction in the pipeline cannot be reduced to the minimum possible value, yet it can be close to that value.

2. Another parameter of the pipeline that is seriously affected by unbalanced stages is clock cycle time. Because the pipeline stages are hooked together, all the stages must be ready to proceed at the same time. The time required to move an instruction one step down the pipeline is a machine cycle. Because all stages proceed at the same time, the length of a machine cycle is determined by the time required for the slowest pipeline stage. In a computer, this machine cycle is just one clock cycle, although the clock cycle may have multiple phases. An instruction pipeline can only run as fast as the slowest stage. If we want to design a pipeline with the fastest clock allowable by the hardware, the pipeline stages must be as perfectly balanced as possible.

3. Clock cycle time also affects the throughput of the pipeline. The throughput of an instruction pipeline is defined as the number of instructions completed per unit time. In the ideal case, when the pipeline is always full, the throughput of a single pipeline can reach its maximum value of one instruction per clock cycle. While each instruction takes d (the number of stages) clock cycles to complete, during each clock cycle the hardware will initiate a new instruction and will be executing some part of the d different instructions. The pipeline increases the CPU throughput in terms of the number of instructions completed per unit time, but it does not reduce the execution time of any individual instruction. The increase in throughput means that a program runs faster and has lower total execution time, even though no single instruction runs faster. The throughput of an instruction pipeline is determined by how often an instruction exits the pipeline.

12.2.2 Asynchronous Pipeline

An asynchronous pipeline does not use staging registers and a synchronizing clock. The data transfer between each pair of neighboring stages is controlled by handshaking signals, *request* and *acknowledge*, as shown in the block diagram in Figure 12.7. Since an asynchronous pipeline does not rely on the timing of a synchronizing clock, it is suitable for environments in which (1) there is no central clock, (2) there are variable-length tasks, or (3) there are tasks not easily decomposed into equal-length subtasks. Like the synchronous pipeline, the throughput of an asynchronous pipeline is determined by its slowest stage. However, the latency of the asynchronous pipeline equals the sum of the delays of all its stages, rather than the delay of the slowest stage times the number of stages, as in a synchronous pipeline. Therefore, the asynchronous pipeline is less sensitive to the imbalance of the speeds of stages than the synchronous pipeline.

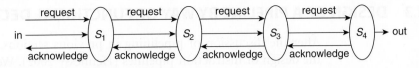

Figure 12.7   Block diagram of an asynchronous pipeline

Examples of asynchronous pipelines can be found in message-passing distributed systems for fine-grain data transmission. Besides the traditional data communication techniques such as circuit switching and packet switching, we have a new switching technique called *wormhole routing*, which is based on the principle of asynchronous pipelining. Circuit switching establishes a physical circuit and reserves it exclusively for transmission of a message. Packet switching performs store-and-forward communication, that is, it stores the entire packet in every intermediate node, which can then forward it to a selected neighboring node on its path to the final destination. Wormhole routing is different from these two methods. It divides the packet into fixed, small-sized *flow control digits*, called *flits*, with the length of each flit as short as a byte. The header flit carries the routing information. As the header flit advances along the path, the remaining flits follow it in a pipelined fashion, as shown in Figure 12.8. Due to a lack of a central clock, asynchronous pipelining is controlled by handshaking, using request and acknowledge signals. From Figure 12.8, the network latency can be derived as follows:

$$Latency = \frac{L}{B} + \frac{L_f}{B}(D-1) \tag{12.4}$$

where L is the length of the packet, L_f is the length of the flit, and B is the network bandwidth. D is the length of the path given by the number of hops between the source node and the destination node. It can be seen that if $L_f << D$, then the effect of D is negligible.

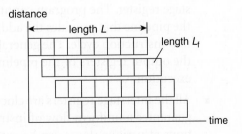

Figure 12.8   Wormhole routing implemented as an asynchronous pipeline

12.3   DESIGN OF A PIPELINE BY WAY OF FUNCTIONAL DECOMPOSITION

After the discussion of pipelining in previous sections, we can now focus on the design of instruction pipelines (Hennessy 2002). We can divide the design process into two major steps: (1) functional decomposition and (2) hazard analysis. The first step is to design a basic datapath for the pipeline based on the functional specification and the block diagram of the parallel datapath to be pipelined. However, this basic datapath is not yet a real pipeline that can run assembly language code. After a detailed hazard analysis, we can modify the basic datapath to resolve hazards and complete the design of a working pipeline. In the current and next sections, we will elaborate on the two steps of this design process. Furthermore, we will design an example pipeline for implementation of the RISC-style instruction set given in Table 9.3.

12.3.1   Special Properties of Instruction Pipelines

In general, an instruction pipeline is constructed according to the following principles:

- To start the design from functional decomposition, the basic instruction cycle of each machine instruction in the instruction set of a processor is decomposed into successive steps of execution.

- Different machine instructions may have different steps of execution, but all the instructions in the instruction set must map their execution steps on the common datapath of the instruction pipeline. So, all these instructions share the same hardware with the same latency, irrespective of whether all the stages of the pipeline are used by each of them. Certain instructions, with complex arithmetic operations, may be exceptions to this requirement. They should be designed to use an extended schedule of execution in the pipeline.

- The successive steps of the instruction cycles mapped on the pipeline stages should have a uniform distribution of execution times such that no stage of the pipeline will become a bottleneck of the datapath.

- Each stage of the pipeline is connected to the next stage through an inter-stage register. The program counter plays the role of an input register of the pipeline that provides the address of the next instruction to initiate a new instruction cycle. The general-purpose register set may be viewed as the output registers of the pipeline to store the results from instruction execution.

- All the interstage registers are clocked by a central synchronizing clock to guarantee a uniform flow of instructions through the pipeline. Instructions at various stages can be executed simultaneously, with each stage completing a different step of a different instruction. Each stage takes one clock cycle time.

- During the work of an instruction pipeline, a new instruction is fetched from the program counter at stage 1 (or accepted at stage i) as soon as the previously fetched (or accepted) instruction leaves stage 1 (or stage i) and enters stage 2 (or stage $i + 1$). Thus, as long as the pipeline is fully utilized, at every clock cycle a new instruction is initiated in the input stage and a completed instruction exits the output stage so that the ideal throughput of the pipeline—one instruction per clock cycle—can be achieved.

- The theoretical throughput of one instruction per clock cycle is not achievable in practice, but we can design the instruction pipeline to maximize its throughput by solving problems of hazards that may cause the pipeline to stall during program execution. This major issue is addressed in the next section, which discusses a design methodology for instruction pipelines.

From the above principles for constructing an instruction pipeline, we can see the special properties of instruction pipelines as distinct from arithmetic operational pipelines.

The first major difference between an operational pipeline and an instruction pipeline is that most operational pipelines are unifunctional pipelines that perform sequences of identical arithmetic operations on continuously supplied vector operands, but the instructional pipelines perform the sequences of instructions in program codes. Therefore, all pipeline stages of a unifunctional operational pipeline are always utilized in full, provided that the operand sequence continues. Conversely speaking, the instructional pipeline frequently has nonuniform utilization of the pipeline stages by different instructions. Particularly in a CISC-style instruction stream, stages specially designed for complex instructions with complex addressing modes are frequently underutilized by simpler instructions with simpler addressing modes. Therefore, the design of an instruction pipeline favors the RISC instruction set, which better utilizes the resources. Another consequence of the difference between an instruction pipeline and an operational pipeline is that the performance achieved by using an instruction pipeline heavily depends on the scheduling of the instructions to provide an optimized order of execution on the pipeline.

The second major difference between an operational pipeline and an instruction pipeline is that the former usually performs sequences of independent operations on array data, while the latter always has to handle sequences of dependent instructions. The instruction dependencies involve many different cases of data dependencies and control dependencies, and these may cause hazards and stalls in the instruction pipelines during the execution of a program. In the design of an instruction pipeline, various mechanisms must be built into the hardware (datapath) and software (compiler) of the instruction pipeline to detect and resolve possible hazards and stalls.

The third major difference between an operational pipeline and an instruction pipeline is that the latter involves less complexity with respect to partitioning the datapath for uniform distribution of subfunctions among the stages. From the examples of operational pipelines in the last section, we have seen that it is difficult to uniformly distribute the steps of an arithmetic algorithm of high complexity among the stages of an operational pipeline. However, it seems to be less complex to uniformly distribute the steps of a basic instruction cycle among the stages of an instruction pipeline. The typical problem in designing an instruction pipeline is how to balance the stages of CPU operations and the stages of memory access operations. We can solve this problem, which arises due to the disparity of speed between the processor and main memory, by employing fast cache memories and avoiding inefficient complex addressing modes.

12.3.2   Mapping the Dataflow Pattern to the Pipeline

In the following sections, we will present the detailed steps involved in designing an instruction pipeline according to the instruction set specification given in Table 9.3. The general organization of the instruction pipeline for implementing a RISC-style instruction set like the one in Table 9.3 suggests proposing the following four-stage pipeline.

- Instruction Fetch (IF)
- Execute (EX)
- Memory Access (MA)
- Write-Back (WB)

From Table 9.3, we know what operations are performed by each instruction. Now, we can decompose each instruction cycle into execution steps and map the steps to the corresponding pipeline stages, as listed in Table 12.1. Instructions with similar execution steps are classified in the same group. Thus, we obtain four groups of instructions. In the IF stage, all the groups perform the same operations—reading instructions from instruction memory and updating the program counter. In the remaining stages, groups perform operations as follows.

1. **ALU group**

   All instructions in this group perform arithmetic or logic operations on two source operands, $Rs1$ and $Rs2$, in the EX stage, load the result in the intermediate register as ALUout, and store this value in the destination register, Rd, in the WB stage. The only exception is the shift instruction, which operates on a single operand in $Rs1$ and may need to use extended cycles to complete its operation, unless we can implement the shift operation in one cycle using a barrel shifter (see Section 5.5.3). The multiply instruction is also a special instruction. Its arithmetic operation in the EX stage is not implemented by the ALU. Instead, we can implement its operation on an operational pipeline

Table 12.1   Mapping the execution steps of the instructions in Table 9.3 to a pipeline

Group	Instr.	IF Stage	EX Stage	MA Stage	WB Stage
ALU	ADD ADDI SUB MUL AND OR XOR LSH SLT SGT	IR ← IM[PC] PC ← NPC = (PC) + 1	ALUout ← (Rs1)op(Rs2)		Rd ← ALUout
LW/SW	LW SW	IR ← IM[PC] PC ← NPC = (PC) + 1	ALUout ← addr = (Rs) + imm	Mout ← M[addr] M[addr] ← (Rs2)	Rd ← Mout(for LW)
Branch	BEQ BNE	IR ← IM[PC] PC ← NPC = (PC) + 1	Target = NPC + imm If (Rs1) = 0 (or ! = 0) PC ← target		
Jump	JR JAL	IR ← IM[PC] PC ← NPC = (PC) + 1	PC ← (Rs1)		Rs ← NPC(for JAL)

such that successive multiply instructions can enter the EX stage every clock cycle. However, individual multiply instructions must use extended cycles to finish their operations and may cause pipeline stalls if subsequent instructions have data dependencies on them.

2. **LW/SW group**

Load/store instructions use the ALU to calculate the effective address in the EX stage and use this address in the displacement addressing mode to read/write data from/into memory in the MA stage. The data read out by the LW instruction is loaded temporarily in the interstage register until it is written back to the destination register, *Rd*, in the WB stage.

3. **Branch group**

This group contains two conditional branch instructions, each of which checks a specified branch condition and generates a target address in order to transfer the program control to a target instruction if the condition is true. These two suboperations of a branch instruction should be mapped to a stage of the pipeline for execution as early as possible. The pipeline will stall and wait until this execution completes. In Table 12.1, the above two suboperations are mapped to the EX stage, resulting in a minimum stall time of one clock cycle. During this stall cycle, the pipeline can be arranged to execute some selected instruction or simply wait with a No-Operation (NOP) instruction depending on the design. We will postpone this discussion until Section 12.4.4. In Table 12.1, we predict an untaken branch, so that the pipeline will continue fetching the next instruction. In case a taken branch is detected in the EX stage, the unused prefetched instruction can be flushed away from the pipeline.

4. **Jump group**
   This group includes two unconditional branch instructions—JAL for calling a subroutine and JR for returning from a subroutine. For both instructions, the target address from register $Rs1$ is loaded into the PC in the EX stage, and for the JAL instruction, the return address is saved in register Rd in the WB stage. The suboperations scheduled in the IF stage are the same as for the Branch group.

12.3.3   Design of the Basic Datapath of the Pipeline

The design of the datapath of the instruction pipeline can be done in two steps. First, a basic preliminary datapath is designed to implement the dataflow pattern in Table 12.1, which maps the execution steps of all the instructions (except MUL and LSH) to the pipeline stages for the given instruction set. This datapath can only be preliminary because it does not consider any additional mechanisms necessary for the resolution of hazards and stall in the pipeline. The second design step will be discussed in the next section, which includes a detailed analysis of the hazards in a pipeline and the modification of the datapath to resolve them.

The basic datapath of the instruction pipeline designed from Table 12.1 is shown in Figure 12.9. From this example, we can see that the design of the basic datapath of an instruction pipeline consists of the following steps.

Step 1.   We can design the logic circuit of each pipeline stage separately from the other stages according to the logic functions derived in Table 12.1. We should first determine the physical placement of the functional units that implement those functions. If a functional unit is dedicated to the logic functions of only one stage, it is placed in that stage. For example, in Figure 12.9, the instruction memory, the ALU, and the data memory should be placed in the IF, EX, and MA stages, respectively. However, if we design the IF and MA stages so that they share a single unified memory, it would result in a structural hazard due to the conflict of usage and a degradation of performance. In some cases, if a functional unit must be shared by two different stages, then it can be shared in a time-multiplexed

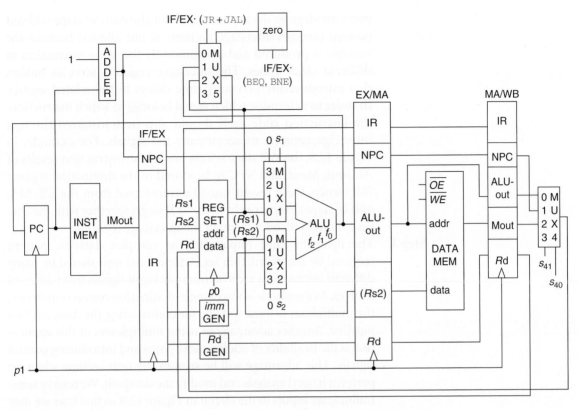

Figure 12.9 The basic datapath implementing the dataflow pattern in Table 12.1

manner. For example, in Figure 12.9, the general-purpose register set must be shared between the EX stage and the WB stage. We place it in the EX stage for Read operations and allow the WB stage to use it for Write operations. This arrangement leads to sharing the Read ports and the Write port of the register set in a two-phase clock cycle, with clock pulse $p0$ controlling the Write operation in phase 0 and clock pulse $p1$ controlling the Read operation in phase 1.

Step 2. As is required in a synchronous pipeline, we must insert an interstage register between each pair of neighboring stages. For example, in Figure 12.9, we inserted three interstage registers, denoted by IF/EX, EX/MA, and MA/WB between the corresponding stages. Interstage registers are used to delimit the stages, synchronize their operations, and pass information between neighboring stages. In Table 12.1, if any stage contains a logic function that uses a variable whose value is produced by a previous stage, then that value must be passed to this stage through an interstage register. Direct connection of the output variable from a previous stage to the input variable of the current stage without passing through interstage registers is not allowed because the variable is produced and consumed by the same instruction in different clock cycles. The interstage registers serve as buffers that introduce the necessary time delays to the related signals. In order to determine which signal belongs to which instruction, the instruction code itself should also be transferred through interstage registers to accompany the signals. For example, in Figure 12.9, the WB stage selects one of the instruction results of ALUout, Mout, and NPC to be stored in the destination register Rd. Hence, these results must be transferred from the EX, MA, and IF stages, respectively, to the WB stage, together with the corresponding OPcodes through the interstage registers.

Step 3. The datapath must implement the complex dataflow pattern required by the instruction set. A functional unit shared by many different instructions receives multiple input signals from different sources. As a multiple-source single-destination connection device, the multiplexer is most suitable for constructing the datapath of a pipeline. Another advantage of using multiplexers in this application is the flexibility of adding more paths and introducing control signals. This advantage will be seen in the next section, when we perform hazard analysis and modify the datapath. We reserve some multiplexer inputs in the circuit of Figure 12.9 so that later we may add new paths to satisfy the needs of hazard resolution.

Step 4. According to the requirement in Table 12.1, branch and jump instructions execute their program-transfer operation in the EX stage in the circuit of Figure 12.9. Like any other instruction, a branch or jump instruction is fetched in the IF stage and uses an adder to update the program counter, PC, to the *next PC* (NPC) value. This NPC value can be loaded into the PC and the interstage register, IF/EX, by the clock pulse $p1$. At this time, the OPcode of the branch or jump instruction has not reached EX stage yet, so the MUX5 selects NPC as its output. After the branch or jump instruction enters the EX stage, its OPcode in the IF/EX register, denoted as either IF/EX.(BEQ + BNE) or IF/EX.(JR + JAL), controls MUX5 to select the target address among NPC, ALUout, and ($Rs1$). Therefore, we can see that MUX5 is placed in the EX stage because its control variables come from the EX stage. However, MUX5 is shared by the IF and EX stages for loading the PC.

Step 5. From the datapath in Figure 12.9, it can be seen that the pipeline is basically a distributed structure. The circuit modules and their control are local to the stages where they are placed to perform the suboperations assigned to them. Some circuits previously designed for the unpipelined control can remain useful for the design of the datapath of the pipeline. For example, in Figure 12.9, two modules named "*imm*GEN" and "*Rd*GEN" in the EX stage can use the same circuit as in Figure 9.20 for the generation of immediate data field and the destination register field. Immediate data generated by *imm*GEN is used in the EX stage, and the destination register number generated by the *Rd*GEN should be propagated to the MA/WB interstage register for use in the WB stage. Similarly, the ALU circuit and its function select code, $f_2 f_1 f_0$, designed for the unpipelined control (e.g., in Figures 9.15 and 9.17) can still be used, with the possible addition of a barrel shifter on the output for LSH and MUL instructions.

12.4 DESIGN OF THE PIPELINE FROM HAZARD ANALYSIS

A simple, basic datapath of an instruction pipeline, as designed in the last section, cannot actually work in practice. It cannot run even a short program with a few instructions owing to the fact that there exist excessive dependencies between instructions, preventing a uniform flow of the instruction stream through the pipeline. These dependencies are called *hazards*. Different types of hazards can be resolved using different methods involving hardware and software (i.e., compiler). Some hazards cannot be resolved by any method except stalling the pipeline. Even stalling the pipeline requires modification of the datapath. We will use the basic datapath of the pipeline in Figure 12.9 and its associated instruction set for a detailed hazard analysis of the pipeline and complete a design of the datapath.

12.4.1 Structural Hazards

Structural hazards can occur in a pipeline when instructions executed in different stages in a time-overlapped manner require the simultaneous use of the same functional units or memory resources. The structural hazard is a special phenomenon that occurs when the hardware resources of the pipeline do not allow all combinations of instructions in the pipeline to execute. For example, if we use a unified memory to fetch the instruction and access the data, then in the same clock cycle two different instructions executed in the IF stage and the MA stage would cause a conflict, resulting in a structural hazard. One instruction may be reading/writing data from/to memory, while the other instruction is just being fetched from the same memory at the same time.

The solution to the structural hazard problem is to add more hardware. As stated in the last section, we are using split memories for fetching instructions and accessing data in two separate stages, IF and MA. Also, we use a separate adder for updating the program counter in the IF stage instead of sharing the same ALU placed in the EX stage. Most importantly, we separate the read ports and write ports of the general-purpose register set and use them in two different phases of a clock cycle. All these solutions can effectively avoid the structural hazards in our example pipeline.

In general, when a pipeline is scheduled statically and the instructions are issued and executed in the program order, structural hazards can be easily solved in hardware by properly designing the datapath. However, when a high-performance pipeline, especially a pipeline in a superscalar processor, needs to execute instructions out of program order for handling complex operations with different latencies, the structural hazards occur more frequently and become more difficult to solve.

12.4.2   Data Hazards—A General Discussion

Data hazards occur when the required data dependencies between instructions cannot be satisfied because of the overlapped execution of the source instruction that produces the data and the destination instruction that consumes the data or two destination instructions that produce data for the same variable.

Data dependencies between instructions are determined by the order of operand access. There are three data hazards that may cause the access order to be changed by the overlapped execution of instructions.

1. *Read After Write* (RAW) hazard caused by a *true dependency*.
    The first instruction writes (produces) data that is read (used) by the second instruction. For example,

    ADD   R3, R1, R2   // R3 ← (R1) + (R2)   produces the result in R3
    SUB   R5, R3, R4   // R5 ← (R3) − (R4)   uses the result (R3) of ADD

2. *Write After Read* (WAR) hazard caused by an *antidependency*.
    The first instruction reads (uses) data that is about to be written (changed) by the second instruction. For example,

    ADD   R3, R1, R2   // R3 ← (R1) + (R2)   uses the data in R1
    SUB   R1, R4, R5   // R1 ← (R4) − (R5)   changes (R1) used by ADD

3. *Write After Write* (WAW) hazard caused by an *output dependency*.
    The first instruction writes (produces) data that is about to be overwritten (updated) by the second instruction. For example,

    ADD   R3, R1, R2   // R3 ← (R1) + (R2)   write the result in R3
    SUB   R3, R4, R5   // R3 ← (R4) − (R5)   overwrite the result in R3

These data dependencies are satisfied in the natural sequences of instructions in a sequential program, but may be violated if the program is to be run on a pipelined or parallel machine, which may execute the first and second instructions in an overlapped or reversed order. In our simple integer pipeline, only the RAW hazards need to be considered. The other two hazards never occur because the "write register" operation is always done in the last stage (WB) and the "read register" operation is done in the second stage (EX).

Furthermore, the three types of dependencies listed above have different properties. The WAR and WAW dependencies are called *name dependencies* because the dependence relations exist only between the names of two identically named variables, and not between their values. They are not true dependencies since we can simply change the name of one variable to remove its dependency on the other variable. The following *register renaming* action between Parts (a) and (b) illustrates this possibility:

(a) ADD $R3, R1, R2$ // $R3 \leftarrow (R1) + (R2)$ $(R3) = (R1) + (R2)$
SUB $R1, R4, R5$ // $R1 \leftarrow (R4) - (R5)$ $(R1) = (R4) - (R5)$
ADD $R1, R1, R6$ // $R1 \leftarrow (R1) + (R6)$ $(R1) = (R1) + (R6)$
$= (R4) - (R5) + (R6)$

(b) ADD $R3, R1, R2$ // $R3 \leftarrow (R1) + (R2)$ $(R3) = (R1) + (R2)$
SUB $Rx, R4, R5$ // $Rx \leftarrow (R4) - (R5)$ $(Rx) = (R4) - (R5)$
ADD $Ry, Rx, R6$ // $Ry \leftarrow (Rx) + (R6)$ $(Ry) = (Rx) + (R6)$
$= (R4) - (R5) + (R6)$

Register renaming does not change the original true data dependence and maintains the equivalence of Ry and $R1$.

12.4.3 Data Hazard Analysis

Now, we will analyze all the possible RAW hazards in our example pipeline generated by different combinations of the instructions from our instruction set. We will use a graphical method for hazard analysis, in which, for each case, we draw a simplified pipeline diagram, identify the hazard, and find a solution to resolve it.

1. *Data Hazard Resolved by Forwarding from ALU Output to ALU Input*

A data hazard exists between two instructions if the first instruction produces an ALU result in the destination register and the second instruction specifies this register as a source register and uses it as an ALU input to perform an operation.

We denote this hazard as Case 1. For example, the following two instruction pairs may cause this type of hazard:

$$
\begin{array}{lll}
\texttt{ADD} & R3, R1, R2 & ; R3 \leftarrow (R1) + (R2) \\
\texttt{SUB} & R4, R3, R2 & ; R4 \leftarrow (R3) - (R2) \\
\texttt{ADD} & R3, R1, R2 & ; R3 \leftarrow (R1) + (R2) \\
\texttt{LW/SW} & R4, disp(R3) & ; R4 \leftarrow M[disp + (R3)] \text{ or } M[disp + (R3)] \leftarrow R4
\end{array}
$$

The writing of the result of the operation into register $R3$ in the WB stage by the first instruction of each pair occurs too late for the second instruction to read it in the EX stage. Hence, a hazard occurs. One method of resolving this type of hazard is the establishment of a forwarding path between the ALU output and one of the ALU inputs through an interstage register so that the second instruction can get the result in advance and bypass the register set. The forwarding path going from the ALUout field of the EX/MA interstage register to the top input of the ALU is shown in Figure 12.10.

To analyze the hazard and derive the logic expression for its detection, we can use a simplified pipeline diagram as shown in Figure 12.11. We use arrows to both indicate the data dependencies in the program and show the forwarding paths in the datapath of the pipeline. In general, each forwarding path should start from an interstage register where the result of the first instruction is stored and end at a device where the forwarded result is to be used. The forwarding path must be used and controlled by the signals that are active in the same clock cycle. For example, in Figure 12.11, the forwarding path is used in the clock cycle when the first instruction is active in the MA stage and the second instruction is active in the EX stage. Therefore, we must use the ALU result stored in the EX/MA interstage register, rather than the result on the output of the ALU (that signal is active only in the EX stage), in the forwarding path.

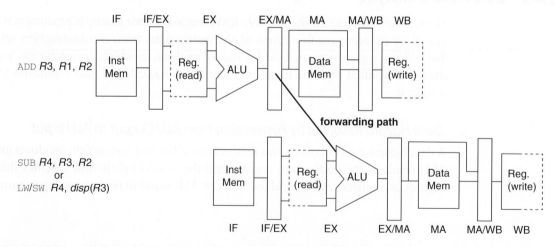

Figure 12.10 Adding a forwarding path to resolve the hazard of Case 1

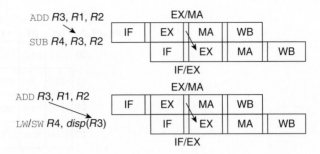

Figure 12.11   A simplified pipeline diagram for the analysis of the hazard of Case 1

To derive logic expressions for detecting the hazard and controlling the forwarding path, we should know what instruction groups may be involved in this type of hazard and what should be the conditions causing the data dependencies to occur. The result of the analysis is as follows:

Concerning the instruction groups in Table 12.1, we know the following:

- Any instruction in the ALU group can serve the first instruction. Any instruction in the ALU group and the LW/SW instructions with Rs (address register) involved in the data dependencies can serve the second instruction for the case of ALU top input. Only the instructions in the ALU group, excluding ADDI and LSH, can serve the second instruction for the case of ALU bottom input.

- All the instructions in the ALU group have the Rd field in IR_3–IR_0 and the $Rs2$ field in IR_7–IR_4 for the case of ALU bottom input (except ADDI and LSH). All the instructions in the ALU group and the LW/SW group have the $Rs1$ or Rs field in IR_{11}–IR_8 for the case of ALU top input.

- Figure 12.12 shows the Karnaugh map of the OPcodes of the instruction set in Table 9.3. We can derive the expressions for the common OPcodes of the ALU group, the LW/SW group, and the ALU group, excluding ADDI and LSH instructions, as follows:

$$\{ALU\} = \overline{IR_{15}} + \overline{IR_{14}}\,IR_{13},$$

$$\{LW/SW\} = IR_{15}\,\overline{IR_{14}} \cdot \overline{IR_{13}},$$

$$\{ALU\} - \{ADDI, LSH\} = \overline{IR_{15}} \cdot \overline{IR_{14}} \cdot \overline{IR_{13}} \cdot \overline{IR_{12}} + IR_{14}\,IR_{13}\,IR_{12}.$$

$$= \overline{IR_{15}} \cdot \overline{IR_{14} \oplus IR_{13}} \cdot IR_{12}$$

(12.5)

- Since the instruction set does not include a NOP instruction, we must use the instruction code of all 0s to replace it. However, the OPcode "0000" is

$IR_{13}IR_{12}$ \ $IR_{15}IR_{14}$	00	01	11	10
00	ADD	AND	BEQ	LW
01	ADDI	OR	BNE	SW
11	MUL	LSH	JAL	SGT
10	SUB	XOR	JR	SLT

Figure 12.12 Karnaugh map of the OPcodes from Table 9.3

an ADD instruction. In order to avoid an erroneous matching condition of $Rs1$ (Rs) and Rd when both are "0000", we must detect the condition when "0000" is incorrectly used as a destination register number.

From the above analysis, we can derive the expressions for controlling the forwarding paths from EX/MA.ALUout to the inputs of the ALU as follows:

To the top input of the ALU:

EX/MA.{ALU} AND   //first instruction in ALU group
IF/EX.({ALU}OR{LW/SW}) AND   //second instruction in ALU or LW/SW
group
$(EX/MA.(IR_3 - IR_0) = IF/EX.(IR_{11} - IR_8))$ AND   //Rd of 1st instruction = $Rs1$
of 2nd instruction
$(EX/MA.(IR_3 - IR_0) \neq 0)$ //Rd of 1st instr. must not be numbered 0   **(12.6)**

To the bottom input of the ALU:

EX/MA.{ALU} AND   //first instruction in ALU group
IF/EX.({ALU} – {ADDI, LSH}) AND   //second instruction in ALU group
//excluding ADDI and LSH
$(EX/MA.(IR_3 - IR_0) = IF/EX.(IR_7 - IR_4))$ AND   //Rd of 1st instruction = $Rs2$
of 2nd instruction
$(EX/MA.(IR_3 - IR_0) \neq 0)$ //Rd of 1st instr. must not be numbered 0   **(12.7)**

2. *Data Hazard Resolved by Forwarding from ALU Output to Branch Input*

A hazard similar to the one in Case 1 exists between two instructions if the first one produces an ALU result in the destination register and the second one is a branch instruction that uses this register as a source register to specify the branch condition. Therefore, the forwarding path to resolve the hazard starts from the ALU output and ends at the input of a zero detector used by the branch instruction.

We denote this hazard as Case 2. For example, the following instruction pair causes this type of hazard:

```
SUB    R3, R1, R2      ; R3 ← (R1) − (R2)
BEQ    R3, offset      ; if (R3) = 0, PC ← (PC) + offset, else
                         PC ← (PC) + 1
                       ; where offset is in the "immediate" field of BEQ
```

A branch instruction uses the ALU only to calculate the target address (PC) + *offset*. This calculation does not involve source and destination registers. However, a branch or jump instruction may have its source register involved in a hazard if its register number coincides with the number of the destination register in an instruction immediately preceding it. This hazard can be resolved by a forwarding path starting from the ALUout field of the EX/MA interstage register to the input of the zero detector.

The simplified pipeline diagram is shown in Figure 12.13. The logic expression for detecting the hazard and controlling the forwarding path for this case is derived as follows:

EX/MA.{ALU} AND   //first instruction in ALU group

IF/EX.({Branch}OR{Jump}) AND   //second instruction in Branch or Jump
$\qquad$ group

$(EX/MA.(IR_3 - IR_0) = IF/EX (IR_{11} - IR_8))$ AND   //Rd of 1st instruction = $Rs1$
$\qquad$ of 2nd instruction

$(EX/MA.(IR_3 - IR_0) \neq 0)$ //Rd of 1st instr. must not be numbered 0 $\qquad$ **(12.8)**

3. *Data Hazard Resolved by Forwarding from ALU Output to Memory Input*

A data hazard exists between two instructions if the first instruction produces an ALU result in a destination register and the second instruction is a Store instruction that specifies this register as a source register and stores it in memory. Therefore, the forwarding path to resolve the hazard starts from the ALU output and ends at the data input of memory through two interstage registers. We denote this hazard as Case 3. For example, in the following instruction pair, ADD produces the sum of (R1) and (R2) and SW stores it in memory.

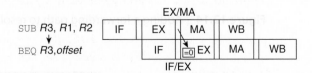

Figure 12.13 A simplified pipeline diagram for the analysis of the hazard of Case 2

ADD $R3, R1, R2$; $R3 \leftarrow (R1) + (R2)$
SW $disp(R4), R3$; $M[disp + (R4)] \leftarrow R3$

The pipeline diagram related to the above example is shown in Figure 12.14. Because the difference between the time of data generation by the ADD instruction and the time of data consumption by the SW instruction equals two clock cycles, the ALUout in the EX stage must be stored in the EX/MA interstage register and then transferred to the MA/WB interstage register in the next clock cycle. The forwarding path connects the ALUout field of the MA/WB interstate register with the data input of the memory as indicated in Figure 12.14.

The hazard in the previous example can be analyzed using the simplified pipeline diagram shown in Figure 12.15. The hazard in Case 3 can be caused by a combination of any instruction from the ALU group (the first instruction) and the SW instruction (the second instruction). Therefore, the logic expression for detecting the hazard and controlling the forwarding path can be derived as follows:

MA/WB.{ALU} AND   //first instruction in ALU group
EX/MA.SW AND   //second instruction must be SW
$(MA/WB.(IR_3 - IR_0) = EX/MA.(IR_7 - IR_4))$ AND   //Rd of 1st instr. = Rd of SW instruction
$(MA/WB.(IR_3 - IR_0) \neq 0)$ //Rd of 1st instr. must not be numbered 0   **(12.9)**

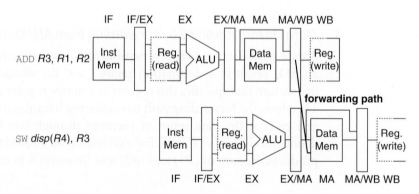

Figure 12.14 Adding a forwarding path to resolve the hazard of Case 3

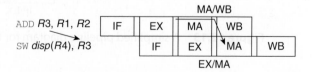

Figure 12.15 A simplified pipeline diagram for the analysis of the hazard of Case 3

4.   *Data Hazard Resolved by Forwarding from Memory Output to Memory Input*

There exists a data hazard between a load memory instruction and a store memory instruction if the first instruction is a Load instruction that produces a memory read result in a destination register and the second instruction is a Store instruction that specifies this destination register as a source register and stores the memory result back to memory. Therefore, the forwarding path goes from the memory output to the memory input through an interstage register. We denote this hazard as Case 4. For example, in the following instruction pair, LW reads the data from a memory location, and SW stores the same data into a different memory location.

LW $R3, disp(R1)$; $R3 \leftarrow M[disp + (R1)]$
SW $disp(R2), R3$; $M[disp + (R2)] \leftarrow R3$

The pipeline diagram related to the above example is shown in Figure 12.16. Because the memory output from the first instruction needs to be delayed one clock cycle in order to be used by the second instruction, we load it into the MA/WB interstage register and forward it from there to the input of the data memory. This forwarding path connecting the memory output with the memory data input is indicated in Figure 12.16.

The above hazard can be analyzed using the simplified pipeline diagram shown in Figure 12.17. This type of hazard only occurs when the LW instruction is the first instruction and the SW instruction is the second instruction. Therefore, the logic expression to detect the hazard and control the forwarding path can be derived as follows:

MA/WB.LW   AND   //First instruction must be LW
EX/MA.SW   AND   //Second instruction must be SW   **(12.10)**
(MA/WB.$(IR_7 - IR_4)$) = EX/MA.$(IR_7 - IR_4)$) //Rd of LW instr. = Rd of SW
                                          instruction

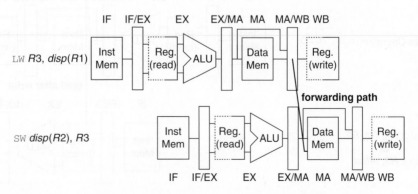

Figure 12.16   Adding a forwarding path to resolve the hazard of Case 4

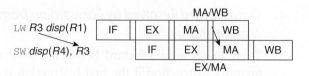

Figure 12.17 A simplified pipeline diagram for the analysis of the hazards of Case 4

5. *Load Interlock*

If the first instruction is a Load instruction that produces a memory Read result in a destination register, and the second instruction is any instruction that uses the memory output in an operation executed in the EX stage, a hazard exists which we will denote as Case 5. This hazard cannot be resolved by forwarding, and it will cause a one-cycle stall of the pipeline. For example, in the following two instruction pairs, LW reads the data from memory, and ADD (or BNE) uses the data in an add (or test) operation which is executed in the EX stage.

LW	$R3, disp(R1)$	; $R3 \leftarrow M[disp + (R1)]$
ADD	$R4, R3, R2$	; $(R4) \leftarrow (R3) + (R2)$
LW	$R3, disp(R1)$	; $R3 \leftarrow M[disp + (R1)]$
BNE	$R3, offset$	; if $(R3) \neq 0, PC \leftarrow (PC) + offset$, else $PC \leftarrow (PC) + 1$
		; where *offset* is in the "immediate" field of BNE

The pipeline diagram related to the above examples is shown in Figure 12.18. Because the time at which the MA stage produces memory data is later than the

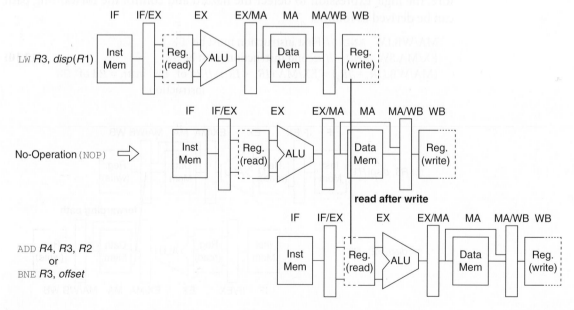

Figure 12.18 A stall plus a RAW mechanism used to resolve the hazard of Case 5

time at which the EX stage consumes the data, no forwarding path can be built to resolve this hazard. The only way to move "forward in negative time" is to delay the data-consuming component. Therefore, we must introduce an alternative method of hazard resolution—a *pipeline stall*. From the pipeline diagram in Figure 12.18, we can see that the pipeline stall is implemented by inserting an instruction of No-Operation (NOP) (sometimes called a *bubble*) into the instruction stream. This NOP instruction can be represented as a series of 0s, which does no activity except delaying the pipelined instruction stream by one clock cycle. After this time delay, the result of instruction 1 can be written into the register set before instruction 2 reads it. Thus, the hazard can be removed automatically by a *read-after-write* mechanism in the hardware of the datapath. The read-after-write mechanism associating the Write port with the Read ports of the register set is indicated by a vertical line in Figure 12.18.

The graphical notation used to represent a stall in the simplified pipeline diagram is shown in Figure 12.19. The delay of the second instruction is represented as a time slot of "stall" inserted in its execution pattern. The EX stage of the second instruction is aligned with the WB stage of the LW instruction, so that a read-after-write mechanism comes into effect that makes any forwarding path unnecessary. This hazard case and its resolution by stalling the pipeline is called *load interlock*. For deriving the logic expression for the condition of load interlock, we observe that the first instruction must be a LW instruction and the second instruction can be any instruction from any of the groups—the ALU group (with respect to either the first source register or the second source register), the LW/SW group (with respect to the address register only), or the Branch and Jump groups (with respect to the source register $Rs1$). Therefore, the logic expression for detecting the hazard and controlling the stall can be derived as follows:

stall for load interlock =
$\quad$ IF/EX.LW AND $\qquad$ //First instruction must be LW
$\quad$ $(\text{IF/EX.}(IR_7 - IR_4) = \text{IM.}(IR_{11} - IR_8))$ OR
$\qquad\qquad\qquad$ //Rd of 1st instr. = Rs of any 2nd instr.
$\quad$ $(\text{IM.}\{\text{ALU}\}$ AND $(\text{IF/EX.}(IR_7 - IR_4) = \text{IM.}(IR_7 - IR_4)))$
$\qquad\qquad\qquad$ //or Rd of 1st instr. = Rs2 of a 2nd ALU instr. $\qquad$ **(12.11)**

where IM denotes the output of the instruction memory in the IF stage.

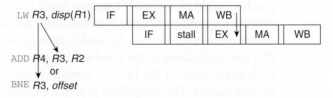

Figure 12.19   A simplified pipeline diagram for the analysis of the hazards of Case 5

Pipeline stalls and their implementation in a datapath will be further discussed in the next section.

12.4.4 Control Hazards

In the last section, we analyzed all the possible data hazards that can occur in our example pipeline. Besides the data hazards, there is another type of hazard called *control hazard* that can be caused by instructions in the Branch and Jump groups. Just as data hazards are caused by unavailability of data, control hazards are due to the unavailability of control information. Control hazards are more difficult to resolve than data hazards. We need to find new solutions that include stalling the pipeline. Since control hazards occur most frequently in loop- and branch-intensive programs, their impact on the pipeline performance in the exploitation of instruction-level parallelism can be very significant. Therefore, methods of resolving control hazards due to branch and jump instructions will be discussed in this section.

For a discussion of control hazards, we need to know how the branch and jump instructions are implemented in the datapath. We will use the following branch instruction as an example:

SUB $R3, R1, R2$; $R3 \leftarrow (R1) - (R2)$
BEQ $R3$, *target*   ; if $(R3) = 0$, transfer to the target
                                              instruction, else continue,
                                   ; where target is a label pointing to
                                              the target instruction

A control hazard occurs when the BEQ instruction is executed by the processor. The outcome of the branch instruction depends on the state of its branch condition, that is, the contents of $R3$. If the branch instruction detects a true condition and changes the PC to its target address, it is a *taken branch*. Otherwise, if a branch detects a false condition and simply updates the PC to its next address, $(PC) + 1$, it is an *untaken branch*. In the preliminary design of the basic datapath in Figure 12.9, we placed the branch control logic in the EX stage. Therefore, the PC is normally not changed until the end of EX stage, after the completion of the comparison in the zero detector and the target address calculation in the ALU. Prior to knowing whether the branch will be taken and where the target address will go, the next instruction that may have already been fetched into the pipeline could be useless. Therefore, there is always a delay of one clock cycle to execute a conditional branch instruction. Similarly, a one-cycle delay exists in the execution of an unconditional branch or jump instruction as well. A hazard that causes the delay of the pipeline due to unavailability of control information, such as the state of the branch condition and/or the target address, is called a *control hazard*. The simplified pipeline diagram to demonstrate this hazard is shown in Figure 12.20.

Figure 12.20 A simplified pipeline diagram for the analysis of a control hazard

There are several methods to resolve the control hazard caused by a branch or jump instruction:

1. **Pipeline stall**

   The simplest way to solve the problem of branch interlock is to stall the pipeline as soon as the branch or jump instruction is detected at the beginning of the EX stage until it finishes the compare operation and the target address calculation. The pipeline stall is implemented by inserting a NOP instruction into the instruction stream running on the pipeline. This solution results in performance loss due to a one-cycle stall per branch instruction.

2. **Branch prediction**

   There are many different methods of branch prediction. The simplest method is to predict the branch outcome as untaken so that the pipeline can continue fetching the next instruction in the program order. The pipeline should be flushed by removing the prefetched instruction only when the branch condition is determined as TRUE and the branch outcome is a branch taken. The control of flushing in this method is similar to the control of stall in the first method, but the flush is done only when the branch is taken.

3. **Delayed branch**

   A method called a *delayed branch* is to reserve a free time slot called *branch delay slot* after each branch instruction. An instruction is placed in this time slot so that it can always be executed irrespective of the branch instruction, conditional or unconditional, or if the branch is taken or untaken.

4. **Multiple streams**

   Another method utilizes two streams for taken and untaken branches. After the outcome of the branch instruction is known, the correct one of two streams is chosen to continue.

5. **Loop buffer**

   Another method uses a small, fast memory in the IF stage for storing the entire loop body. The IF stage can prefetch the next instruction after the branch instruction while executing the loop program.

1. *Pipeline Stall Due to Branch Interlock*

A stall due to a branch or jump instruction is sometimes called a *branch interlock*. It is similar to the load interlock discussed in Section 12.4.3.5. Both interlocks can be solved by the same pipeline stall logic in the datapath. Both interlocks require that a NOP instruction be inserted into the instruction stream. For example,

Load Interlock:

LW $R3, disp(R1)$; $R3 \leftarrow M[disp + (R1)]$
No operation
ADD $R4, R3, R2$; $(R4) \leftarrow (R3) + (R2)$

Branch interlock:

BEQ $R3, target$; if $(R3) = 0$, branch to the instruction labeled as "*target*"
No operation
Target instruction

We will analyze branch interlock using a simplified pipeline diagram and a timing diagram as shown in Figure 12.21. The timing diagram in Part (b) depicts the detailed steps in time, $t_0, t_1, \ldots, t_4$, of the execution process of the above instruction stream with an inserted NOP. We can see that all four instructions flow through the pipeline continuously. The NOP should be detected at time interval t_2 and then inserted into the EX stage at time interval t_3. So, the target instruction (if branch taken) or the next instruction (if branch untaken) will be delayed until time interval t_3 before it enters the pipeline. To detect the NOP at time interval t_2, we derive the logic expression for a control signal, "stall for branch interlock," as follows:

$$\text{stall for branch interlock} = \text{IF/EX}.(\{\text{Branch}\}\text{OR}\{\text{Jump}\}) \tag{12.12}$$

and use this signal to insert a NOP into the IF/EX interstage register. The implementation of the pipeline stall logic is shown in Figure 12.24 as follows:

1. Connect a set of 2×1 multiplexers on the input of the IR field of the IF/EX interstage register.
2. Use the multiplexers to select between the output of the instruction memory (IM) and the NOP instruction (all 0s).
3. Use "stall" as the control voltage on the multiplexers so that if stall = 0, it selects the output of the instruction memory, else, if stall = 1, it selects NOP as the instruction code to be loaded into the IR field of the IF/EX interstage register.
4. Use $\overline{stall}$ to inhibit the operation of (PC) + 1 by the adder, so that if a branch is untaken, the next instruction at time interval t_3 will be the same as the next instruction at time interval t_2.

The above pipeline stall logic designed for solving branch interlock can be used to solve load interlock as well. We can derive exactly the same expression for the stall signal as Expression (12.11) using the simplified pipeline diagram and the timing diagram for the analysis of the load interlock as shown in Figure 12.22 for detecting the NOP at time interval t_1. The expression (12.11) should be ORed with Expression (12.12) to form a single signal "stall" for controlling the pipeline stall due to either branch interlock or load interlock. The above-stated four-step implementation of the pipeline stall logic for the branch interlock also applies to the load interlock.

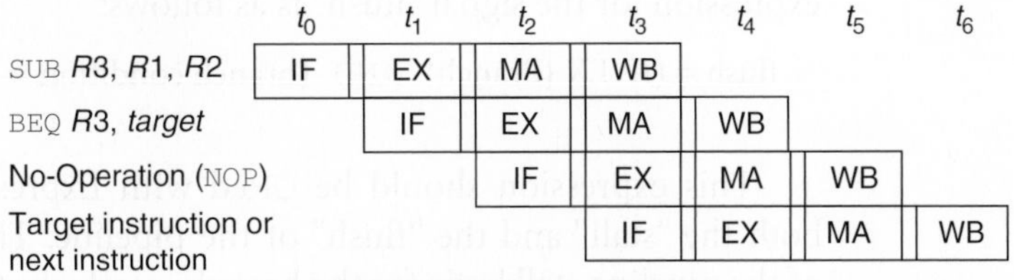

	t_0	t_1	t_2	t_3	t_4	t_5	t_6
SUB $R3, R1, R2$	IF	EX	MA	WB			
BEQ $R3$, target		IF	EX	MA	WB		
No-Operation (NOP)			IF	EX	MA	WB	
Target instruction or next instruction				IF	EX	MA	WB

(a) Simplified pipeline diagram

Time	IF Stage	EX Stage	MA Stage	WB Stage
t_0	SUB			
t_1	BEQ	SUB		
t_2	next instr.	BEQ	SUB	
t_3	target or next instr.	NOP	(BEQ)	SUB
t_4	....	target or next instr.	NOP	(BEQ)

(b) Timing diagram of the execution process

Figure 12.21   Pipeline and timing diagrams for the analysis of branch interlock

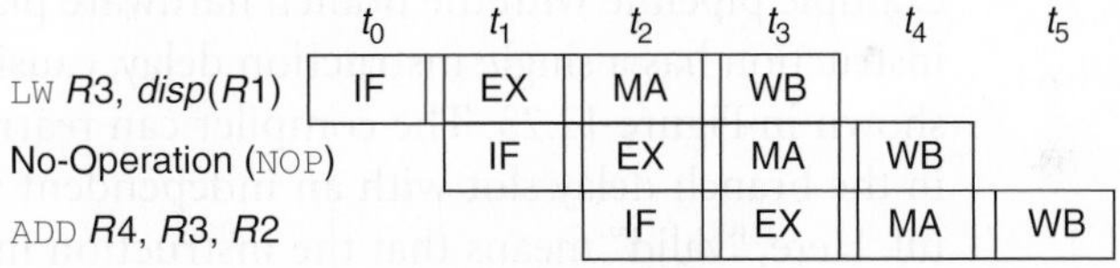

	t_0	t_1	t_2	t_3	t_4	t_5
LW $R3, disp(R1)$	IF	EX	MA	WB		
No-Operation (NOP)		IF	EX	MA	WB	
ADD $R4, R3, R2$			IF	EX	MA	WB

(a) Simplified pipeline diagram

Time	IF Stage	EX Stage	MA Stage	WB Stage
t_0	LB			
t_1	ADD	LW		
t_2	ADD	NOP	LW	
t_4	...	ADD	NOP	LW

(b) Timing diagram of the execution process

Figure 12.22   Pipeline and timing diagrams for the analysis of load interlock

2. Flushing the Pipeline during a Branch Taken

This section describes the implementation of the method of "Predict branch untaken." In this scheme, the next instruction in the program order is prefetched after each branch instruction. If the prediction succeeds by having a branch untaken, continue the prefetched instruction without penalty. Otherwise, flush the pipeline and fetch a new instruction from the target address of the branch instruction.

Using Figure 12.21 for the analysis of branch interlock, we can derive the logic expression for the control signal, which flushes the pipeline when the branch instruction has a misprediction and detects a branch taken. The logic expression for the signal "flush" is as follows:

$$\text{flush} = (\text{IF/EX.\{Branch\}} \text{ AND } (\text{branch condition} = \text{TRUE})) \text{ OR } \text{IF/EX.\{Jump\}}$$
$$(\textbf{12.13})$$

This expression should be ORed with Expression (12.12) for controlling both the "stall" and the "flush" of the pipeline. The four-step implementation of the pipeline stall logic for the branch interlock stated above in the last section also applies to this case of flush control.

Besides the prediction of branch untaken, there are many other branch prediction schemes, static (at compile time) or dynamic (depending on the execution history), by software or hardware. "Predict untaken" is the simplest one. It should be noted that for such a simple prediction scheme, "Predict taken" has no benefit on our example pipeline because the branch condition is known at the same time as the target address is known.

3. *Delayed Branch*

A pipeline stall after each branch instruction results in performance loss. It creates branch delay slots normally not used by subsequent instructions. For our example pipeline with the branch hardware placed in the EX stage, each branch instruction has a single instruction delay, causing only one branch delay slot, as shown in Figure 12.23. The compiler can rearrange the instructions so as to fill in the branch delay slot with an independent instruction that is valid and useful. Here, "valid" means that the instruction inserted into the branch delay slot can be executed whether or not the branch instruction is taken. If the compiler cannot choose an eligible instruction, a NOP instruction will fill the branch delay slot instead. Hence, no special hardware is necessary for stalling or flushing the pipeline. This method is especially attractive for a simple processor that does not need extra hardware to resolve control hazards, but provides more opportunities for the compiler to improve performance.

Branch	IF	ID	EX	MEM	WB		
Branch delay instr.		IF	ID	EX	MEM	WB	(Branch delay slot)
Successor instr. of branch			IF	ID	EX	MEM	WB

Figure 12.23   Resolving a control hazard by a delayed branch

Example 12.5   A Short Assembly-Language Code with a Delayed Branch

The following code calculates the sum of two data arrays, A and B, of size $n = 32$, stored in memory with the starting addresses, *Astart* and *Bstart*, respectively. The result $C = A + B$ is to be stored in memory with the starting address *Cstart*.

```
        ADD   R1, R0, R0      ; R1 ← 0
        ADDI  R2, R0, #4      ; R2 ← 0 + 4 = 4
        LSH   R2, R2, #-3     ; R2 ← (R2)<<3 = 32
LOOP:   LW    R3, Astart(R1)  ; R3 ← M[Astart + (R1)]
                              ;      = A[i]
        LW    R4, Bstart(R1)  ; R4 ← M[Bstart + (R1)]
                              ;      = B[i]
        ADD   R5, R3, R4      ; R5 ← (R3) + (R4)
        SW    Cstart(R1), R5  ; M[Cstart + (R1)] ←
                              ;      (R5) = C[i]
        ADDI  R1, R1, #1      ; R1 ← (R1) + 1
        SLT   R6, R1, R2      ; if (R1)<(R2), R6 ← 1,
                              ;   else R6 ← 0
        BNE   R6, LOOP        ; loop until (R1) = 32
        EXIT
```

It is not easy to obtain an instruction in the above code to fill in the branch delay slot without changing instructions inside the program. If some minor change in the original program is allowed, solutions to overcome the difficulty can be found. The following are two possible solutions.

Solution 1
The instruction "`ADDI R1, R1, #1`" could be moved into the branch delay slot, but we must change the value in $R2$ from 32 to 31, so that the loop still repeats 32 times by comparing $(R1) = 0$ to 31 with the value $(R2) = 31$.

Solution 2
The first `LW` instruction in the loop could be moved into the branch delay slot, but we must add one `LW` instruction to the original code, which is used in the first iteration of the loop body. Then, starting from the second iteration, the first operand, $A[i]$, will be accessed after the `BNE` instruction, and the second operand, $B[i]$, will be accessed at the beginning of the loop. In the last iteration, the extra operand $A[i]$ accessed after the `BNE` instruction will be useless and not affect the program's results.

■

12.4.5 The Complete Datapath of the Pipeline

From the results of the hazard analysis obtained above, we can now modify the basic datapath we designed (shown in Figure 12.9) and obtain a final version of the datapath of our example pipeline as shown in Figure 12.24. The major differences between this modified datapath and the one shown in Figure 12.9 are the additions of the forwarding paths and the pipeline stall logic to implement the design discussed in Sections 12.4.3 and 12.4.4. We have added multiplexers and inputs to multiplexers to provide hardware support for these additional functions.

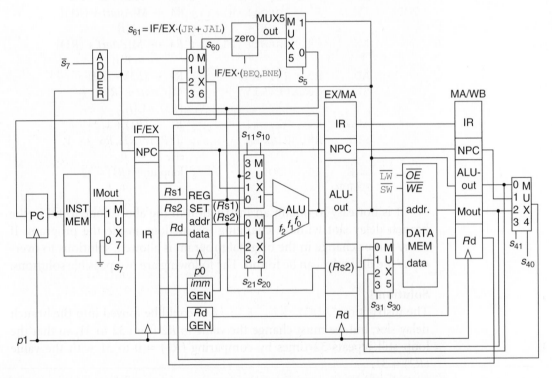

Figure 12.24 Complete datapath of the example pipeline that modifies Figure 12.9

All the multiplexers and their control signals in Figure 12.24 are listed as follows.

1. MUX1 at the top input of the ALU:

   $s_{11}s_{10} = 00$:   input ($Rs1$), default, no control

   $s_{11}s_{10} = 01$:   input NPC controlled by IF/EX.{Branch} = s_{10}

   $s_{11}s_{10} = 10$:   input EX/MA.ALUout controlled by Expression (12.6) = s_{11}

2. MUX2 at the bottom input of the ALU:

   $s_{21}s_{20} = 00$:   input ($Rs2$), default, no control

$s_{21}s_{20} = 01$: input *imm* controlled by IF/EX.(ADDI + {LW/SW} + {Branch}) = s_{20}

$s_{21}s_{20} = 10$: input EX/MA.ALUout controlled by Expression (12.7) = s_{21}

3. MUX3 at the data input of the data memory:

$s_{31}s_{30} = 00$: input EX/MA.(*Rs2*), default, no control

$s_{31}s_{30} = 01$: input MA/WB.ALUout controlled by Expression (12.9) = s_{30}

$s_{31}s_{30} = 10$: input MA/WB.Mout controlled by Expression (12.10) = s_{31}

4. MUX4 at the data input of the register set:

$s_{41}s_{40} = 00$: input MA/WB.ALUout, default, no control

$s_{41}s_{40} = 01$: input MA/WB.NPC controlled by MA/WB.JAL = s_{40}

$s_{41}s_{40} = 10$: input MA/WB.Mout controlled by MA/WB.LW = s_{41}

5. MUX5 at the input of the zero detector:

$s_{51}s_{50} = 0$: input (*Rs1*), default, no control

$s_{51}s_{50} = 1$: input EX/MA.ALUout controlled by Expression (12.8) = s_{50}

6. MUX6 at the input of the PC:

$s_{61}s_{60} = 00$: input (PC)+$\overline{stall}$, default, no control

$s_{61}s_{60} = 01$: input ALUout controlled by Expression (12.15) = s_{60}

$s_{61}s_{60} = 10$: input (*Rs1*) controlled by IF/EX.{Jump} = s_{61}

where the logic expression for the logic circuit of the zero detector is:

$$zero\ detector\ out = (\text{IF/EX} \cdot \text{BEQ AND } \overline{MUX6out})$$
$$\text{OR } (\text{IF/EX} \cdot \text{BNE AND } MUX6out) \tag{12.14}$$

7. MUX7 at the output of the instruction memory:

$s_7 = 0$: input IMout, default, no control

$s_7 = 1$: input NOP controlled by Expression (12.12) OR (12.13) = s_7 if branch stall or Expression (12.12) OR (12.14) = s_7 if branch prediction

12.5 SUPERSCALAR PROCESSOR

In this section, we describe the features of a superscalar processor and its conceptual structure. The instruction-issue and instruction-completion of the processor is also discussed in detail.

12.5.1 Special Features of a Superscalar Processor

A superscalar processor is a high-performance scalar processor that can offer superior speed. Speed is measured in units of *CPI*, and a superscalar processor can achieve a speed equal to a small fraction of one *CPI*. If a processor with a single instruction pipeline can achieve a maximum speed of *CPI* = 1, then a superscalar processor has the ability to execute multiple instruction streams independently in multiple instruction pipelines at the same time. Superscalar processors are usually ranked by the number of instructions, k, issued per clock cycle, and a particular processor is referred to as a k-issue processor. For example, different instruction pipelines in a superscalar processor can be of several types, as follows:

- Integer instruction pipelines
- Floating-point instruction pipelines
- Load/store instruction pipelines

...

The pipeline diagram of a two-issue superscalar processor can be represented as shown in Figure 12.25(b). Each pipeline consists of five stages—and one extra stage to perform Instruction Decode (ID). We will see the important function performed by the ID stage for a superscalar processor in the following discussion.

IF	ID	EX	MA	WB		
	IF	ID	EX	MA	WB	
		IF	ID	EX	MA	WB

(a) Base machine

IF	ID	EX	MA	WB		
IF	ID	EX	MA	WB		
	IF	ID	EX	MA	WB	
	IF	ID	EX	MA	WB	
		IF	ID	EX	MA	WB
		IF	ID	EX	MA	WB

(b) Two-issue superscalar processor

Figure 12.25   Pipeline diagram of a two-issue superscalar processor vs. a one-issue base machine

The second special feature of a superscalar processor, distinct from a base machine, is its ability to issue and execute instructions in an order different from the program order. This ability is necessary to fully utilize multiple instruction pipelines to exploit instruction-level parallelism in the program. Thus, the parallel jobs performed by multiple instruction pipelines can be scheduled as follows:

- Fetch multiple instructions at an instant in time.
- Dispatch nearby independent instructions.

- Issue multiple instructions at the same time (this can be in-order issuing or out-of-order issuing).
- Have multiple resources (functional units, memory modules, and so on) execute instructions in parallel (this can be in-order completion or out-of-order completion).

12.5.2 Conceptual Structure of a Superscalar Processor

The general conceptual structure of a superscalar processor is shown in Figure 12.26. It gives an overview of superscalar execution of programs on multiple instruction pipelines of a processor. The structure consists of the following steps (Shen 2003):

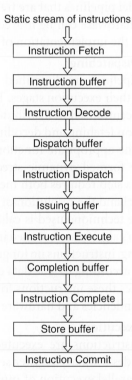

Figure 12.26 Conceptual structure of a superscalar processor

1. **Instruction Fetching**

   For a superscalar processor, multiple instructions should be fetched from the I-cache in every machine cycle. The I-cache should have a wide physical organization with the row width of the cache array equal to the fetch width. Typically, a cache block corresponds to a physical row or spans several physical rows of the cache array. The Instruction Fetch stage should maximize the instruction fetching bandwidth so that the access latency of the I-cache equals one machine cycle. The instructions in a fetch group are deposited in the same instruction buffer. In order to fetch multiple instructions simultaneously, this step requires the use of multiple pipeline fetch, decode stages, and branch prediction logic.

2. **Instruction Decoding**

All the instructions in the fetch group are decoded collectively by a centralized parallel decoder. The decoding involves the identification of individual instructions, determination of their types, and detection of interinstruction dependencies. The objective of this step is to form a dynamic stream of instructions that involves the solution of various types of dependencies and branch prediction policies. To alleviate the complexity of decoding and to create parallel pipelines that are free from sequential bottlenecks, some of the decoding hardware can be moved to the input side of the I-cache. This has motivated the implementation of a technique called *predecoding*.

3. **Instruction Dispatching**

Superscalar pipelines are diversified pipelines that employ different functional units in their execution stages. Therefore, the overall pipeline structure changes from centralized to distributed at the instruction dispatching stage. After instruction fetching and decoding, different types of instructions must be routed to the appropriate functional units for execution. The processor dispatches the formed dynamic stream of instructions into a window of execution. This step requires both mechanisms for issuing multiple instructions in parallel and the resolution of name dependencies by way of register renaming. The technique used is called *dynamic scheduling*, and originated with Tomasulo's algorithm first used in the IBM 360/91 system. After instruction dispatching, instructions no longer form a sequential stream, but instead are structured according to true data dependencies. The dynamic scheduling algorithm issues these instructions for execution in an order determined by true data dependencies and hardware resource availability.

4. **Instruction Execution**

The issued instructions are executed in parallel in multiple instruction pipelines. Besides ordinary register set and memory modules, the resources required for parallel execution of multiple instructions in this step, according to Tomasulo's algorithm, include the following:

- Multiple pipelined functional units.
- Reservation stations serving the temporary instruction buffers attached to different functional units.
- Memory load/store buffers capable of simultaneously servicing multiple memory references.
- A common data bus (CDB) interconnecting all the resources for data transfer.

5. **Instruction Completion and Instruction Retiring**

An instruction is considered completed when it completes execution, but has not yet updated the machine state. Completing execution is represented by exiting the functional units and entering the completion buffers. After execution, instructions are conceptually put back into sequential order and their results are recorded. Thus, the completed instructions enter a step of Instruction Commit or Retiring. This is a special step needed by the use of parallel, multiple instruction pipelines because some data may be changed or abandoned due to out-of-order execution, out-of-order completion, or branch prediction. This step will provide the mechanisms for committing the process state in a correct order. Before commit, the results are stored temporarily. Commit moves the final results into permanent storage (to update CPU registers and memory).

12.5.3 Instruction-Issue and Instruction-Execute Policies

In a superscalar processor, machine parallelism is not simply a matter of having multiple instruction pipelines. The processor must also be able to identify instruction-level parallelism and schedule the fetching, decoding, and execution of instructions in parallel. Therefore, it is very important to have good instruction-issue and instruction-completion policies. In essence, the processor should be able to look ahead from the current point of execution to locate instructions that can be brought into the pipeline and executed. This look-ahead scheduling should determine three types of orderings, namely:

- The order in which instructions are fetched.
- The order in which instructions are executed.
- The order in which instructions update the contents of registers and memory locations.

In general, superscalar instruction issue and completion policies can be grouped into the three categories to be addressed in the following sections (Stallings 2003).

1. In-Order Issue with In-Order Completion

Instructions are issued in the exact order that would be achieved by sequential execution (in-order issue) and write results in that same order (in-order completion). This policy is too simplistic to be used even in ordinary scalar pipelines. However, it is useful to consider this policy as a baseline when discussing more sophisticated approaches.

Figure 12.27 provides an example of this policy. The superscalar pipeline is assumed to be capable of fetching and decoding two instructions at a time. It has three separate functional units and two instances of write-back pipeline stages.

This example assumes the following constraints on a six-instruction code fragment:

```
I1:    MUL    R3, R1, R2   // MUL executes in 2 cycles
I2:    AND    R4, R1, R2   // The rest executes in 1 cycle
                           //   each
I3:    ADD    R5, R1, R2
I4:    SUB    R6, R1, R2
I5:    ADDI   R7, R6, #4
I6:    SUBI   R8, R2, #4
```

- If I3 and I4 are paired, they conflict for the same functional unit
- If I5 and I6 are paired, they conflict for the same functional unit
- I5 depends on the value of *R6* produced by I4

Instructions are fetched two at a time and passed to the decode unit. To ensure in-order completion, when functional units are not available due to conflict or long execution time, the issuing of instructions temporarily stalls. The scheduling result is shown in Figure 12.27. The total execution time is eight cycles.

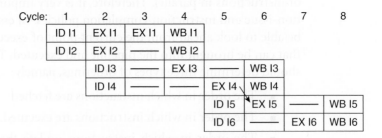

Figure 12.27 An example with in-order issue and in-order completion

2. In-Order Issue with Out-of-Order Completion

With out-of-order completion, any number of instructions may be in the execution stage simultaneously up to the maximum number of available functional units. Instruction issuing is stalled by a resource conflict, a data dependency, or a control dependency. The scheduling of the example is shown in Figure 12.28. Instruction I2 is allowed to run to completion prior to I1. This allows I3 to be completed earlier. The total execution time is seven cycles, with a savings of one cycle.

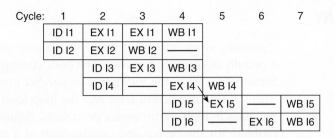

Figure 12.28 An example with in-order issue and out-of-order completion

3. Out-of-Order Issue with Out-of-Order Completion

To allow out-of-order issue, it is necessary to decouple the decode and execute stages of the pipeline. This is done with a buffer referred to as an *instruction window*, which temporarily stores the instructions that have finished decoding, but are waiting for execution. Any instruction can be issued by the instruction window provided that the required functional unit is available and no data dependencies block its execution. The scheduling of the example is given in Figure 12.29. Instruction I6 can be issued ahead of I5 because it does not depend on I4, even though I5 does. Thus, one cycle is saved in both the execute and write-back stages, and the total execution time is six cycles.

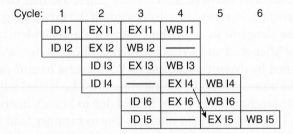

Figure 12.29 An example with out-of-order issue and out-of-order completion

SUMMARY

Pipelining is an important concept in many areas of science and technology, especially in computer science. The basic concept of pipelining is introduced in Section 12.1 from the viewpoint of parallel processing. Exploitation of parallelism at the instruction level and the loop level is the major purpose of using pipelines in high-performance processors. Balancing the pipeline stages is a key problem for the design and construction of a pipeline as discussed in Section 12.2. The pipeline must be fed with a continuous stream of tasks so that it can deliver its maximum throughput of one task per clock cycle. The design procedure of an instruction pipeline consists of two steps: design from functional decomposition as stated in Section 12.3, and design from hazard analysis as stated in Section 12.4. The detailed design process is illustrated using an example of designing a specific instruction pipeline, which implements the same instruction set used in Chapter 9 for designing the hardwired and microprogrammed control of a RISC processor. So, we can see how a processor can be designed in three different organizations.

Resolving three types of hazards—structural hazard, data hazard, and control hazard—is the key to fully utilizing the high-performance pipelines. It also constitutes the fundamental topics of analysis and design of an instruction pipeline. A structural hazard can be resolved by hardware replication and/or dynamic scheduling to avoid possible conflict in the usage of pipeline resources. Data hazards most frequently occur as a consequence of read-after-write data dependencies between instructions. These are true data dependencies that can be satisfied, in most cases, by designing the forwarding and bypassing hardware in the datapath of a pipeline. Other data dependencies exist in a program as write-after-read and write-after-write. These are name dependencies that can be satisfied by dynamic scheduling. Whenever a hazard cannot be resolved by any of the above methods, the pipeline must be stalled with a loss of performance of the pipeline. The control hazard due to branch instructions discussed in Section 12.4.4 and the load interlock due to memory load instructions discussed in Section 12.4.3.5 are the cases that need to be solved by instruction stall. Other methods for resolving control hazards are stated in Section 12.4.4.

Superscalar processors are introduced in Section 12.5. A superscalar processor has multiple, typically diversified instruction pipelines in a processor and delivers a throughput of cycles per instruction of less than one. The distinctive speed characteristics of a superscalar processor depend on how well the instruction-level parallelism can be exploited, both by hardware and by software. The structure (Section 12.5.2) and the instruction issue and completion policies (Section 12.5.3) are the fundamental technical issues.

EXERCISES

12.1 Amdahl's Law determines the speedup of parallel computation relative to the sequential computation on the compatible hardware of equal uniprocessor performance. The problem is to evaluate the speedup of pipelined computation relative to unpipelined computation. The method is to convert a pipelined computation into an equivalent parallel computation with an explicit serial portion, such that Amdahl's Law can be equally applied to the pipelined computation. The timing diagram of a pipelined computation is shown in Figure 12.30(a). It does not have an explicit serial portion of computation. However, if we move the shaded busy region to the idle region, then the timing diagram can be converted into a form as shown in Figure 12.30(b), which is equivalent to a typical parallel pattern that allows Amdahl's Law to be applied.

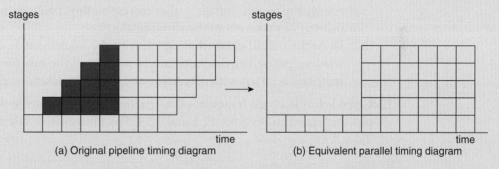

Figure 12.30 Pipelined execution vs. parallel execution for Problem 12.1

(a) Explain the original pipeline timing diagram to determine how the task stream flows through the pipeline, how many stages (d) the pipeline has, and how many tasks (n) are executed in this pipeline. Based on your analysis, derive the formula for the speedup of the pipelined relative to the unpipelined execution of the same number of tasks.

(b) Check the correctness of your formula in Part (a) by applying Amdahl's Law to the equivalent parallel timing diagram as obtained in Part (b) of Figure 12.30.

12.2 Let us study a five-stage pipeline with an extra stage named ID (Instruction Decode) added between the stages IF and EX [see Hennessy (2002)]. Given the following cases of implied data hazards:

(i)

```
ADD   R1, R2, R3
SUB   R4, R5, R1
AND   R6, R1, R7
OR    R8, R1, R9
```

```
(ii)     ADD     R1, R2, R3
         LW      R4, 0(R1)
         SW      12(R1), R4

(iii)    LW      R3, 0(R1)
         SUB     R4, R1, R3
         SW      12(R1), R4
```

Design the forwarding paths in the above five-stage pipeline for resolving the data hazards implied in these cases. If some hazards cannot be resolved by forwarding, simply identify them and explain. If you find any other types of data hazards that can be resolved by forwarding, you may include them in your analysis and design.

Your design in this problem should show the following results:

(a) Indicate the source and destination of every forwarding path and the resolved data hazard (i.e., the corresponding pair of data-dependent instructions taken from the above cases).

(b) Draw the overall datapath diagram with the implementation of these forwarding paths. The diagram should include all the functional blocks, the interstage registers with data fields, and the multiplexers used for switching.

12.3 Given below is a code fragment of instructions to be executed on the four-stage pipeline stated in Sections 12.3 and 12.4. For the available instruction set, see Table 9.3.

```
         ADDI    R7, R0, #n
         ADD     R6, R0, R7
LOOP:    SUB     R5, R7, R6
         LW      R1, Astart(R5)
         LW      R2, Bstart(R6)
         ADD     R3, R1, R2
         SW      Astart(R5), R3
         SUB     R4, R1, R2
         SW      Bstart(R6), R4
         ADDI    R6, R6, #-1
         SLT     R8, R6, R0
         BEQ     R8, LOOP
         EXIT
```

(a) Assume two data arrays A and B in memory, whose starting addresses are given as *Astart* and *Bstart*, respectively. What task does this code fragment perform? Write the simplest C code to describe it.

(b) Show the timing of this instruction sequence for the basic four-stage pipeline specified in Section 12.3, Figure 12.9, without any forwarding or bypassing hardware, except that the register set itself has the forwarding function between its Write port and Read ports (i.e., Read After Write).

Use a pipeline timing chart like Figure 12.11. Assume that the branch is handled by flushing the pipeline. If all memory references hit in the cache, how many cycles (in terms of n) does this loop take to execute?

(c) Show the timing of this instruction sequence on the pipeline with normal forwarding and bypassing hardware as shown in Figure 12.24. Assume that the branch is handled by predicting it as not taken. If all memory references hit in the cache, how many cycles (in terms of n) does this loop take to execute?

(d) Assuming the pipeline has a single-cycle delayed branch and normal forwarding and bypassing hardware, schedule the instructions in the loop including the branch delay slot. You may reorder instructions and modify the individual instruction operands, but do not undertake other loop transformations. Show a pipeline timing diagram and compute the number of cycles (in terms of n) needed to execute the entire code.

12.4 Given the following code segment:

```
            ADDI        R1, R0, #1
            LW          R2, Astart(R0)
    LOOP:   LW          R3, Astart(R1)
            SUB         R4, R2, R3
            SLT         R5, R4, R0
            BEQ         R5, SKIP1
            SUB         R4, R0, R4
    SKIP1:  SW          Astart(R1), R4
            ADDI        R1, R1, #1
            SLT         R6, R1, #100
            BNE         R6, SKIP2
            ADD         R1, R0, R0
    SKIP2:  ADD         R2, R3, R0
            ADDI        R7, R1, #-1
            BEQ         R7, LOOP
            EXIT
```

(a) Assume a data array A in memory, whose starting address is *Astart*.

   (i) What task is done by the above code? How many iterations does the loop program execute? Write its algorithm in the simplest high-level-language code in C using variable A as the name of the data array in memory. Don't interpret the given program instruction by instruction using registers as the variables.

   (ii) Draw a map to show the allocation of initial data and final results in memory.

(b) Draw the timing diagram for the execution of the above code on the four-stage integer pipeline with full forwarding and bypassing hardware studied in Section 12.4. Assume that the branch delay slot is left unfilled.

    (i)   Use arrows to show all data hazards between instructions.

    (ii)   Using arrows for all the data hazards in Part (i) that can be resolved by forwarding, show the forwarding paths in your pipeline timing diagram.

    (iii) If all memory references are hit in the cache, how many cycles in total does the above code take to execute? (For the branch instructions with unpredictable outcomes, assume the worst case, i.e., always untaken.)

(c)   Assume the pipeline with a single-cycle delayed branch and full bypassing and forwarding hardware, schedule the instructions, especially the branch delay slots, for the minimum time of execution. You may reorder instructions and modify the individual instruction operands, but do not undertake other loop transformations. Draw a pipeline timing diagram and calculate the total number of cycles needed to execute the code.

12.5 A computer has the following configuration:

- Word length: 8 bits
- Register set: 16×8 bits, $(R0) = 0$
- Data memory: 256×8 bits
- Instruction memory: 256×16 bits, word addressing
- The instruction format is given in Figure 12.31
- The instruction set is given in Table 12.2

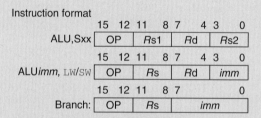

Figure 12.31   Instruction format for Problem 12.5

Table 12.2   Instruction set for Problem 12.5

OPcode IR_{15-12}	Mnemonic	Name	Operation
0000	NOP	no-operation	
0001	(not used)		
0010	ADD Rd,Rs1,Rs2	add	$Rd \leftarrow (Rs1) + (Rs2)$
0011	SUB Rd,Rs1,Rs2	subtract	$Rd \leftarrow (Rs1) - (Rs2)$
0100	AND Rd,Rs1,Rs2	and	$Rd \leftarrow (Rd) \wedge (Rs2)$
0101	XOR Rd,Rs1,Rs2	xor	$Rd \leftarrow (Rd) + (Rs2)$

OPcode IR_{15-12}	Mnemonic	Name	Operation
0110	SGT Rd,Rs1,Rs2	set on greater than	if $(Rs1) > (Rs2)$, $Rd \leftarrow 1$, else $Rd \leftarrow 0$
0111	SLT Rd,Rs1,Rs2	set on less than	if $(Rs1) < (Rs2)$, $Rd \leftarrow 1$, else $Rd \leftarrow 0$
1000	ADDI Rd,Rs,imm	add *imm*	$Rd \leftarrow (Rs) + imm_{\text{sign-ext.}}$
1001	ANDI Rd,Rs,imm	sub *imm*	$Rd \leftarrow (Rs) \wedge imm_{\text{sign-ext.}}$
1010	LW Rd,Rs,imm	load word	$Rd \leftarrow \text{Mem}[(Rs) + imm_{\text{sign-ext.}}]$
1011	SW Rd,Rs,imm	store word	$\text{Mem}[(Rs) + imm_{\text{sign-ext.}}] \leftarrow (Rd)$
1100	BEQZ Rs,imm	branch equal	if $(Rs) = 0$, $PC \leftarrow (PC)_{\text{updated}} + imm$
1101	BNEZ Rs,imm	branch not equal	if $(Rs) \neq 0$, $PC \leftarrow (PC)_{\text{updated}} + imm$
1110	(not used)		
1111	(not used)		

Design the pipeline of the computer with five stages:

- IF—Instruction Fetch
- ID—Instruction Decode
- EX—Execute
- MA—Memory Access
- WB—Write-Back

(a) Draw a detailed and complete datapath diagram including all functional units, all multiplexers, and all interstage registers. Give the names and sizes of all the component registers inside each interstage register. Give the input number (0, 1, …) of each multiplexer. Do not draw a black box to denote the control unit because the control is distributed throughout the pipeline.

(b) Analyze all the cases of data hazards and control hazards that can be resolved by forwarding. For each case, indicate the forwarding path in a timing diagram and derive the logic expression of the condition for detecting the hazard.

(c)   Repeat Part (b), but analyze all the cases of pipeline interlock. Derive the logic expressions of the conditions for detecting the interlock.

(d)   Using the results of analysis in Parts (b) and (c), complete the datapath and derive the expressions for the control signals acting on all the related functional units and all the multiplexers in it.

12.6 Given the following branch frequencies as the percentages of all the instructions running on our four-stage pipeline stated in Section 12.4: unconditional branches such as jumps—5%; conditional branches—20%, 60% of which are taken and the remaining are not taken. Furthermore, branch delay slots cannot be filled at all in 20% of the total branches. How much faster would the machine be without any branch penalties?

References

Ashenden, P.J. 1998. *The Student's Guide to VHDL.* San Francisco, CA: Morgan Kaufmann Publishers.

———. 2002. *The Designer's Guide to VHDL.* 2nd ed. San Francisco, CA: Morgan Kaufmann Publishers.

Azimi, M., Cherukuri, N., Jayasimha, D.N., Kumar, A., Kundu, P., Park, S., Schoinas, I., and Vaidya, A.S. 2007. Integration challenges and tradeoffs for Terascale architectures. *Intel Technology Journal*, 11(3), pp. 178–184. Available at: http://www.intel.sg/content/dam/www/public/us/en/documents/technology-briefs/intel-labs-tera-scale-challenges-paper.pdf [last accessed 15 July 2013].

Bartee, T.C. 1991. *Computer Architecture and Logic Design.* New York, NY: McGraw-Hill Education.

Brown, S. and Vranesic, Z. 2000. *Fundamentals of Digital Logic with VHDL Design.* New York, NY: McGraw-Hill Education.

Capilano Computing Systems. 1999. *LogicWorks™ 4 Interactive Circuit Design Software for Windows and Macintosh.* Boston, MA: Addison-Wesley.

Caragea, G., Keceli, F., Tzannes, A., and Vishkin, U. 2010. General-purpose vs. GPU: Comparison of many-cores on irregular workloads. In: *USENIX, HotPar '10: Proceedings of the 2nd workshop on hot topics in parallelism.* Berkeley, CA, June 14–15, 2010.

Carpinelli, J.D. 2001. *Computer Systems: Organization and Architecture.* Boston, MA: Addison-Wesley.

Charlton, C. and Leng, P. 1990. *Principles of Computer Organization: A First Course Using the 68000.* Maidenhead, UK: McGraw-Hill Education.

Chiang, S. 2001. Foundries and the dawn of an Open IP era. *Computer*, 34(4), pp. 43–46.

Chen, P.M., Lee, E.K., Gibson, G.A., Katz, R.H., and Patterson, D.A. 1994. RAID: High-performance, reliable secondary storage. *ACM Computing Surveys*, 26(2), pp. 145–185.

Clements, A. 2000. *The Principles of Computer Hardware.* 3rd ed. New York, NY: Oxford University Press.

———. 2014. *Computer Organization and Architecture: Themes and Variations.* Boston, MA: Cengage Learning.

Dasgupta, S. 1989. *Computer Architecture: A Modern Synthesis.* New York, NY: John Wiley & Sons.

De Blasi, M. 1990. *Computer Architecture.* Boston, MA: Addison-Wesley.

Dewey, A. 1997. *Analysis and Design of Digital Systems with VHDL.* Boston, MA: PWS Publishing and International Thomson Publishing.

Diefendorff, K., Dubey, P.K., Hochsprung, R., and Scales, H. 2000. AltiVec extensions to PowerPC accelerates media processing. *IEEE Micro*, 20(2), pp. 85–95.

Dulong, C. 1998. The IA-64 architecture at work. *Computer*, 31(7), pp. 24–32.

Feldman, J.M. and Retter, C.T. 1994. *Computer Architecture: A Designer's Text Based on a Generic RISC.* New York, NY: McGraw-Hill Education.

Flynn, M.J. 1995. *Computer Architecture: Pipelined and Parallel Processor Design.* Boston, MA: Jones and Bartlett Publishers.

Forouzan, B.A. 2001. *Data Communications and Networking.* 3rd ed. New York, NY: McGraw-Hill Education.

van de Goor, A.J. 1989. *Computer Architecture and Design.* Boston, MA: Addison-Wesley.

Gschwind, M., Hofstee, P., Flachs, B., Hopkins, M., Watanabe, Y., and Yamazaki, T. 2005. A novel SIMD architecture for the Cell heterogeneous chip-multiprocessor. In: *Proceedings of Hot Chips 17: A symposium on high performance chips*, Stanford, CA, August 14–16, 2005.

Hamacher, V.C., Vranesic, Z.G., and Zaky, S.G. 2002. *Computer Organization.* 5th ed. New York, NY: McGraw-Hill Education.

Hayes, J.P. 1993. *Introduction to Digital Logic Design.* Boston, MA: Addison-Wesley.

Hennessy, J.L. and Patterson, D.A. 2002. *Computer Architecture: A Quantitative Approach.* 3rd ed. San Francisco, CA: Morgan Kaufmann Publishers.

Herzog, J.H. 1996. *Design and Organization of Computing Structures.* Wilsonville, OR: Franklin, Beedle & Associates.

Heuring, V.P. and Jordan, H.F. 1997. *Computer Systems Design and Architecture.* Boston, MA: Addison-Wesley.

Horel, T. and Lauterbach, G. 1999. UltraSPARC-III: Designing third-generation 64-bit performance. *IEEE Micro*, 19(3), pp. 73–85.

Intel Corporation. 2009. An introduction to the Intel QuickPath Interconnect, Intel White Paper, January 2009. Available at: http://www.intel.sg/content/dam/doc/white-paper/quick-path-interconnect-introduction-paper.pdf [last accessed 15 July 2013].

Janukowicz, J. and Reinsel, D. 2007. Evaluating the SSD total cost of ownership. IDC White Paper, November 2007.

Kain, R.Y. 1989. *Computer Architecture: Software and Hardware.* Englewood Cliffs, NJ: Prentice Hall.

———. 1996. *Advanced Computer Architecture: A Systems Design Approach.* Englewood Cliffs, NJ: Prentice Hall.

Karam, G.M. and Bryant, J.C. 1992. *Principles of Computer Systems.* Englewood Cliffs, NJ: Prentice Hall.

Katz, R., Borriello, G., and Ebeling, C. 1994. *LogicWorks: Instructor's Laboratory Manual.* Menlo Park, CA: Benjamin Cummings.

Kavi, K., Browne, J.C., and Tripathi, A. 1999. Computer systems research: The pressure is on. *Computer*, 31(1), pp. 30–39.

Kumar, R., Tullsen, D.M., and Jouppi, N.P. 2005. Heterogeneous chip multiprocessors. *Computer*, 38(11), pp. 32–38.

Langholz, G., Francioni, J., and Kandel, A. 1989. *Elements of Computer Organization.* Englewood Cliffs, NJ: Prentice Hall.

Maccabe, A.B. 1993. *Computer Systems: Architecture, Organization, and Programming.* Homewood, IL: Richard D. Irwin.

Mano, M.M. 1988. *Computer Engineering: Hardware Design.* Englewood Cliffs, NJ: Prentice Hall.

Mano, M.M. and Kime, C.R. 1997. *Logic and Computer Design Fundamentals.* Englewood Cliffs, NJ: Prentice Hall.

Mattson, T., van der Wijngaart, R., and Frumkin, M. 2008. Programming Intel's 80 core Terascale processor. In: *SC'08 Proceedings of the 2008 ACM/IEEE conference on supercomputing,* Austin, TX, November 15–21, 2008. Piscataway, NJ: IEEE Press.

Micron Technology. 2008. *Wear-Leveling Techniques in NAND Flash Devices.* Micron Technical Note TN-29-42.

Murdocca, M.J. and Heuring, V.P. 2000. *Principles of Computer Architecture.* Englewood Cliffs, NJ: Prentice Hall.

Oliver, B. 2008. Comparison of 32GB SSD vs. 10,000 RPM HDs *(32GB MemoRight GT SSD vs. WD Raptor and WD VelociRaptor), accelerate your mac,* June 16, 2008. Available at: http://www.xlr8yourmac.com/IDE/SSD_vs_VelociRaptor_vs_Raptor/SSD_vs_VelociRaptor_Raptor.html [last accessed 15 July 2013].

Patterson, D.A. and Hennessy, J.L. 1998. *Computer Organization and Design: The Hardware/Software Interface.* 2nd ed. San Francisco, CA: Morgan Kaufmann Publishers.

Peacock, C. 2010. *USB in a Nutshell.* BeyondLogic.org. Available at: http://www.beyondlogic.org/usbnutshell/ [last accessed 15 July 2013].

Ramakrishna Rau, B. and Schlansker, M.S. 2001. Embedded computer architecture and automation. *Computer,* 34(4), pp. 75–83.

Raman, S.K., Pentkovski, V., and Keshava, J. 2000. Implementing streaming SIMD extensions on the Pentium® III processor. *IEEE Micro,* 20(4), pp. 47–57.

Sailer, P.M. and Kaeli, D.R. 1996. *The DLX Instruction Set Architecture Handbook.* San Francisco, CA: Morgan Kaufmann Publishers.

Samaras, W.A., Cherukuri, N., and Venkataraman, S. 2001. The IA-64 Itanium processor cartridge. *IEEE Micro,* 21, pp. 82–89.

Scragg, G.W. 1992. *Computer Organization: A Top-Down Approach.* New York, NY: McGraw-Hill Education.

Sheldon, T. 2001. *Encyclopedia of Networking & Telecommunications.* New York, NY: McGraw-Hill/Osborne.

Shen, J.P. and Lipasti, M.H. 2003. *Modern Processor Design: Fundamentals of Superscalar Processors.* 2nd ed. New York, NY: McGraw-Hill Education.

Shiva, S.G. 1996. *Pipelined and Parallel Computer Architectures.* New York, NY: Harper Collins Publishers.

Sima, D., Fountain, T., and Kacsuk, P. 1997. *Advanced Computer Architectures: A Design Space Approach.* Boston, MA: Addison-Wesley.

Stallings, W. 2003. *Computer Organization and Architecture: Designing for Performance.* 6th ed. Upper Saddle River, NJ: Prentice Hall.

Stone, H.S. 1993. *High-Performance Computer Architecture.* 3rd ed. Boston, MA: Addison-Wesley.

Tanenbaum, A.S. 1999. *Structured Computer Organization.* 4th ed. Englewood Cliffs, NJ: Prentice Hall.

The Economist. 2009. The military-consumer complex. 12 December 2009. Available at: http://www.economist.com/node/15065709 [last accessed 15 July 2013].

Thorne, M. 1990. *Computer Organization and Assembly Language Programming for IBM PCs and Compatibles.* 2nd ed. Menlo Park, CA: Benjamin Cummings.

Toshiba America Electronic Components. 2009. Solid state drives: Separating myths from facts, Version 1.3, June 2009. Available at: http://www.toshiba.com/taec/components/Generic/SSD_Myths.pdf [last accessed 15 July 2013].

Tremblay, M. and O'Connor, J.M. 1996. Ultra SPARC I: A four-issue processor supporting multimedia. *IEEE Micro,* 16(2), pp. 42–50.

Triebel, W.A. and Singh, A. 1986. *The 68000 Microprocessor: Architecture, Software, and Interfacing Techniques.* Englewood Cliffs, NJ: Prentice Hall.

Vajapeyam, S. and Valero, M. 2001. Guest editors' introduction: Early 21st century processors. *Computer,* 34(4), pp. 47–50.

Wang, A., ed. 2000. *Computer Organization and Architecture.* 3rd ed. [in Chinese.] Beijing: Tsinghua University Press.

Ward, S.A. and Halstead, R.H., Jr. 1990. *Computation Structures.* New York, NY: The MIT Press and McGraw-Hill Education.

Williams, R. 2001. *Computer Systems Architecture: A Networking Approach.* Boston, MA: Addison-Wesley.

Wolf, W. 2001. *Computers as Components: Principles of Embedded Computing System Design.* San Francisco, CA: Morgan Kauffmann Publishers.

Zargham, M.R. 1996. *Computer Architecture: Single and Parallel Systems.* Englewood Cliffs, NJ: Prentice Hall.

INTERNET RESOURCES

Intelligent RAM Project

Computer Science Division, University of California at Berkeley. *The Berkeley Intelligent RAM (IRAM) Project.* Available at: http://iram.cs.berkeley.edu/ [last accessed 15 July 2013].

Hardware-related Magazines and Websites

Ars Technica (part of the Condé Nast Group). Available at: http://arstechnica.com/ [last accessed 15 July 2013].

SearchStorage (part of the TechTarget Storage Media Group). Available at: http://searchstorage.techtarget.com/ [last accessed 15 July 2013].

Tom's Hardware (part of the Bestofmedia Group). Available at: http://www.tomshardware.com/ [last accessed 15 July 2013].

Integrated Circuits

Intersil. Available at: http://intersil.com/ [last accessed 15 July 2013].

PCI Specifications

PCI-SIG Developers Home. Available at: http://www.pcisig.com/developers/ [last accessed 15 July 2013].

USB Specifications

USB-IF Developers Area. Available at: http://www.usb.org/developers/ [last accessed 15 July 2013].

Index